Perspectives on Environment

Essays Requested by the Panel on Environmental Education,
Commission on College Geography

Edited by

Ian R. Manners
University of Texas
at Austin

and

Marvin W. Mikesell
University of Chicago

ASSOCIATION OF AMERICAN GEOGRAPHERS

Commission on College Geography
1710 Sixteenth Street, N.W.
Washington, D.C. 20009

PUBLICATION No. 13

Library of Congress Catalog Card Number 73-88849

Supported by a grant from the National Science Foundation

PREFACE

The origin of this volume can be traced to the decision made by the Commission on College Geography in February of 1971 to establish a "Panel on Environmental Education" and its subsequent approval of this Panel's recommendation that a collection of essays devoted to geographic research on environmental problems would be a desirable addition to the Commission's program of publications. Informal surveys conducted by Panel members later in 1971 produced evidence that a substantial number of geographers were offering courses with an environmental or ecological emphasis and that an assessment of professional commitments in this complex field would be useful. It was not thought that a publication designed to meet this need could be comprehensive. Nevertheless, the Panel felt that an appropriate selection of papers might indicate the breadth and depth of geography's past and potential contributions to environmental education.

In discussing the possible character of this collection, the Panel was well aware that the commitment of geographers to environmental education represented a convergent movement from several fields. Geographers concerned with the effects of human activities on vegetation and soil had begun to take account of man's impact on air and water, while geographers devoted to perception had been investigating attitudes and decision-making in regard to natural hazards and the role of values and taste in landscape evolution. Physical geographers had also begun to take account of current environmental problems and had been applying old and new skills in studies of modified climates and land forms. It was equally evident that both human and physical geographers had become aware of the fact that environmental deterioration is most clearly manifest in cities. In short, there seemed to be good reason to believe that the widespread interest among geographers in environmental problems was producing combinations and associations that had not previously been conspicuous in geographic education.

It was also evident that these research commitments had not been summarized and that suitable materials for classroom use were not widely available. Hence it was hoped that a volume designed to review old commitments and expose the dimensions of new ones would enhance the efforts of teachers who were trying to respond effectively to the national interest in environmental problems. That many of these teachers were facing larger and more enthusiastic classes than they had ever faced before gave added impetus to the Panel's rationale.

It was also hoped that the several papers commissioned for the publication might document and demonstrate those distinctive aspects of geographic training that are of particular value in dealing with environmental issues and hence might enable the profession to play a more active role in the initiation and development of environmentally-focused education programs. These professional traits were thought to include (1) a long-standing commitment to environmental studies, (2) understanding of the significance of factors of location, diffusion, and scale, (3) awareness of the complexity of man-environment interactions,

(4) recognition that problems of environmental quality must be considered not only in physical and biological terms but also in relation to human perceptions, needs, and desires, and (5) experience in dealing with both systems and processes.

With these objectives in mind, the Panel asked for contributions from the several authors whose essays are published here. They were invited to prepare review articles designed to acquaint college teachers with environmental problems that have been, are, or should be of interest to geographers. The members of the Panel are grateful to these authors for their willingness to respond to a difficult charge and are also indebted to John F. Lounsbury, Director of the Commission on College Geography, for serving as host for a meeting of the contributors and organizers of the volume in Tempe, Arizona in January of 1973. Thanks must be offered in addition to Salvatore J. Natoli, Educational Affairs Director of the Association of American Geographers, for advice on format, design, and style, editorial assistance, and for the cover design. The index was prepared by Jane F. Castner of the AAG National Office who also assisted with technical editing and with checking bibliographies. In addition, Marie K. Nixon of the AAG National Office offered her editorial assistance during the galley stage of the work.

Since the basic rationale for this effort is a belief that it will be useful in environmental education, "feedback" from teachers and students will be deeply appreciated.

Panel on Environmental Education of the Commission on College Geography

Ian R. Manners, University of Texas (Co-chairman)

Marvin W. Mikesell, University of Chicago (Co-chairman)

Ian Burton, University of Toronto

Melvin G. Marcus, Arizona State University

Harold A. Winters, Michigan State University

TABLE OF CONTENTS

Geography as the Study of Environment: An Assessment of Some Old and New Commitments

Marvin W. Mikesell
University of Chicago

Toward the end of the 1960's the American public was overwhelmed with declarations of an impending environmental crisis. In some parts of the country, most notably in California, awareness of air pollution and other cases of environmental deterioration had occurred more than a decade earlier. Still for most Americans 1969 marked the beginning of an "environmental crusade," and the rallying cry of those who initiated this movement ("Clean Air, Clean Water!") focused attention on what seemed to be the critical issues (Lowenthal: 1970a).

Since that time, crisis rhetoric and a yearning for simple answers to complicated questions has given way to a more sophisticated and deliberate search for environmental understanding. Ecology has been institutionalized, as both the federal government and many of our colleges and universities have launched programs of environmental research and education. The rapid transition from "Earth Day" to a "United Nations Conference on Human Environment" and from "teach-ins" to an "Environmental Protection Agency" constitutes one of the remarkable developments of recent history.

This development is certainly well known, for it has been amply covered in both scientific and popular journals. However, it is less well known that the environmental crusade initiated in the 1960's had antecedents in the conservation movement of the 1880's (Graham: 1971). Moreover, it is possible to identify at least two prior periods of intense preoccupation with environmental problems. In the 1930's a similar crusade was inspired by drought, crop failure, and wind erosion on the Great Plains. Beginning with crisis rhetoric and prophecies of "deserts on the march," this expression of public concern was also institutionalized after the establishment of the Soil Conservation Service in 1935 (Bennett: 1939). During a still earlier period of American history the major environmental preoccupation was deforestation. Initiated by Marsh's discourse of 1864 on the adverse effects of the clearing of woodlands, official and public concern encouraged the publication of a massive *Report on Forestry* (Hough: 1878-1884) and the creation of the American system of National Forests.

1

The focus of these popular and official concerns—vegetation, soil, air and water—has long been regarded as a particular interest of geographers. Yet, ironically, developments within geography have been such that the several phases of national preoccupation with environmental problems have not produced a general awareness of our interests and skills. The first phase occurred prior to the establishment of geography as a university discipline in this country. The second phase occurred during a period when geographers had begun to reject "environmentalism" and were about to recast their discipline in an empirical and inductive mold as an enterprise devoted to "areal differentiation." Hence although Warren Thornthwaite and his associates played an active role in the research program of the Soil Conservation Service, it cannot be said that geographers displayed much interest in the causes and consequences of the "dust bowl."

The current quest for environmental understanding promises to be different, for there is ample evidence of a more active and creative response to the several issues raised during the past few years and perhaps even an aura of confidence about the advantages of geographic education and the power of geographic tools. Yet the fact that environmental education represents a new commitment for many geographers (and perhaps even a forgotten commitment for some) means that the trials and errors of our prior endeavors need to be placed in sharp focus if we are to take advantage of the current opportunity. Knowledge of where we might be going will obviously be enhanced by some knowledge of where we have been.

FROM PHYSIOGRAPHY TO ENVIRONMENTALISM

When the first departments of geography were established in the United States shortly after the beginning of the twentieth century their self-proclaimed charge was to function as a bridge between the natural and social sciences. For example, the catalogue of the University of Chicago for 1903 indicates that its newly established Department of Geography would offer courses "intermediate between geology, on the one hand, and history, sociology, political economy, and biology, on the other." Three years later the first president of the Association of American Geographers proclaimed that "any statement is of geographic quality if it contains . . . some relation between an element of inorganic control and one of organic response" (Davis: 1906). This conception of the nature of geography was appealing to the first generation of American geographers, who were trained for the most part as geologists and hoped to apply this knowledge in the study of mankind. By moving deliberately from geology to physical geography and then to human geography defined in reference to the presumed influence of natural environment, American geographers were in fact redefining their field as "geographical history." For example, Semple's *American History and its Geographic Conditions*, published in 1904, was essentially a physical-geographic interpretation of American history, a vigorous assertion that the development of the American landscape could be interpreted as a consequence of the distinctive features of the American environment.

The line of inquiry initiated during the period when human geography was still firmly tied to physical geography was denounced in time as a one-sided determinism, an example of special pleading and selectivity in the search for evidence. Yet the scholar who reads these works today is left with an uneasy feeling, for far more qualification is evident than one might expect from the deprecatory caricatures of environmentalism that were published in our textbooks after this mode of thought had ceased to be fashionable. For example, Semple placed major emphasis in each of her works on the importance of location, and Huntington's persistent attempt to understand the role of climatic change in human history and the human consequences of different habitats can be described as a search for standards of correlation and measurement (Huntington: 1945). Indeed, it is not an exaggeration to describe Semple as a "location theorist" and Huntington as the first American geographer, perhaps even the first American, to try to find indices of "environmental quality." Moreover, the third major figure in environmentalism might well be described as a proponent of the now fashionable concept of "limits to growth" (Taylor: 1940). A "revisionist attitude" toward the works of these authors, or at least a more objective attitude toward them (Lewthwaite: 1966), seems clearly to be overdue.

CRITICISMS OF ENVIRONMENTALISM

The retreat of geographers from environmentalism began in the 1920's and by the end of the 1930's had resulted in a nearly total abandonment of the research program initiated prior to the First World War. This retreat is evident even in Barrows' conception (1923) of geography as the study of the mutual relations between man and his natural environment or "human ecology," for he asserted that geographers, as thus identified, could abandon their responsibility to conduct original research in physiography and climatology.

The negative attitude toward environmentalism was expressed in different terms by Sauer (1927), who held that rejection of this doctrine should be based not on any denial of the importance of studies of environment but rather on the following methodological grounds: (1) a field of science cannot be defined by a particular causal relationship; (2) the environmentalist inquiry could not claim a class of data as its own; (3) this lack of specificity could lead only to a parasitic existence; (4) the environmentalists could not claim to define or justify their inquiry by a particular method; and (5) special pleading was difficult to avoid in an enterprise that depended upon demonstration that natural environment has played a decisive role in human history. The last objection was probably the most telling because it implied that studies thus motivated could not be pursued scientifically. But this was not the primary basis for the rejection of environmentalism, which was prescriptive rather than philosophical, i.e., environmentalism was held by its critics to be merely an hypothesis, subject to verification or rejection, and hence could not be regarded as a definition of the content or objective of geography as an academic field. In this sense "environmentalism was not disproved, only disapproved" (Rostlund: 1962).

In addition to these methodological or prescriptive objections critics of environmentalism often stressed the philosophical hazards of the doctrine of "determinism." Yet unbridled "free will" was not an acceptable framework for teaching or research. Hence the long, scholastic debate on this issue, which occupied many of the best minds in geography and concluded with an endorsement of "possibilism," the idea that environment acts to constrain or encourage mankind but cannot be regarded as the principal initiating force of human activity (Tatham: 1951). This mode of thought was congenial to the empirical and skeptical spirit of the second generation of American geographers, who were critical of the premature generalizations and grand speculations of their predecessors. Embarrassed by the latter's apparent failures, geographers trained in the 1920's and 1930's looked for different programs, and for many this quest led not to greener pastures but to smaller and safer pastures.

ALTERNATIVES TO ENVIRONMENTALISM

For most geographers the alternative to environmentalism was to disregard the ecological commitments of the discipline in favor of distributional or locational studies that paid only perfunctory attention to environment. Thus although land use and land forms might both be mapped, the only generalization offered about a connection between the two would be one of coincidence or correlation, e.g., steep slopes have different uses than gentle slopes. Not a few geographers simply ignored environment and devoted themselves to functional or classificatory studies of economic activities. The excitement created by the concept of "nodal regions" and the vast energy expended on the mapping of land use were sufficient to discourage more than a casual second look at environmentalism.

Moreover, human and physical geographers began to drift apart in the 1930's and were almost totally separated in the 1940's and 1950's. The conception of geography as a bridge between the natural and social sciences was still proclaimed in some textbooks, but was seldom evident in research. The separation of geography's "two cultures" is manifest in *American Geography: Inventory and Prospect*, the "official" survey of the field published by the Association of American Geographers in 1954, for although this volume includes studies of both nature and culture no chapter is devoted explicitly to their relationship (James and Jones). Between physical geography cultivated without reference to human activities and human geography cultivated with only perfunctory reference to nature there could be few opportunities for collaboration, especially when both sides were influenced by a residual fear of environmentalism.

Yet concern for the operation of man in nature had not been abandoned totally, for many geographers had followed Sauer's example (Leighly, ed.: 1963) and had devoted themselves to studies of deforestation, erosion, reclamation, and other processes of environmental modification. These studies were inspired by a belief that man's role as an ecological dominant should be a primary focus of geographic investigation. The literature produced within this framework is large and cumulative and it is noteworthy that geographers appear prominently in the symposium volume on *Man's Role in Changing the Face of the Earth* (Thomas, ed.: 1956). Unfortunately, this impressive collection appeared about a dozen years before public interest in environmental problems produced a craving for its message. Nevertheless, the research tradition it represents provides an attractive point of departure for the interest in "polluted environments" that is so widespread among American academics today, for it demonstrates the importance of several processes, initiated by man, that have resulted in environmental deterioration and provides an impressive documentation of the contribution geographers have made to the study of these processes. The volume even includes an essay on the prospect of an "energy crisis," the most likely focus of America's next environmental crusade.

The fate of *Man's Role in Changing the Face of the Earth*, which seems to have been appreciated only by a relatively small group of scholars, has an interesting parallel in the fate of the collection of articles on *Limits of Land Settlement* published by the Council on Foreign Relations in 1937. Geographers are correspondingly prominent in this volume, which is devoted to problems of population growth in relation to food supply and the prospects for population redistribution—topics of overriding importance today. The "ultra-relevant" character of these two volumes, which were published "out of phase" in regard to public interest in their contents, encourages happy speculation about what might happen if works of such character were to appear in concert with a national interest in their messages. One can only hope that *Geography and a Crowding World*, the symposium on "population pressures upon physical and social resources in the developing lands" (Zelinsky, Kosiński, and Prothero, eds.: 1970) will be more successful than its predecessors.

RECENT COMMITMENTS

The "Report of the AAG Task Force on Environmental Quality" (Lowenthal *et al.*: 1973) includes a list of some of the most important commitments of geographers devoted to study of the relations of nature and culture. Since this list was designed to indicate the range and persistence of professional interest in environmental problems, it is worth repeating here:

(1) "Geographical History" (e.g., Semple: 1904);
(2) "Prehistoric Geography" (e.g., Butzer: 1964);
(3) "Limits of the Habitable World" (e.g., Bowman: 1937);
(4) "History of Ideas on the Relations of Nature and Culture" (e.g., Glacken: 1967);
(5) "Philosophical Debates on Determinism, Possibilism, and Probability" (e.g., Tatham: 1951);
(6) "Impact of Human Activities on Environment" (e.g., Thomas, ed.: 1956);
(7) "Natural Hazards Research" (e.g., Saarinen: 1966);
(8) "Studies of Environmental Perception" (e.g., Lowenthal, ed.: 1967, 1972);
(9) "Medical Geography" (e.g., May: 1958);
(10) "Resources Management" (e.g., Burton and Kates, eds.: 1965); and
(11) "Designs for Ecological Human Geography" (e.g., Wagner: 1960; Eyre and Jones, eds.: 1966).

That all but one of these commitments, geographical history, continue to be "going concerns" adds up to a substantial contribution. Moreover, human modifications of air and water have already commanded sufficient interest to be listed as additional commitments (Tyson: 1970; Wolman: 1971; and the articles by Mrowka and Terjung in this volume), as is the growing interest among geographers in urban environments (Detwyler and Marcus: 1972; and Schmid in this volume). Other preoccupations not yet evident or overlooked when the AAG Task Force prepared its report, are represented in the present collection (see especially, the chapters by Watts, Butzer, Doughty, and Manners) and still others are bound to emerge as a new generation of geographers, alert to the potentialities of ecological reasoning, begins to make its contribution.

COMPARATIVE ADVANTAGE

The AAG Task Force on Environmental Quality also called attention to aspects of the professional background of geographers that should make them especially effective as educators and researchers. These characteristics of geographic thought, which might be described as a comparative advantage, include the following:

(1) *Synthesizing.* Geographers are self-selected for their curiosity about, and ability to handle, a wide range of scholarly approaches. Geographical training generally fosters these traits and expands the range of accessible insights and materials. This is especially true for interactions between man and environment, for which geographers are apt to assume that any subject matter may be germane and must be taken into account more or less systematically.

(2) *Complexity of explanations.* The wide range of often conflicting insights that geographers normally acquire and the profession's past experience with simplistic explanations—notably environmental determinism—makes most geographers reluctant to accept single-factor propositions about cause-and-effect relations. Already sensitive to the need for complex and multiform explanations, geographers ought to bring mature leadership to environmental problems that are usually less simple and less easily resolved than they seem. The inability of any single discipline to formulate, let alone answer, some of the basic environmental problems suggests a need for the synthesizing, holistic approach long and successfully developed in geography.

(3) *Range of information sources.* Environmental understanding is apt to require enormously diverse kinds of information, ranging from the location and dispersal mechanisms of specific chemical agents, for example, to the attitudes and behavior of individuals and groups stemming from their images of such agents. More than most other scholars, geographers are early exposed to and trained in a variety of data-gathering techniques, from field observations and laboratory analyses to interviews and questionnaires, from historical, archival, and library sources to attitudinal surveys, from cartographic and statistical analyses to descriptive and holistic syntheses. We do not contend that any geographer is competent to handle all such techniques, nor that many geographers are well trained in most of them; what is significant, in our view, is that geographical education presupposes the potential utility of any or all such techniques. Geographers are usually willing to recognize the value of evidence drawn from fields in which they themselves lack expertise. Catholicity and eclecticism of this nature are invaluable in many problems of environmental understanding and action.

(4) *Location and spatial relationships.* Interest and training alert most geographers to features of distribution and diffusion, both as to environmental factors and information and as to value systems bearing on those factors.

(5) *Man as a part of environment, and vice versa.* More than other professions, geography is aware of the complexity of the man-nature

interface. Geographers have examined landscapes and artifacts seen to varying degrees as both 'natural' and 'cultural'; they avoid sharp dichotomies between these realms. And geographers are constantly reminded that the physical environment is felt and responded to through screens of perception and cognition, screens that deserve to be studied along with environment and man.

The most persuasive feature of this assessment is its reminder of geography's unique position as a discipline devoted to both natural and social science. On the natural science side, geographers have the advantage of a perspective that encourages awareness of the relationship of climate, water, land forms, vegetation, and soils. Such cannot be claimed by many meteorologists, hydrologists, or geologists, and biologists and soil scientists may nor may not be willing to look beyond their particular phenomena. In contrast, physical and biogeographers have always had a comprehensive ecological rationale. The range of investigations conducted by geographers who identify themselves as social scientists is similarly broad and eclectic and has the additional advantage of including both predictive and retrospective orientations. To be sure, the pedagogic problems created by the separation of physical and human geography have not yet been resolved. Nevertheless, the growing interest among geographers in modified environments and cultural ecology provides ample opportunity for rapprochement (Mikesell: 1970).

This comment brings our discussion back to its point of departure, for it seems clear that each of the major phases of national environmental concern has called for the combined wisdom of natural and social scientists and it was this wisdom that the first academic geographers hoped to acquire. Yet the several research and teaching commitments now evident among geographers interested in environment differ notably from the program initiated by these academic pioneers. The most important feature of this difference is a greater awareness of ecological principles and a desire to deal with specific linkages within ecosystems. The most serious failing of the early environmentalists was their tendency to regard nature and culture as separate entities or opposing forces rather than as interlocking components of such systems. The trials and errors of their effort have taught us that man acts in and upon nature rather than merely in response to the dictates of nature. We have also learned that "the surface of the earth is shaped for each person by refraction through cultural and personal lenses of custom and fancy" (Lowenthal: 1961, p. 260).

These confident remarks should not be taken as an indication that geographers can pursue their environmental interests in an atmosphere of splendid isolation. The fact that our accomplishments and perhaps even our trials and errors add up to a richer heritage than can be claimed by any other group concerned with environmental problems does not give us reason to be complacent about our ability to solve new problems or train a new generation of students without help from other disciplines. The essays in this volume provide emphatic and rather sobering evidence on this point. For example, the understandings and methods of chemistry, physics, and meteorology are evident in the essays of Terjung and Watts, while Butzer draws upon research in archeology and geology, Mrowka reviews the findings of geologists and hydrologists, Doughty considers the work of biologists and students of wild-life management, and Manners draws upon studies in demography and agronomy. A similar range of specific knowledge is evident in the works cited by Hills, and both Mitchell and Saarinen have drawn support from several of the social sciences. Finally, the essays of Nelson and Butler, and Schmid suggest the existence of or need for integrating disciplines devoted to recreation and urban environments.

An additional challenge is posed by the fact that environmental problems not only exceed the grasp of any one scholar or scholarly discipline but have also become the focus of public interest and government policy. The reference to an "environmental crusade" at the beginning of this chapter and the fact that the range of persons participating in this movement or at least exposed to it includes persons of every conceivable interest and background provides ample evidence that more than a leisurely reexamination of old commitments will be required of geographers.

THE ENVIRONMENTAL CRUSADE

That environment is now widely and even pervasively regarded as a "problem" means that public attitudes have to be taken into account in any program of environmental studies. In the United States these attitudes were influenced by the atmosphere of crisis, contention, and confusion that was evident when the environmental crusade was launched toward the end of the 1960's. We will probably never know why this movement acquired such extraordinary force at that time, for it might have started much earlier and indeed was evident in California in the 1950's. However, it is possible to identify a number of concepts that were characteristic of the crusade.

Most important, perhaps, was the *doomsday theme*, an anticipation of environmental disasters of such vast scope that the survival of the human species would be threatened. The handbook prepared for the first national environmental "teach-in" or "Earth Day" (Bell, ed.: 1970) abounds in prophecies of this sort, including predictions that human life is threatened by rising or declining temperatures, pesticides, air pollution, water pollution, starvation caused by population growth, and exhaustion of fuel supplies and essential raw materials. This conception of impending disaster naturally encouraged a *sense of urgency*, a belief not only that "something had to be done," but also that something had to be done *immediately*. It is indicative of this attitude of impatience that only two years after the appearance of more than a dozen books with the word "crisis" in their titles, a new book appeared (Armstrong, ed.: 1972) that posed the question "why do we still have a crisis?"

A second prominent theme of the crusade was *guilt*, a belief that Americans in particular and the urban-industrial realm of the world in general were responsible for the planetary crisis. As the leading consumers of the world's resources and polluters of its air and water, Americans and Europeans were encouraged to feel apprehensive not only about their own fate, but also about the role they were playing in determining the fate of others.

Another theme of the crusade was the notion of *the earth as a spaceship or closed system*. This idea was probably encouraged by the first photographs from orbiting satellites, which suggested that the planet might indeed be likened to a spaceship with a "life support system." In any case, what Graham (1969) describes as the "illusion of dilution" was dispelled by such vivid evidence of the limited extent of the earth's atmosphere.

Still another prominent theme was the assertion of a *need for "recycling."* The logical answer to the depletion of resources and mountainous accumulations of waste was to re-use as well as use, and "re-cycling centers" (now often abandoned) were established throughout the country. Moreover, by using biodegradable products and conserving energy *ecology could be practiced in the home.*

It is probably also fair to suggest that most of the people who wrote or thought about environmental problems in 1969 or 1970 felt that they were dealing with an *immediate issue*, that the various problems being described were uniquely associated with modern urban and industrial societies. Consequently, historical perspective is hard to find in the lore of the environmental crusade. The fact that deforestation and soil erosion have been evident in many parts of the world for several millennia, or that air pollution has been evident since the beginning of the Industrial Revolution was of little consequence in a movement devoted almost exclusively to problems thought to be peculiar to the experience of its participants.

This *timeless quality* of the crusade, which seems in retrospect to have been suspended between an unpleasant present and a frightening future, is evident even in the writing of one of the few authors who expressed interest in the past experience of mankind, for in his often cited—and reprinted—essay on the "historical roots" of the crisis, White (1967) conveys the misleading impression that the relationship between nature and culture had not previously been given serious consideration by historians or philosophers (cf. Glacken: 1967).

These several concepts encouraged a more radical idea that deterioration could be arrested only by a *reexamination of material needs* and a *change of "life styles."* The American Indian, "who used only according to his needs," was offered as an ideal, and modern Americans were admonished to abandon or at least reconsider their once sacrosanct "standard of living." This conception of *virtue in simplicity* led inevitably to a corresponding notion of *sin or danger in artificiality.* The popularity of "organic farming" and "health foods" was a clear reflection of this combination of positive and negative ideology.

The concept of *zero population growth* was also presented, most vigorously by Ehrlich (1968; see also Ehrlich and Ehrlich: 1970), as a necessary requirement for human survival, although many found it difficult to accept the substance or style of the more passionate arguments in favor of this concept (Callahan, ed.: 1971). Moreover, the virulent and much publicized debate between Ehrlich and Commoner (*Environment*, April, 1972; *Science*, July 21, 1972; see also Commoner: 1971), in which "too many people" and "faulty technology" are offered as the ultimate causes of environmental deterioration and "birth control" and "improvement of technology" as the ultimate solutions, seems to have been disregarded by most scholars in favor of eclectic arguments of greater subtlety. In any case, the perceptive bookstore managers who combined population explosion literature with pollution literature were responding to an automatic association in the minds of most of the people who participated in the crusade.

Finally, it seems clear that many of the writers on environmental problems believed that *radical changes were required* if the threat of massive environmental contamination were to be avoided. Yet dispute was also evident between those who advocated revolutionary or merely evolutionary policies. The many special issues of popular magazines on the environmental crisis reveal this range of opinion. *Newsweek* (January 26, 1970), *Fortune* (February 1970), *Time* (February 2, 1970), and the *National Geographic* (December, 1970) display some confidence about the ability of "the system" to correct itself, whereas the *Progressive* (April 1970) and *Ramparts* (May 1970) offer a more pessimistic point of view, particularly in regard to the wisdom of "planners" and "developers." The eagerness of most participants in the crusade to condemn bureaucrats and businessmen seems to have been combined with a reluctance to condemn academics engaged in "pure" research. That the latter were thought to have been unprepared for the environmental crisis prior to its exposure is implicit in the lore of the crusade. Yet academics were also presumed to be innocent by reason of their impotence. From the perspective of the Ivory Tower, "the practitioners of superficial planning" seemed to be "wielding their bows in competition with Nero," and "the developing conflagration" promised "to be a holocaust" (Eyre: 1971, p. 27).

These features of the environmental crusade provide some insight into its character and style. But perhaps even more revealing is its pattern of cause and effect argumentation, mostly addressed to the question "who or what should be blamed?" In addition to ignorance, greed, shortsightedness, and a host of other persistent human failings, many contributors to the lore of the crusade felt that they could be confident about specific causation. As already indicated, White's essay of 1967 on "The Historical Roots of Our Ecological Crisis" was widely read during the most intense period of environmental activisim and debate. In it, he argued that the Judeo-Christian doctrine with its conception of the superiority of man made in God's likeness had encouraged an exploitative attitude toward nature. White's argument was challenged directly or indirectly by a vast array of counter-arguments. Capitalism and the profit-motive impressed some authors as offering a more plausible explanation of the destructive practices of Western and especially American civilization (e.g., Gellen: 1970); while others offered broadly cultural explanations (e.g., Moncrief: 1970), and the case against capitalism was countered by evidence of pollution in the Soviet Union (Goldman: 1972). Perhaps "Imperialism" could be blamed, at least for the destruction of soils and forests in areas of plantation economy; or the "frontier spirit," evident in the United States, Canada, South Africa, Australia, the Soviet Union, and other countries that had enjoyed the advantage of "new land" to which restless pioneers might move after resources had been exhausted. Yet attempts to invoke "national character" as a cause of environmental disruption entailed formidable difficulties, for projection of ideals into realities (or vice versa) is a hazardous exercise (Tuan: 1970).

Another focus of cause and effect argumentation, especially in the United States, was the environmental damage caused by automobiles or, more precisely, by the internal combustion engine. Early recognition that automobiles are one of the largest, if not the largest, contributors of air-born contamination led promptly to recognition that the vehicle seemingly best suited to the American settlement system was obviously not well suited to the American environment or indeed to any environment. Hence debates on whether adequate emission standards could be set or enforced for such engines and the merits and feasibility of vehicles powered by steam or electricity figured prominently in the crusade (Bell, ed.: 1970; Schneider: 1971; Buel: 1972), as did criticisms of the seeming irresponsibility of the automobile industry (e.g., Ayres: 1970) and the latter's persistent rebutals (e.g., General Motors Corporation: 1973).

Finally, one might blame uncontrolled technology (or blind faith in the power of technology); urbanization, which had created monumental problems of air pollution and waste disposal; or the unforeseen consequences of environmental manipulation. The last argument, which had been presented forcefully by Carson in 1962, was probably the most compelling of all—and the most discouraging to those who sought simple answers. Its spirit was captured by a cartoonist (*New Yorker*, April 4, 1970) who showed a forlorn figure in a bed and wrote:

> This is the man who ate the steak that came from the steer that nibbled the grass that grew in the field where roamed the cat that caught the bird that ate the fish that fed on the bug that floated in the oil slick.

This fabulous (but plausible) lament is a fitting conclusion to a discussion of the environmental crusade, for it seems clear that the most serious problem for mankind is to prevent such unforeseen developments. More often than not environmental deterioration is produced not by deliberate (or malicious) action but by a chain of causes and effects that is neither intended nor controlled. Innovation "A" is introduced to product effect "B" and eventually produces effects "X," "Y," and "Z." Hence the importance of the concept of ecosystem, which demands understanding of such linkages. The assumption that this concept encourages "holistic" thinking has probably been overstated, for its more obvious and attainable virtue is its encouragement of a search for specific causes and effects (Odum: 1971, 1972; see also the giant symposium volume published under the title *The Careless Technology*, Farvar and Milton, eds.: 1972).

GOVERNMENT INITIATIVES

In retrospect, many of the publications issued during the environmental crusade, and especially those associated with "Earth Day," seem extravagant and simplistic today. Passionate arguments about *the* cause of environmental damage or what *must* be done *immediately* are encountered less frequently today. This change reflects several developments.

In the first place, there seems now to be general recognition that the environmental problems considered during the crusade are exceedingly complicated, that some of them will never be solved, and that effective research and planning will require decades and even generations of sustained effort. This recognition is both a cause and a consequence of the more sophisticated character of the "second generation" of crisis publications. Indeed, the qualitative difference between the "Earth Day" publications and such later presentations as the "Blueprint for Survival" issued as a special number of *The Ecologist* (Goldsmith *et al.*, eds.: 1972) is enormous. This generalization also applies to the difference between *Eco-Tactics* issued by the Sierra Club in 1970 and *Stop It! A Guide to Defense of the Environment* (Sanders: 1972).

It is also significant that the environmental movement has been "institutionalized." Teach-ins and newsletters have been replaced by institutes, schools, departments, government agencies, and a host of associated publications. Conversely, it seems clear that public interest and the attention of the news media have waned, at least in comparison with the atmosphere in 1970. Therefore, it might be reasonable to suppose that more is being done and less merely being said about environmental problems. In any case, there is now ample evidence of the beginning of a negative reaction against environmental planning, a realization that cleaner air and water might mean fewer jobs and less individual or corporate freedom. One can also see evidence of lobbying against anti-pollution legislation.

Still it has to be said that government agencies have moved more rapidly and vigorously than was thought possible during the initial phase of the "environmental crusade." The record of the Environmental Protection Agency, particularly in regard to emission standards for new automobiles (CO and hydrocarbon to be 90 per cent below 1970 standards by 1975) has unquestionably been one of vigorous advocacy, in spite of its acceptance, after considerable pressure from the automobile industry, of a one-year extension of this deadline. Moreover, in June of 1973 this agency announced that it would propose stringent controls that would drastically restrict the use of automobiles in several cities, including New York and Los Angeles, that seem unlikely to be able to meet its standards for substantial reduction of air pollution. If effectively enforced, and not too compromised by anticipated "extensions," the proposed controls would force commuters to make wider use of public transportation facilities. In any case, these suggestions, which bring to mind Mumford's recommendations of 1958, are radical even by the standards of "Earth Day."

Government policy, mostly backed by specific legislation, calls for the reduction of several other categories of pollution. For example, federal water pollution controls require that industry must use the "best practical technology" of treating wastes by 1977, and must have installed the "best available" treatment equipment by 1983. The target year for achieving the national goal of eliminating all polluting discharges is 1985, when American waters are supposed to be safe for fish, other wildlife, and people. Government controls also relate to noise, solid waste, and radioactive materials, pesticides, or other toxic substances, which means that there is hardly an aspect of pollution that is not now subject to actual or impending controls. As in the case of emissions from automobiles, government policy has been to hold fast to recommended standards but permit flexibility in regard to deadlines. The estimate of the amount of money the nation must put into efforts to clean up its environment was put at $287 billion in the third annual report (1972) of the Council on Environmental Quality.

Most of the government initiatives undertaken in recent years relate to the National Environmental Policy Act of 1969. This act and its subsequent amendments have become the primary basis of authority for insuring that federal officials consider the environmental consequences of contemplated actions. In instances where a proposed action may "significantly" affect environment, federal officials are required to prepare an "environmental impact statement," concerning the consequence of the action, adverse effects that cannot be avoided, alternatives to the proposed action, the relationship between short- and long-term uses, and any irreversible commitment of resources. Such statements normally include comments of state and local as well as federal agencies, and are supposed to be available to the public prior to the initiation of an action. The definition of impact statements stipulates use of "a systematic, interdisciplinary approach which will insure the integrated use of the natural and social sciences and the environmental design arts in planning and in decision-making which may have an impact on man's environment."

As White (1972, p. 303) remarks, the effect of these regulations "is to require the agencies to specify the likely impacts of their proposed projects, to obtain the comments of other interested agencies, to make public their own findings and the comments of others, and to expose themselves to critical review of both findings and method. Enough time is provided [90 days for draft reports and 30 days for final statements] for individuals, groups, or agencies opposed to a project to gather their forces quickly and make their views known to whatever congressional or executive units may have responsibility for undertaking the project."

White adds that "it is too early to judge the full consequences of the procedures now being followed: there have been no searching studies published of what is happening, and the process itself is so new that adjustments are made rapidly as it unfolds." Indeed, it is fair to suggest that the legislation stating the need for and general character of environmental impact statements did not consider the complexities of implementation. It demanded performance without defining its nature precisely and without recognizing the lack of tools or resources required. Hundreds—perhaps thousands—of government and private groups are engaged in the preparation of impact statements or submitting material for such statements, yet guidelines on what constitutes a good or even adequate statement are only now beginning to appear. Perhaps the impressive methodological contribution is the elaborate "Information Matrix for Environmental Impact Assessment" prepared by Leopold and associates (1971) as part of a report of the U.S. Geological Survey on *A Procedure for Evaluating Environmental Impact*. Reports of varying length and quality have also been published by other government agencies charged with explicit responsibility for the preparation of impact statements. (See, for example, Committee on Merchant Marine and Fisheries, *Administration of the National Environmental Policy Act: Appendix to Hearings Before the Subcommittee on Fisheries and Wildlife Conservation*, Ninety-Second Congress, Second Session, 1972, which includes the reports of 28 agencies.)

The question of what might constitute an ideal environmental impact statement poses perplexing problems. For example, White (1972) suggests that there "can be no fully satisfactory statement," because it would require two virtues that are inevitably lacking: "(1) A complete description of the likely biological, physical, and economic impacts of the proposed work, and (2) a complete description of the impacts of all practical alternatives to the proposed work." It is probably best, therefore, to anticipate relatively complete or convincing statements. In any case, the attraction to geographers of the National Environmental Policy Act is self-evident, for the stipulation that the methods and understandings of both natural and social science must be utilized should be appealing to a discipline that includes both natural and social scientists. Moreover, if physical geography is defined as "the study of the earth ecosystem in terms of its sub-systems and their spatial and temporal attributes" (Marcus: 1967) it offers if not the wisdom then at least the perspective that is apparently encouraged by the environmental impact legislation.

Finally, the directives on the design of impact studies relating to federally funded "new communities" (U.S. Department of Housing and Urban Development: 1972) come close to the framework for detailed regional investigation that was once widely employed by the writers of theses and dissertations in geography. Needless to say, one can press this aspect of comparative advantage too far, for prediction as well as description is required, and it cannot be claimed that much progress has been made in designing training programs for geographers seeking careers in impact research. Still a challenge for geographers is evident even in the *idea* of environmental impact studies.

Another feature of government policy has been a persistent search for environmental indices. In regard to most categories of pollution, these indices have been set according to presumed standards of public health. However, as the

Chairman of the Council on Environmental Quality suggests (Train: 1972), this quest has posed numerous problems:

> Good indices depend upon good data, but the environmental data now being collected are deficient in many respects. Inadequate sampling is probably the most pervasive problem. Much of our air pollution data, for example, is based on results from only one monitoring station in each community. It makes a big difference whether that single station is located next to a power plant or on the outer fringes of the suburbs. Similarly, water pollution readings are only rarely adjusted to take into account the location of the stations collecting the data. Another major problem is the excessive length of time between collections of data. Unsatisfactory systems for data storage and dissemination are often notable deficiencies.
> Finally, in many cases the scientific knowledge necessary to properly weigh the components of an index is lacking. How important is dissolved oxygen compared to turbidity in estimating the quality of our nation's water? How much park space does a typical urban dweller need or want? Until sound standards are set for major aspects of the environment, a number of somewhat arbitrary assumptions will have to be made in the computation of indices.

THE MEANINGS OF ENVIRONMENTAL QUALITY

The reference to "want" and "need" in the statement just quoted introduces the difficult question of what should be understood by "environmental quality." The fact that the Executive Office of the President includes a "Council on Environmental Quality" and that this body has produced three substantial reports does not mean that the problem of definition has been solved. In his preface to the first report, President Nixon suggested that we should "strive for an environment that not only sustains life but enriches life, harmonizing the works of man and nature for the greater good of all." The last phrase implies an equalitarian principle, but not all or perhaps even most Americans perceive wilderness to be a "good" or care much about endangered wildlife. Conversely, open space, almost universally perceived to be a "good," is surely not good in equalitarian terms if it is utilized for a golf course.

The subtle and seemingly intractable problems involved in trying to define "quality" are certainly not new, for a good deal of the intellectual effort of mankind—since the time of Socrates—has been devoted to attempts to understand human values. Indeed the cumulative lore of ethics and aesthetics provides a million-volume reading list on this topic! But the key issue in most current discussions of environmental quality seems not to be ethics or aesthetics nor perhaps even truth in any metaphysical sense: it is survival. Thus the indices offered by the Council on Environmental Quality have to do mainly with levels of pollution or contamination, and the goal for the nation is to reduce such levels below what is thought to be dangerous. But one can be prosperous and contented in an environment that seems by some standards to be intolerably polluted and ugly, and danger may be rationalized or ignored. Even the smog problem in Los Angeles tends to be excluded from acceptable conversation. "Perhaps a passing comment is acceptable, or even a witty jibe at the weather. But to get serious about what one is daily forced to inhale can label one an oddball, a person who can't adjust to the inconveniences of modern life" (Winn: 1973, p. 294).

This is not to suggest that environmental quality is a hopeless issue or an invitation to intellectual anarchy. The Council on Environmental Quality has displayed awareness of the subjective and objective dimensions of its charge, and a few individual authors have struggled admirably with the problem of reconciling environmental ideals and realities (Marx: 1970; McCamy: 1972; Ward and Dubos: 1972). Among geographers, the most persistent effort to deal with this issue has been made by Lowenthal (1961, 1962, 1968, 1970a, 1970b; see also Lowenthal and Prince: 1965).

However, since it seems unlikely that environmental quality can be defined adequately by any one scholar or policy-maker, it is perhaps best to seek its meaning indirectly by trying to discover the array of ideas and perceptions that can or should be taken into account. During the past four years this writer has asked students in his undergraduate course on "Nature and Culture" to prepare essays on "The Meanings of Environmental Quality." The assignment has always been given at the beginning of the course, in order that the responses might not be unduly influenced by assigned readings or lectures. Approximately 200 students have responded to the challenge of this deliberately open-ended charge, and their opinions give some indication of what will have to be taken into account in any serious assessment of environmental quality.

Most students began by trying to define the key terms, "environment" and "quality," and then conceded that neither could be defined objectively. Yet they were unwilling to regard the issue as being wholly subjective, and hence struggled to achieve a balance between their own views and what might be good for the nation or the planet. The awesome range of issues to be considered was summarized effectively by one student who wondered if "visual blight" and "starvation" could possibly be considered under a common heading. Yet all agreed that environmental quality could be judged according to at least one absolute standard: survival of the human species. Hence the students in these classes tended to adopt the strategy of the Council on Environmental Quality and think initially of human health.

In 1970 the general tone of the essays was one of anger and fear. A year later the essays were melancholic rather than angry, and by 1972 most students demonstrated patience and a realization that answers to most environmental problems were not likely to be found soon. This progression—from awareness of urgency to awareness of difficulty and complexity—probably parallels and no doubt reflects the development of public and official opinion. However, it is noteworthy that it was so clearly revealed, not only between 1970 and 1973 but even between 1970 and 1971.

The realization that solutions to major environmental problems will not be found easily or quickly did not encourage cynicism or nihilism. Virtually all of the students were confident that substantial progress could be made if changes could be achieved in public attitudes. Initiative, in other words, seemed to lie with the consuming and wasting public as well as with government and industry. The plea so often heard during the environmental crusade for a re-ordering of priorities and change of life style was reiterated by a large majority of the students. One spoke of the need to think of "more than personal space;" and several suggested that "control of humans" was the decisive issue. In other words, the behavioral and perceptual dimension of environmental quality seems to have been recognized intuitively or empirically.

On the other hand, no great confidence was expressed about human behavior. It is not surprising, therefore, that most of the students indicated a need for planning and strict regulations. Indeed, one student thought that environmental quality was inconceivable without "world government." The prospect of a loss of individual freedom did not arouse fears to any considerable degree, since control was envisioned to conclude mainly regulation of industry and curtailment of conspicuous consumption. Hence another message of the environmental crusade, the doctrine of virtue in simplicity, seems to have been heard and believed. And, whether naively or not, most of the students felt confident that they could enjoy adequate personal freedom in a controlled environment.

The questions implicit in the last remark (how much freedom and how much control?) were not really answered in the essays. If faced with the hypothetical alternatives of "unlimited growth" and "back to nature," most of these students would probably have elected a moderate position: "limited growth" and "less disturbance of nature." In any case, growth versus non-growth was not regarded as a realistic option. Correspondingly, although American urban environments impressed many of the students as being ugly, dangerous, and even "inhuman," little enthusiasm was expressed for rural life or wilderness areas served only by hiking trails.

The prospect of zero population growth was almost universally accepted as desirable and many students thought it was essential. Yet they were not very well informed at the beginning of the course on the reasons for disagreement among demographers and had only a vague understanding of what the "green revolution" is supposed to mean. Still most of the students saw a clear correlation between population growth and exhaustion of resources and did not feel that birth control should be endorsed only in the underdeveloped regions of the world. In other words, the essential argument of the proponents of zero-population growth had been understood and accepted, even by those who had done little specific reading.

As for the assumption that the environmental crusade encouraged "whole earth" rather than "national" thinking, the essays of these students displayed only afterthoughts about areas outside the United States. Yet, conversely, the ethnocentrism seemingly evident in the essays was only rarely matched by a disciplinary bias. This is especially interesting, since with only about a dozen exceptions each of the 200 students was committed to be a "major" in a particular academic discipline, and the disciplines represented included most of the social and natural sciences and several of the humanities. The fact that attitudes clearly identifying a student with his or her "major" were hard to detect in the essays, suggests that courses with an environmental focus can indeed encourage inter-disciplinary or extra-disciplinary thinking. A tendency for anthropology majors to seek cross-cultural comparison and psychology majors to think of environment in reference to mental health is the only real exception to this generalization. The most "rigorous" of the essays was written by a law student and the most "poetic" came from a mathematics major. The highest level of sophistication and greatest awareness of the range and character of environmental problems undoubtedly was exhibited by biology majors. Yet the biologists in the four classes were no more successful than their fellow students in dealing with the meanings of "quality."

Another theme revealed in about forty of the essays was a realization that the need for environmental planning was creating difficulties for the mode of thought that is commonly identified with science. Several students pointed out that the progression constantly recommended to them by their professors (data gathering–correlation–experimentation–formulation and testing of hypotheses—legislation—planning) was ill-suited to environmental problems that often demand anticipatory planning. Indeed, the prospect that one might have to plan even before adequate data have been collected was accepted by these students as it has been accepted by the Council on Environmental Quality and the Environmental Protection Agency.

Finally, it is significant and perhaps disturbing that few of these students offered visual images of quality. The essays were philosophical in tone and rarely included more than a paragraph of description. And when these paragraphs did appear, they were negative in character—accounts of the undesirable. The fact that these students had no difficulty, when challenged, in describing environments of poor quality but were reticent or contentious when asked to describe environments of good quality might be a reflection of current American character, which seems deficient in the traits that encourage utopian speculation. In any case, if this tendency to approach the meaning of environmental quality abstractly and negatively is at all representative of public opinion, it will present a severe challenge to the policy makers and planners of our society.

THE LIMITS TO GROWTH DEBATE

In June of 1972 the environmental crusade was proclaimed from a new platform—a United Nations Conference on Human Environment. This conference, held in Stockholm, offered impressive evidence of the diffusion of anxiety about environmental problems (Ward and Dubos: 1972; Strong: 1973). Yet the atmosphere in Stockholm differed from the American movement in one important respect: the official participants in the conference were delegates and hence spokesmen for their respective countries. Consequently, the rhetoric of crisis ecology was blended with the more familiar rhetoric of political and economic rivalry. "Capitalist" and "socialist" countries, "crowded" and "empty" countries, and above all "developed" and "developing" countries presented arguments and counter-arguments about what was wrong or threatening in the world and what should be done to improve or save it. Yet the official "declaration" of the conference was sufficiently broad to receive general approval. For example, its fourth proclamation declares that

> In the developing countries most of the environmental problems are caused by underdevelopment. Millions continue to live far below the minimum levels required for a decent human existence, deprived of adequate food and clothing, shelter and education, health and sanitation. Therefore, the developing countries must direct their efforts to development, bearing in mind their priorities and the need to safeguard and improve the environment. For the same purpose, the industrialized countries should make efforts to reduce the gap between themselves and the developing countries. In the industrialized countries, environmental problems are generally related to industrialization and technological development.

By proclaiming the need for development in "developing countries" and pointing to the environmental problems created by development in "developed countries," the conference declaration offered an evasive response to a hotly debated issue. And no wonder; for any argument in favor of global curtailment of growth would have been fiercely resisted by the "Third World" and hence by most of the world. As ecology seemed to be in conflict with economics during the American "environmental crusade," so ecology was revealed to be in conflict with both economics and national aspirations when it was presented to an international audience.

The different perception of people in "developing countries" has been summarized by the person most responsible for the organization of the conference (Strong: 1973, pp. 691-692):

> ... In Asia, Africa, and Latin America, the disposition was to regard the environment as something remote from the interests and concerns of the poor. To a man faced with immediate starvation and other diseases of poverty, the risks he runs from contamination of the seas or the atmosphere seem so remote as to be irrelevant. To him factory smoke smells of money—and of jobs and needed consumer goods . . . I also found in the poorer countries a widespread fear that preoccupation by the rich with the new environmental 'fad' would divert attention and resources from the basic and compelling needs of the developing world—needs arising mainly out of their poverty and underdevelopment . . . They also wanted to know how the growing environmental concern of the more industrialized countries would affect the flow of finances for their development, the cost of the capital equipment they buy, their access to markets for products that may be subject to new environment-based restrictions, and their ability to attract new industry to their countries.

The major focus of attention in the continuing debate on the problems and prospects of development has been a report prepared for the Club of Rome's project on "The Predicament of Mankind" (Meadows *et al.*: 1972). The team responsible for this report, which appeared under the now famous title *The Limits to Growth*, built a computer model of the world and fed into it data on population and industrial growth rates, farm yields, and resources, and then constructed "feedback loops" to assess the effects of changes in particular variables. The results of these simulations encouraged a view that continued exponential growth will produce a sudden and uncontrollable decline in both population and industrial capacity sometime before the year 2100. These developments were deduced from the assumption that projections of current rates of population increase (about 2 per cent per year) and industrial output (about 7 per cent per year), would result in exhaustion of essential natural resources, collapse of industrial production, associated agricultural failures caused by shortages of fertilizers and pesticides, and a population decline caused by famine and epidemics.

The several developments that might arrest these trends are discounted in the report. For example, technological innovations designed to multiply usable resources would simply encourage continued exponential growth of industry and consequent environmental deterioration, whereas reduction of production and pollution would not solve the problem of exponential growth of population. In short, the only alternative to the projected collapse is a "no growth" policy for both industry and population. "Global equilibrium" in these respects would result in a drastic reduction in the standard of living of "developed countries" and effectively prohibit realization of the material aspirations of "developing countries."

Needless to say, the alternative of global cataclysm or global equilibrium has not gone unchallenged, and the cumulative comment on the report already exceeds its modest size (cf. Gillette: 1972; Klein: 1972; Slesser: 1972; and Cole *et al.*: 1973). Some critics have argued that exponential growth can be maintained by use of new raw materials and sources of energy, intensification of food production, curtailment of pollution, and recycling. Others have challenged the quality of the data used in the report. Yet few have suggested that the projected catastrophe is inconceivable or have claimed that exponential growth of both industry and population can continue indefinitely. Nor has it been denied that curtailment of growth will require controls on a global scale that are bound to be resisted.

In any case, what is significant in the context of this chapter is that the assumptions and projections of the report of the Club of Rome, and also most of the issues raised in the debate about its quality, are essentially geographic. Resource uses and distributions, population densities and trends, national policies in regard to production and trade—these and most of the other variables built into the model are fundamental considerations in human geography. Yet, ironically, although Eyre (1971) has offered a projection that certainly equals the report of the Club of Rome in pessimism, the debate on this most relevant of all issues has attracted remarkably little attention from geographers.

RECAPITULATION

This chapter opened with an assertion that the recent development of public interest in environment offers both an opportunity and a challenge for geographers and then approached the relationship between public interest and professional interest indirectly by means of an historical survey. The progression from physiography to environmentalism is easy to understand, given the origin of American geography as an offshoot from geology and the subsequent attempt to fashion a discipline that could function as a mediator between the natural and social sciences. The abandonment of that initial effort was a consequence of inherent difficulties or inadequacies and the reluctance of many geographers to define their enterprise as a search for specific causal connections. Yet interest in environment did not disappear, but rather persisted in the form of "pure" physical geography and cultural geography defined in reference to the impact of human activities on vegetation and soil.

When the environmental crusade burst on the American scene toward the end of the 1960's, geographers were well prepared to comment on the relationship of man and land but were less well prepared to join in the discussion of the causes and consequences of air and water pollution. Moreover, the separation of physical and human geography created difficulties for those who sought to design courses or conduct research that would be responsive to the national interest. An additional problem was created by the tendency of some spokesmen to present an atrophied description of geography as a social science devoted exclusively to studies of "spatial organization" (Taaffe, ed.: 1970). Yet for those who accepted Pattison's conception (1964) of four traditions—i.e., a "spatial tradition," an "area studies tradition," a "man-land tradition," and an "earth science tradition"—at least half of what had been called geography could be regarded as a contribution to environmental studies. Moreover, as Parsons (1971) suggests, much of the lore of the area studies tradition, especially in reference to Latin America, has also been devoted to environmental studies. In addition, there is abundant evidence that a spatial tradition has always been implicit in ecology (Major: 1969). In short, all four of the persistent traditions of geography have contributed to and drawn from a larger tradition, shared by several disciplines, of environmental studies.

It is in this context that one can speak of "comparative advantage" and point hopefully to the role that geographers might play in the search for environmental wisdom. But having said this much, one must add hastily that many of the environmental problems exposed in recent years and also many of the social and philosophical issues debated during the environmental crusade have not been given adequate attention by geographers. Therefore, the easy assumption that Huntington, Marsh, and perhaps even Strabo would have had little difficulty understanding the atmosphere of "Earth Day" is only partly reassuring, for "Earth Day" would also have been comprehensible to Marx, Rousseau, and Diogenes!

If one turns from "Earth Day" to the present day, it seems clear that attention has continued to be focussed on the elusive concept of environmental quality. This focus does not entail a new commitment for geographers interested in perception or behavior. Yet even the most optimistic champions of these interests could not claim that the problem of what might constitute environmental quality is going to be easy to solve or that more than a few of the necessary questions have even been asked by geographers. It follows that we will not soon be able to offer answers; and since belief is a more comfortable state of mind than doubt, it also follows that pursuit of the meanings of environmental quality will be a frustrating experience.

As for the efforts being made by the several government agencies charged with responsibility under the Environmental Policy Act, it is impossible to resist the temptation to view these efforts as a "challenge" and hope that there will be an appropriate "response." The requirement that impact studies include the understandings of both natural and social science is of particular importance to geographers and may spur the development of a new commitment, in both teaching and research, that will bring together representatives of physical and human geography.

Finally, the continuing debate on "limits to growth" calls for a commitment from geographers concerned with population and resources and also from geographers without these interests who are excited by the prospect of prediction and simulation. Indeed, it is astonishing that the report of the Club of Rome, a controversial *tour de force* of model-building, has apparently not attracted the attention of theoretical geographers.

Early in the nineteenth century Humboldt (1808) expressed confidence that nature would "continue to unfold her germs, regardless though sinful man, ever at war with himself, tramples beneath his foot the ripening fruit." The fact that such optimism is seldom encountered in our time means that the disciplines of environmental study have to be practiced in a harsh light. As a purely academic and almost private enterprise, the environmentalism of our formative decades did not suffer or profit from such exposure. It was little noticed by other scholars and had no discernible influence on human welfare. Perhaps it is still possible (and proper) to regard environmental study as a purely individual and intellectual exercise. But this effort can never again be wholly private or academic, for it is no longer possible to separate the study of environment from issues that will determine the fate of mankind.

REFERENCES

Armstrong, Terry R. (ed.), 1972, *Why Do We Still Have an Ecological Crisis?* Englewood Cliffs, N.J.: Prentice-Hall.

Ayres, Edward, 1970, *What's Good for GM.* Nashville: Aurora Publishers.

Barrows, Harlan H., 1923, "Geography as Human Ecology," *Annals of the Association of American Geographers*, Vol. 13, pp. 1-14.

Bell, Garrett de (ed.), 1970, *The Environmental Handbook Prepared for the First National Environmental Teach-In.* New York: Ballantine Books.

Bennett, Hugh H., 1939, *Soil Conservation.* New York: McGraw Hill.

Bowman, Isaiah (ed.), 1937, *Limits of Land Settlement.* New York: Council on Foreign Relations.

Buel, Ronald, 1972, *Dead End: The Automobile in Mass Transportation.* Baltimore: Penguin Books.

Burton, Ian and Robert W. Kates (eds.), 1965, *Readings in Resource Management and Conservation.* Chicago: University of Chicago Press.

Butzer, Karl W., 1964, *Environment and Archeology: An Introduction to Pleistocene Geography.* Chicago: Aldine.

Callahan, Daniel (ed.), 1971, *The American Population Debate.* Garden City, N.Y.: Doubleday.

Carson, Rachel, 1962, *Silent Spring.* Boston: Houghton Mifflin.

Cole, H. S. D. *et al.*, 1973, *Models of Doom: A Critique of the Limits to Growth.* New York: Universe Books.

Committee on Merchant Marine and Fisheries, 1972, *Administration of the Environmental Policy Act*, Appendix to Hearings Before the Subcommittee on Fisheries and Wildlife Conservation of the Committee on Merchant Marine and Fisheries, House of Representatives, Ninety-Second Congress, Second Session. Washington, D.C.: U.S. Government Printing Office.

Commoner, Barry, 1971, *The Closing Circle: Nature, Man, and Technology.* New York: Alfred A. Knopf.

Council on Environmental Quality, 1970-1973, *Environmental Quality.* 3 vols., Washington, D.C.: U.S. Government Printing Office.

Davis, William Morris, 1906, "An Inductive Study of the Content of Geography," *Bulletin of the American Geographical Society*, Vol. 38, pp. 67-84.

Detwyler, Thomas R. and Melvin G. Marcus (eds.), 1972, *Urbanization and Environment: The Physical Geography of the City.* Belmont, California: Duxbury.

Ehrlich, Paul, 1968, *The Population Bomb.* New York: Ballantine Books.

Ehrlich, Paul and Ann H. Ehrlich, 1970, *Population, Resources, Environment: Issues in Human Ecology.* San Francisco: W. H. Freeman and Company.

Eyre, S. R., 1971, "Man the Pest: The Dim Chance of Survival," *The New York Review*, November 18, pp. 18-27.

Eyre, S. R. and G. R. Jones (eds.), 1966, *Geography as Human Ecology: Methodology by Example.* London: Edward Arnold.

Farvar, M. T. and J. P. Milton (eds.), 1972, *The Careless Technology: Ecology and International Development.* Garden City, N.Y.: Natural Press.

Gellen, Martin, 1970, "The Making of a Pollution-Industrial Complex," *Ramparts*, Vol. 8, pp. 22-28.

General Motors Corporation, 1973, *Report on Progress in Areas of Public Concern.* Warren, Michigan: G.M. Technical Center.

Gillette, Robert, 1972, "The Limits to Growth: Hard Sell for a Computer View of Doomsday," *Science*, Vol. 175, pp. 1088-1092.

Glacken, Clarence J., 1967, *Traces on the Rhodian Shore: Nature and Culture in Western Thought from Ancient Times to the End of the Eighteenth Century.* Berkeley: University of California Press.

Goldman, Marshall I., 1972, *The Spoils of Progress: Environmental Pollution in the Soviet Union.* Cambridge, Mass.: M.I.T. Press.

Goldsmith, Edward *et al.* (eds.), 1972, "A Blueprint for Survival," *The Ecologist*, Vol. 2, No. 1. Also published (1972) as a book. Boston: Houghton Mifflin.

Graham, Frank, 1969, *Since Silent Spring.* Boston: Houghton Mifflin.

_____, 1971, *Man's Dominion: The Study of Conservation in America.* New York: M. Evans and Lippincott.

Hough, Franklin B., 1878-1884, *Report on Forestry.* 4 vols., Washington, D.C.: U.S. Government Printing Office.

Humboldt, Alexander von, 1850, *Views of Nature.* London: H. G. Bohn, p. 173. First published as *Ansichten der Natur* (Stuttgart, 1808).

Huntington, Ellsworth, 1945, *Mainsprings of Civilization.* New York: Wiley and Sons.

James, Preston E. and C. F. Jones (eds.), 1954, *American Geography: Inventory and Prospect.* Syracuse: Syracuse University Press.

Klein, Rudolph, 1972, "Growth and its Enemies," *Commentary*, Vol. 53, pp. 37-44.

Leighly, John (ed.), 1963, *Land and Life: A Selection From the Writings of Carl Ortwin Sauer.* Berkeley: University of California Press.

Lewthwaite, G. R., 1966, "Environmentalism and Determinism: A Search for Clarification," *Annals of the Association of American Geographers*, Vol. 56, pp. 1-23.

Lowenthal, David, 1961, "Geography, Experience, and Imagination: Towards a Geographical Epistemology," *Annals of the Association of American Geographers*, Vol. 51, pp. 241-260.

_____, 1962, "Not Every Prospect Pleases: What is Our Criterion for Scenic Beauty?" *Landscape*, Vol. 12, pp. 19-23.

_____ (ed.), 1967, *Environmental Perception and Behavior.* University of Chicago, Department of Geography Research Paper No. 109.

_____, 1968, "The American Scene," *Geographical Review*, Vol. 58, pp. 61-68.

_____, 1970a, "The Environmental Crusade: Ideals and Realities," *Landscape Architecture*, Vol. 60, pp. 290-296, 343.

_____, 1970b, "Recreation Habits and Values: Implications for Landscape Quality," in Pierre Dansereau (ed.), *Challenge for Survival.* New York: Columbia University Press, pp. 103-117.

_____ (ed.), 1972, "Human Dimensions of Environmental Behavior," *Environment and Behavior*, Vol. 4, pp. 251-342.

Lowenthal, David and Hugh C. Prince, 1965, "English Landscape Tastes," *Geographical Review*, Vol. 55, pp. 186-222.

Lowenthal, David and Ian Burton, Richard Cooley, and Marvin Mikesell, 1973, "Report of the AAG Task Force on Environmental Quality," *Professional Geographer*, Vol. 25, pp. 39-47.

Major, Jack, 1969, "Historical Development of the Ecosystem Concept," in George M. Van Dyne (ed.), *The Ecosystem Concept in Natural Resource Management.* New York: Academic Press, pp. 9-22.

Marcus, Melvin G., 1967, "Introductory Physical Geography in the College Curriculum," in *Introductory Geography: Viewpoints and Themes.* Publication No. 5, Commission on College Geography. Washington, D.C.: Association of American Geographers.

Marsh, George Perkins, 1864, *Man and Nature; or, Physical Geography as Modified by Human Action.* New York: Scribner.

Marx, Leo, 1970, "American Institutions and Ecological Ideals," *Science*, Vol. 170, pp. 945-952.

May, Jacques M., 1958, *The Ecology of Human Disease.* New York: Hafner.

McCamy, James L., 1972, *The Quality of the Environment.* New York: Free Press.

Meadows, Donella H. and Dennis L. Meadows, Jørgen Randers, and William W. Behrens, 1972, *The Limits to Growth: A Report for the Club of Rome's Project on the Predicament of Mankind.* New York: Universal Books.

Mikesell, Marvin W., 1970, "Cultural Ecology," in Philip Bacon (ed.), *Focus on Geography: Key Concepts and Teaching Strategies.* 40th Yearbook, National Council for the Social Studies. Washington, D.C., pp. 39-61.

Mitchell, John G. and Constance L. Stallings, 1970, *Ecotactics: The Sierra Club Handbook for Environmental Activists.* New York: Pocket Books.

Moncrief, Lewis W., 1970, "The Cultural Basis for Our Environmental Crisis," *Science*, Vol. 170, pp. 505-512.

Mumford, Lewis, 1958, *The Highway and the City.* New York: Harcourt, Brace and World.

Odum, Eugene P., 1971, *Fundamentals of Ecology.* 3rd edition, Philadelphia: W. B. Saunders.

_____, 1972, "Ecosystem Theory in Relation to Man," in John A. Wiens (ed.), *Ecosystem Structure and Function.* Corvallis: Oregon State University Press, pp. 11-24.

Parsons, James J., 1971, "Ecological Problems and Approaches in Latin American Geography," in Barry Lentnek, Robert L. Carmin, and Tom L. Martinson (eds.), *Geographical*

Research on Latin America: Benchmark 1970, Proceedings of the Conference of Latin Americanist Geographers, Vol. 1. Muncie, Indiana: Ball State University, pp. 13-32.

Pattison, William D., 1964, "The Four Traditions of Geography," *Journal of Geography*, Vol. 63, pp. 211-216.

Rostlund, Erhard, 1962, "Twentieth Century Magic," in Philip L. Wagner and Marvin W. Mikesell (eds.), *Readings in Cultural Geography*. Chicago: University of Chicago Press, pp. 48-53.

Saarinen, Thomas F., 1966, *Perception of the Drought Hazard on the Great Plains*. University of Chicago, Department of Geography Research Paper No. 106.

Sanders, Norman K., 1972, *Stop It! A Guide to Defense of the Environment*. San Francisco: Rinehart Press.

Sauer, Carl O., 1927, "Recent Developments in Cultural Geography," in E. C. Hayes (ed.), *Recent Developments in the Social Sciences*. Philadelphia: Lippincott, pp. 154-212.

Schneider, Kenneth, 1971 *Autokind versus Mankind*. New York: W. W. Norton.

Semple, Ellen C., 1904, *American History and its Geographic Conditions*. Boston: Houghton Mifflin.

Slesser, Malcolm, 1972, "Disaster Postponed," *The Ecologist*, Vol. 2, pp. 43-47.

Strong, Maurice F., 1973, "One Year After Stockholm: An Ecological Approach to Management," *Foreign Affairs*, Vol. 51, pp. 690-707.

Taaffe, Edward J. (ed.), 1970, *Geography*. Englewood Cliffs, N.J.: Prentice-Hall.

Tatham, George, 1951, "Environmentalism versus Possibilism," in Griffith Taylor (ed.), *Geography in the Twentieth Century*. New York: Philosophical Library.

Taylor, Griffith, 1940, *Australia: A Study of Warm Environments and Their Effect on British Settlement*. London: Methuen.

Thomas, William L. (ed.), 1956, *Man's Role in Changing the Face of the Earth*. Chicago: University of Chicago Press.

Train, Russell E., 1972, "The Quest for Environmental Indices," *Science*, Vol. 178, p. 121.

Tuan, Yi-Fu, 1970, "Our Treatment of the Environment in Ideal and Reality," *American Scientist*, Vol. 58, pp. 244-249.

Tyson, P. D., 1970, *Urban Climatology: A Problem of Environmental Studies*. Johannesburg: University of Witwatersrand Press.

U.S. Department of Housing and Urban Development, 1972, *Instructions for Loan and Guarantee Assistance, Urban Growth and New Committee Assistance Act of 1970*. Washington, D.C.: Department of Housing and Urban Development.

Wagner, Philip L., 1960, *The Human Use of the Earth*. Glencoe, Illinois: Free Press.

Ward, Barbara and René Dubos, 1972, *Only One Earth: The Care and Maintenance of a Small Planet*. New York: Norton and Company.

White, Gilbert F., 1972, "Environmental Impact Statements," *Professional Geographer*, Vol. 24, pp. 302-309.

White, T. Lynn, 1967, "The Historical Roots of Our Ecological Crisis," *Science*, Vol. 155, pp. 1203-1207.

Winn, Ira J., 1973, "The Psychology of Smog," *The Nation*, March 5, 1973, pp. 294-298.

Wolman, M. Gordon, 1971, "The Nation's Rivers," *Science*, Vol. 174, pp. 905-918.

Zelinsky, Wilbur, L. A. Kosiński, and R. M. Prothero (eds.), 1970, *Geography and a Crowding World*. New York: Oxford University Press.

Biogeochemical Cycles and Energy Flows in Environmental Systems

David Watts
University of Hull

This paper will be concerned with environmental systems from a functional point of view. To suit this purpose, the broadest interpretation of the words "environment" and "system" will be employed. Environment will be taken to mean all those physical and chemical, organic and non-organic components of the atmosphere, lithosphere (soil and bedrock), and oceans. Man is clearly an important organic part of the total environment and in view of his proven ability to modify the overall inter-relationships of other component parts, it is perhaps inescapable that he should be treated as a special case. Nevertheless one must never forget the fact that, equally inescapably, man must operate within the physico-chemical restraints imposed upon all members of the organic world and that ultimately his activities, and his survival, are dependent upon other biological communities.

The concept of systems study as applied in biogeography implies that the environment should be seen to function, both as a whole and in the interlinkages of its discrete parts, under the control of the laws of thermodynamics. Interactions between the organic and inorganic components of an environmental system, involving the input, transfer, storage and output of energy and essential materials through the system, are in the final analysis energy dependent (Figure 1). Under natural conditions, or when largely undisturbed by man, environmental systems tend to be self-regulatory. Through the process of ecological succession, they develop towards a stable, steady state condition where the maximum amount of biomass is maintained per unit of available energy flow. A steady state condition in environmental systems implies that a dynamic equilibrium between the input and outflow of energy and materials has been achieved. This condition is usually associated with the presence of a high degree of diversity of organic life forms. Should this degree of diversity be disturbed, a regression from steady state may occur to a situation in which patterns of input and outflow no longer balance. Steady state conditions are maintained by feedback mechanisms, concepts of which have been borrowed from the study of cybernetics to illustrate the idea that the precise patterns of

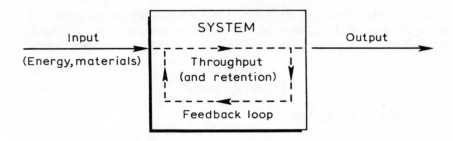

Figure 1. The Essential Function Controls of an Environmental System.

functioning of any system are largely controlled by a wide range of interlinked reactions among its component parts. Feedback mechanisms that serve to maintain a steady state condition are termed regulatory (or negative), such as that formed by the thermostatic control of a heating unit. Other feedback mechanisms, however, may be disruptive (or positive), as in the spread of epidemic diseases. In environmental systems, a simple negative feedback mechanism is that controlling the relationships between predator and prey, in which any increase in the numbers of a particular species is brought under control by the predator population. Most feedback mechanisms, however, are much more complicated than this and sometimes difficult to comprehend fully. To some extent, the appearance (i.e., form or structure) of systems will also reflect their functional status; thus a system which displays a steady state condition will tend to have a mature, or "climax," vegetation assemblage.

It should be emphasized that in most environmental systems undisturbed by man, it is the biological component that is of prime importance to the maintenance of the system. Moreover, the biotic community in its natural state is virtually self-supporting once it has received a supply of energy. As will be discussed in a later section of this paper, this is especially the case with respect to the demand for nutrients in mature systems. In the real world, the functioning of all environmental systems depends in large measure on three factors: (1) the transfer of energy through plants (either terrestrial or aquatic) and animals to provide the basic "drive" for the system; (2) the formation and maintenance of matter through complex molecular arrangements and rearrangements of chemical elements, a process which not only involves the storage and expenditure of energy (and hence facilitates the transfer of energy through the system), but which requires that the circulation of those chemical elements which constitute the growth substances of living organisms should not be impaired; and (3) the ability of a wide range of living organisms to adapt successfully to the environmental and demographic restraints that are imposed upon them. It is the first two of these which are to be examined in detail in this paper. It should also be stressed that environmental systems are open systems (as opposed to the closed systems so beloved of physical theorists, which allow for no outside interference) in that even when their boundaries can be clearly defined, they will be vulnerable to random inputs and outputs of energy and materials, as when dead leaves (and therefore energy) or animals move across the boundaries of the system. Under these circumstances, one may perhaps best study the functioning of systems by considering the transfers (or flux) of energy and materials across particular boundaries, as for example those between atmosphere and lithosphere, atmosphere and ocean, lithosphere and ocean, leaf and atmosphere, plants and animals, and it is this practice, the rationale of which was first formally suggested by Margalef (1968), which is to be followed herein.

ENERGY FLOW

The Atmospheric Energy Balance

Solar energy, the receipt of which by environmental systems is an essential prerequisite for most life forms, is transmitted through space to the earth's atmosphere along a broad spectrum of shortwave radiation bands. These may be broadly classified into visible light waves (0.36 to 0.76 μ), infrared radiation (in excess of 0.76 μ), and ultraviolet radiation (less than 0.36 μ). (One μ refers to a micron, or one millionth of a meter. Incoming solar energy falls mainly between 0.3 and 2.0 μ at sea-level, where visible light rays comprise about 50 percent and infrared about 40 percent, with the remainder in the ultraviolet segment.) Currently, radiation emitted from the sun is received at the outer fringes of the earth's atmosphere at a steady rate of two calories per cm^2 per minute, a value which despite being described as the solar constant is likely to have fluctuated slightly from time to time. The input of this shortwave energy through the outermost atmospheric interface (i.e., the theoretical upper limit of the atmosphere where it adjoins deep space) must ultimately be balanced by the equivalent outflow of both short and long-wave (heat) radiation, as described below.

The role of the earth's atmosphere as a shield which intercepts incoming radiation is well known. Certain constituents of the atmosphere, notably free oxygen (O_2), ozone (O_3), carbon dioxide (CO_2) and water vapor, absorb particular segments of the solar spectrum exceedingly well. Thus much of the ultraviolet radiation which penetrates the outermost atmospheric interface is absorbed by ozone layers in the upper stratosphere and to a lesser extent by oxygen throughout the whole vertical spread of the atmosphere. A good deal of the infrared radiation is absorbed by water vapor, carbon dioxide and oxygen along very specific and narrow spectral bands. Finally, some visible light waves are actively intercepted by ozone and oxygen. Atmospheric water vapor also serves to restrict the outward movement of long-wave radiation generated at the earth's surface and so encourages heat retention in the lower reaches of the atmosphere in a "greenhouse" effect. The overall consequences of atmospheric interference with the free input and outflow of energy to and from the earth's surface are demonstrated in Figure 2, which shows the patterns of mean energy exchange within the atmosphere and at the extreme upper and lower interfaces of the atmosphere (the latter being where it adjoins land and ocean surfaces), as calculated by Gates for the whole of the northern hemisphere (1956). This suggests that if the total quantity of incoming solar energy at the outermost edge of the atmosphere is taken to be 100 units, 34 units (25 units reflected from cloud surfaces plus 9 units scattered to space through refraction) are returned directly to space in unaltered form, leaving a balancing deficit of 66 units to be filled by long-wave units of terrestrial radiation from the earth's surface (10 units) and from the atmosphere (56 units). Atmospheric interception produces a situation in which, on average, only 47 per cent of the radiant energy

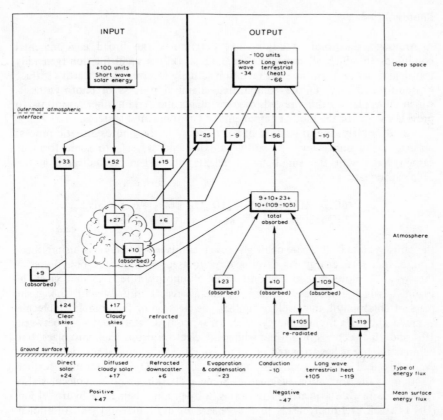

Figure 2. Patterns of Mean Energy Exchange or Energy Flux Within the Atmosphere for
the Whole of the Northern Hemisphere. Data from Gates: 1956.

received at the outer atmosphere reaches the earth's surface. These 47 units are
balanced by an equivalent outflow of longwave units, comprised of a net loss of
14 units by way of reflection and degraded heat energy (respiration) from plants
and animals, 23 units through evaporation and transpiration, and 10 units
through conduction. Of course, the actual amounts of incoming energy received
at particular points on the earth's surface may range considerably from this
mean. Due to the tilt of the earth's axis, for example, greater proportions of
incoming energy are lost through atmospheric reflection and refraction in higher
latitudes. Feedback mechanisms operate to ensure that a portion of the
correspondingly larger amounts of energy received in low latitudes is transported
to mid- and high-latitudes, so maintaining a hemispheric energy balance. The
complex processes, including the transfer of energy by advective means, i.e.,
through ocean currents and the major wind systems that contribute to the
maintenance of the earth's energy budget, are discussed in more detail in articles
by Hare (1960, 1965) and Stewart (1969) and in a later chapter by Terjung in
this volume. In a similar way, significant variations in radiant energy income will
occur on a diurnal basis, while even hourly variations in income may result from
cloud patchiness on a micro-scale (Garnier and Ohmura: 1969).

Photosynthesis

Although the total radiation flux determines the broad environmental conditions to which all organisms must adapt, only a small fraction (generally less than 5 per cent) of the solar radiation actually received at the earth's surface is transformed through the complicated chemical process of photosynthesis, which takes place within the cells of green plants and certain other organisms, to provide energy for the biotic components of environmental systems.

Stated crudely, the utilization of solar energy in the photosynthetic process results in the conversion of carbon dioxide and water into some form of carbohydrate with the simultaneous release of oxygen, as indicated in the following equation:

$$6CO_2 + 6H_2O \longrightarrow C_6H_{12}O_6 + 6O_2 + 673 \text{ kcals}$$
[One kilocalorie (or kcal) equals 1000 calories]

the carbohydrate in this case being glucose. But this is an extreme oversimplification, in that solar energy can never be *directly* used to produce carbohydrates in this way. A more precise demonstration of photosynthesis is that given in Figure 3, which indicates that radiant energy reacts initially with the green pigment chlorophyll, the result being that one electron of this complex molecule is raised above its normal energy level. This "excited" state lasts only between 10^{-7} and 10^{-8} seconds, following which the electron drops back into place, but before so doing it has triggered off other complicated chemical reactions, which eventually lead to the fixing of one molecule of CO_2 and through further reaction to the formation of glucose. Some reduction of other molecules also takes place in this sequence of reactions, a by-product being the hydroxyl ion (OH^-), which eventually leads to the release of molecular oxygen. Additional details of these processes may be found in a recent article by Hutchinson (1970). The glucose produced by the plant in this way represents a fairly large store of energy (673 kcals), which is then used for growth and respiration. Freshwater algae and oceanic phytoplankton are equally capable of fixing solar energy through photosynthesis and provide basic energy requirements for organisms in water bodies. Those organisms which can transform radiant energy in this way, and so manufacture food from simple chemical substances, are termed *autotrophic* organisms.

Although the rate of fixation of solar energy by autotrophs is usually between 0.1 and 1 per cent of the energy received at the ground or water surface, some notable exceptions do occur. Certain extremely productive plant communities (including sugar beet, some deciduous forests, and algae in shallow water) may at peak rates of growth convert solar energy at rates of over five per cent of the amount reaching the earth's surface. In contrast, energy in open oceans may be so diffused by scattering downwards among the water particles as to reduce the availability of energy per unit area. This, plus the relative scarcity of nutrients in the upper layers of the ocean, may reduce the rate of energy fixation by phytoplankton to a good deal less than 0.1 per cent. Rates of photosynthesis among *individual* species in terrestrial systems are also known to vary substantially not only on an annual basis, but also diurnally and seasonally (often being much greater towards midday and in spring) as a response to minor changes in environmental conditions (Hodges: 1967; Watts: 1971). Other factors affecting individual rates of photosynthesis, which have been reviewed by

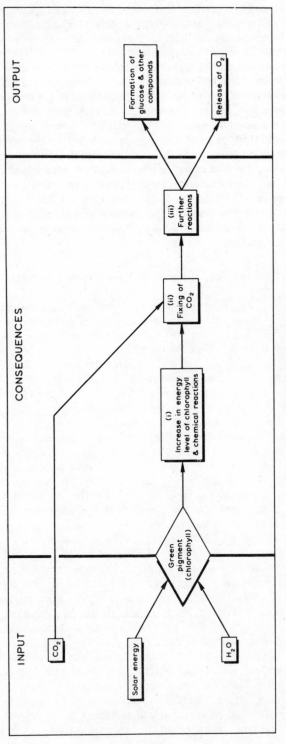

Figure 3.   The Photosynthetic Process.

Jahnke and Lawrence (1965), relate to the density of species spacing and to the geometric form of species, particularly the height of the crown and the reflectivity and transmissivity to light of vegetation surfaces as determined by leaf shape, texture, thickness and orientation.

Once fixed by autotrophs, energy is then available for transfer down the food chain to *heterotroph* consumer organisms (e.g., herbivores, carnivores, and omnivores such as man), which are entirely dependent upon the energy stored in autotrophs for their own energy requirements. At each stage in the transfer of energy from one organism to another (plant eaten by animal; animal eaten by animal), the overall store of energy in organic cells within the food chain is reduced, since energy is needed to do the work involved in effecting the transfer. As this work is done, the used energy is transformed to, and released as heat, to form part of the long wave quotient of energy leaving the earth's surface. This long wave energy is of course no longer available for use by the biotic component of environmental systems. The several implications of these patterns of energy transfer as far as the structure of such systems are concerned are discussed in the next section.

Potential Restraints on the Flow of Energy in Environmental Systems

It has already been suggested that, under natural conditions, mature environmental systems will customarily have a large number of different species within them. Indeed, the proposition that the greater the species diversity found within a system, the more stable will that system be, is one which has been supported by a large number of ecologists, but perhaps nowhere more lucidly than in the writings of Charles Elton, whose studies of Wytham Wood in Oxfordshire, England and of the ecology of invasions are classics in their field (1958, 1966). Other researchers have commented on the marked instability of systems which have an impoverished fauna and flora, this being particularly notable in the case of isolated oceanic island systems (Harris: 1965; MacArthur and Wilson: 1967; Watts: 1970). It has further been argued convincingly by Hutchinson (1959) that the species diversity which is characteristic of stable systems is ultimately essential to the survival of life as we know it. Certainly, to take a simple example, an organic community comprised solely of herbivores would eventually die of starvation, in that they could not convert solar energy into the chemical energy required for basic life processes.

Particular patterns of species diversity may be affected by two important constraints on organic life forms, the availability of food (energy and matter), and the existence of an environment suited to their body metabolism. Limitations on plant life, dependent as they are on the receipt of solar energy, will normally be defined only by the space available for growth, other environmental conditions permitting; in contrast, those for animals will be much more specific, being determined essentially by the organization of the system and the patterns of energy flow within it. As regards the second potential constraint, given time both plants and animals will tend to adapt successfully to a wide range of environmental conditions, which may at times be quite adverse. This adaptation may involve anatomical modifications and/or the evolution of superior patterns of competition among plants; and the establishment of particular behavioral mechanisms and patterns of competition and avoidance in the case of animals. Perhaps the all-important point raised by a consideration of these inter-relationships is the functional interdependency of the components that make up an environmental system.

Environmental systems must also function within the constraints set by the first two laws of thermodynamics, which must operate at every level of energy exchange. The first of these laws, the *law of the conservation of energy*, states that energy may be altered from one form (i.e., state) into another, but may neither be created nor destroyed. Thus the chemical energy of food which is consumed and utilized in work by an organism, will ultimately be transformed into an exactly equivalent amount of heat energy, assuming that none is stored within the organism. In a similar manner, the quantity of energy leaving an environmental system through heat loss must equal the amount of energy entering it, again assuming that there is no change in storage of energy within the system. Such a concept may be expressed in a very simple equation:

$$\Delta E = Q + W$$

in which ΔE represents changes in the internal energy of the system (or changes in input), Q represents the heat (of respiration) given off by the system, and W represents the work (of growth, etc.) done within the system *and* by implication the latent energy stored in the bodies of plants and animals within the system. This may be related to real life situations by considering the transfer of energy within the producer level of a simple ecosystem—Silver Springs, Florida—first studied by H. T. Odum in 1957 (Figure 4). Here, the solar energy transformed in photosynthesis (E), or the *gross primary productivity* of this spring system, amounted to 20,810 kcals/m^2/year. The heat given off in respiration by the autotrophic community (Q) amounted to 11,977 kcals/m^2/year, while the energy stored by autotrophs (i.e., the *net primary productivity*, or W), was 8,428 kcals/m^2/year, this being the amount of energy available for passage down the food chain to consumer organisms. But in this, as in most other natural situations, a strict accounting of energy use by particular groups of organisms does not result in a completely balanced budget, leaving some energy apparently unaccounted for (405 kcals/m^2/year). In point of fact, this energy is transferred in a subsidiary *decomposer* food chain (as opposed to the *grazing* food chain noted above), providing the energy requirements of those microorganisms (e.g., bacteria, fungi) which are responsible for the decay of organic matter after death. Relationships between the two food chains are complex, there being many interlinkages involving the transfer of energy and matter between a wide range of organisms within each chain.

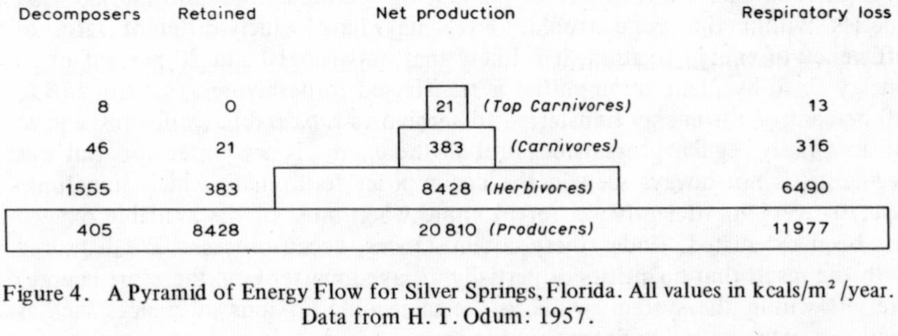

Decomposers	Retained	Net production		Respiratory loss
8	0	21	(*Top Carnivores*)	13
46	21	383	(*Carnivores*)	316
1555	383	8428	(*Herbivores*)	6490
405	8428	20810	(*Producers*)	11977

Figure 4.   A Pyramid of Energy Flow for Silver Springs, Florida. All values in kcals/m^2/year. Data from H. T. Odum: 1957.

While the first law of thermodynamics sets out the framework for energy exchange, the second is more concerned with the pattern of energy flow and relates specifically to the decline in the quantity of energy available for work, growth and storage after each stage of energy transfer in food chains. It states that entropy, a term which relates to the degree of disorder among the elementary particles of matter, will increase after each energy conversion. Since of all forms of energy in environmental systems, heat most closely approaches a state of maximum entropy, being characterized by a high degree of disordered particles, this law may be invoked to explain the energy which leaves such systems in the form of heat energy (respiration) after each transfer of energy along the food chain and which contributes towards the longwave fraction of our global energy loss. It has already been demonstrated in Figure 4 that the quantities of energy transformed into heat through respiration at the producer level can be considerable, and a similar relationship exists at each subsequent transfer of energy along a food chain.

How does this second law affect the structure of environmental systems? To answer this, we need to refer in greater detail to the concept of energy passing through a system by means of a food chain, though it is usually the case that organisms will transfer energy in a manner more indicative of a food web than a simple chain. Steps in the transfer of food within the chain or web are termed *trophic levels.* The first trophic level on land (the producers) will therefore be green plants, the next will be comprised of herbivores or omnivores, and subsequent levels will be of carnivores or omnivores. Often, a graphic representation of the energy or biomass totals present in each trophic level will result in a pyramidical form, such as that presented in Figure 4, termed an Eltonian pyramid after Charles Elton who first used them (1927). Usually the restrictions on energy availability imposed by the accumulative heat loss through respiration, means that each environmental system will normally support no more than five trophic levels, though exceptions may occur if the efficiency of energy transfer between levels is very good. In the case of Silver Springs, Florida, for example, it will be seen that the energy input, and the types of organism present in the system, were unable to support more than four trophic levels.

Theoretical considerations relating to the differential rate of energy fixation and loss at each trophic level were first considered by Lindemann (1942). His work suggested that in natural systems some percentage of the energy flow entering any population would always be available for transfer to those subsequent populations that fed upon it, without in any way endangering the stability of the system. In fact, the actual amount of energy transferred from one level to another will vary according to environmental circumstances and the type of food chain. In the case of the grazing food chain, despite the fact that species within the same trophic level may have widely-different rates of efficiency of energy fixation, it is likely that between 10 and 20 percent of all energy fixed by plant communities is transferred to herbivores, that from 10 to 20 percent of the energy transferred to herbivores is passed to carnivores, and so on in a fairly regular progression until all the energy is accounted for. But this regularity is not always seen in the decomposer food chain which sometimes operates very inefficiently, as for example when most of the available oxygen has been exhausted. Under these circumstances, decay processes are disrupted with the result that quantities of partially-decayed matter (and therefore energy) are left within the system, while at the same time noxious substances such as methane, alcohols and hydrogen sulfide are produced.

Energy Flow, Function and Form of Environmental Systems

It has already been implied, though not explicitly stated, that environmental systems will attain a steady state condition only when the input of energy equals the output of energy from the system. In reality, this means that if a steady state situation is to be achieved, the gross primary production of the system must be equalled by the total respiration of all organisms within the system, once the work required to maintain the system has been completed. If this is not the case, some energy must have been stored in new biomass, so initiating changes in structure. From this, one may hypothesize that plant communities which are in the early stages of succession will be characterized by a reasonably high degree of retention of energy, but that the amounts retained will decrease as mature, "climax" conditions are approached. Although for technical reasons it is difficult to record complete respiration totals in natural conditions, such detailed measurements as do exist tend to bear out these suppositions. Thus in a late-successional mixed oak-pine forest at the Brookhaven National Laboratory on Long Island, New York, Woodwell (1970) has estimated that the mean annual respiration over one year amounted to approximately 80 percent of the energy input into the forest, although some distinct fluctuations from this mean occurred between summer and winter.

Productivity Pattern: Regional and Local Differences

Over the world as a whole, the total annual production of dry organic matter is of the order of 164,000 million tons, of which approximately two-thirds occurs on land and one-third in the oceans. New biomass, or the net primary production of biological systems, is of course not distributed equally over the face of the earth. Probably the first reasoned attempt at summarizing both regional and local differences in productivity was that prepared by E. P. Odum (1959), which classified environmental systems into those which were relatively unproductive, such as open oceans and land deserts; those which were moderately productive, such as continental shelf areas, shallow lakes, moist grasslands, mesophytic and dry forests, and "ordinary" agricultural lands; and those which had high production rates, such as estuaries, coral reefs, moist forest, alluvial plains and intensively cultivated lands. Extremely high rates of production (in excess of 20 grams of dry organic matter/m^2/day) are likely to be found in a very few natural communities, in polluted waters, and in some intensively farmed croplands. Odum's conclusions have been largely confirmed by subsequent investigators (Ovington: 1965; Gerloff: 1963; Olson: 1964; Westlake: 1963; Menhinick: 1967; Woodwell: 1970; Woodwell and Whittaker: 1968; Bray and Gorham: 1964), who have compiled summaries of net rates of primary production (or of litter production) in a wide range of land and water communities. Characteristic values of net primary production for several types of environmental systems, as abstracted from these works, are presented in Table 1. This table demonstrates that on land, tropical mountain areas which have both a high level of energy income and an ample supply of moisture fix most energy. Productivity rates fall away generally in subtropical and temperate latitude forests, although there is some considerable variation between different temperature communities. The decline in productivity continues as one approaches the taiga spruce and tundra systems of high latitudes. Major grassland

TABLE 1—Rates of Net Primary Productivity in Selected Environmental Systems

Values in gms of dry organic matter/m^2/yr.·

	Rate		Rate
Natural vegetation communities		*Freshwater communities*	
Tropical rain forest	3000-3700	Denmark	1500
Tropical mountain forest		Cattail swamp, Minnesota	2500
(Caribbean)	6000	*Spartina* swamp	2980
Sub-tropical deciduous		Grass swamp, USSR	7880
forest	2450		
Beech forest (Denmark)	1350	*Agricultural communities*	
Oak-pine forest		Sugar cane, Java	9400
(New York)	1195	Sugar cane, Hawaii	7500
Scots pine forest (U.K.)	1600	Palm plantations	3700
Taiga spruce forest		Rice	1200
(Siberia)	950	Maize, U.S.A.	2500-4000*
Dry savanna grassland		Small grain, potatoes, hay	340-1000*
(Ghana)	440	Grassland (New Zealand)	3200
Meadow steppe	1800	Meadowland	1240
Tall grass prairie	1200		
Tundra	180	*Polluted water*	
Harsh desert	110	Sewage ponds, California	5600
Oceans			
Mean (open ocean)	100		
Mean (coastal zone)	200		
Zones of upwelling	600		
Algae (Denmark)	400		
Algae, coral reefs	4900		

* Not including production of chaff, and other unused parts.

Data from Ovington: 1965; Gerloff: 1963; Olson: 1964; Westlake: 1963; Menhinick: 1967; Woodwell: 1970; Woodwell and Whittaker: 1968; Bray and Gorham: 1964.

areas vary substantially in production, but those which have an adequate water supply (e.g., tall grass prairie) may have substantially higher rates of productivity than dry savanna grasslands. Rates which are equivalent to those found in the harsh deserts may also be found in open oceans, except where above-average quantities of nutrients are available through upwelling or the mixing of major currents. In contrast, tropical reefs are usually extremely productive, as are also certain freshwater communities (especially swamps) in which the supply of nutrients is abundant, and many lakes and rivers polluted by fertilizing nutrients such as phosphates and nitrates.

Bearing in mind that approximately five per cent of all solar energy fixed by land plants occurs in agricultural systems designed solely for the support of man—a very imbalanced situation when one considers the myriad other species present on land surfaces—the current recorded values of productivity in cropland stand out as being generally high. However, as discussed by Manners in a later chapter, these values are to some extent misleading in that many of these agricultural systems depend not only on solar sources for their energy requirements, but on an artificial input of energy and other materials if they are to be kept free of weeds, cultivated satisfactorily, and harvested and marketed efficiently. This is especially true of modernized, "occidental" patterns of cropping which frequently demand the simplification of an agricultural system so as to obtain maximum economic gain, an extreme example of this being the repetitive cultivation of a single crop or monoculture. Yet even with artificial inputs of energy, highly simplified agricultural systems are sometimes less efficient in terms of transforming solar energy than the more complex natural communities standing adjacent to them, although, of course, the food yield to man is substantially higher. Note, for example, the lower range of productivity values found under mid-latitudinal small grain agriculture in comparison with the much higher rates characteristic of beech, oak-pine and Scots pine forest in similar latitudes. Indeed it is usually the case that the most efficient transformation of solar energy in agriculture occurs in those systems which best imitate natural conditions, i.e., those which have a full crop canopy with no bare soil (which of course has no means of converting solar energy). Many traditional agricultural systems, and especially those which have a mixed tree-herb canopy, such as the olive-wheat/barley agriculture of the Mediterranean small-scale farmer or the much more intricate association of cultivated trees and herbs found in tropical slash-burn agriculture, are exceptionally good in this respect. In contrast, the mechanized simplicity of modern agriculture, which often demands large open spaces between plants or a fallow period when soil is left bare of vegetation for part of the year, is often grossly inefficient. One other proposition which may be put forward from a consideration of these comparative values is that plant resources such as tree leaves and roots may at times represent a very effective means of transferring solar-derived energy to the human body, always assuming that sufficient quantities of the protein required by animal cells can be readily extracted from them.

In contrast to the generally high rates of net primary productivity found in cropland, the low rates found in open oceans suggest that food resources in this milieu may not be as great as is sometimes thought. Detailed studies of the trophic structure of oceans by Ryther (1963) have confirmed that as a whole the oceans cannot be expected to form the basis of any future food resource for man, even after taking into account those areas which are nutrient rich through upwelling and mixing. Ryther suggests that the sustainable yield of fish from all oceanic waters probably does not exceed 100,000,000 metric tons (wet weight), and, in view of the current annual catch of some 70,000,000 metric tons, concludes that the chances for future expansion of the world's fishing industry are limited. Moreover his calculations do not take into account the possible effects of oceanic pollution, including fish kills and the destruction of food chains, which undoubtedly have already depleted fish resources in some seas.

Recent Changes in the Pattern of Energy Transfer

So far, man's influence on the functioning of environmental systems has largely been ignored. It has, however, been stressed that many modern agricultural systems are artificially maintained by a large input of energy resources which are not directly solar-derived. The land area occupied by such systems has expanded greatly over the last two centuries at the expense both of natural communities and traditional agricultural systems. This expansion has resulted from the pressing need to provide more arable land for the production of a relatively small number of staple crops (notably small grains such as wheat, barley, and rice) to feed a rapidly-growing world population (Table 2), a steadily-increasing percentage of which is concentrated in major conurbations. Modern agricultural systems may indeed be viewed as the end-product of an experimental revolution in cropping no less real than that which followed the evolution of the first small-grain agriculture in the Near East approximately 10,000 years ago, which allowed the global population of mankind to advance well beyond the ten million hunters, gatherers, and collectors directly supported by the photosynthetic transformation of solar energy. Our current and continuing revolution has been stimulated by the adoption of radically new technologies including mechanization, irrigation, the chemical control of weeds and insects, and the breeding of plants and animals with ever-greater yields, with the result that for the first time approximately ten percent of the world's land surface has been put under the plough, with more under an intensive grass culture. This, in association with the developing patterns of urbanization and industrialization, represents a massive disturbance of natural systems on a scale hitherto unknown, many further details of which are discussed in detail elsewhere in this volume by Manners and Schmid.

In what ways do these developments directly affect the workings and the stability of environmental systems? Two trends are perhaps most critical. The first is directly concerned with a possible hemispheric reduction in the rates of solar energy fixation through photosynthesis following the replacement of complex and mature natural biological systems by extremely simple agricultural systems and concrete-and-brick urban and industrial sites. Added to this is the fact that many of the remaining natural communities are constantly modified by human pressures (the hunting of animals, amenity development), so that the grazing food chain is increasingly disturbed, and its efficiency accordingly lowered. A frequent consequence of these modifications is that a good deal of energy which normally would have flowed through the grazing food chain is diverted into the decomposer chain. At the same time, the closed nature of systems which was stressed at the beginning of this paper, begins to break down, causing interactions in both nutrient and energy flow *between* systems (e.g., land-ocean; mountain-plain) rather than within them.

Changes towards simplified, inefficient and unstable systems have been further compounded by a second major trend, man's interference with the delicate chemical balance of the environment. Although this is a topic which impinges on the next section of this paper, a few remarks which relate one such

TABLE 2—Increase in World Population and Arable Land since 1650

Date	Estimated world population (millions)	Estimated arable land (millions of ha.)
1650	545	250
1750	728	300
1800	906	370
1850	1171	490
1900	1608	720
1950	2550	1000
1970	3700	1290

Data from Carr-Saunders: 1936; United Nations Food and Agricultural Organization: 1970.

pattern of interference—the dumping of a wide range of toxic chemicals and pollutants on land and in water bodies—to the pattern of energy flow will be pertinent here. The initial impact of these activities is usually reflected in some structural modification of affected systems in that many organisms which live therein cannot adapt quickly enough to the man-induced chemical changes in the environment. As a result, formerly complex systems may quickly be changed to simple ones whose populations are instable. On land, grazing food chains tend to be shortened, while the decomposer chain is favored. Surviving plants may be small and hardy, as in the case of the mountains surrounding Los Angeles, California, where scrub oaks are replacing pines which are no longer able to survive the effects of drifting photochemical smog. Small herbivores, especially those which can reproduce quickly and frequently, may become more common. In polluted aquatic habitats, food chains are also simplified, and many of those organisms which lie at the top of the chain (mainly fish and certain birds) are removed, to be replaced by scavengers such as gulls and crabs. Even the food chains of decay, which are favored in these circumstances, may become so overburdened that they are unable to cope with the vast amounts of dead organic material found in heavily polluted waters, in which case dissolved oxygen is likely to be exhausted quickly and anaerobic life forms begin to predominate.

BIOGEOCHEMICAL CYCLING

In addition to a continuing source of energy, environmental systems need an adequate supply of chemical materials if they are to function satisfactorily. These are derived from simple substances which form a multiplicity of molecular arrangements and rearrangements as they pass through the organic world. The formation of each molecular combination involves the use of a certain amount of energy. Unlike the passage of energy, which is one-way, nutrients are continually being circulated within systems in a complex manner and so are potentially capable of being reused many times. These complicated movements, termed biogeochemical cycles by Vernadskii (1934) in recognition of the fact that they involve exchanges between the organic and inorganic world, are facilitated by the presence of a wide variety of living organisms. As in the case of energy flow, the ease of circulation of such elements is improved as the number of organisms and species in a system increases, while the maintenance of effective patterns of nutrient movement is essential to the stability of the system. Although miniscule exchanges have been detected both high in the upper troposphere and in deep bedrock (in which microorganisms live off oily liquids), most exchanges take place in the lowest levels of the atmosphere and the surface layers of land and ocean. In this zone, organic life is abundant and the annual turnover of materials enormous. Mason has calculated that assuming an average life cycle of one year for all the organisms within this zone and a relatively constant mass of organisms, the total turnover mass (i.e., the quantity of chemical materials taken up by living organisms and then returned to the environment following their death) for the period of known organic life would be approximately equivalent to the total mass of the earth (Mason: 1960).

All organisms within environmental systems take up a wide selection of nutrients from "pool" areas to be found in the atmosphere, oceans, soil and bedrock, process them to form the biological compounds needed for growth, and then return them to the environment through litter fall, decay and respiration. In oceans, the availability of nutrients for growth varies substantially according to the degree of mixing and upwelling, while on land environmental and physiological restraints curb their uptake to some extent. For most organisms, 17 elements are considered to be essential to life. Of these carbon (C), hydrogen (H), oxygen (O) and nitrogen (N) are derived mainly from atmospheric sources, and the remainder, namely potassium (K), calcium (Ca), magnesium (Mg), phosphorus (P), sodium (Na), sulfur (S), iron (Fe), copper (Cu), manganese (Mn), zinc (Zn), molybdenum (Mo), boron (B) and chloride (Cl), originate largely in soil and bedrock. Of these, only hydrogen and oxygen are freely available to organic life forms, and intricate routeways of recycling are needed before the others may be taken up by plants and animals. This means that under normal circumstances, neither the soil, bedrock, atmosphere nor oceans can by themselves support stable organic communities; some interaction between at least two and sometimes all of these is almost always required at least initially, though once mature systems have become established, such interactions may become less important. Altogether six elements (H, N, O, C, P, and S) show exceptional mobility in environmental systems, and we shall look in particular at the means and methods of movement of each of these; however, one should not forget that all of the other nutrients mentioned above have indispensable roles to play in the maintenance of life.

The Importance of Water to Biogeochemical Cycling

As a result of its existence in vapor, liquid, and solid form in the environment, and its ability to act as a solvent for most substances, much of the movement of nutrients in systems takes place through the medium of that most uniquely-flexible of all chemical substances—water. Moreover it is water which provides the hydrogen required by all living organisms. About 1500 million cubic kilometers of water are located on the earth's surface, of which approximately 97 percent is located in oceans and seas as salt water, 2.25 percent is locked up as ice in the Arctic and Antarctic and in continental glaciers, and 0.70 percent is present as ground water. The balance is distributed between lake water, atmospheric water vapor, and water within vegetation and animal biomass in the approximate ratio of 100:10:1. All of this water is potentially able to move along the complicated pathways of the hydrological cycle, a term used to describe the circulation of water between atmosphere, oceans, lithosphere, and living organisms. An understanding of the hydrological cycle involves a consideration of evaporation and transpiration rates from water bodies and life forms, condensation rates, the distribution of precipitation, rates of soil moisture recharge, surface runoff and a host of other factors. For a detailed account of the mechanisms of these aspects of the cycle, written by a geographer, the reader is referred to a comprehensive study by Ward (1967). The importance of water to the functioning of environmental systems has also been stressed in the concept of the solusphere, as introduced by Rainwater and White (1958), which incorporates all milieus through which chemical migrations occur, and in studies of water quality (Douglas: 1971).

Possibly the most critical phase of the hydrological cycle is that which involves the interchange of moisture between atmosphere and biosphere, for it is this which controls to a large extent many of the patterns of life and growth in the organic world. Once water has been absorbed by plants through their root systems, some hydrogen atoms will be extracted to be bound into plant structures through photosynthesis, but a much greater amount of water (about four times greater) will be retained in the main transpiration stream. The actual amounts of water which move in this way will vary considerably from place to place, depending in part upon the atmosphere's capacity to hold moisture, which is substantially greater in low latitudes than elsewhere (Table 3). The atmospheric controls that are primarily responsible for determining rates of evapotranspiration have been analyzed by several climatologists (Budyko: 1958; Penman: 1963; Thornthwaite: 1948; Carter and Mather: 1966; Thornthwaite and Hare: 1955), who have positively correlated the rates of uptake and movement of water in vegetation communities with the availability of energy.

Movements of water within major oceans through currents, tides, upwelling and so on, are also essential to the distribution and adequate provision of nutrients for marine organisms. Even the deepest ocean basins have their water (and thus their nutrients) replaced over periods of approximately one thousand years. However, it should be remembered that even though the replacement of water in deep ocean basins represents a fairly long-term cycle when compared to the cycling of other nutrients in environmental systems (e.g., the same carbon atoms respired from animals may be fixed again within the same species 300 years later), it is still much shorter in duration than either that of oxygen atoms which take 2000 years to cycle between the atmosphere and organic life forms, or of hydrogen atoms which may require 2 million years to be reconstituted in water molecules following their extraction from water in photosynthesis. This differential in the time factor of nutrient cycling clearly adds immeasurably to the complexity of organic system functioning.

The Cycling of Oxygen and Carbon

Oxygen is a particularly interesting element in that while it is essential to all forms of differentiated multicellular life, it is also potentially destructive of such life forms in oxidative metabolism. Accordingly, chemical defenses against the potential effects of oxidative metabolism are required within plant and animal cells. In this context, it should be noted that most cells use the energy of oxidative metabolism anaerobically, mainly through the removal of hydrogen from food materials rather than through the addition of oxygen. As a result of this dual role and of its presence in so many different molecular arrangements in both the organic and inorganic world, the pathways of oxygen cycling are almost impossible to trace in full.

Much more is known about the overall movement of carbon, the single most important element of organic chemistry. The main reservoir pool of available carbon is to be found as carbon dioxide (CO_2) in the atmosphere (Figure 5). Carbon is absorbed from this pool quickly and directly by plants through

TABLE 3—The Capacity of the Atmosphere to Hold Moisture

Temperature °C	Capacity g/liter
40	40.06
30	24.22
20	13.86
10	7.53
0	3.85

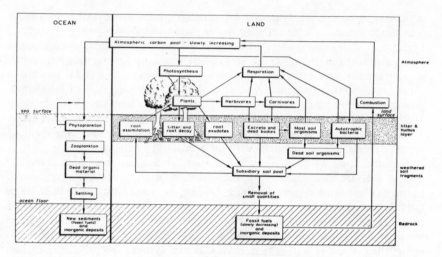

Figure 5.   The Carbon Cycle.

photosynthesis, to be converted in part into sugars and other growth substances. Some of the carbon incorporated into plant biomass in this process, however, is returned to the atmosphere through respiration and only approximately one half of the carbon removed from the atmosphere during photosynthesis is eventually added to the soil in decomposing litter. Carbon materials are also passed along the food chain from plants to consumer levels, with more carbon being returned to the atmosphere through animal respiration, and to the soil through decomposition and decay. The carbon which eventually reaches the soil forms an important subsidiary pool of this element. Small amounts may be secreted into this pool directly from plant roots in the forms of sugars, amino-acids, or other compounds, but much more is usually derived from the decay of plant roots. The greatest quantities of carbon within the soil pool, however, customarily come from the decay of surface litter. Thus in tropical rain forests, 548 kg/ha/year of soil carbon is derived from the decay of plant roots compared with 911 kg/ha/year from surface litter (Jackson and Raw: 1966). Patterns of decay in themselves are an extremely complex environmental phenomena, since different types of debris will be decomposed at varying rates depending upon the particular chemical structure, the prevailing climatic conditions and the degree of soil aeration. In addition to these major routeways of carbon on land, small amounts of atmospheric carbon are also used by autotrophic bacteria to directly synthesize organic compounds. This carbon is also eventually moved to the atmospheric or soil pools by means of respiration or decay. Roughly the same quantities of carbon transferred from the atmosphere to land systems (between 20,000 and 30,000 million metric tons each year) are also fixed in the oceans, although much less is known about the pathways of movement in aquatic environments.

Regional differences in the overall rate of carbon fixation on land can be broadly correlated with latitude, approximately 100 times more carbon being incorporated into plant biomass within tropical rain forest environments than in tundra or desert environments (Figure 6; see also the biomass totals of Table 4). More subtle influences, of a seasonal and diurnal nature, are also known to operate. In mid-latitudes, for example, plants take up noticeably more carbon dioxide in spring than at other times of the year, with the result that the rate of carbon fixation greatly exceeds the amount of carbon being returned to the atmosphere in respiration by surface and soil organisms. In consequence, a marked decrease in the carbon dioxide content of the atmosphere (at peak, a reduction to 70 percent of the normal total) occurs north of $30°N$ between April and September. According to Bolin (1970), this results in the fixation of about 6,000 million metric tons of carbon in new growth, about one-quarter to one-fifth of the world's annual total. Diurnal variations result from the fact that whereas respiration is a continuous process, photosynthesis is purely a daytime phenomenon. Observations have indicated, for example, that during summer months in certain mid-latitudinal forests CO_2 is present at tree top levels in concentrations of just over 300 parts per million at noon, as opposed to readings of 400 parts per million near the soil surface of the same communities at midnight.

Between 400,000 and 500,000 million metric tons of carbon are currently retained within the world's vegetation, while a further 700,000 million metric tons exist within the atmospheric pool. But much more than this (roughly 99 percent of the earth's carbon, or 20×10^{15} metric tons) is not readily available to living organisms, being locked semipermanently in inorganic deposits (carbonates, such as limestones or chalk) or organic fossil fuels (e.g., coals, petroleum, oil shale). One recent modification of the delicate balance of the carbon cycle has been the release to the atmosphere of a substantial quantity of this stored carbon (*ca.* 5,000 to 6,000 million metric tons) since the industrial revolution through the burning of fossil fuels for domestic and industrial purposes. This has resulted in an increase in mean atmospheric CO_2 concentrations over the last hundred years from 290 to 320 parts per million, with forecasts of a further increase to between 375 and 400 parts per million by the

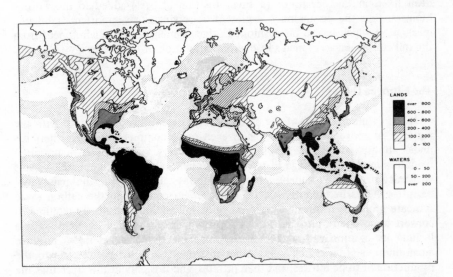

Figure 6.   The Annual Worldwide Fixation of Carbon. All values in grams of carbon per square meter per year. Adapted from Lieth: 1964-1965.

end of this century if recent exponential rates of growth in the consumption of fossil fuels are maintained (Bolin: 1970; Keeling: 1970). At the same time, the massive clearance of natural and semi-natural vegetation communities on a world scale since the eighteenth century has affected the overall rate of movement of carbon dioxide between the atmosphere and the biosphere. The implications of such changes are obviously immense, though no clear indications as to what they may ultimately entail have as yet been forthcoming. It has, however, been suggested by Plass (1956) that the increase in the atmospheric carbon dioxide may be sufficient to inhibit outgoing longwave radiation, thereby resulting if present trends continue in an amelioration of mean world temperatures by approximately $2°C$ by 2000 A.D., with consequential changes in sea level through icecap melting. Others have argued that the increasing cloudiness and turbidity which have characterized world climates since 1960 will offset any such trend and point to the fact that world temperatures over this period have fallen by about $0.1°C$ rather than risen as might have been anticipated (Mitchell: 1961; Davitaya: 1969; Wendland and Bryson: 1970; Bryson: 1968). Peterson (1969) has postulated that whether or not turbidity increases, any initial rise in world temperatures due to an increase in atmospheric carbon dioxide automatically paves the way for an increase in atmospheric moisture, a greater degree of cloudiness, and, accordingly, higher world atmospheric reflectivity quotients which would affect the overall patterns of solar energy income at ground surface level. The eventual effects of these interactions might be not to raise, but rather to reduce air temperatures. Further consideration of these several hypotheses are to be found in papers by Keeling (1970), Pales and Keeling (1965), Eriksson and Welander (1956) and Lieth (1963), in a recent book by Bach (1972), and in the chapter by Terjung in this volume.

That such changes will affect *all* environmental systems may be surmised from the fact that the increased quantity of CO_2 in the atmosphere is known to account for only one-third of the amount emitted through the burning of fossil fuels since the beginning of the industrial revolution. The rest has presumably been fixed in the oceans or (a small fraction at best) added to the world's biomass; thus the oceans may at present be serving as an important stabilizing mechanism which has so far cushioned other segments of the environment from the full consequences of man's inadvertent alteration of this cycle.

The Nitrogen Cycle

If man's modification of the carbon cycle is great, his interference with the patterns of movement of nitrogen is even more comprehensive. An inert gas under atmospheric conditions, but one with a very large number of potential oxidation levels, the passage of nitrogen through natural environmental systems is characterized by extremely complex routeways. Like carbon, the major pool of nitrogen lies in the atmosphere. However, in contrast to the carbon cycle intricate processes involving a wide range of soil microorganisms are required to convert atmospheric nitrogen into a form which can be used by plants. These include its fixation within the soil, its mineralization by bacteria to produce ammonium salts, at which point other microorganic activity gives rise to the production of toxic nitrites, and then nitrates; and it is only at this stage that the nutrient may be safely absorbed by plant roots. Subsidiary sources of soil nitrogen, which are derived from decaying organic material, must also undergo these chemical transformations before being available for plant use. Other bacteria, through the process of denitrification return nitrogen to the atmosphere in gaseous form, so completing the cycle (Figure 7). Only very small amounts of nitrogen are present in bedrock.

Of the many stages in the nitrogen cycle, the passage of nitrogen from atmosphere to soil and from soil to atmosphere, is perhaps most critical to the efficient functioning of environmental systems. Nitrogen moving from the atmosphere is fixed within the soil in several ways. Some may be added to the soil as ammonium and nitrate ions in rainwater or other forms of precipitation, and while this normally results in the input of only very small quantities (0.38 to 3.8 kg/ha/year), on occasions the amount deposited in this way may be very significant (Nye and Greenland: 1960). Much more nitrogen fixation occurs through the activities of soil microorganisms. Some of these microorganisms live symbiotically on the roots of particular plant species, while others have "free-living," non-symbiotic relationships with other life forms. In particular regions, both groups of microorganisms may be almost equally important to the nitrogen cycle: thus 18.2 to 23.7 kg/ha/year of nitrogen is fixed non-symbiotically in Nigerian grasslands as opposed to 18.2 to 36.4 kg/ha/year through symbiotic fixation (Nye and Greenland: 1960). The latter is of course only viable if suitable host plants exist for the nitrogen-fixing microorganisms, and legumes are especially important in this context. Often the associations between microorganisms (usually bacteria) and host plants are very specific. Those strains, for example, which fix nitrogen in lucerne may be totally ineffective on clovers and *vice versa*. *Rhizobium* bacteria, two species and many strains of which exist, are the predominant nitrogen-fixers on legumes. But many other plants play a similar role in nitrogen fixation in association with so far unidentified bacteria; among these are cycads, ginkgoes, alders, sea buckthorn (*Hippophae rhamnoides*), bog myrtle (*Myrica gale*), *Ceanothus* species, and the tropical *Casuarina*. The non-symbiotic fixation of nitrogen may also be accomplished by several groups of microorganisms, the most widely distributed of which are three species of *Azotobacter* bacteria, which commonly live in environments characterized by well aerated soils. Members of the *Beijerinckia* genus often fulfill an identical bacterial role in the tropics, while on wet acid soils the anaerobic bacterial genus *Clostridium* may be another very effective nitrogen-fixer. Nitrogen may also be fixed in soil and water by blue-green algae which, unlike other nitrogen-fixers, can also photosynthesize. In certain agricultural environments, notably wet rice fields, such algae may be able to fix nitrogen so efficiently as to provide all the nitrogen requirements of the crop.

While there are still many gaps in our knowledge of the nitrogen-fixing process, many more exist in our understanding of denitrification. As a general rule, however, it may be said that denitrification is often unimportant in aerobic environments, in which free oxygen tends to be used most efficiently in oxidizing organic compounds rather than in reducing nitrate salts. Waterlogged conditions, such as those found in swamps, bogs or tundra, are much better suited for the return of nitrogen to the atmosphere as a result of the activities of anaerobic bacteria such as *Pseudomonas denitrificans* and *Micrococcus denitrificans*, while other denitrification processes may also take place close to soil water tables. It is difficult to overemphasize the importance of the denitrification process to environmental systems, for without such a process much of the atmospheric nitrogen required by living organisms would now be locked in new sediments or in the oceans in forms unavailable for use by the biotic community.

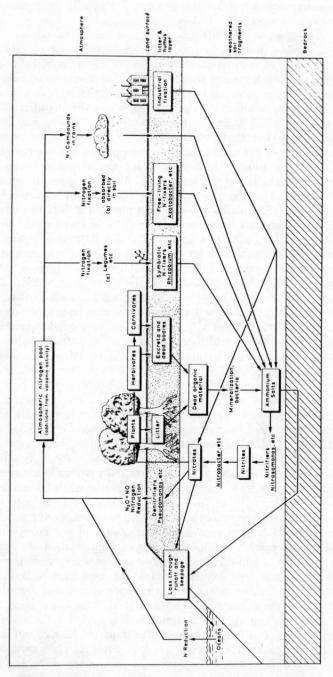

Figure 7.   The Nitrogen Cycle.

Recently, the balancing mechanisms of this cycle have been massively interfered with by man in two major respects. First, an enormous quantity of nitrogen has been fixed industrially and applied to the soil as synthetic fertilizer during the last century. The total amount of nitrogen fixed in this way is now in the order of 30 million tons annually, a figure which is equivalent to that fixed naturally by all terrestrial systems before the development of modern agriculture (Delwiche: 1970). Reliable estimates suggest that industrial nitrogen-fixation could reach 100 million tons annually by the end of the twentieth century. Secondly, a much wider use of nitrogen-fixing legumes, from which as much as 350 kg/ha of nitrogen may be produced each year under favorable cropping routines (Delwiche: 1970), has further increased the quantities of nitrogen fixed in modern agricultural systems. Yet at the same time denitrification processes are not keeping pace with the increased rate of nitrogen fixation, with the result that there has been a gradual buildup of fixed nitrogen in certain environments, particularly rivers and lakes. It has been suggested that the buildup of nitrates in water bodies contributes to the process of eutrophication, although recent research suggests that it is the availability of phosphates rather than nitrates that is critical. In a subsequent chapter in this volume by Manners, this, together with some further effects of the nitrate buildup in particular environments, are examined more closely. One other general consequence of the application of artificial nitrogen fertilizers in modern agricultural systems is that it may trigger off a greater demand for other elements needed in plant growth (especially K, P, Mo), thus leading to additional chemical imbalances in affected areas.

The Phosphorus and Sulfur Cycles

The two remaining major elements which are absolutely indispensable for the maintenance of life (phosphorus and sulfur) have very different patterns of movement to those of carbon and nitrogen. Phosphorus, once described as the weakest link in the chain of elements necessary to life (Wells, Huxley and Wells: 1931) and without which photosynthesis could not take place, has its sole pool area in bedrock. Moreover, its movement from bedrock to ocean would be one-way were it not for the feedback loop provided by organic systems (Figure 8). Within this loop, the uptake of orthophosphate ions ($H_2PO_4^-$) or mineral phosphate is encouraged either directly by plant roots, or, more especially, indirectly through the activities of mycorrhizae (certain fungi which live symbiotically on roots). The phosphate taken up in this way is then transferred along the food chain before being returned to the soil as a result of decomposition and decay. The operational efficiency of this loop is known to vary seasonally as more phosphorus is in circulation in the spring and early summer than at other times of the year, a feature which may reflect its gradual storage in the basal internodes of plant systems during the winter months and its subsequent rapid release during the main growing season. If the loop is interfered with to any great extent, as in the case of vegetation clearance, the movement of phosphorus could revert at least in the short term to being one-way, with a gradual accumulation of phosphorus in the oceans. As the return of phosphorus to the land is almost entirely dependent upon the geological uplift of ocean sediments, for all practical purposes this represents a permanent loss to other terrestrial systems, only a small amount being returned to land in fish catches (*ca.* 3 to 6 percent of the total reaching the ocean

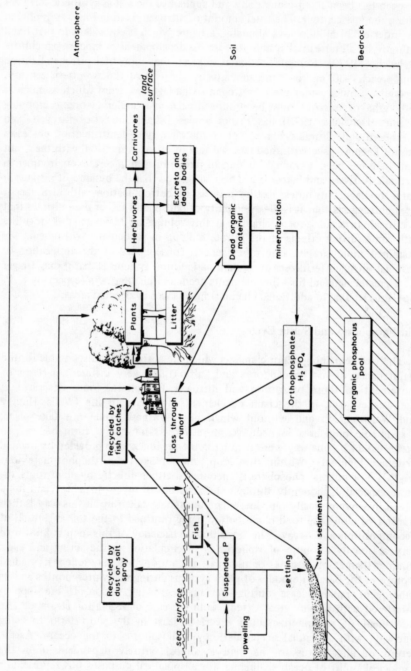

Figure 8. The Phosphorus Cycle.

according to Hutchinson), salt spray, or occasional dust (Hutchinson: 1954). As in the case of nitrogen, the phosphorus cycle has also been drastically modified in the last two centuries through the use of large amounts of phosphatic fertilizers (guano, or mined phosphatic rock) in agricultural systems. But much of the fertilizer is removed easily and quickly from such systems through erosion, to eventually settle, like nitrates, in lakes and ponds and so further encourage eutrophication.

The main pool of sulfur is also to be found in the bedrock, from where it moves through the biological component of environmental systems in a manner which resembles phosphorus. The major difference as far as the sulfur cycle is concerned is that an additional feedback loop operates to recycle sulfur from water bodies or swamps back to land systems through the atmosphere. The existence of this was first suggested by the discovery that the amount of sulfur released from the bedrock was too small by a factor of about three to account for the annual movement of sulfate to water bodies (Eriksson: 1959, 1960; Deevey: 1970). It is now estimated that over the world as a whole, about two-thirds of the sulfur present within the atmospheric feedback loop reaches the atmosphere as sulfides through the action of bacteria living in muds (especially fresh-water muds) and decomposition under anaerobic conditions. The sulfides are then oxidized to sulfur dioxide, ultimately giving rise to sulfate and sulfuric acid after being dissolved in rain water. The rest of the atmospheric sulfur dioxide is a recent addition, caused through emission of sulfur dioxide from industrial sources. This may be sufficiently important to account for almost all sulfate deposited by rain in and around heavily polluted areas. Before being deposited as sulfate, however, the industrially-derived SO_2 may give rise to greatly accelerated rates of erosion of metal and stone and to the aggravation of irritant lung diseases such as bronchitis and emphysema. The amount of sulfur dioxide present in the atmosphere in heavily polluted areas is often substantial; thus in the industrial West Riding of Yorkshire, sulfur dioxide quantities have reached values as high as 100 parts per million under exceptional circumstances, though values are usually very much lower than this (Gorham: 1958).

Major Regional Differences in Biogeochemical Cycling Patterns

As well as considering the global circulation pattern for individual nutrients, it is also necessary to examine the general pattern of nutrient cycling within particular systems since major regional differences both in the quantity of nutrients in circulation and in the nature of the overall circulation pattern are known to occur. As a general proposition, one would expect greater quantities of materials to circulate in those carbon-rich systems characterized by the greatest amounts of biomass and litter, i.e. in humid forested areas of the tropics. Table 4 indicates that this is indeed the case. These systems, however, are not necessarily the most effective movers of elements in terms of the *relative* quantities of elements in circulation per unit of biomass. Indeed, certain deserts, grasslands and tundra systems are often much more effective in this respect (see column 6 of Table 4), though at times this effectiveness may be either of a seasonal nature or (as in the case of savanna grasslands as described by Hills in a subsequent chapter in this volume) confined to particularly favorable sites. One would further infer some degree of relative advantage for nutrient circulation in

TABLE 4—Biomass & Element Circulation in Selected Environmental Systems

System	Biomass				Ash elements & nitrogen in circulation					
	Total Biomass kg/ha	% Green part	Total litter fall kg/ha	Floor litter kg/ha	Total elements in circ. (kg/ha/yr)	Elements in circ./ biomass	N in circ. (kg/ha/yr)	Ash elements in circ. kg/ha/yr	%N/Ash	Major elements in litter fall
Tropical rain forest	>5000	8	250	20	11081	2.22	2940	8141	27/73	Si,N,Ca
Subtropical decid- uous forest	4100	3	210	100	5283	1.29	1359	3924	26/74	N,Ca,K
Beech forest	3700	1	90	150	4196	1.13	1608	2588	38/62	Ca,N,Si
Taiga spruce forest	1000	8	35	300	970	0.97	350	620	36/64	N,Ca,K
Dry savanna (Ghana)	268	11	72	–	978	3.65	238	740	24/76	Si,N,Ca
Meadow steppe (USSR)	250	32	137	120	1183	4.73	274	909	23/77	Si,N,Ca
Semishrub desert	125	14	95	–	185	1.48	61	124	33/67	N,Ca,K
Harsh desert	16	13	6	<1	143	8.94	31	112	22/78	Cl,Na,N
Arctic tundra	50	30	ca.10	35	159	3.18	81	78	51/49	N
Forest-sphagnum bogs	370	41	25	<1000	609	1.65	229	380	38/62	N,Si,Ca

Data from Rodin and Basilevic: 1967.

those systems whose green-part biomass (e.g., leaves) forms a large proportion of the whole, as opposed to those systems in which nutrients are fixed for some time in non-photosynthetic woody growth. Other things being equal, the rates of biogeochemical cycling are likely to be facilitated in those systems where the processes of decomposition operate very quickly, as in tropical and equatorial rain forests, as compared to those forests of mid- and high-latitudes, in which rates of decay are slower and litter accumulation is greater.

In a thorough analysis of available world-wide data, Rodin and Basilevic (1967) have further suggested that five major and biologically meaningful types of nutrient circulation pattern may be broadly delimited by considering variations in the quantity of ash elements and nitrogen taken up from and returned to the soil by plant assemblages over the course of a year. (Carbon will, of course, be taken in from the atmosphere in all plant communities by means of the photosynthetic process but is by no means as significant a criterion in the differentiation of nutrient circulation patterns.) First, in regions which are predominantly marshy and potentially anaerobic (e.g., the tundra), the movement of nitrogen exceeds that of all other such elements. Second, a group of communities exist in which nitrogen circulation, although somewhat less important, still retains its overall preponderance: this is the case in certain coniferous and deciduous temperate forests and in sub-tropical forests. Third, calcium is the most common of the ash elements in circulation in many broad-leaved temperate forests (e.g., beech), where it can comprise between 40 and 54 percent of the ash litter. Fourth, steppe and savanna grasslands as well as many deserts and tropical rain forests are characterized by a pattern of ash element and nitrogen cycling dominated by silicon, with subsidiary amounts of iron and aluminum (50 to 60 percent silicon in ash litter, 10 to 15 percent iron and aluminum). And fifth, some harsh deserts may have more chloride in circulation than any other of these elements.

Local Patterns of Element Circulation: Stable and Instable Systems

Often our understanding of the movement of critical nutrients, and the ways in which these various cycles might be affected by man's disruptive influence, may be best furthered by detailed local studies. A clear advantage of this approach is that with care very precise balance sheets may be drawn up showing the input, output and retention for a variety of elements, so clarifying the interactions between organic community, lithosphere and atmosphere. This is not an easy task for the effective measurement of certain elements (especially nitrogen) under natural conditions presents the observer with many problems. However, a good deal of progress has recently been made in this direction, initially by ecologists and subsequently by geographers. The results of three such studies are indicated below in the form of three completed sets of data, two for mid-latitude forest areas and the other for a degraded moorland system.

The two forest communities are a young mixed oak forest growing on limestone at Virelles in Belgium, studied by a team led by Duvigneaud and Denaeyer-de-Smet, and a maturing second-growth deciduous forest in hilly country within the Hubbard Brook Experimental Station in the White Mountains of New Hampshire, U.S.A. (Duvigneaud and Denaeyer-de-Smet: 1970; Bormann and Likens: 1969; Likens, Bormann, Johnson and Pierce: 1967). Not only oak (*Quercus robur*), but hornbeam (*Carpinus betulus*) and beech (*Fagus sylvatica*) are dominant at Virelles, where rich shrub and ground layers are also present. At Hubbard Brook, sugar maple (*Acer saccharum*), beech (*Fagus grandifolia*) and yellow birch (*Betula alleghaniensis*) are the most common canopy species. Figure 9 displays the pathways for six elements within the Virelles forest and indicates that the rates of movement of particular nutrients may vary significantly within even a small area. Variations in the rate and pattern of movement of a particular nutrient occur, for example, from one dominant species to another. Ground flora is important to the cycling of certain elements (particularly K and P), while small quantities of all six elements are imported in rainwater and stream flow. The essential role played by litter in nutrient circulation is also demonstrated. An annual balance sheet (Table 5) suggests that even in nutrient-rich environments such as those which exist at Virelles, mature communities can be extremely frugal in their nutrient demands, needing only a few kilograms per hectare each year to maintain themselves. Similar conclusions may also be drawn from the Hubbard Brook data (Table 7), which shows an almost balanced budget for potassium and only minor losses of calcium, sodium and magnesium each year, despite the presence of slopes of up to 40 percent (with a few up to 70 percent) and an active stream which might have encouraged nutrient removal in solution or through erosion. These values strongly support the notion that it is the biological component which is primarily responsible both for the initial retention of nutrients and for the subsequent recirculation of nutrients, in that inputs from outside through precipitation, weathering and other means are relatively unimportant in mature environmental systems.

TABLE 5—Annual Element Balance (kg/ha) of Forest at Virelles

Element	K	Ca	Mg	N	P	S
Retained (increment)	16	74	5.6	30	2.2	4.4
Returned (losses)	53	127	13.0	62	4.7	8.6
Uptake	69	201	18.6	92	6.9	13.0

Data from Duvigneaud and Denaeyer-de-Smet, 1970.

From their research, Duvigneaud and Denaeyer-de-Smet conclude that even in small areas, clear sub-types of forest can be distinguished according to the pattern of element circulation. Indeed this is a proposition which follows naturally from the observation that one species may take up certain elements in very different proportions to its neighbors. Thus while the Virelles forest was particularly frugal in its uptake of potassium and nitrogen relative to that of calcium, a rather more mature adjacent forest with oak (*Q. robur*) and ash (*Fraxinus excelsior*) dominants and coppiced hazel (*Corylus avellana*) and hornbeam, had a much more marked pattern of uptake in which much greater amounts of potassium (99 kg/ha/yr), magnesium (24 kg/ha/yr), nitrogen (123 kg/ha/yr) and phosphorus (9.4 kg/ha/yr) were in circulation. In fact throughout Europe, mature oak forests are characterized by high nutrient demands, especially for potassium and nitrogen, and may be contrasted markedly with the much more restricted intake of beech, spruce and pine forests (Neshtateyev *et al.*: 1966).

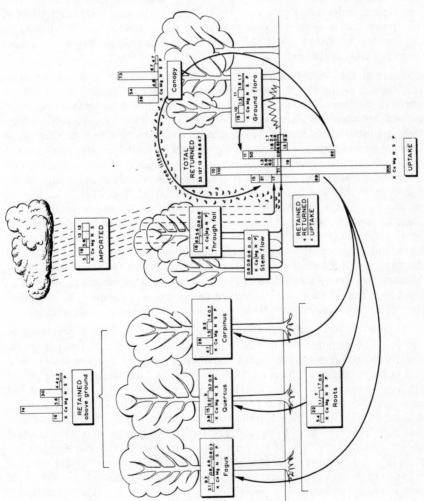

Figure 9. Annual Mineral Cycling of Selected Nutrients (kg/ha) in a Young Mixed Oak Forest at Virelles, Belgium. Retained: in the annual wood and bark increment of roots and aerial parts of each species. Returned: by tree litter, ground flora, washing, and leaching of the canopy by throughfall and stem flow. Imported: by incident rainfall. Macronutrients contained in the crown leaves when fully grown (July) are shown as canopy values on the right side of the figure. These amounts are higher than those returned by leaf litter, except for Ca. The total biomass of the forest amounted to 156 tons per hectare, and the annual productivity was 14.4 tons per hectare. Adapted from Duvigneaud and Denaeyer de Smet: 1970.

The idea that most mature vegetation systems are largely self-sustaining as far as their need for nutrients is concerned has been stressed. However, there will normally be a small input of nutrients into any system through precipitation, the settling of dust particles, nitrogen fixation, or the weathering of bedrock. Losses of elements from mature systems through stream drainage are usually not large, except possibly in the case of calcium (4-12 kg/ha/yr at Hubbard Brook). In all such systems, a readily-available store of nutrients is present in soil and litter, and it is of course this which tends to be quickly and steadily removed through erosion following forest clearance. Recent experiments at Hubbard Brook have demonstrated that once forest plots have been cut down, rates of nutrient loss from soil and litter immediately increase enormously. Thus in some plots, quantities of nitrogen equivalent to the normal annual turnover of this element were lost in the first year following cutting, while the removal of calcium, magnesium, sodium and potassium took place at rates that were respectively 9, 8, 3, and 20 times greater than normal. If forest species are not allowed to regenerate, the system itself will become less effective in terms of nutrient retention and circulation.

Some of the longer-term consequences of forest removal in similar latitudes may be seen in the Rough Sike catchment, a degraded moorland in the hills of northern England. This moorland is typical of many in this region having been covered by mixed oak forest until between 3000 and 4000 years ago when they were gradually cleared, first by Mesolithic and then Neolithic farmers. More comprehensive clearance by monastic settlers occurred in the twelfth- and thirteenth-century development of major sheep ranges. The close-grazing habits of sheep, coupled with a slight but significant deterioration in climate which lasted until the seventeenth century (equivalent to the Little Ice Age of continental Europe and North America), resulted in the almost total replacement of trees by bleak and desolate, acidic and peaty moorlands covered by small woody shrubs such as heather (*Calluna vulgaris*) and bell heather (*Erica spp.*), and a variety of tough grasses, mosses and bog species. The continued dominance of these species has been assured not only by the year-round grazing of sheep but also by the custom of burning away shrub vegetation at intervals of eight to fifteen years so as to stimulate the growth of palatable young heather shoots for the sheep and game birds (e.g., red grouse) raised on many estates.

A detailed input-output nutrient budget for Rough Sike is presented in Table 6. This demonstrates that only a very small fraction of the output results directly from contemporary human activities (the sale of sheep or wool), most arising from physical processes such as leaching, the downstream flow of elements in solution or in particulate matter, and peat erosion, the latter being an accelerating phenomenon at present. All elements suffered a net loss from the system. In most cases, this appears to be accounted for by the release of new materials from bedrock; however, two exceptions to this were nitrogen and phosphorus. The net loss of nitrogen was more than double the input. Since there are few reserves of this in bedrock, it would appear that the fund of nitrogen in this system is being rapidly depleted, mainly through the agency of peat erosion. The removal of phosphorus by identical means is also significant. In both these instances (Table 7) this form of erosion is sufficient to turn positive budgets, showing a net gain, into negative ones. Table 7 also suggests that degraded moorland systems are losing their nutrient resources at rates which are in general substantially greater than areas recently cleared of forest such as

TABLE 6—Annual Element Loss in Rough Sike Catchment (83 ha.)

	Na	K	Ca	P	N
Output					
Stream water	3755	744	4461	33	244
Peat erosion	23	171	401	37	1214
Faunal drift in stream	0.1	0.4	0.1	0.4	4.8
Sale of sheep & wool	0.2	0.4	1.6	1.0	4.4
Total Output	3778	916	4864	71	1467
Input	2120	255	745	39	681
Difference	1658	661	4119	32	786
Net loss/ha	20.0	8.0	50.0	0.4	9.5

Data from Crisp: 1966. Note that this study does not deal with the release of elements from bedrock. More recent work by a geographer (Imeson: 1971) suggests that most of the output of minerals on these moorlands takes place immediately after burning and before the heather canopy has been able to re-establish itself.

Hubbard Brook. Nitrogen and calcium are exceptions but both are very susceptible to heavy leaching in the period immediately following clearance. In other words, the longer systems are degraded, the easier it is for them to be degraded still further, and the greater the difficulty in bringing them back to their former nutrient status. It is to be noted that these conclusions echo in large measure those reached by geomorphologists such as Douglas (1967), who after using a very different approach also claim that present rates of erosion (and therefore of nutrient loss) in humid, mid-latitude environments are, through human interference, often far in excess of those which may have prevailed in the geological past.

TABLE 7—Comparisons of Precipitation Input, Streamflow Output, and Net Changes in the Nutrient Balance of Six Elements at Hubbard Brook, U.S.A. and Rough Sike, U.K.

	K	Ca	Mg	N	Na	P
Input in Precipitation						
Hubbard Brook	1.4	2.6	0.7	6.5	1.5	
Rough Sike	3.1	9.0		8.2	25.5	0.5
Output in Streamflow						
Hubbard Brook (forested)	1.5	10.6	2.5	2.0	6.1	
Rough Sike	9.0	53.8		3.0	45.3	0.4
Net Gain or Loss						
Hubbard Brook (forested)	−0.1	−8.0	−1.8	+4.5	−4.6	
Hubbard Brook (cutover)*	−2.0	−72.0	−14.4	−52.8	−13.8	
Rough Sike (minus peat erosion)	−5.9	−44.8		+5.2	−19.8	+0.1
Rough Sike (with peat erosion)	−8.0	−50.0		−9.5	−20.0	−0.4

* Approximate values only.

CONCLUSIONS

The importance of the biological community to the efficient functioning and stability of environmental systems has been emphasized throughout this paper. Over the last 1500 million years, the input of radiant energy into mature systems through the medium of photosynthetic organisms, which themselves depend upon an adequate provision of a variety of chemical elements, has led to an array of interactions between plants, animals, saprobes, and the inorganic world, interactions which contribute to the stability of environmental systems. Three basic controls seem critical to the functioning of the system: first, the photosynthetic process itself, which provides the ultimate "drive" for systems; second, the movement of water between the organic world, atmosphere, lithosphere, and water bodies; and third, the continued recirculation of the elements for growth, of which phosphorus and nitrogen seem particularly critical. When plant and animal communities are modified to any great extent, the initial consequence may be that the number of pathways of energy and nutrient flow following input is reduced. If this continues over a prolonged period, system instability or even breakdown is produced, leading to greater reactions *between* systems (e.g., increased erosion in mountain systems and sedimentation in lowlands) rather than the conservation of elements and energy *within* them. As educated citizens, we are by now only too well aware of the potential implications of severe environmental disturbance to our future well-being. As geographers, we are confronted with the challenge of explaining our own particular sense of the environment as a working whole, *all* of whose interlinkages are important to all forms of organic life, and many of which, in the words of the Zen Buddhist saying, are so often "too clear, and thus so very hard to see."

ACKNOWLEDGEMENTS

I should like to acknowledge with thanks the advice given by Dr. John Pethick, of the Department of Geography, Hull University, in the preparation of this paper.

REFERENCES

Bach, W., 1972, *Atmospheric Pollution.* New York: McGraw-Hill.

Bolin, B., 1970, "The Carbon Cycle," *Scientific American*, Vol. 223, pp. 124-135.

Bormann, F. H. and G. E. Likens, 1969, "The Watershed-Ecosystem Concept and Studies of Nutrient Cycles," in G. M. Van Dyne (ed.), *The Ecosystem Concept in Natural Resource Management.* New York and London: Academic Press, pp. 49-76.

Bray, J. R. and E. Gorham, 1964, "Litter Production in Forests of the World," *Advances in Ecological Research*, Vol. 2, pp. 101-157.

Bryson, R. A., 1968, "All Other Factors Being Constant . . . ," *Weatherwise*, Vol. 21, pp. 56-61.

Budyko, M. I., 1958, *The Heat Balance of the Earth's Surface*, (translated by N. A. Stepanova). Washington, D.C.: U.S. Weather Bureau.

Carr-Saunders, A. M., 1936, *World Population: Past Growth and Present Trends.* Oxford: Oxford University Press.

Carter, D. B. and J. R. Mather, 1966, "Climatic Classification for Environmental Biology," *C. W. Thornthwaite Associates Laboratory of Climatology, Publications in Climatology*, Vol. 19, pp. 305-395.

Crisp, D. T., 1966, "Input and Output of Minerals for an Area of Pennine Moorland: the Importance of Precipitation, Drainage, Peat Erosion and Animals," *Journal of Applied Ecology*, Vol. 3, pp. 314-327.

Davitaya, F. F., 1969, "Atmospheric Dust Content as a Factor Affecting Glaciation and Climatic Change," *Annals of the Association of American Geographers*, Vol. 59, pp. 552-560.

Deevey, E. S., Jr., 1970, "Mineral Cycles," *Scientific American*, Vol. 223, pp. 148-159.

Delwiche, C. C., 1970, "The Nitrogen Cycle," *Scientific American*, Vol. 223, pp. 136-147.

Douglas, I., 1967, "Man, Vegetation and the Sediment Yield of Rivers," *Nature*, Vol. 215, pp. 925-928.

_____, 1971, "The Interpretation of River Quality Data," *Progress in Geography*, Vol. 4, pp. 5-81.

Duvigneaud, P. and S. Denaeyer-de-Smet, 1970, "Biological Cycling of Minerals in Temperate Deciduous Forests," in D. E. Reichle (ed.), *Analysis of Temperate Forest Ecosystems*. London: Chapman and Hall, pp. 199-225.

Elton, C. S., 1927, *Animal Ecology*. London: Sidgwick and Jackson.

_____, 1958, *The Ecology of Invasions by Animals and Plants*. London: Methuen.

_____, 1966, *The Pattern of Animal Communities*. London: Methuen.

Eriksson, E., 1959-1960, "The Yearly Circulation of Chloride and Sulfur in Nature: Meteorological, Geochemical and Pedological Implications," *Tellus*, Vol. 11, pp. 375-403; Vol. 12, pp. 63-109.

Eriksson, E. and P. Welander, 1956, "On a Mathematical Model of the Carbon Cycle in Nature," *Tellus*, Vol. 8, pp. 155-175.

Garnier, B. J. and A. Ohmura, 1969, *Estimating the Topographic Variations of Short-Wave Radiation Income*. Washington, D.C.: Office of Naval Research.

Gates, D. M., 1956, *Energy Exchange in the Biosphere*. New York: Harper & Row.

Gerloff, G. C., 1963, "Comparative Mineral Nutrition of Plants," *Annual Review of Plant Physiology*, Vol. 14, pp. 107-124.

Gorham, E., 1958, "The Influence and Importance of Daily Weather Conditions in the Supply of Chloride, Sulphate and Other Ions to Fresh Waters from Atmospheric Precipitation," *Philosophical Transactions of the Royal Society of London*, Series B, Vol. 241, pp. 147-178.

Hare, F. K., 1960, "The Westerlies," *Geographical Review*, Vol. 50, pp. 345-367.

_____, 1965, "Energy Exchanges and the General Circulation," *Geography*, Vol. 50, pp. 229-241.

Harris, D. R., 1965, "Plants, Animals and Man in the Outer Leeward Islands," *University of California Publications in Geography*, Vol. 18, pp. 1-164.

Hodges, J. D., 1967, "Patterns of Photosynthesis under Natural Environmental Conditions," *Ecology*, Vol. 48, pp. 234-242.

Hutchinson, G. E., 1954, "The Biogeochemistry of the Terrestrial Atmosphere," in G. P. Kuiper (ed.), *The Earth as a Planet*. Chicago: University of Chicago Press, pp. 371-433.

_____, 1959, "Homage to Santa Rosalia, or Why are There so Many Kinds of Animals," *American Naturalist*, Vol. 93, pp. 145-159.

_____, 1970, "The Biosphere," *Scientific American*, Vol. 223, pp. 44-53.

Imeson, A. C., 1971, "Heather Burning and Soil Erosion on the North Yorkshire Moors," *Journal of Applied Ecology*, Vol. 8, pp. 537-542.

Jackson, R. M., and F. Raw, 1966, *Life in the Soil*. London: Institute of Biology.

Jahnke, L. S. and D. B. Lawrence, 1965, "Influence of Photosynthetic Crown Structure on Potential Productivity of Vegetation, Based Primarily on Mathematical Models," *Ecology*, Vol. 46, pp. 319-326.

Keeling, C. D., 1970, "Is Carbon Dioxide from Fossil Fuel Changing Man's Environment?" *Proceedings of the American Philosophical Society*, Vol. 114, pp. 10-17.

Lieth, H., 1963, "The Role of Vegetation in the Carbon Dioxide Content of the Atmosphere," *Journal of Geophysical Research*, Vol. 68, pp. 3887-3898.

_____, 1964/1965, *Geographisches Taschenbuch*. Wiesbaden: Steiner Verlag Gmbh.

Likens, G. E., F. H. Borman, N. M. Johnson, and R. S. Pierce, 1967, "The Calcium, Magnesium, Potassium, and Sodium Budgets for a Small, Forested Ecosystem," *Ecology*, Vol. 48, pp. 772-785.

Lindemann, R. L., 1942, "The Trophic-Dynamic Aspect of Ecology," *Ecology*, Vol. 23, pp. 399-418.

MacArthur, R. H. and E. O. Wilson, 1967, *The Theory of Island Biogeography*. Princeton, New Jersey: Princeton University Press.

Margalef, R., 1968, *Perspectives in Ecological Theory*. Chicago & London: University of Chicago Press.

Mason, B., 1960, *Principles of Geochemistry*. New York: Wiley.

Menhinick, E. F., 1967, "Structure, Stability and Energy Flow in Plants and Arthropods in a *Sericea lespedeza* Stand," *Ecological Monographs*, Vol. 37, pp. 255-272.

Mitchell, J. P., Jr., 1961, "Recent Secular Changes of Global Temperature," *Annals of the New York Academy of Sciences*, Vol. 95, pp. 235-250.

Neshtateyev, Yu. N., *et al.*, 1966, "Entry into the Soil of Ash Elements and Nitrogen with Leaf Fall from Trees and Grasses in the Main Types of Oak Stands in the 'Forest on the Vorskla'," *Soviet Soil Science*, Vol. 12, pp. 1372-1379.

Nye, P. H., and D. J. Greenland, 1960, *The Soil under Shifting Cultivation*. Harpenden, U. K.: Commonwealth Bureau of Soils.

Odum, E. P., 1959, *Fundamentals of Ecology* (2nd edition). Philadelphia: W. B. Saunders.

Odum, H. T., 1957, "Trophic Structure and Productivity of Silver Springs, Florida," *Ecological Monographs*, Vol. 27, pp. 55-112.

Olson, J. S., 1964, "Gross and Net Production of Terrestrial Vegetation," *Journal of Ecology*, Vol. 52, (Supplement), pp. 98-118.

Ovington, J. D., 1965, "Organic Production, Turnover and Mineral Cycling in Woodlands," *Biological Review*, Vol. 40, pp. 295-336.

Pales, J. C. and C. D. Keeling, 1965, "The Concentration of Atmospheric CO_2 in Hawaii," *Journal of Geophysical Research*, Vol. 70, pp. 6053-6076.

Penman, H. L., 1963, *Vegetation and Hydrology*. Farnham Royal, U.K.: Commonwealth Agricultural Bureau.

Peterson, E. K., 1969, "Carbon Dioxide Affects Global Ecology," *Environmental Science Technology*, Vol. 3, pp. 1162-1169.

Plass, G. N., 1956, "The Carbon Dioxide Theory of Climatic Change," *Tellus*, Vol. 8, pp. 140-154.

Rainwater, F. H. and W. F. White, 1958, "The Solusphere—its Inferences and Study," *Geochemica et Cosmochemica Acta*, Vol. 14, pp. 244-249.

Rodin, L. E. and N. I. Basilevic, 1967, *Production and Mineral Cycling in Terrestrial Vegetation*. Edinburgh: Oliver and Boyd.

Ryther, J. H., 1963, "Geographic Variations in Productivity," in M. N. Hill (ed.), *The Sea: Ideas and Observations on Progress in the Study of the Seas*. New York: Interscience.

Stewart, R. W., 1969, "The Atmosphere and the Ocean," *Scientific American*, Vol. 221, pp. 76-105.

Thornthwaite, C. W., 1948, "An Approach Towards a Rational Classification of Climate," *Geographical Review*, Vol. 38, pp. 55-94.

Thornthwaite, C. W. and F. K. Hare, 1955, "Climatic Classification in Forestry," *Unasylva*, Vol. 9, pp. 51-59.

United Nations Food and Agricultural Organization, 1970, *Provisional Indicative World Plan for Agricultural Development*. Rome: FAO.

Vernadskii, V. I., 1934, *Studies in Geochemistry* (2nd Russian edition). Leningrad.

Ward, R. C., 1967, *Principles of Hydrology*. London: McGraw-Hill.

Watts, D., 1970, "Persistence and Change in the Vegetation of Oceanic Islands: An Example from Barbados, West Indies," *Canadian Geographer*, Vol. 14, pp. 91-109.

———, 1971, *Principles of Biogeography*. London and New York: McGraw-Hill.

Wells, H. G., J. S. Huxley, and G. P. Wells, 1931, *The Science of Life*. Garden City, New York: Doubleday, Doran and Company.

Wendland, W. M. and R. A. Bryson, 1970, "Atmospheric Dustiness, Man and Climatic Change," *Biological Conservation*, Vol. 2, pp. 125-128.

Westlake, D. F., 1963, "Comparisons of Plant Productivity," *Biological Review*, Vol. 38, pp. 400-419.

Woodwell, G. M., 1970, "The Energy Cycle of the Biosphere," *Scientific American*, Vol. 223, pp. 64-97.

Woodwell, G. M. and R. H. Whittaker, 1968, "Primary Production in Terrestrial Eco-systems," *American Zoologist*, Vol. 8, pp. 19-30.

Accelerated Soil Erosion: A Problem of Man-Land Relationships

Karl W. Butzer
University of Chicago

Accelerated soil erosion has posed a latent if not chronic environmental problem ever since agriculture became the dominant mode of subsistence in parts of the Old World, almost 10 millennia ago. Cultivation and the pressures of livestock grazing marked the first serious impact of man on ecosystems, and thus opened a Pandora's Box of complications in regard to the balance of vegetation cover, soil mantle, and runoff. No food-producing culture or environment has been immune to the threat of accelerated soil erosion, and soil-conserving agricultural methods have been applied locally and temporarily since pre-historic times. But by and large, farmers and herders have tended to be ruthless rather than conservative in their exploitation of the environment. Mainly through ignorance, population pressures have usually been countered by over-intensive land use, with a concomitant, self-defeating deterioration of natural resources. However, until the 16th century A.D. the ecological crises provoked by man were of limited area and duration, and essentially confined to parts of Eurasia. Since then the exponential increase of population and an unprecedented global colonization by western society has provided the people and the technology essential to severe environmental deterioration in all but the desert and polar worlds.

As the second half of the 20th century progresses there is a growing awareness of overcrowding, of the false panacea of unrestricted technology, and of the inability of society at large to deal with the processes that threaten the planetary ecosystem. One of the few advantages of the growing current of pessimism is that blind trust in the efficacy of expanding G.N.P.'s is being replaced by a search for new perspectives. Educators are now confronted with students more sympathetic to innovative curricula, less intolerant of cultural diversity, and above all willing to admit to the existence of current problems.

Soil destruction is one such problem, and its solution demands more than the conservation programs of an earlier generation that knew the Dust Bowl years or formed the subject matter of *The Grapes of Wrath*. At issue is an aspect of man-land relationships: a matter of universal education in the value of the precarious soil resource, in the use and abuse of the land, and of the relative suitability of new and traditional technologies. Apart from instilling ecological values at home, where most of the damage may already have been done, there is urgent need to educate subsistence farmers of underdeveloped areas in methods of optimal land use, while preserving those techniques or attitudes that may be most harmonious with local conditions.

SOIL FORMATION AND EROSION

Soil can be defined as a shallow zone of intermixed mineral and organic matter, exhibiting one or more horizons that differ from the underlying regolith in morphology, particle size, chemical composition, and biological character-istics. Soils, in this restricted sense, are common to perhaps 75 percent of Earth's land surface and are lacking only in certain polar, desert, and mountain settings. Even where man has not interfered with ecosystems, soils are subject to some degree of erosion. In fact, the ideal condition is a balance between weathering and erosion (Bunting: 1965, Chapter 6) as expressed by the equation

$$E = W + S$$

> where E is erosion by runoff and mass movement,
>   W is the rate of weathering and soil formation, and
>   S is soil wash and other colluvium added from upslope.

Under most normal conditions a balance will be maintained, with the thickness of soil profile varying according to the steady-state defined by conditions that reflect climate, vegetation mat, bedrock, gradient and length of slope, as well as degree of human interference.

On undisturbed moderate or steep slopes, "natural" erosion is persistent and requires continuous formation and replacement of soil products. Consequently even without interference, most slope soils are not inherently stable and remain permanently "young" since they are ever composed of fresh products.

A rupture of the ecological balance, produced by deforestation, overgrazing, or cultivation can promote an *active balance* with $E > W + S$, until a new balance is attained or until bare rock is exposed. Strictly speaking, an active balance cannot be maintained indefinitely except in unconsolidated rocks. However, it is useful to employ a broader definition of active balance whereby $E > W + S$ whenever a lithosol or bare rock is present. By this criterion, convex facets or segments of most intermediate-gradient slopes have an active balance. This is also the case wherever backwearing is dominant, as a result of steep initial slopes, continued slope undermining, or climatically-inhibited chemical weathering in very dry or very cold environments.

Where soil profiles deepen through time, $E < W + S$ and a *passive balance* prevails. Soils on convex slopes thicken until increasingly fine texture and greater inherent soil moisture decrease the shear strength of the soil. At that point mass movements and possibly sheetwash promote erosion of any excess soil on increasingly unstable slope segments, until a steady state is reestablished. Consequently a passive balance cannot persist indefinitely, even on concave slopes, except in a very relative way whereby profiles thicken almost imper-ceptibly over centuries and millennia.

When an *established* soil is suddenly removed faster than it forms, there obviously is a disruption of the normal balance between weathering, soil formation, erosion, and deposition. Lithosols and other "immature" soil profiles may be a permanent feature in steep mountain country, the polar world, or in hyperarid deserts as a result of topography or climate. However, when an existing soil in an intermediate environment begins to show net erosion, there are two possible explanations: (1) a change of climate and macro-environment, affecting the vegetation cover and other aspects of the ecosystem, or (2) human interference. Practically all such *accelerated soil erosion* visible today is the result of man's manifold activities.

SOIL ERODIBILITY

The erodibility of a soil mantle varies considerably according to a variety of environmental parameters, including:

(1) Intensity and duration of precipitation. High-intensity or protracted rains increase amount and proportion of runoff and accelerate overland flow, whereas light rains do not increase soil or slope instability.

(2) Slope angle and length. Steep slopes favor runoff over infiltration and accelerate overland flow, particularly on long slopes that increase water velocity as a function of time and mass, the latter as a result of greater local concentration (Horton: 1945).

(3) Vegetation type. Trees, closed grass cover, or shrubs with contiguous crowns will intercept raindrops, break their impact, and reduce splash erosion. Deforestation, overgrazing, or cultivation reduce or eliminate this vegetation mantle.

(4) Organic mat. The rooting network, sod and leaf or grass litter of an undisturbed vegetation/soil interface increase infiltration, reduce runoff velocities, impede concentrated overland flow, and provide general protection and stabilization for the mineral soil. Plowing and intensive overgrazing destroy this organic mat.

(5) Soil texture. Permeability and porosity strongly affect infiltration rates, which are greatest in sands. Equally important are coherence and structure imparted by texture: clay content favors aggregation, while cohesivity is also high in mixed-grade soils where "binding" clays and silts are well dispersed among the larger sand grains. On the other hand, well sorted silts or sands are highly susceptible to erosion. Plasticity and cohesiveness are also increased by excess lime or colloidal silica, although increased water content decreases shear strength regardless of texture.

(6) Parent material. Subsurface lithologies are important both indirectly as parent materials and directly as a precondition for gross slope stability. In particular, unconsolidated materials are prerequisite for deep gullying, while large-scale mass movements are inhibited by most compact, unweathered rock types.

All in all, erodibility is determined by multivariate factors and is difficult to evaluate. Bryan (1968) has reviewed the various indices that attempt to express erodibility in practical terms, while Wischmeier and Smith (1965) provide a soil-loss equation in relation to rainfall factors, soil erodibility, slope length and gradient, crop/vegetation cover factors, and conservation practices.

Clearly a great deal of regional information is necessary before such an equation can be solved. More recently, Wischmeier *et al.* (1971) have devised nomographs that incorporate only five soil parameters: percent of silt, percent of sand, organic matter content, structure, and permeability.

THE MECHANICS OF SOIL EROSION

Disturbance or elimination of the vegetation mantle by man introduces a new geomorphic agent capable of upsetting an ecosystem within as little as a few years. In basic terms, deforestation or cultivation reduce the proportion of rain water that infiltrates, increase the ratio and rate of surface runoff, permit splash erosion (Hudson: 1971, Chapters 3-4) as well as accelerated erosion by overland flow (Strahler: 1952), or gullying (Ireland *et al.*: 1939), and increase sediment yield (Leopold: 1956; Golley: 1972). Specifically, three degrees of interference can be recognized:

(1) Deforestation or removal of grassy vegetation by lumbering, cultivation, grazing, or burning eliminate raindrop interception and permit splash erosion as well as accelerated soil creep and rill erosion. Experimental work on a small, devegetated watershed in New Hampshire showed that summer discharge increased 40 percent while almost 15 times as much dissolved inorganic material is now removed from the catchment (Likens *et al.*: 1970). Hydrographic observations from 219 rivers in Russia also show that smaller, forested watersheds have significantly less overland flow and runoff, but greater spring and seepage-derived base flow during dry weather (Bochkov: 1970). The accelerated loss of solubles, and particularly soil nutrients, is confirmed by this Russian study as well as by recent French work. For example, calcium and magnesium ions are removed 4 to 5 times more rapidly on cultivated fields in south France and 20 to 25 times more rapidly in Ivory Coast, West Africa (Clauzon and Vaudour: 1971). This chemical erosion reflects the removal of ions, colloids, and clays in solution and suspension, both by surface sheet flow and lateral seepage of percolating waters through the topsoil.

(2) Plowing and severe overgrazing destroy the litter or fermentation horizons that constitute much of the organic mat. This further reduces infiltration capacity, increasing the volume and velocity of surface runoff, and exposes bare soil to alternating rain and drought. The last result in turn accelerates oxidation of organic matter and reduces the variety and number of soil micro-organisms that generate beneficial humus. As a result, soil structure is modified, with heavy soils taking on forms that are less permeable and aerated, and therefore more erodible and less fertile; light soils, on the other hand, lose their aggregation properties and become incohesive. Depletion of organic matter through soil overuse has similar effects on structure. At this stage of disturbance the probability and destructiveness of soil slumping, debris slides, earthflows, or deflation are greatly increased.

(3) Bad cultivation practices enhance the trend already established. Plowing across the contours provides countless ready-made channels for concentrated overland flow after each rainstorm, allowing appreciable sheet

erosion on slopes of as little as $2°$ and rill erosion on slopes of $5°$. Planting of open row crops such as corn, cotton, or tobacco will provide bare soil not only during the sowing season and after the harvest, but throughout the growing season with its maximum-intensity rainstorms. Removal of natural vegetation along stream banks and headwaters further invites bank and headwater erosion. Finally, without terracing, cultivation of slopes steeper than $8°$ is an invitation to disaster.

The individual processes of accelerated erosion are broadly similar to those normally operating on gentle or intermediate slopes through a broad range of environments. The primary difference is that rates of erosion are higher, gentler slopes are affected, and a greater variety of processes can be seen at work in any one area. Apart from the chemical erosion already referred to, the mechanical processes include the following (compare Happ *et al.*, 1940):

(1) *Sheet wash*, the gradual removal of topsoil over wide areas by successive rainstorms. Sheet wash becomes conspicuous when light-colored B or even C-horizons are exposed on convexities and dark, A-horizon topsoil in concavities.

(2) *Rill wash,* the rapid removal of topsoil along plow furrows or natural lines of concentrated drainage. The effectiveness of rill wash is commonly obscured by plowing that erases temporary rills, but that cannot restore lost topsoil.

(3) *Gullying*, the rapid and catastrophic erosion of all soil horizons by deep channels that eat back from permanent drainage lines. Gullies deepen, widen and cut headward after each rainstorm, mainly in unconsolidated parent materials. Headward erosion in silts may be aided by subsurface piping (Figure 1).

(4) *Mass movements*, including soil creep, soil slumping, earth flows and debris slides. Such processes accelerate and intensify the impact of running water on slopes of over $5°$, and can lead to catastrophic destruction of hillsides with clayey substrates. Bank slumping and collapse as well as soil falls also aid in the growth of gullies.

(5) *Deflation* or wind erosion, primarily of dry, incohesive soils. Although most common and effective in semiarid and coastal areas, deflation can attack exposed soil in humid lands during periods of drought.

EROSIONAL RATES IN DIFFERENT ENVIRONMENTS

The close relationship between environmental parameters and erodibility presupposes that erosion rates vary from one environment to another. Fournier (1960, pp. 123ff.) has devised a quasi-empirical formula

$$E \propto p^2/P$$

where E is erosion, p is the mean precipitation of the wettest month, and P is the mean annual precipitation.

This function expresses a simple relationship with seasonal periodicity and ignores the crucial variations of rainfall intensity (Greer: 1971). Applying the

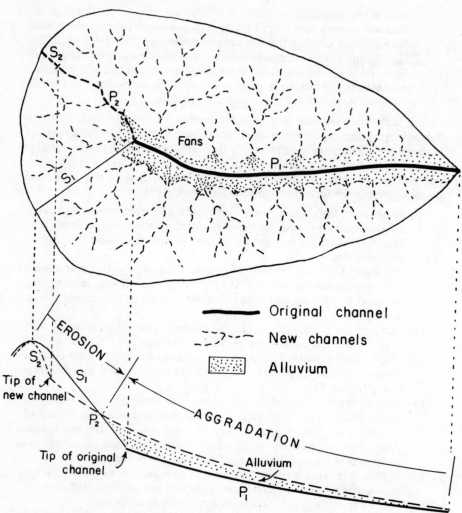

Figure 1. Diagrammatic Illustration of Severe Gullying on Slopes, Alluviation of a Valley
Floor, and Increase of Both Channel and Slope Gradients. Reproduced from Strahler:
1956, by permission of the University of Chicago Press.

index to station data from the conventional Koeppen climatic provinces we
obtain the following results for p^2/P:

Dcw and *Dd*	(9 stations)	0.77
Dcf	(15 stations)	0.39
Dbf	(17 stations)	0.43
Daf	(16 stations)	0.46
Cbf	(15 stations)	0.73
Caf	(19 stations)	0.81
Caw (monsoonal only)	(12 stations)	2.99
Csb	(14 stations)	0.92
Csa	(31 stations)	0.77

BSkw	(12 stations)	0.36
BShs	(13 stations)	0.76
BWh	(18 stations)	0.55
BShw	(15 stations)	1.29
Aw	(16 stations)	2.95
Am	(15 stations)	4.11
Af	(15 stations)	2.63

The high erosional rates suggested here for tropical and monsoonal climates are given a greater measure of reality by their generalized correspondence with high rainfall intensities. In fact, Hudson (1971, p. 74ff.) estimates the erosive force of tropical rains to be 16 times greater than that of mid-latitude rains, while the removal of soil nutrients from vegetated ground is 5 to 20 times greater in Ivory Coast than in southern France, and the corresponding values for cultivated fields are 30 to 100 times greater (Clauzon and Vaudour: 1971). Similarly, the critical gradient threshold for large-scale erosion from cultivated fields is 8° in western Europe compared with 2° in Rhodesia, reflecting primarily on rainfall intensity and periodicity (Stocking, 1972).

The available quantitative data on regional denudation rates unfortunately are inadequate either to support or question such generalizations. A variety of regional estimates of sediment yield and erosional rates based on river sampling have been offered by Corbel (1964), Fournier (1960, p. 33ff.), Livingstone (1963), Judson and Ritter (1964), Schumm (1965), and Strakov (1967). These are all based on short-term measurements, seldom standardized, fraught with assumptions (Meade, 1969), and in part mutually contradictory. Major difficulties lie in the lack of usable data on bed-load sediments, and in the fact that accelerated soil erosion primarily involves localized erosion and deposition that may show little output beyond small watersheds. The only generalizations that can be drawn at this time are that (1) overall denudation is 2 to 5 times greater in mountain country than on plains, (2) chemical denudation is significantly greater in humid than in dry lands, and (3) the yield of suspended sediment in middle latitudes is greatest in semiarid climates.

In effect, these materials caution against the overemphasis of zonal climates in evaluating problems of regional soil erosion. Once the vegetation has been removed it appears that slope and the nature of the soil itself are primary criteria. Furthermore, in this writer's experience in North America, Europe, and Africa, the constellation of "accelerated" geomorphic processes in operation, as well as the micro-landforms generated, most conspicuously reflect initial slope and lithology.

CULTURAL FACTORS IN ACCELERATED SOIL EROSION

Land use provides variable opportunities for accelerated soil erosion. Some practices are patently exploitative, disrupting ecosystems and maintaining a permanent state of imbalance. Others establish new ecosystems capable of a reasonable steady state. Factors such as technology, subsistence economies, and social attitudes are critical in assessing the following man-soil interactions:

(1) Forest clearance. Patterns of plot clearance or general deforestation vary greatly. On the one hand, slash-and-burn cultivators may clear small woodland plots, killing the larger trees (which are frequently not

removed) and cutting or burning away only the undergrowth and that minimum of mature trees inimical to successful cultivation; some rain-drop interception remains and the rooting network commonly continues to stabilize the soil mantle. On the other hand, cultivation based on heavy, wheeled plows generally leads to complete clearance of large plots, with destruction of stumps and roots. Additional deforestation for timber, fuel, or herding opportunities can intensify this denudation by destroying the cover of adjacent steeper slopes or roughlands. Even within these broad types of clearance, attitudes to the maintenance of forest stands and of ornamental or shade trees range from the sublime disinterest of the Near Eastern cultivator to the tree-consciousness of the transalpine peasant.

(2) Soil preparation. The shallow and incomplete soil upturning associated with hoe and digging-stick cultivation may not favor good crop yields, but it does help preserve soil moisture and reduce the depletion of organic matter and biota. Similarly, the scratch-plow commonly preserves the base of the humic A-horizon and does not expose the heavier and more erodible B-horizons to rain splash and the compaction associated with periodic, intensive dehydration. The deep-delving wheeled plough, while favoring more sustained yields—and almost essential on heavy soils—is a potential menace on erodible land. Without fertilization, deep plowing destroys the biota, organic matter, and structure of the A-horizon, ultimately favoring maximum erodibility. Most of the recent and rapid soil destruction in the New World was predicated on deep plowing, and many Western technologists are still attempting to intro-duce similar implements to tropical nations where the tractor-drawn steel plow can have a catastrophic impact.

(3) Planting techniques. Dissemination of seeds or root cuttings affects erodibility in several ways. Broadcast seeds provide even and relatively dense stands of crops, compared with row planting. As a result grains and alfalfa provide good to excellent ground cover for most of the growing season, while row crops of maize, cotton, and tobacco expose much bare and disturbed ground at all times. By contrast, tropical "mound" planting of seed or root plants leaves most of the ground undisturbed. Crop rotation reduces erodibility, at least in part because legume plantings help restore organic matter and biotic activity. Leaving plots in bare-ground fallow may be advantageous for restoring soil fertility, but the minimum of ground cover invites intensive erosion on sloping land. A quantitative example, derived by Bennett (1939, p. 148) from rates of denudation on an 8° Ohio slope, illustrates some of these differences of cover. The theoretical time necessary to erode 175 mm. of soil is as follows:

forest	173,700 years
grass	28,900 years
rotation (maize-wheat-alfalfa)	100 years
fallow (bare ground)	17 years
maize	16 years

Intercropping is far more favorable than monocultures, by providing longer and more complete ground cover: e.g., alternating rows of vines and fruit trees, interspersed with grains and vegetables in Mediterranean vineyards; almond or olive trees with winter wheat and capers in other Mediterranean areas; yams and rice in southeast Asia; or maize and root crops in Latin America.

(4) Special landscaping. Several cultures inhibit soil erosion by landscaping techniques that may be necessary for hydraulic or slope cultivation. Wet-rice fields on level land or behind water-retaining terrace embankments suffer next to no erosion. Contoured or terraced vineyards commonly occupy slopes too steep or stoney for other cultivation but manage to reduce accelerated soil erosion to an acceptable minimum. Other terraced slopes have traditionally been created through the painstaking efforts of cultivators to collect or preserve slope soils, sometimes in connection with water distribution from elaborate irrigation devices. Many such attempts at cultural landscaping succeed only for a time, and their willful destruction or abandonment can be disastrous, because once breached, terraced or embanked soils erode rapidly and extensively. Other ancient landscaping techniques include such "modern" remedial measures as contour plowing and strip cropping.

(5) Pastoral activities. Although livestock raising does not involve deliberate eradication of the vegetation mantle, its effects are mainly negative. Pasture is often temporarily improved by burning of grassland or open woodland. Trees are browsed by many kinds of livestock, and the cropping of leaves for cattle feed is still practiced in some areas. Overstocking—beyond the carrying-capacity of pasture at its seasonal minimum productivity—is bad with all species. Sheep have the additional trait of grazing down to root level, often destroying beneficial grasses and permanently opening up the ground mat, with only partial recolonization by shrubby vegetation. Goats are notorious for indiscriminate grazing, resulting in destruction of trees and their seedlings. Large aggregations of livestock in fenced plots or through nightly collecting of herds in enclosures also serves to destroy the plant cover, not the least through trampling. In many ways, therefore, pastoralism can promote accelerated soil erosion on a scale that vies with the impact of cultivation. Traditional dairy farming is the notable exception here, and the European version of manured hay crops provides a striking counter-example to tribal herding.

The cultural factors outlined above help explain why the visible evidence for accelerated soil erosion bears little relationship to rainfall intensity, slope, or the innate erodibility of soils. They show that the Eurasian grain-farming tradition is far more destructive than the much-maligned shifting cultivation of the tropics. They single out paddy cultivators, horticulturalists, dairy farmers, and wine growers as successful specialists in the spectrum of rural achievement. And they provide the explanatory key for understanding of accelerated erosion in an historical context.

HISTORICAL PERSPECTIVES: THE OLD WORLD

Agricultural communities were already established in western Asia and along the Greek shores of the Aegean Sea by 8000 B.P. (before present time), in the Hungarian Plain and Italy by 7000 B.P., in central Europe and eastern Spain by about 6400 B.P., and in northwestern France and Britain by about 5300 B.P. (Ammerman and Cavalli-Sforza: 1971; Berger and Protsch: 1973). This gives a *de facto* time depth of 6 to 9 millennia for primary village-farming communities in Europe and its Asiatic borderlands, although it should be noted that C^{14} dates in the time range discussed here are approximately 800-1000 years younger than true calendar years, as corrected by bristlecone pine calibration.

Some degree of deforestation was involved in most of the environments used by early agriculturalists and, as Dimbleby (1972) has pointed out, the removal of the dominant organism—the tree—inevitably altered naturally balanced eco-systems and frequently led to ecological disaster. Yet, early "primitive" agriculture was not inherently destructive and seems to have been surprisingly well-adapted to local environments. Soil preparation was done by hoe or digging stick, plots were small and used for short periods only, and only level lands were cultivated (Butzer: 1971, Chapter 33).

A potential change was first introduced with the ox-drawn scratch plow or *ard* in the 3rd millennium B.C. (Fowler: 1971). The first suggestions of large-scale deforestation and cultivation on unstable slopes, with resulting soil erosion, are recorded within lake sediments of the English Lake District (Mackereth: 1965) and by valley hillwash in Kent (Evans: 1971*b*), both incidents also dating to the 3rd millennium B.C. Yet, despite the evidence of man's increasingly intensive impact on vegetation, there is little evidence for either significant or extensive soil erosion in temperate Europe or the Mediterranean Basin until the end of the Bronze Age, about or shortly after 1000 B.C. (Evans: 1971*b*; Huckriede: 1971; Yassoglou and Nobeli: 1972, p. 174ff.).

The Mediterranean World after 1000 B.C.

Several classical Greek authors were the first to draw attention to deforestation and soil erosion problems, and the commentary of Plato (Critias, 111, D-E), in the 4th century B.C., is the first of its kind:

> In consequence of the successive violent deluges ... there has been a constant movement of soil away from high elevations; and, owing to the shelving relief of the coast, this soil, instead of laying down alluvium as it does elsewhere, has been perpetually deposited in the deep sea around the periphery of the country or, in other words, lost. ... All the rich, soft soil has molted away, leaving a country of skin and bones [so that rainfall] is allowed to flow over the denuded surface [directly] into the sea. ...

Elsewhere Plato attributes this soil erosion to deforestation. His views find some confirmation in the observation of Pausanias, in the 2nd century A.D., who related siltation on the coast of Asia Minor to increased stream sedimentation as a result of soil erosion due to cultivation. Although also affected by relative movements of land and sea, this coastal progradation in Asia Minor began *ca.* 750 B.C., reached its maximum from 300 to 100 B.C., and came to a close by 700 A.D. (Eisma: 1962). Alluviation of a coastal plain was also underway in the northwestern Peloponnese by the 2nd century B.C., reaching its maximum in Roman times and essentially coming to a close in the 3rd century A.D. (Raphael: 1973).

Rediscovery of the Greek and Roman authors, and the antiquarians that began to seek out the ancient Mediterranean world since the late 17th century, created a false impression of the ravages of soil erosion. It has become commonplace to attribute denuded mountain slopes and alluvial lowland soils everywhere to the impact of historical soil erosion (see, for example, Bennett: 1939, p. 24 ff., and Stallings: 1957, p. 2 ff.). This gross exaggeration has unfortunately found its way, by implication, into many general texts, whereas in fact the Mediterranean Basin is no more scarred by soil erosion than is the United States.

Two points deserve elaboration in connection with Mediterranean soil erosion: the true age of the red soil sediments often attributed to historical erosion, and the chronology of documented, historical erosion.

Red Mediterranean soils are today found primarily in piedmont alluvial plains or river floodplains, with little more than discontinuous veneers on uplands or hillsides (Durand: 1959, part 3 and map). Closer examination shows most of the lowland occurrences to be silty or sandy, reworked soil derivatives. Yet even the apparently intact profiles of *terra rossas* (and equivalent red-yellow podsolic soils on non-carbonate parent material) appear to be relict, and no longer developing today. It can be demonstrated geologically that red Mediterranean soils were last formed on a regional scale during the early Upper Pleistocene (before 70,000 B.P.), that such soils are relict and have not developed on freshly exposed sediments during the last 10,000 years, and that related soil mantles were repeatedly and intensively eroded by episodes of natural erosion during Pleistocene times (Butzer: 1963, 1964, 1971, pp. 306 ff., 378 ff.; Fränzle: 1965). For example, below the plain of Palma de Mallorca, Spain, situated at the foot of high, denuded, limestone sierras, there are over 150 m. of interdigitated red soil sediments and fanglomerates. These Mallorquin piedmont deposits span the late Pliocene and most of the Pleistocene, and the only post-Pleistocene wash is limited to isolated 1-1.5 m. channel fills and restricted coastal veneers that interfinger with +1 to 2.5 m. beach deposits, all containing post-Reconquista pottery, i.e., post-dating A.D. 1228. Numerous similar examples could be cited from Mallorca and Catalonia. The implication is that in the case of hills or mountains formed of compact bedrock, the great bulk of the piedmont soil colluvia are of Pleistocene age. By contrast, unconsolidated sediments such as the late Tertiary shales of southern Italy and southeastern Spain gully rapidly (Bennett: 1960) and catastrophic mass movements occur persistently in response to human activities (Kayser: 1961; Franceschetti and Masone: 1968).

As to the chronology of Mediterranean soil erosion, a classic example is provided by the original Olympic site, in the western Peloponnese. The shrine of Olympia was originally built on a non-functional stream confluence fan in the 8th century B.C. A drainage culvert was constructed there about A.D. 130 and an adjacent Byzantine fort was built in the 5th century A.D. The site continued to be used for settlement until *ca.* A.D. 680 (Büdel: 1965). Aggradation of silty hillwash probably began after A.D. 500, when records of catastrophic floods begin. At any rate, all of these structures were buried by 7 m. of colluvium before the first traveller's description in 1776. However, by that time the stream channels had once again cut down 7 m. below the post-680 valley floor, although remaining 2 m. higher than in ancient Greek times (Büdel: 1965).

This denudation of slope soils in post-Roman or Medieval times was not restricted to Olympia but rather was widespread in the Mediterranean Basin: (1) A 4-5 m. sandy alluvial terrace of the Gornalunga River in east-central Sicily dates to Medieval times (Judson: 1963); (2) Some 5-8 m. soil wash and alluvium buried Roman buildings and roads in southern Etruria after A.D. 209 and before 1534, with C^{14} dates suggesting a specific age of A.D. 500-1000 (Judson: 1963;

also Vita-Finzi: 1969, p. 72); (3) 2 m. of soil wash, eroded from Roman vineyards, buried latifundia in Catalonia that were abandoned between 258 and *ca.* A.D. 400 (Butzer: 1964, p. 48 f.).

Vita-Finzi (1969) has collected a variable body of data to show that during late Roman or early Medieval times many of the streams of the Mediterranean Basin were in fact subject to a significant change of geomorphologic equilibrium: vertical cutting of older alluvial fill gave way to alluviation in the lower stream courses. As a result, longitudinal stream profiles were steepened and smoothened, while broad tracts of loamy agricultural soils were created along the valley floors by silt-laden floods. In recent centuries these "post-Classical alluvia" have once again been subject to dissection. Unfortunately these valley alluvia are discussed by Vita-Finzi (1969) with little attention to colluvial deposits and the complex of slope processes; interactions of vegetation mat, soil properties, and denudational forces are neglected at the specific level; and interpretations are not based on sedimentological studies. Finally, changes of land use, gradual or repeated devegetation, and other human influences are discounted or relegated to secondary and local significance by this author. Instead, the "post-Classical fill" is thought to reflect vague climatic factors affecting the whole Mediterranean Basin simultaneously, possibly the "Little Ice Age."

It need not be emphasized that alluviation which had terminated before A.D. 1500 cannot be ascribed to the "Little Ice Age" of the 16th and 17th centuries. More significantly, Vita-Finzi can make no case for strictly synchronous slope denudation and valley alluviation over a possible range of 1000 years. Finally, there have indeed been earlier episodes of soil destruction, as witnessed by the early siltation of the Asia Minor or Peloponnesian coasts or, in the Gornalunga, by the 5-6 m. of alluvial sand and silt washed together after the beginning of Greek colonization in Sicily, but before the digging of burials that date from *ca.* 325 B.C. (Judson: 1963). Consequently, the Mediterranean Basin suggests localized soil erosion problems as early as the mid-first millenium B.C., and far more general soil stripping in the wake of the economic decline of the Roman Empire, with its attendant rural depopulation, barbarian invasions, and land abandonment.

It seems that the onset of "post-Classical" erosion varied over a span of 500 years, between the 3rd and 8th centuries, depending on the history of local land use. Although some sets of climatic anomalies may have aided in the process, a series of pollen studies including the central Spanish sierras (Welten: 1954), the Valencian and Mallorquin coasts (Menéndez-Amor and Florschütz: 1961*a*, 1961*b*), Dalmatia (Beug: 1967*b*), western and northern Greece and Crete (Wright: 1972; Wijmstra: 1969; Rossignol and Pastouret: 1971), Israel (Horowitz: 1971), and Asia Minor (Beug: 1967*a*; Van Zeist *et al.*: 1970) show conclusively that there was no regional climatic oscillation or change during the last 2500 years. In other words, man must assume the primary responsibility. Whether the process of soil erosion was ultimately and inadvertently beneficial to agriculture as claimed by Vita-Finzi (1969, p. 117 ff.) is debatable. To suggest that valley floor alluvia are easier to cultivate and irrigate than hillside soils may be true, but the hillside soils were much more extensive before being reworked into deep but restricted valley fills, and those valley fills that have been described are at best loamy, and many are sandy or gravelly. Fertility would have been quite low on crude mineral soil and slope derivatives.

Soil erosion remains a chronic problem, particularly in overpopulated, marginal environments of the Mediterranean Basin to the present day, e.g., the

Apennines and the Atlas Mountains (Kayser: 1961; Aubert and Monjauze: 1946).

Temperate Europe after 1000 B.C.

Soil erosion in temperate Europe, although less conspicuous, was in many areas no less significant than in the Mediterranean world. Evidence to this effect is so far restricted to soils developed in veneers of unconsolidated parent material, such as till and particularly loess.

In central Europe loessic slope soils were first swept into the river valleys at the transition from the Bronze to the Iron Age, *ca.* 750 B.C., and further evidence of accelerated erosion comes from several areas of Halstatt-La Tène (Celtic) settlement in subsequent centuries (Lüttig: 1960; Jäger: 1962; Strautz: 1963; Huckriede: 1971). Older, Bronze Age valley settlements were buried by as much as 1-2 m. of loessic soil wash, and accelerated floodplain sedimentation locally destroyed riverine forests. It remains uncertain whether deforestation and increased runoff played a key role in this process, whether cultivation of precarious intermediate slopes was responsible, or whether abandonment of hillside plots during successive periods of widespread unrest triggered off episodes of disequilibrium. The ancillary role of cool-wet climatic oscillations with the onset of the Subatlantic phase (*ca.* 800-300 B.C.) also remains to be considered.

Celtic and Roman cultivators continued to employ the scratch-plow and concentrated their plots on upland plains and some intermediate-slope hillsides. By the time of the Germanic migrations the uplands of Britain and Gaul had lost much of their topsoil to erosion and the Germanic tribes colonized the mainly unused lowlands, where they were able to till the heavy-textured soils with the heavy, mould-board plow that had been first introduced to northwestern Europe in Roman times. Thus in southern England cultivation shifted to the lowlands, with the old, eroded upland fields partly abandoned to pastoralism (Crawford: 1923; Bowen: 1962; Fowler: 1971). In northern and eastern Gaul, on the other hand, a dichotomy of settlements arose, similar to that of central Europe. Population pressure built up in central Europe during the 13th century, leading to extensive deforestation and cultivation on the rougher uplands. By the time the more marginal of these settlements were abandoned, *ca.* 1350-1450, most of the topsoil had been destroyed and a second wave of loessic soil sediments inundated footslopes and floodplains (Jäger: 1962; Strautz: 1963; Huckriede: 1971). The truncated B-horizons of abandoned fields can still be recognized under the forests of today (Machann and Semmel: 1970), and some German valleys are mantled by 1-8 m. of corresponding "haugh loams."

The third episode of soil erosion in temperate Europe is dated between about 1760 and 1880, a time of renewed rural population pressure, consolidation of fields, shifts to monocultures, resurveying along geometric grids, upland deforestation, and destructive herding in once-protected woodlands. These manifestations are richly documented in the archives and have been described from France (Vogt: 1953, 1971) and Germany (Hard: 1971), with close modern parallels evident for post-1918 Poland (Miszczak: 1960), and comparable trends related to deforestation can be recognized in many uplands of the Mediterranean world. This last major wave of soil erosion was eventually halted by conservation measures such as strip-cropping and reforestation.

The Asiatic Monsoon Lands

Although southern and eastern Asia qualify as ancient agricultural lands, there is as yet little precise information as to the adaptation or innovation of agricultural traits. On the Indian subcontinent there is an embarrassing lack of substantive evidence for domesticated plants or animals until shortly before the appearance of the Harappan civilization (Allchin: 1969). In China there happens to be no isotopic dating or even a developed relative stratigraphy for the Neolithic, so that we can only assume that grain-farming was established there relatively early (Watson: 1969). For Southeast Asia there are tantalizing indications that independent domestication may have begun as early as in the Near East and southeastern Europe (Gorman: 1971), but regional and temporal patterns have not yet begun to be understood.

The difficulty of establishing a datum for early agriculture in the Asiatic monsoon lands underscores the inadequacies of archeological and historical research in land use in such vital areas where population pressures and soil deterioration appear to have been chronic for at least several centuries. Conservatively speaking there is an agricultural time depth of at least 4 or 5 millennia in most of this region, significantly greater in parts. Destructive monocultures such as jute, cotton, and wheat were long favored by the export-oriented economy of the British raj in India. Above all, however, these same lands are characterized by maximum erodibility in climatic terms, and the sediment yields of Indian and southeast Asian rivers are almost phenomenal.

The degree of gullying in India is catastrophic, and no less so than in the unconsolidated volcanic hillsides of Java. Soil stripping has almost denuded the uplands of southern China, while deflation and gullying of the loessic regions of the north is also in an advanced stage (Min Tieh: 1941). It is unfortunate, therefore, that there are no comprehensive surveys of erosion problems today, let alone in historical perspective. Here, even more than in the Mediterranean world and temperate Europe, there is a fruitful field for interdisciplinary research.

HISTORICAL PERSPECTIVES: THE NEW WORLD

Serious soil erosion in the 18th century was essentially limited to the ancient agricultural lands of Eurasia and North Africa. Almost nowhere else did technological levels and population pressures present significant problems of overintensive or abusive land use. However, in the past two centuries soil erosion has become commonplace in the New World as well as in large parts of subsaharan Africa. The obvious exploitation of the earliest European *conquistadores* and frontiersmen was perpetuated with a vengeance by the colonists and settlers. Only, the object of their pillage was neither gold nor slaves nor furs but the land itself. Unlike the Old World peasant who was committed to making a livelihood from his holdings, from one generation to the next, the New World farmer was patently speculative in his land use. When one farm failed it was abandoned and a new start made elsewhere.

The American colonization of the mid-central U.S.A. may be the most flagrant example of land abuse. Farming populations began to cross the Appalachians in the late 1700's and westward colonization only succumbed on the Great Plains amid the 1930's Dust Bowl. Preceded by systematic deforestation to the prairie margins (Schmid: 1974), and following a disastrously conceived geometric grid system (Pattison: 1957) these pioneers in reckless land use at first attempted to farm on all available slopes, plowing up- and downhill. Specialization rapidly followed mixed general farming, and monocultures became dominant with intercropping practically unknown. In about 150 years the agricultural soil resources of the United States have been cut by perhaps a half, and in some areas such as Oklahoma, a single generation sufficed to destroy almost 30 percent of the soil mantle. Such a systematic if unconscious rape of the land has had an impact that rivals or exceeds that of 6 to 10 millennia of cultivation in the Mediterranean world.

Early signs of accelerated soil erosion were apparent in the hilly farmlands of New England by the early 18th century (Stallings: 1957, p. 12 ff.) and remedial measures were already the subject of debate well before the appearance of the major work of George Perkins Marsh (1864). As the cutters slashed westward and the settlers shifted from farm to farm in their wake, ecosystems were thoroughly disrupted. This has been tangibly documented for southwestern Wisconsin by Happ (1944) and particularly by Knox (1972 a, b; Knox and Corcoran: 1972), who has resurveyed stream widths first recorded in the Federal Land Survey of 1832-33. Existing forest cover was reduced 80 to 90 percent by the earliest settlers, increasing the frequency and magnitude of flood flows and disrupting the balance between slope, sediment, and discharge. Soils were truncated and the eroded silts and clays systematically distributed over downstream floodplains. This increased sediment yield created alluvial fans at tributary confluences and significantly increased bed-load fractions and channel width. An older, but equally valuable paper by Gottschalk (1945) describes the impact of soil erosion since colonial times on sedimentation in Chesapeake Bay.

A fine historical documentation of accelerated soil erosion has been provided for another region, the upper Georgia piedmont, by Trimble (1969, 1970). Settlement of the bottom lands began there between 1780 and 1805, but erosion first became apparent when sloping lands were cleared and was locally accentuated by the impact of plantation agriculture after the 1840's and 1850's. In contrast to the older cotton plantation areas, major erosion was delayed until the 1880's when forest acreage was significantly decreased and row crops, especially cotton, became dominant. By the 1930's, when the efforts of the U.S. Soil Conservation Service began to take effect, the impact of man on the soil mantle, hydrography, and sedimentation had exceeded that of any natural climatically-induced ruptures of equilibrium experienced in the southeastern U.S.A. during all of Pleistocene times.

The American Southwest has also been ravaged by soil erosion but here, surprisingly, the major culprit has been climate rather than man. A relatively well-known hemi-cycle of gullying and range deterioration has drastically reduced land values for grazing purposes since the 1880's. Ongoing research has shown that rainfall at all seasons was well below normal during the intervals 1872-89 and especially 1895-1904 (Stockton and Fritts: 1971), which resulted in a reduction of soil moisture and a weakening of the grass cover. Coincident with a rapid increase of livestock, a unique combination of climatic and cultural stress produced the results in evidence today (Hastings and Turner: 1965).

The present state of soil erosion in the U.S.A. and the varying degree of success in combating it are described by Bennett (1939), Stallings (1957), and in several regional studies. In much of the eastern United States the state of erosion as of 1934 was documented by field mapping at 1:62,500 and published (state) maps at 1:500,000 (U.S. Department of Agriculture, Soil Erosion Service, *Reconnaissance Erosion Survey*, Washington, 1935). A wealth of historical data was also collected at that time, and various specific studies and a monumental card file of historical references to soil erosion were reposited in the National Archives, Washington (Files of the Section of Climatic and Physiographic Research, Soil Conservation Service, "Thornthwaite Collection," especially Record Groups 114 and 221. S. W. Trimble, personal communication).

Comparable problems are, of course, shared by Canada, especially the Prairie provinces, and by most of Latin America (F.A.O.: 1954), particularly in areas of overpopulation such as central Chile and central Mexico (Cook: 1949), or exploitative monocultures, such as the coffee plantations of Colombia and southern Brazil (Maack: 1956). Similar pictures of agricultural disaster can be given for large tracts of those other two "colonial" lands, Australia and South Africa.

To this overall picture of limited encouragement comes the more recent impact of urban sprawl and associated construction that has introduced an unprecedented level of intensity to disturbance and now threatens to ravage large parts of the United States. Sobering examples have been provided by Wolman (1967) from Baltimore, Vice *et al.* (1969) from Fairfax County, Virginia, and Thompson (1970) from Detroit (see also the chapter of Mrowka in this volume). The need for "urban" geomorphologists begins to be alarmingly obvious!

FUTURE PERSPECTIVES

With the geometric increase of accelerated soil erosion and the exponential increase of world population, the soil resource has become at once both more precarious and more essential. A potential solution depends on the development and application of remedial measures on the one hand, and on social attitudes and capital resources on the other.

Methods of soil conservation, as developed in North America, have been outlined by Bennett (1939) and Stallings (1957), and a refreshingly cosmo-politan approach has recently been presented by Hudson (1971), whose field experience comes primarily from Africa and Britain. Remedial or preventative measures can be summarized only at the certain risk of over-generalization, since directional change within any one complex ecosystem is difficult to predict. The suggestions discussed below are therefore offered with reservation:

(1) The basic options for coping with soil erosion include: (A) On severely eroded surfaces (bad gullying and 75 percent of topsoil removed)—reforestation or reestablishment of a permanent grass cover is commonly recommended. (B) In areas where gullying has begun or is actively underway—construction of check dams or obstructions is essential to attempt gully stabilization, with contour plowing and strip cropping another "must." (C) Where topsoil erosion by sheetwash is significant—contour plowing, strip cropping (e.g., alternating field strips of hay and crops), and avoidance of open row crops are recommended. In general, terracing may be the only solution on steep slopes used for anything but woodland or hay.

(2) The time to initiate conservation measures is *before* accelerated erosion

begins. Contour plowing should always be employed if slopes exceed $2°$, and on almost level land checkerboard plowing (each adjacent plot with furrows at right angles) helps to retard sheetwash. Plowing as well as construction should avoid the edges of steep bluffs, leaving areas of potential gullying or mass movements along river breaks in permanent grass or woodland. Alternation between open and close-grown crops and even strip cropping are recommended on all slopes of 3 to $5°$ or more. In areas of potential wind erosion, woodland shelter belts or windbreaks may well be necessary. Finally, soil organic matter and structure must be maintained at reasonably good levels.

(3) In all environments, every form of cultivation or grazing activity will produce *some* accelerated soil erosion. But with careful cultivation or pasturing of limited numbers of suitable livestock, soil erosion can be kept to an acceptable minimum that, given access to fertilizers, will not affect soil productivity over extended periods of time. On the other hand, poor land management can produce catastrophic and often irreversible damage in a remarkably short time.

Beyond this lowest common denominator of conservation guidelines there is a crying need for ecological thinking. One reflection of this problem can be seen in the controversies surrounding shelter-belt construction in southern Russia and on the Great Plains (George *et al.*: 1957). Another case in point is the reforestation of many central European uplands with pine and spruce, in areas where hardwood forests had once been in equilibrium with eutrophic soils; the resulting timber yield has been commercially profitable, but man-made podzolization has rapidly created acidic, low base-saturation soils (Duchaufour: 1956). Perhaps one of the greatest planning mistakes of the 20th century was the "virgin lands" cultivation in Soviet Central Asia, in what seemed to be a grim attempt to emulate, in 1960, the American Dust Bowl calamity of the 1930's. Any program that plans to institute conservation measures or to "improve" existing land use patterns must be carefully scrutinized within overall landscape ecology.

This is particularly important in the tropics, where a third of the world's population is concentrated, and where standard approaches derived from higher latitudes must be considered suspect. What is good for Missouri may well not be appropriate for Malaysia! Most tropical soils have different clay minerals, so that exchange capacities are highly variable and often so low that fertilization methods must be drastically modified. Many tropical soils have a consistency, porosity, and permeability that bears no obvious relationship to texture, depending on variables such as colloidal silica. Above all, crops, crop seasons, plot size, and technology must all be geared to local conditions. Underdeveloped nations may never have the resources to provide the fertilizers necessary for overambitious agricultural schemes once inaugurated, nor to pay for costly conservation measures necessary once the subsistence cultivator is persuaded to turn in his digging stick for a tractor-drawn, steel plow.

The success or failure of conservation methods depends on social attitudes as much as anything. The traditional values of the Eurasiatic peasantry (Wolf: 1966; Tuan: 1968) have, by and large, preserved soil resources indefinitely, regardless of the odds. The family group or restricted community has had to be more or less self-sufficient in dealing with its land, with no higher power to guarantee continued soil productivity and few if any options to find new land.

The resulting ethic of responsibility for the state of the land and its preservation stood the Eurasiatic peasant in good stead but, unfortunately, did not cross the ocean to the Americas, Australia, and South Africa.

Farms are commonly bought and sold in New World areas of recent colonization, and most North American farmers' overriding concern is short-term investment and profit. Whatever success the U.S. Soil Conservation Service has had in checking erosion can be attributed to its educational program in convincing the farmer that erosion means less cash. The United States farmer expects outside assistance to tackle any environmental problem, and environmental hazards have become equated with governmental responsibility (Leopold: 1966, part IV). As a result, conservation is not practiced independently but becomes a matter of politics at the county, state, and even federal level. Erosion once out of hand becomes an expensive problem to check, but the responsibilities that were shirked by the offending farmer ultimately require major capital expenditures, a tax burden to be shared by the nation at large.

Another conservation problem that has yet to be faced is the direct agency of man in creating or modifying landforms. Highways, strip mines (U.S.D.I.: 1971) and, above all, the "creation" of subdivisions continue to upset the ecological balance on a local but intensive scale that makes agricultural soil erosion seem relatively minor. When social attitudes and capital interests fail as effective deterrents, then clearly there must be political activity and legislation. This is both the critical threshhold and focus where all concerned individuals of a depersonalized, industrial society must act in concert.

ACKNOWLEDGEMENTS

I am indebted to G. W. Dimbleby (London), D. B. Luten (Berkeley), J. A. Schmid (Jack McCormick and Associates, Inc.), and S. W. Trimble (Milwaukee) for their helpful comments on an interim draft of this paper.

REFERENCES

Allchin, F. R., 1969, "Early Domestic Animals and Cultivated Plants in India and Pakistan," in P. J. Ucko and G. W. Dimbleby (eds.), *The Domestication and Exploitation of Plants and Animals.* Chicago: Aldine, pp. 317-29.

Ammerman, A. J. and L. L. Cavalli-Sforza, 1971, "Measuring the Rate of Spread of Early Farming in Europe," *Man,* Vol. 6, pp. 647-88.

Aubert, G. and A. Monjauze, 1946, "Observations sur quelques sols de l'Oranie nord-occidentale: influence du déboisement, de l'érosion sur leur évolution," *Comptes Rendues Sommaires Société de Biogéographie,* No. 23, pp. 44-51.

Bennett, H. H., 1939, *Soil Conservation.* New York: McGraw-Hill.

_____, 1960, "Soil Erosion in Spain," *Geographical Review,* Vol. 50, pp. 59-72.

Berger, R. and R. Protsch, 1973, "Earliest Radiocarbon Dates for Domesticated Animals from Europe and the Near East," *Science,* Vol. 179, pp. 235-39.

Beug, H. J., 1967a, "Contributions to the Postglacial Vegetational History of Northern Turkey," in E. J. Cushing and H. E. Wright (eds.), *Quaternary Paleoecology.* New Haven: Yale University Press, pp. 349-56.

_____, 1967b, "On the Forest History of the Dalmatian Coast," *Review of Paleobotany and Palynology,* Vol. 2, pp. 271-79.

Bochkov, A. P., 1970, "Forest Influence on River Flows," *Nature and Resources* (UNESCO), Vol. 6, pp. 10-11.

Bowen, H. C., 1962, *Ancient Fields.* London: British Association for the Advancement of Science.

Bryan, R. B., 1968, "The Development, Use and Efficiency of Indices of Soil Erodibility," *Geoderma*, Vol. 2, pp. 5-26.

Bunting, B. T., 1965, *The Geography of Soil*. Chicago: Aldine, 213 pp.

Büdel, Julius, 1965, "Aufbau und Verschüttung Olympias: mediterrane Flusstatigkeit seit der Frühantike," *Tagungsberichte und Wissenchaftliche Abhandlungen*, Deutscher Geographentag, Heidelberg, 1963. Wiesbaden: Steiner, pp. 179-83.

Butzer, K. W., 1963, "The Last 'Pluvial' Phase of the Eurafrican Subtropics," *Arid Zone Research* (UNESCO), Vol. 20, pp. 211-21.

_____, 1964, "Pleistocene Geomorphology and Stratigraphy of the Costa Brava Region, Catalonia," *Abhandlungen, Akademie der Wissenschaften und der Literatur* (Mainz), Math.-Naturw. Klasse, 1964, No. 1, pp. 1-51.

_____, 1971, *Environment and Archeology: an Ecological Approach to Prehistory*. Chicago: Aldine.

Clauzon, G. and J. Vaudour, 1971, "Ruissellement, transports solides et transports en solution sur un versant aux environs d'Aix-en-Provence," *Revue de Géographie Physique et de Géologie Dynamique*, Vol. 13, pp. 489-504.

Cook, S. F., 1949, "Soil Erosion and Population in Central Mexico," *Ibero-Americana*, Vol. 34, pp. 1-86.

Corbel, Jean, 1964, "L'érosion terrestre, étude quantitative," *Annales de Géographie*, Vol. 73, pp. 385-412.

Crawford, O. G. S., 1923, "Aerial Surveys and Archaeology," *Geographical Journal*, Vol. 61, pp. 342-66.

Dimbleby, G. W., 1972, "The Impact of Early Man on his Environment," in P. R. Cox and J. Peel (eds.), *Population and Pollution*. London: Academic Press, pp. 7-13.

Duchaufour, P., 1956, *Pedologie: applications forestières et agricoles*. Nancy: Ecole Nationale des Eaux et Forêts.

Durand, H. H., 1959, *Les sols rouges et les croutes en Algerie*. Alger: Service des Etudes Scientifiques.

Eisma, D., 1962, "Beach Ridges near Selçuk, Turkey," *Tijdschrift K. nederlandsche aardrijkskundige Genootschaap*, Vol. 79, pp. 234-46.

Evans, J. G., 1971a, "Habitat Change on the Calcareous Soils of Britain: the Impact of Neolithic Man," in D. D. A. Simpson (ed.), *Economy and Settlement in Neolithic and Early Bronze Age Britain and Europe*. Leicester: Leicester University Press, pp. 27-73.

_____, 1971b, "Notes on the Environment of Early Farming Communities in Britain," in D. D. A. Simpson (ed.), *Economy and Settlement in Neolithic and Early Bronze Age Britain and Europe*. Leicester: Leicester University Press, pp. 11-26.

Food and Agricultural Organization, 1954, "Soil Erosion Survey of Latin America," *Journal of Soil and Water Conservation*, Vol. 9, pp. 158-68, 214-19, 223-29, 237.

_____, 1960, *Soil Erosion by Wind: Measures for its Control on Agricultural Lands*. F. A. O. Developmental Paper 71, London: H. M. S. O.

_____, 1965, *Soil Erosion by Water: Some Measures for its Control on Cultivated Lands*. F. A. O. Developmental Paper 21, London: H. M. S. O.

Fournier, Frédéric, 1960, *Climat et Erosion*. Paris: Presses Universitaires de France.

Fowler, P. J., 1971, "Early Prehistoric Agriculture in Western Europe: Some Archaeological Evidence," in D. D. A. Simpson (ed.), *Economy and Settlement in Neolithic and Early Bronze Age Britain and Europe*. Leicester: Leicester University Press, pp. 153-82.

Franceschetti, P. and G. Masone, 1968, "Aspetti della degradazione accelerate nei dintorni di pocapaglia in Provincia di Cuneo," *Rivista Geografica Italiana*, Vol. 74, pp. 435-86.

Fränzle, Otto, 1965, "Die Pleistozane Klima-und Landschaftsentwicklung der nordlichen Po-Ebene," *Abhandlungen, Akademie der Wissenschaften und der Literatur* (Mainz), Math.-Naturw. Klasse, 1965, No. 8, pp. 1-141.

George, E. J., R. A. Reed, and others, 1957, "Shelterbelts and Windbreaks," in *Yearbook of Agriculture 1957*. Washington, D.C.: Government Printing Office, pp. 715-21.

Golley, F. B., 1972, "Energy Flux in Ecosystems," in J. A. Wiens (ed.), *Ecosystem Structure and Function*. Portland: Oregon State University Press, pp. 69-90.

Gorman, C. F., 1971, "The Hoabinhian and After: Subsistence Patterns in Southeast Asia during the Late Pleistocene and Early Recent Periods," *World Archaeology*, Vol. 2, pp. 300-20.

Gottschalk, L. C., 1945, "Effects of Soil Erosion on Navigation in Upper Chesapeake Bay," *Geographical Review*, Vol. 35, pp. 219-38.

Greer, J. D., 1971, "Effect of Excessive-Rate Rainstorms on Erosion," *Journal of Soil and Water Conservation*, Vol. 26, pp. 196-97.

Happ, S. C., 1944, "Effect of Sedimentation on Floods in the Kickapoo Valley, Wisconsin," *Journal of Geology*, Vol. 52, pp. 53-68.

Happ, S. C., G. Rittenhouse and G. C. Dobson, 1940, "Some Principles of Accelerated Stream and Valley Sedimentation," *U.S. Department of Agriculture Technical Bulletin* No. 695, pp. 1-134.

Hard, Gerhard, 1971, "Excessive Bodenerosion um und nach 1800," *Erdkunde*, Vol. 24, pp. 290-308.

Hastings, J. R. and R. M. Turner, 1965, *The Changing Mile*. Tucson: University of Arizona Press.

Horowitz, A., 1971, "Climatic and Vegetational Developments in Northeastern Israel during Upper Pleistocene-Holocene Times," *Pollen et Spores*, Vol. 13, pp. 255-78.

Horton, R. E., 1945, "Erosional Development of Streams and their Drainage Basins," *Bulletin of the Geological Society of America*, Vol. 56, pp. 275-370.

Huckriede, Reinhold, 1971, "Uber jungholozäne, vorgeschichtliche Löss-Umlagerung in Hessen," *Eiszeitalter und Gegenwart*, Vol. 22, pp. 5-16.

Hudson, Norman, 1971, *Soil Conservation*. London: Batsford.

Ireland, H. A., C. F. S. Sharpe and D. H. Eargle, 1939, "Principles of Gully Erosion in the Piedmont of South Carolina," *U.S. Department of Agriculture Technical Bulletin* No. 633, pp. 1-143.

Jäger, K. D., 1962, "Uber Alter und Ursachen der Auelehmablagerung thüringischer Flüsse," *Praehistorische Zeitschrift*, Vol. 40, pp. 1-59.

Judson, Sheldon, 1963, "Erosion and Deposition of Italian Stream Valleys during Historic Time," *Science*, Vol. 140, pp. 898-99.

Judson, S. and D. F. Ritter, 1964, "Rates of Regional Denudation in the United States," *Journal of Geophysical Research*, Vol. 69, pp. 3395-3401.

Kayser, B., 1961, *Recherches sur les sols et l'erosion en Italie meridionale (Lucanie)*. Paris: SEDES.

Knox, J. C., 1972a, "Valley Alluviation in Southwestern Wisconsin," *Annals of the Association of American Geographers*, Vol. 62, pp. 401-10.

——, 1972b, "Post-1820 Valley Sedimentation in Southwestern Wisconsin," abstract of paper presented to meeting of the West Lakes Division, AAG, Saint Louis, Oct. 6-7, 1972.

Knox, J. C. and W. T. Corcoran, 1972, "River Adjustment to Deforestation 1832-1971, Platte River, Grant Co., Wisconsin," abstract of paper presented during Midwest Regional Meeting, Geological Society of America, Vol. 4, p. 331.

Leopold, Aldo, 1966, *A Sand County Almanac*. New York: Oxford University Press.

Leopold, L. B., 1956, "Land Use and Sediment Yield," in W. L. Thomas (ed.), *Man's Role in Changing the Face of the Earth*. Chicago: University of Chicago Press, pp. 639-47.

Likens, G. E. and others, 1970, "Effects of Forest Cutting and Herbicide Treatment on Nutrient Budgets in the Hubbard Brook Watershed-Ecosystem," *Ecological Monographs*, Vol. 40, pp. 23-47.

Livingstone, D. A., 1963, "Chemical Composition of Rivers and Lakes," *U.S. Geological Survey Professional Paper*, No. 440-G.

Lüttig, Gerd, 1960, "Zur Gliederung des Auelehms im Flussgebiet der Weser," *Eiszeitalter und Gegenwart*, Vol. 11, pp. 39-50.

Maack, R., 1956, "Uber Waldverwüstung und Bodenerosion im Staate Parana," *Die Erde*, pp. 191-228.

Machann, R. and A. Semmel, 1970, "Historische Bodenerosion auf Wüstungsfluren deutscher Mittelgebirge," *Geographische Zeitschrift*, Vol. 58, pp. 250-60.

Mackereth, F. J. H., 1965, "Chemical Investigation of Lake Sediments and their Interpretation," *Proceedings of the Royal Society*, Vol. B-161, pp. 295-309.

Marsh, G. P., 1864, *The Earth as Modified by Human Action*. New York: Scribners.

Meade, R. H., 1969, "Errors in Using Modern Stream-Load Data to Estimate Natural Rates of Denudation," *Bulletin, Geological Society of America*, Vol. 80, pp. 1265-74.

Menéndez-Amor, J. and F. Florschütz, 1961a, "Contribución al conocimiento de la historia de la vegetacion en España durante el Cuaternario," *Estudios Geologicos*, Vol. 17, pp. 83-99.

——, 1961b, "La concordancia entra la composición de la vegetacion durante la segunda mitad del Holoceno en la costa de Levante y en la costa W. de Mallorca," *Boletin, Real Sociedad Española de Historia Natural* (G), Vol. 59, pp. 97-100.

Min Tieh, T., 1941, "Soil Erosion in China," *Geographical Review*, Vol. 31, pp. 570-90.

Miszczak, A., 1960, "Amalgamation of Land-Holdings–an Agent of Increasing Soil Erosion," *Czasopismo Geograficzne*, Vol. 31, pp. 179-90.

Pattison, W. D., 1957, *Beginnings of the American Rectangular Land Survey System 1784-1800*, University of Chicago, Department of Geography Research Paper No. 50.

Pouquet, Jean, 1951, *L'Erosion*. Paris: Presses Universitaires de France (Collection "Que Sais-Je?", No. 491).

Raphael, C. N., 1973, "Late Quaternary Changes in Coastal Elis, Greece," *Geographical Review*, Vol. 63, pp. 73-89.

Rossignol, M. and L. Pastouret, 1971, "Analyse polliniques des niveaux sapropéliques postglaciaires dans une carotte en Méditerranée orientale," *Reviews of Palaeobotany and Palynology*, Vol. 11, pp. 227-38.

Schmid, J. A., 1974, *Urban Vegetation: A Review and Chicago Case Study*. University of Chicago, Department of Geography Research Paper, in press.

Schumm, S. A., 1965, "Quaternary Paleohydrology," in H. E. Wright, and D. G. Frey (eds.), *The Quaternary of the United States*. Princeton: Princeton University Press, pp. 783-794.

Stallings, J. H., 1957, *Soil Conservation*. Englewood Cliffs, N.J.: Prentice-Hall.

Stocking, M. A., 1972, "Relief Analysis and Soil Erosion in Rhodesia Using Multivariate Techniques," *Zeitschrift für Geomorphologie*, Vol. 16, pp. 432-43.

Stockton, C. W. and H. C. Fritts, 1971, "Conditional Probability of Occurrence for Variations in Climate Based on Width of Annual Tree-Rings in Arizona," *Tree-Ring Bulletin*, Vol. 31, pp. 3-24.

Strahler, A. N., 1952, "Dynamic Basis of Geomorphology," *Bulletin of the Geological Society of America*, Vol. 63, pp. 923-38.

———, 1956, "The Nature of Induced Erosion and Aggradation," in W. L. Thomas (ed.), *Man's Role in Changing the Face of the Earth*. Chicago: University of Chicago Press, pp. 621-38.

Strakov, N. M., 1967, *Principles of Pedogenesis*. Vol. 1, S. I. Tomkieff and J. E. Hemingway (eds.), London: Oliver and Boyd.

Strautz, W., 1963, "Auelehmbildung und -gliederung im Weser- und Leinetal mit vergleichenden Zeitbestimmungen aus dem Flussgebiet der Elbe," *Beiträge zur Landespflege* (Stuttgart), Vol. 1, pp. 273-314.

Thompson, J. R., 1970, "Soil Erosion in the Detroit Metropolitan Area," *Journal of Soil and Water Conservation*, Vol. 25, pp. 8-10.

Tricart, Jean, and André Cailleux, 1972, *Introduction to Climatic Geomorphology*. London: Longmans.

Trimble, S. W., 1969, *Culturally Accelerated Sedimentation on the Middle Georgia Piedmont*. M. A. thesis, University of Georgia. Reproduced and distributed by U.S. Soil Conservation Service, Fort Worth, Texas, 1970.

———, 1970, "The Alcovy River Swamps: the Result of Culturally Accelerated Sedimentation," *Bulletin, Georgia Academy of Science*, Vol. 28, pp. 131-41.

———, 1973, *A Geographic Analysis of Erosive Land Use on the Southern Piedmont, ca. 1700-present*. Unpublished Ph. D. Dissertation, University of Georgia.

Tuan, Yi-Fu, 1968, "Discrepancies Between Environmental Attitude and Behavior: Examples from Europe and China," *Canadian Geographer*, Vol. 12, pp. 176-91.

U.S. Department of the Interior, 1971, "Impact of Surface Mining on Environment," in T. R. Detwyler (ed.), *Man's Impact on Environment*. New York: McGraw-Hill, pp. 348-69.

van Zeist, W., R. W. Timmers and S. Bottema, 1970, "Studies of Modern and Holocene Pollen Precipitation in Southeastern Turkey," *Paleohistoria*, Vol. 14, pp. 19-39.

Vice, R. B., H. P. Guy and G. E. Ferguson, 1969, "Sediment Movement in an Area of Suburban Highway Construction, Scott Run Basin, Fairfax County, Virginia, 1961-64," U.S. Geological Survey Water Supply Paper 1591-E, pp. 1-41.

Vita-Finzi, Claudio, 1969, *The Mediterranean Valleys: Geological Changes in Historical Times*. Cambridge: Cambridge University Press.

Vogt, Jean, 1953, "Erosion des sols et techniques de culture en climat tempéré maritime de transition," *Revue de Géomorphologie Dynamique*, Vol. 4, pp. 157-83.

———, 1971, "Aspects de l'érosion historique des sols en Bourgogne et dans les régions voisines," *Annales de Bourgogne*, 1971, pp. 30-50.

Watson, William, 1969, "Early Animal and Cereal Domestication in China," in P. J. Ucko and G. W. Dimblebey (eds.), *The Domestication and Exploitation of Plants and Animals*. Chicago: Aldine, pp. 393-402.

Welten, Max, 1954, "Pollenniederschlagstypen aus höhern Lagen Spaniens und ihre subrezenten Veränderungen," *Veröffentlichungen, Geobotanisches Institut Rübel* (Zürich), Vol. 31, pp. 199-216.

Wijmstra, T. A., 1969, "Palynology of the First 30m of a 120m Deep Section in Northern Macedonia," *Acta Botanica Nederlandia*, Vol. 18, pp. 511-27.

Wischmeier, W.H. and D.D. Smith, 1965, "Predicting Rainfall-Erosion Losses from Cropland East of the Rocky Mountains," *U.S. Department of Agriculture Handbook* No. 282, pp. 1-47.

Wischmeier, W. H., C. B. Johnson, and B. V. Cross, 1971, "A Soil Erodibility Nomograph for Farmland and Construction Sites," *Journal of Soil and Water Conservation*, Vol. 26, pp. 189-93.

Wolf, E. R., 1966, *Peasants*. Englewood Cliffs, N.J.: Prentice-Hall.

Wolman, M. G., 1967, "A Cycle of Sedimentation and Erosion in Urban River Channels," *Geografiska Annaler*, Vol. 49A, pp. 385-95.

Wright, H. E., 1972, "Vegetation History," in W. A. McDonald and G. R. Rapp (eds.), *The Minnesota Messenia Expedition: Reconstructing a Bronze Age Regional Environment.* Minneapolis: University of Minnesota Press, pp. 188-99.

Yassoglou, N. J. and C. Nobeli, 1972, "Soil Studies," in W. A. McDonald and G. R. Rapp (eds.), *The Minnesota Messenia Expedition: Reconstructing a Bronze Age Regional Environment.* Minneapolis: University of Minnesota Press, pp. 171-76.

Man's Impact on Stream
Regimen and Quality

Jack P. Mrowka
University of Chicago

Man's impact on stream regimen and quality has been multifarious and often synergistic throughout his period of habitation of this planet. Although there is a long history of research on this topic, we have only begun to comprehend some of the intricacies involved. In this chapter an attempt is made to illustrate the nature and complexity of man's impact upon the earth's freshwaters, and comments are offered on some of the many significant past research efforts to gain understanding of these relationships.

A great wealth of knowledge is now available concerning hydrology and man's interaction with the hydrosphere. This generalization is easily verified by reference to two outstanding compilations of water knowledge: Ven Te Chow's (1964*a*) monumental and peerless *Handbook of Applied Hydrology* and the more recent and geographically-oriented *Water, Earth and Man*, edited by R. J. Chorley (1969). The serious scholar will be amply rewarded for time expended in digesting the great quantity of knowledge in these two volumes. Among the many attempts to review the problems of man and water are Thomas' "Changes in Quantities and Qualities of Ground and Surface Waters" (1956), which includes an excellent bibliography of relevant articles published before the mid-1950's, and "Water Problems" (1965), a later review also by Thomas.

The terms "river regimen" and "water quality" have been defined in a variety of ways. Beckinsale (1969*a*: p. 455) has broadly defined river regimen as "the variations in its discharge." Following his lead, river regimen can be defined as the trace of streamflow with time at a given channel cross section. In engineering parlance, river regimen would be illustrated by the station hydrograph. At a very general scale the hydrograph (and thus the river regimen) is illustrated by means of monthly values for a complete year, either a water year (October 1 through September 30) or a calendar year (January through December). However, in actuality, the river regimen consists of the continuous streamflow with all its variations in daily and hourly flow.

Stream quality is a more complex concept, as is ably demonstrated by Wolman (1971) in his recent article on our nation's rivers. River quality embodies both characteristics of the fluid in transit and physical attributes of the channel. River quality is also a very subjective concept, being evaluated as perceived by the investigator and his particular value system, which is subject to change with time. The complexity and subjectivity of the concept of water quality has been the topic of much recent discussion and debate in the attempts of United States Council on Environmental Quality to set up uniform standards for the control of water pollution (Council on Environmental Quality: 1972).

For the purposes of this article the concept of river quality can be defined as the total of all the physical and chemical characteristics of the fluid and the physical channel at any given cross section along the length of the watercourse.

Working within a general systems framework, Chorley and Kennedy (1971, pp. 79, 93-101) have identified the basic structure of hydrology as a cascading system. This being a specific subtype of an open system, the investigator's attention is immediately focused upon the inputs, outputs, and changes in the state of a particular variable through time. If viewed within this framework, river regimen and quality at a particular point in space and time may be considered as a function of characteristics and inputs of the watershed upstream, the outputs downstream, the initial state of streamflow, and quality at the point of observation. Examples of watershed characteristics are interception storage and infiltration capacity, while examples of downstream characteristics are back-water effects of a riffle, tidal fluctuations, and estuarine circulation.

Owing to the linkage between the watershed characteristics both upstream and downstream and the stream at any given point, man's alteration of any of the watershed attributes should be reflected in changes in the character of the stream flow and quality at all locations throughout the drainage basin. However, the effects of man's alteration may be masked or filtered by a variety of phenomena associated with the structure of a specific hydrologic system and its state at the time of analysis. These phenomena include feedback mechanisms and variables affecting relaxation time or period of system reorganization following man's input. The input-output relationships can probably be analyzed most effectively by means of queueing theory including analysis of the arrival pattern, i.e., magnitude and frequency, lag time, queue discipline, attrition rate, and so on (Chorley and Kennedy: 1972, pp. 13-20, and Chow: 1964b, pp. 48-49).

If it is valid to consider the hydrologic processes within a systems framework and if the theoretical model illustrated in Figure 1 is physically correct, then any alteration by man of any of the storages or linkages in the hydrologic system, with perhaps the exceptions of deep percolation, deep storage, and deep outflow, must have an impact upon the stream flow and water quality. Two basic models of the hydrologic cycle that include man's impact are illustrated in Figures 2 and 3. Figure 2 is a general model for the hydrologic system after H. E. Thomas (1956, p. 545), while Figure 3 is a specific model for the hydrologic system of Nassau and Suffolk Counties, New York after Franke and McClymonds (1972, p. 39).

A review of some of the recent literature was attempted in order to provide empirical data for some of the links involved in the man-river system. However, instead of examining individual storages and processes as indicated in these models, most of the recent studies have investigated the combined effects of some general complex human activity. These impact studies can be grouped under four major headings: (1) direct channel manipulation, (2) rural watershed alterations, (3) the effects of urbanization, and (4) water pollution activities.

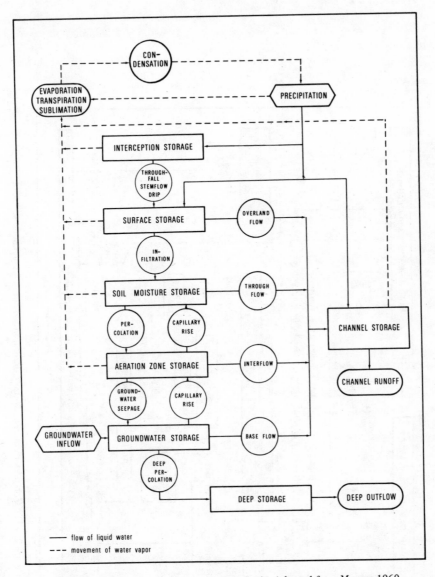

Figure 1. Model of a Basin Hydrological Cycle. Adapted from Moore: 1969.

Before expanding on these four themes, it should be noted that one of the problems encountered in the preparation of this review was the abundance of theoretical articles presenting hypotheses and speculation and the relatively small number of articles presenting empirical data. Major exceptions to this generalization are various publications by the U.S. Department of Agriculture, Forest Service, and Soil Conservation Service, U.S. Geological Survey, and also publications emanating from the experimental watersheds and the recently established National Hydrologic Bench-Mark Network. (For more information on the National Network of Hydrologic Bench-Marks, see Leopold: 1962; Cobb and Biesecker: 1971.)

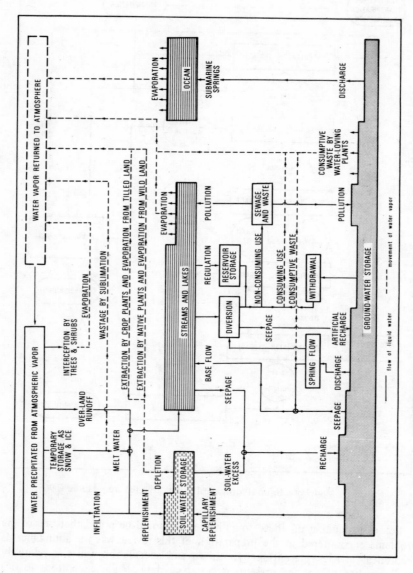

Figure 2.   The Complex Pattern of Water Circulation. Adapted from Thomas: 1956.

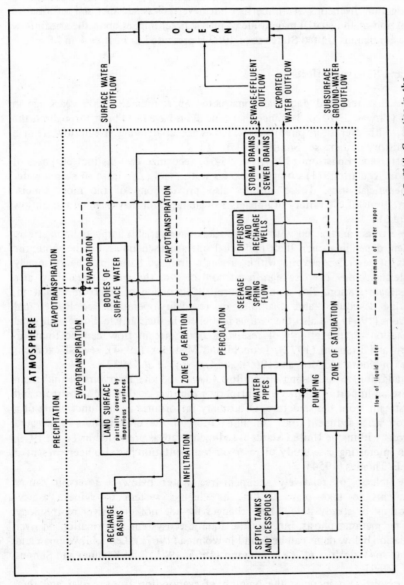

Figure 3. Flow Diagram of the Hydrologic System of Nassau and Suffolk Counties in the 1960's. Adapted from Franke and McClymonds: 1972.

MAN'S DIRECT CHANNEL MANIPULATION

Perhaps the most obvious and visible impact of man upon stream regimen and river quality has been his direct physical manipulation of river channels. These projects can be divided into three classes of activities: (a) dam and reservoir construction, (b) channelization, bank manipulation and levee construction and (c) irrigation diversions. An imperfect but nevertheless succinct and informative illustration of the spatial magnitude of man's direct impact upon the streamflow of the contiguous United States as of 1969 is presented in Figures 4 and 5.

Dam and Reservoir Effects

The first recorded dam was constructed approximately 5000 years ago in Egypt (Biswas: 1970, p. 3). Since that time dams have been built throughout the world, with ever more ambitious schemes for controlling streamflow. (For a brief history of dams see Smith: 1971.)

Rutter and Engstrom (1964, pp. 25-61) recognize two distinct purposes of reservoir regulation: (1) storage of excess water, and (2) release of stored water for beneficial uses. These authors also provide one of the most concise presentations of the variety of impacts a single reservoir may have on streamflow (Figure 6).

Reservoirs constructed with gated outlets have variable impacts upon stream regimen, depending upon their individual operating schedules. Furthermore, the effects of several reservoirs within a single drainage basin may be extremely complex and may exercise significant control over the entire streamflow at a downstream station. For a more thorough discussion of reservoir regulation, operating schedules, and examples of reservoir operation see Rutter and Engstrom (1964) and also the various references in their article. Some additional information on the effects of reservoirs upon stream flow can be found in Linsley and Franzini (1972), Leopold and Maddock (1954), several excellent articles in Moore and Morgan (1969), and Oglesby, et al. (1972).

In addition to regulating streamflow, dams and the reservoirs behind them exercise an important degree of control over the river quality both upstream and downstream from the structure. Of primary importance is the functioning of a reservoir as a sediment trap. An illustration of the effectiveness of selected reservoirs within the United States as sediment traps is presented in Todd: 1970, and an interesting case study of reservoir sedimentation has also been presented by H. E. Thomas (1954).

The release of relatively sediment-free water below a reservoir causes adjustments to take place within the channel system to achieve a new equilibrium or steady-state. These changes include not only river morphology and river metamorphosis, but also the aquatic ecosystem. Information on river degradation below dams can be found in Wolman (1967a), Leopold, Wolman and Miller (1964), deVries (1968), Schumm (1969, 1971), and Komura and Simons (1967, 1969).

Reservoirs also increase the amount of evaporation from a river and thus increase the salinity of the water downstream, which may further affect the aquatic ecosystem. This great agency of water loss has led to much recent research on the use of monomolecular films on the surface of reservoirs in an attempt to reduce evaporation. Chorley and Kennedy (1971, p. 317) report that the spraying of a monomolecular film of cetyl alcohol reduced evaporation from a 130 acre Tanzanian reservoir by about 12 percent, and that this method was even more effective in reservoirs of less than 1 acre, where the reduction is up to 25 percent.

The temperature characteristics of the water may also be affected by the presence of a reservoir. Odum (1971) differentiates two different types of heat budgets for the impounded water on the basis of the type of dam design. If water is released from the surface, the reservoir is a "nutrient trap and heat exporter," whereas if water is released from the bottom, as is generally the case for dams which generate hydro-electric power, the reservoir is a "heat trap and nutrient exporter." In addition to the thermal effects Odum (1971: p. 314) lists the following effects of dams with deep-water penstocks:

(1) Water is released with a higher salinity than would be obtained from surface water withdrawal.
(2) Essential nutrients are lost from the reservoir, thus tending to deplete the productive capacity of the reservoir and at the same time causing eutrophication downstream.
(3) Evaporative loss is increased as a result of storing warm incoming water and releasing cold hypolimnial water.
(4) Low dissolved oxygen in the discharged water reduces the capacity of the stream to receive organic pollutants.
(5) The discharge of hydrogen sulfide and other reduced substances lowers downstream water quality and in extreme cases, results in fish-kills.

Dams also terminate the migration of various aquatic species unless elaborate fish ladders are provided. Trefethen (1972) gives an interesting discussion of man's impact on the Columbia River, with emphasis on the effects upon the Pacific salmon migrations.

Channelization and River Bank Treatment

The term channelization generally implies the straightening and shortening of a natural river channel. The primary effect of this process is to increase gradient and reduce the time of transmission of discharge through the channelized reach, thus steepening the rising segment of the flood hydrograph.

Normally large quantities of water are stored in river banks and on the flood plain as the river stage rises and overflows its banks. This water is later released as the river stage falls (Ward: 1967, pp. 319-20). However, if the river banks have been lined with concrete or if the higher stages have been confined to the channel by means of artificial levees or dikes, bank or floodplain storage is not possible and therefore the effect will be to increase the flood peak in the downstream reaches (Spieker: 1970, pp. 114-117; Gilbert: 1917).

The impact of channelization upon river quality is many-fold and can be especially catastrophic to the aquatic community. These effects may include increased velocity, both the mean velocity and point velocity throughout the cross-section, reduction of sheltered areas, increased temperature range and greatly reduced nutrient input due to destruction of overhanging bank vegetation, and disruption of the food chain. A nationwide study of the effects of channelization on the aquatic ecosystems is currently in progress and was reported on at the annual meeting of the Geological Society of America in

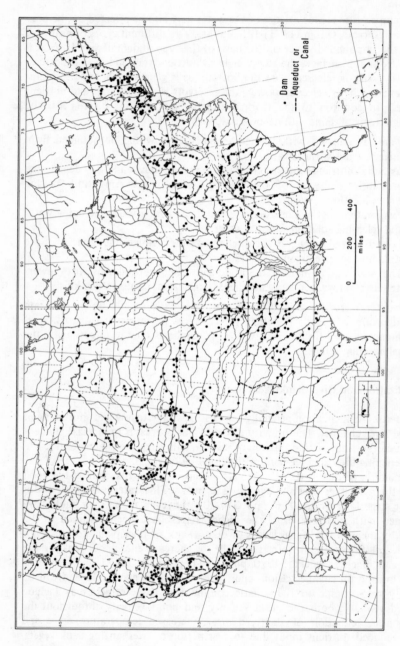

Figure 4. Distribution of Dams and Aqueducts or Canals in 1968. Adapted from map of Water Resources Development, U.S. Geological Survey: 1969.

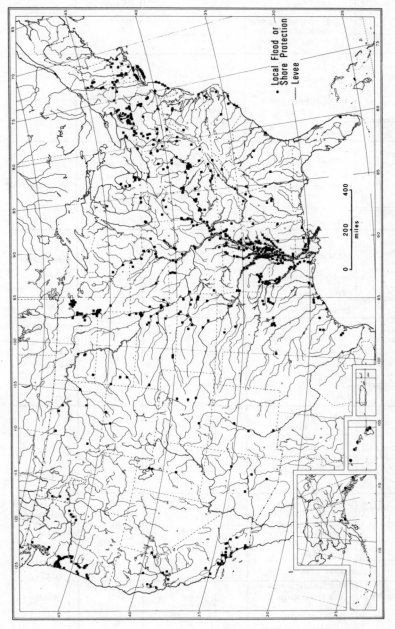

Figure 5. Distribution of Local Flood or Shore Protection Works and Levees in 1968. Adapted from map of Water Resources Development, U.S. Geological Survey: 1969.

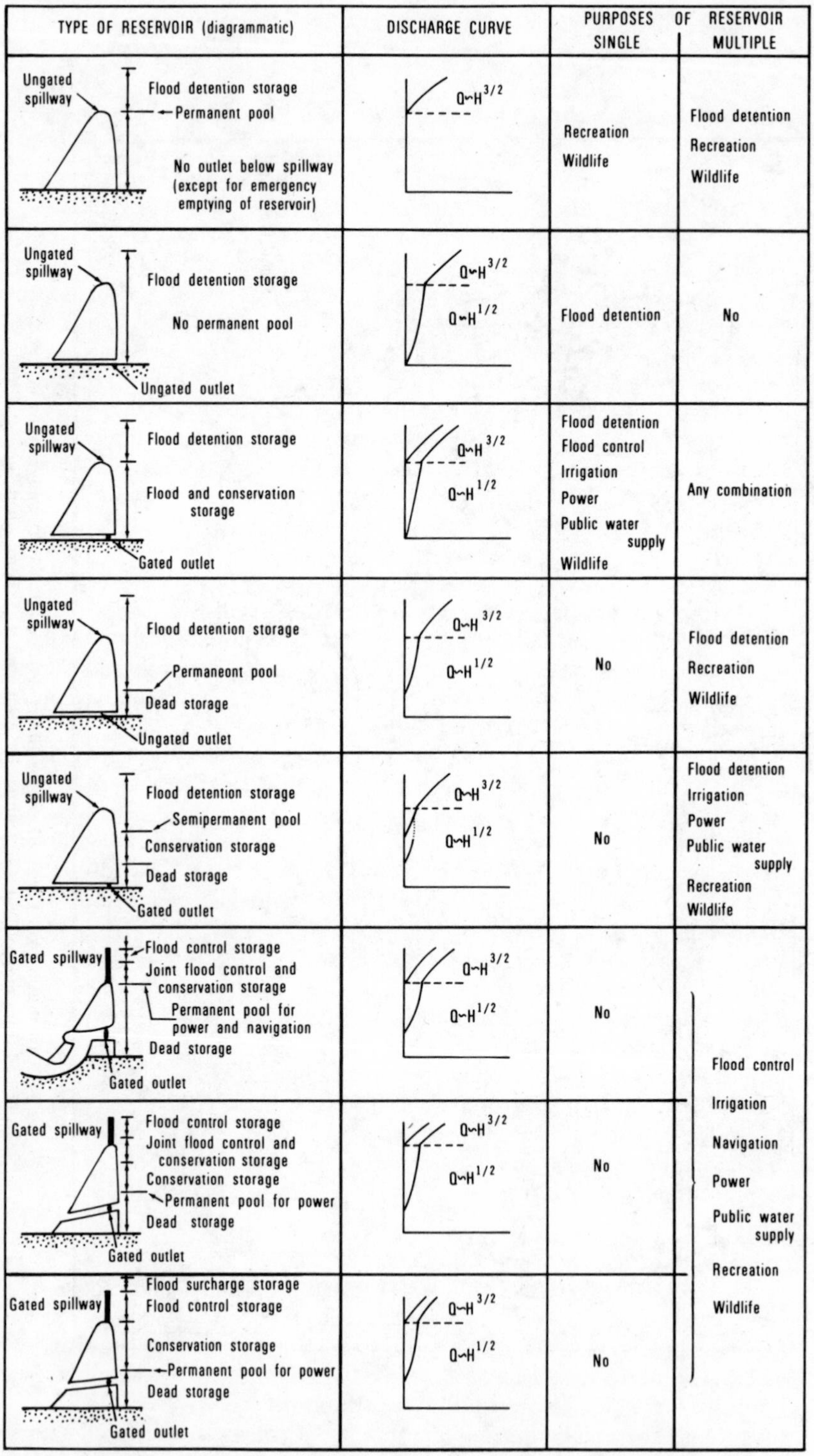

TYPE OF RESERVOIR (diagrammatic)	DISCHARGE CURVE	PURPOSES OF RESERVOIR SINGLE	MULTIPLE
Ungated spillway — Flood detention storage ← Permanent pool — No outlet below spillway (except for emergency emptying of reservoir)	$Q \sim H^{3/2}$	Recreation Wildlife	Flood detention Recreation Wildlife
Ungated spillway — Flood detention storage — No permanent pool — Ungated outlet	$Q \sim H^{3/2}$ $Q \sim H^{1/2}$	Flood detention	No
Ungated spillway — Flood detention storage — Flood and conservation storage — Gated outlet	$Q \sim H^{3/2}$ $Q \sim H^{1/2}$	Flood detention Flood control Irrigation Power Public water supply Wildlife	Any combination
Ungated spillway — Flood detention storage — Permaneont pool — Dead storage — Ungated outlet	$Q \sim H^{3/2}$ $Q \sim H^{1/2}$	No	Flood detention Recreation Wildlife
Ungated spillway — Flood detention storage — Semipermanent pool — Conservation storage — Dead storage — Gated outlet	$Q \sim H^{3/2}$ $Q \sim H^{1/2}$	No	Flood detention Irrigation Power Public water supply Recreation Wildlife
Gated spillway — Flood control storage — Joint flood control and conservation storage — Permanent pool for power and navigation — Dead storage — Gated outlet	$Q \sim H^{3/2}$ $Q \sim H^{1/2}$	No	Flood control Irrigation Navigation Power Public water supply Recreation Wildlife
Gated spillway — Flood control storage — Joint flood control and conservation storage — Conservation storage — Permanent pool for power — Dead storage — Gated outlet	$Q \sim H^{3/2}$ $Q \sim H^{1/2}$	No	
Gated spillway — Flood surcharge storage — Flood control storage — Conservation storage — Permanent pool for power — Dead storage — Gated outlet	$Q \sim H^{3/2}$ $Q \sim H^{1/2}$	No	

Figure 6.   Classification of Reservoirs. Adapted from Rutter and Engstrom: 1964.

November of 1972 (Vannote: 1972). Table 1 gives an impression of the extent of river bank treatment by one agency within the United States.

Irrigation Diversion Effects

Man has been practicing irrigated agriculture for at least six millennia in the Tigris-Euphrates Valleys, five millennia in the Nile Valley of Egypt, two and a half millennia in the Hwang and Yangtze Valleys and two millennia in the Indus Valley. From these modest beginnings the practice of irrigation has spread throughout the world into humid as well as arid areas, to the projected extent of more than 500 million acres during the 1970's (Beckinsale: 1969b, p. 495).

The most prominent effect of irrigation upon stream regimen is the direct reduction in discharge downstream from the diversions. There is generally some return flow to the channel due to seepage and drainage from the irrigated fields. However, it is usually substantially less in volume than the original diversion owing to conveyance losses, increased evaporation rates (stemming from more surface exposure when spread across the fields), infiltration into the soil, plant consumptive use, both within the plant structure and through transpiration although there have been recent attempts to reduce these losses by means of chemical sprays (Chorley and Kennedy: 1971, pp. 317-318).

There is also an alteration in the water quality of the river below the irrigated fields due to return flow. This deterioration in water quality results from increased salinity and sediment concentration in the drainage waters owing to evapotranspiration, ionic exchange, and the solution of any additional chemicals applied to the fields such as pesticides and fertilizers.

On the basis of these generalizations it might be assumed that the water quality would change in direct response to increases in the amount of irrigated acreage. However, as is the case with almost every phase of the hydrologic system, the complexity of the actual physical system militates against such a simple generalization. J. D. Rhoades and L. Bernstein (1971, p. 194) clearly demonstrate on the basis of a comparison of conditions before and after approximately fifty years of irrigation development, that different stream systems may respond in quite different fashion to similar human actions. These findings are illustrated in Table 2.

The article of Rhoades and Bernstein also contains useful information on the chemical, physical, and biological characteristics of irrigation and soil water and includes a comprehensive bibliography of 283 works.

This discussion of irrigation which involves direct channel withdrawals and utilization by crops within the catchment provides a natural introduction to the second major area of hydrologic impact research—the effects of watershed manipulation or alterations.

MODIFICATIONS OF WATERSHED CHARACTERISTICS

Undoubtedly some of man's most significant impacts upon stream regimen and water quality can be traced to modification of watershed characteristics. Possibly the most geographically significant of these actions has been the intentional and unintentional alteration of the native vegetation of watersheds.

Reference to Figure 1 will impress upon the reader the complexity of responses of the stream regimen which are initiated by changes in watershed

TABLE 1—Riverbank Treatment in the United States

[Values in miles as of 1966; Corps of Engineers projects only.]

Region	Mattress	Jetties	Training walls	Riprap	Revetment	Dikes	Other	Total treated
North Atlantic	—	18	18	—	—	—	—	36
South Atlantic-Gulf	35	67	—	—	—	—	—	102
Great Lakes	—	—	—	—	—	—	—	—
Ohio	—	—	—	50	10	—	—	60
Tennessee	—	—	—	—	—	—	—	—
Upper Mississippi	573	—	—	—	—	—	—	—
Lower Mississippi	—	—	—	—	—	75	5,836	6,484
Souris-Red-Rainy	—	—	—	—	—	—	—	—
Missouri	—	735	—	—	735	—	—	1,470
Arkansas-White-Red	250	1	80	—	—	140	—	471
Texas-Gulf	0	0	0	0	0	0	0	0
Rio Grande	—	250	—	—	—	—	0	250
Upper Colorado	—	—	—	—	—	—	—	—
Lower Colorado	—	—	—	—	—	—	—	—
Great Basin	0	0	0	0	0	0	0	0
Columbia-North Pacific	—	—	—	261	—	—	—	261
California	—	—	—	—	—	—	19	19
Alaska	—	—	6	—	—	—	—	6
Hawaii	0	0	0	0	0	0	0	0
Puerto Rico	—	—	—	—	—	—	—	—

Source: U.S. Water Resources Council: 1968 and Todd: 1970.

TABLE 2—Chemical Composition (meq/liter) of River Water Before and After Intensive Irrigation Developments

Constituent	Colorado River		Missouri River		Rio Grande River	
	1893	1962	1906	1953	1893	1945
Ca	3.3	4.5	3.2	3.1	2.95	4.5
Mg	1.1	2.4	1.6	1.5	0.67	1.5
Na	8.5	5.8	2.1	2.6	2.85	6.3
$CO_2 + HCO_3$	2.8	2.7	3.3	3.1	2.26	3.6
Cl	5.2	3.5	0.3	0.4	1.52	3.4
SO_4	4.8	6.8	3.5	3.7	2.61	5.3
Total solute contents, mg/liter	774	814	514	523	380	850
Millions of irrigated acres and year:	0.9 (1902)	3.5 (1950)	2.9 (1902)	5.1 (1950)	0.5 (1902)	2.5 (1950)

Source: Rhoades and Bernstein: 1971, p. 194.

vegetation. Directly affected are evapotranspiration, interception storage, stemflow and drip, surface storage, infiltration, overland flow, soil moisture storage, throughflow, and, in areas of high groundwater table, ground water storage, and base flow.

The alteration of catchment vegetation by means of fire may have been man's earliest, most constant, and most universally applied impact upon stream regimen and river quality (Stewart: 1956, pp. 115-133).

The results of investigations on the effects of watershed vegetation alterations have been presented at several recent conferences. Three such conferences of national and international significance were the Symposium on the Results of Research on Representative and Experimental Basins (1970, Wellington, New Zealand), Forest Watershed Management Symposium (1963, Corvallis, Oregon), and the International Symposium on Forest Hydrology (1965, University Park, Pennsylvania). (See IASH—UNESCO: 1970; Society of American Foresters: 1963; and Sopper and Lull: 1967.)

During the 1970 symposium, Sartz (p. 286) reported as follows on the effect of land use on the hydrology of small watersheds in Southwestern Wisconsin:

> Forest watersheds produced overland flow only after heavy rains, and the amounts of flow and peak rates were low compared with those from open land watersheds. Peak flow rates from a major storm ranged from 64 millimeters per hour for tilled land to no flow for undisturbed forest. Analysis of the flows from five large storms in one year showed that peak rates from tilled land averaged 2.5 times those from an abandoned field. Peak rates from heavily grazed pasture were 3.0 times those from lightly grazed pasture. Suspended sediment content was low for forest, abandoned field, and meadow, but high for tilled land and heavily grazed pasture.

In addition Pierce et al. (1970) reported on the effect of total elimination of the forest vegetation of a New Hampshire watershed on stream water quantity and quality. They found streamflow increases of 240 millimeters to 346 millimeters per water year, with a large part of this augmentation during the previous low flow season. These investigators also announced radical changes in the stream chemistry in response to the vegetation removal, including a 50 percent rise in nitrate concentration, a three to twenty fold elevation in cation levels, and particulate matter increases to 9 times the previous concentrations.

The antithesis of the study of Pierce *et al.* was conducted in Wales (Green: 1970) in a watershed that had been planted with Sitka Spruce trees. The initial effect of this afforestation was to increase mean streamflow for 5 years by 83 millimeters. The inconsistency in the findings of these two studies demonstrates the complexity of the relationships between watershed alteration and stream-flow. Green (1970, p. 344) postulated that the large area of basin surface (32 percent) which resulted from ploughing the catchment prior to the planting of the trees, sustained reduced evaporation loss, brought about by a reduction in soil moisture following the ploughing. Additional light on this problem is shed by the reports of Swank and Helvey (1970), Sopper and Lynch (1970), and Bochkov (1970).

There still appears to be some controversy on the "state of the art" of present knowledge about the effects of vegetation alteration upon streamflow. As may be judged by the preceding discussion much of the research effort within this particular realm of impact has been focused upon the relationships between forest vegetation and runoff. The monograph of H. W. Lull and K. Reinhart on *Forests and Floods in the Eastern United States* (1972) provides an excellent summary of research on this problem and includes a very useful bibliography. However, even in this sub-branch of hydrologic research the opinions of the scientists are varied, which may be comprehended from the following passage (Bochkov: 1970):

> In spite of the antiquity of the problem and numerous publications on hydrological and climatic influences of forests, 'to review which a man's life wouldn't be enough,' as P. Y. Ototsky wrote in 1905, and in spite of a substantial amount of field and laboratory experiments there is still no universal scientific opinion on the hydrological role of forests.

However, there is promise that many of the complexities of this problem will be better understood as more information is gained from the research efforts during the International Hydrological Decade (1965-74).

Modification of the distribution of forests is only one of the ways in which vegetation can be altered. The river channel quality and streamflow charac-teristics have been radically modified by man's attempts to convert scrub growth to grassland (Orme and Bailey: 1971; Hadley: 1972). In addition, there have been and continue to be attempts to control or eliminate the growth of phreatophytes (plants that absorb their water from permanent supplies in the ground) within semiarid or arid regions, with subsequent increases in streamflow (Bowie and Kam: 1968; Hughes: 1968; Muckel: 1966; and McDonald and Hughes: 1968).

As Table 3 indicates, man may produce significant effects upon stream regimen by means of changes in non-native vegetation distributions within the catchment such as particular crops grown with their associated differences in transpiration and consumptive use. Other tables listing values of transpiration for various crops and vegetation types as well as consumptive water use within the United States are given by D. K. Todd (1970, pp. 88-115).

Man has modified stream regimen and water quality through a wide spectrum of other impacts upon watersheds. A particularly significant source of informa-tion on this problem is *Effects of Watershed Changes on Streamflow* edited by

TABLE 3—Variations in Consumptive Use by Crops

Crop	No. of tests	Range in water requirements, ft.
A. Farm Crops in the Southwest		
Alfalfa	369	3.47-5.08
Rhodes grass	12	3.49-4.43
Sudan grass	25	2.88-3.16
Barley	3	1.24-1.83
Oats	2	1.90-2.09
Wheat	46	1.46-2.24
Corn	42	1.44-1.99
Kafir	16	1.32-1.54
Flax	3	1.23-1.59
Broomcorn	9	0.97-1.15
Emmer	6	1.19-1.87
Feterita	8	0.97-1.10
Millet	5	0.91-1.09
Milo	35	0.96-1.67
Sorghum	34	1.69-2.08
Cotton	103	2.35-3.51
Potatoes	12	1.59-2.04
Soybeans	36	1.66-2.81
Sugar beets	5	1.77-2.72
Sugar cane*	41	3.48-4.56
B. Vegetable Crops in the Southwest		
Beans, snap	9	0.83-1.44
Beets, table	28	0.87-1.37
Cabbage	21	0.94-1.49
Carrots	6	1.27-1.60
Cauliflower	6	1.43-1.77
Lettuce	49	0.72-1.35
Onions	4	0.73-1.52
Peas	8	1.21-1.56
Melons	3	2.48-3.40
Spinach	12	0.80-1.07
Sweet potatoes	3	1.77-2.25
Tomatoes	17	0.95-1.42
C. Crops in the Missouri and Arkansas Basins		
Forage, including alfalfa	648	1.94-2.62
Barley	335	1.33-1.82
Oats	409	1.35-1.81
Wheat	542	1.36-1.80
Corn	70	1.23-1.83
Kafir corn	15	1.43-1.57
Flax	50	1.47-1.85
Millet	14	0.81-0.94
Milo maize	27	1.09-1.70
Sorghum	26	1.06-1.47

TABLE 3–(*Continued*)

Crop	No. of tests	Range in water requirements, ft.
Apples	4	2.10-2.60
Beans	4	1.30-1.60
Buckwheat	3	1.05-1.30
Cantaloupes	10	1.50-2.30
Peas	168	1.36-1.94
Potatoes	350	1.38-1.70
Sugar beets	128	1.60-2.50
Sunflowers	16	1.20-1.40
Tomatoes	6	2.10-2.80
Cucumbers	7	1.73-3.75

Source: U.S. Water Resources Council: 1968; Todd: 1970.

Moore and Morgan (1969). This spectrum of impacts has broadened in scope, geographical distribution, and intensity of effect as man's technological skills have advanced. For example, man has influenced the amount of precipitation input into the drainage basin and thus influenced streamflow regimen both through deliberate attempts such as cloud seeding, and unintentionally through the production of hygroscopic nuclei as a result of air pollution (Chorley and Kennedy: 1971, pp. 311-315; Changnon: 1968). Furthermore, as technology increases man may unintentionally greatly affect the streamflow of the southern and eastern United States through hurricane dissipation (Chorley and Kennedy: 1971, pp. 316-317).

It is necessary to emphasize that owing to the present state of our knowledge of the various complex processes of the hydrologic cycle, many of the human impacts on streamflow regimen are expressed as statistical relationships, which is particularly true concerning watershed alterations. This has created a major problem in evaluating the effectiveness of cloud seeding as a means of increasing streamflow, particularly in semi-arid and arid areas. For example, Ives (1972) has recently discussed this problem in association with investigations of man's impact upon ecosystems within the San Juan Mountains of Colorado.

Streamflow regimen and water quality have been significantly influenced by the various hydrologic responses to the diverse actions included under the term agricultural practices. In addition to the regulation of interception, evapotranspiration, and consumptive water use owing to the distribution of crops grown, these activities include: (1) the effects upon surface storage-infiltration and overland flow owing to plowing, terracing and other cultivation practices; (2) the effects upon soil moisture storage, throughflow and interflow owing to deep plowing, tiling and various drainage practices, as well as irrigation practices; and (3) the effects upon water quality of fertilizers, pesticides, herbicides, and manure to name just a few of the possible impacts. For a more thorough discussion of the effects of agriculture upon streamflow and water quality see Hockensmith (1960), Willrich and Smith (1970), and the chapter by Manners in the present volume.

Possibly the most radical modification of a catchment results from the process of urbanization. This topic is of growing significance throughout the world and has become the object of much of the modern research on man's impact upon his environment.

URBANIZATION

There have been several recent reviews of the effects of urbanization upon various components of the hydrologic system. Thomas (1956) composed a very good general survey of the relationships between man and water (both surface flow and ground water) including over eighty references published before the middle 1950's. Thomas has also published two subsequent articles on the effects of urbanization on hydrology in 1965 and 1970. In addition, Savini and Kammerer (1961, p. 1) produced "a review, classification, and preliminary evaluation of the significance of the effects of urbanization on the hydrologic regimen." These authors provide a good review of the literature up to the mid-1950's and a good introduction to this complex problem, focusing primarily upon the sub-problems of urban consumptive water use and the effects of urban land use. They complete their discussion with a plea for research concerning storm runoff.

> With the possible exception of the Raymond Basin, there have been no comprehensive and detailed studies of multiple hydrologic changes created by urbanization of an area and, without exception, no such studies have been made which document pre-urban hydrologic conditions of the same area (p. A-39). Except for consulting engineers reports to their clients, there appear to have been no more than 5 to 10 studies of storm runoff specifically related to urban areas and documented in hydrologic literature generally available to the public. These studies, to which reference already has been made, have been made principally in St. Louis, Mo., Los Angeles, California, Champaign, Ill. and most recently, in Baltimore, Md. (p. A-38).

There followed a concentrated attempt on the part of the U.S. Geological Survey to study the many aspects of urban hydrology including a whole series of water supply papers on the hydrologic effects of urban growth; another series on water in the urban environment; several papers concerned with hydrology and urban planning; several circulars on water in the urban environment; six professional papers on hydrology and effects of urbanization on Long Island, New York; and numerous relevant articles in the annual research reports of the Geological Survey beginning with Carter's "Magnitude and Frequency of Floods in Suburban Areas" (1961). (See also Savini and Kammerer: 1961; Harris and Rantz: 1964; Martens: 1968; Dawdy: 1969; Vice, *et al.*: 1969; Anderson: 1970; Spieker: 1970; Leopold: 1968; Schneider and Spieker: 1969; Rantz: 1970; Sheaffer, *et al.*: 1970; Thomas and Schneider: 1970; Seaburn: 1969, 1970; Pluhowski: 1970; Franke and McClymonds: 1972; Carter: 1961; Waananen: 1961; Sawyer: 1963; Riggs: 1965; Crippen: 1965; and Wilson: 1967.)

In 1963 a Task Force on Effect of Urban Development on Flood Discharges of the Committee on Flood Control of the American Society of Civil Engineering was organized and given the following task:

> To seek out information pertaining to changes in runoff characteristics of watersheds due to urban development and to the effects of such changes on the concentration of flood waters in stream channels; to compile a bibliography of works and papers that provide such information (see

Appendix I.—Annotated Bibliography); to prepare an inventory of investigations being conducted on this subject or pertinent parts thereof; and to identify areas in which research is needed to broaden knowledge of runoff rates for flood control or protective purposes.

This group published a progress report entitled "Effect of Urban Development on Flood Discharges—Current Knowledge and Future Needs" in 1969, which includes a very informative 71-piece annotated bibliography of research on the urban hydrology problems up to the mid-1960's. Also in 1969, the American Society of Civil Engineers produced *An Analysis of National Basic Information Needs in Urban Hydrology* for the U.S. Geological Survey in a document which emphasized the need for research in storm drainage from urbanized areas.

One can also point to the report of Wolman and Schick (1967) on the effects of construction and fluvial sediment in urban and suburban areas of Maryland. On the basis of this study as well as extensive past research on fluvial geomorphology, Wolman (1967*b*) developed "A Cycle of Sedimentation and Erosion in Urban River Channels." This cycle of land use, sediment yield and channel response for the Piedmont area of Maryland is illustrated in Figure 7 below.

Wolman's work was followed in England by Walling and Gregory's study "The Measurement of the Effects of Building Construction on Drainage Basin Dynamics" (1970). They found suspended sediment concentrations 2 to 10 times and occasionally 100 times greater for disturbed as opposed to undisturbed conditions. See also Leopold's earlier attempt to summarize existing knowledge of the effects of urbanization on hydrologic factors in his 1968 circular entitled *Hydrology for Urban Land Planning—A Guidebook on the Hydrologic Effects of Urban Land Use*.

Owing to the lack of adequate data, it was recommended that his report be considered as a compilation of tentative suggestions. It is interesting to note that

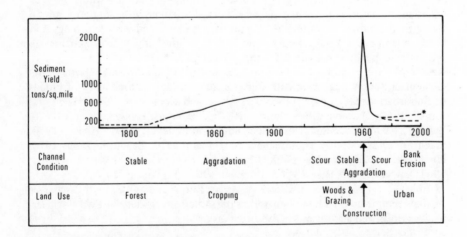

Figure 7. Schematic Sequence of Land Use, Sediment Yield, and Channel Response in a Part of the Piedmont Region. Adapted from Wolman: 1967*b*. * = Revised interpretation suggested by Leopold: 1972.

the sediment production rates were compared between two streams, one urban and one rural. Watts Branch, the rural stream or control, has recently been affected by the urbanization of its drainage basin. At the annual meeting of the Geological Society of America, Leopold (1972) in his presidential address, discussed the recent history of Watts Branch and demonstrated some additional complexities in the impact of urbanization upon stream channels. He effectively illustrated the importance of differentiating short term from long term changes in channel character. Generally Watts Branch illustrated Wolman's cycle of sedimentation and erosion, carving a channel at places twice the pre-urbanization size; however, more recently the channel has become much smaller in size than even the initial pre-urbanization stream channel, thus confounding the earlier finding of channel enlargement. (For additional information see Hammer: 1972a and 1972b.)

A very important source of information on the effects of urbanization upon streamflow including many references to the recent literature is section three, "Urban water," in *Effects of Watershed Changes on Streamflow,* Water Resources Symposium Number Two, Center for Research in Water Resources, The University of Texas at Austin (Moore and Morgan: 1969; see also Schaake: 1972). Finally, a recent article by Jones (1971) entitled "Where is Urban Hydrology Practice Today?" illuminates common engineering practice and some of the fallacious assumptions which must be investigated.

Initial conclusions concerning the impact of urbanization upon stream attributes can be summarized as follows:

(1) The roofing of the watershed surface greatly reduces infiltration of precipitation thus increasing the peak runoff and shortening the lag time between precipitation and peak runoff.

(2) The reduction in ground water recharge in response to the decreased infiltration of precipitation, reduces the amount of base flow or low water flow in the stream channel.

(3) The initial construction accompanying urbanization produces greatly increased sediment loads for the stream channels.

(4) There appears to be initial channel erosion and enlargement accompanying urbanization and at least some sedimentation owing to construction activity; however, the long term effects of urbanization upon channel size and shape is obscure at the present time.

More information on the effects of urbanization upon hydrology on a world-wide scale may be forthcoming as results from the International Hydrological Decade. One of the subgroups of the working group on the influence of man on the hydrological cycle, is concerned with the effects of industrial and urban development, with emphasis upon the geographical concentration of the need for good quality water and the alternations in runoff and infiltration resulting from urbanization (UNESCO: 1967).

There are additional effects of man upon streamflow and river quality through the activity encompassed by the term urbanization. These activities include modification of the drainage network through the construction of storm drains, thus influencing the lag time (shortening it) between precipitation and peak discharge. Also included are several actions previously discussed under the heading of direct channel manipulation, including channelization, concrete lining of channels, reduction of bed, bank, and floodplain storage. Increased water consumption within the catchment and streamflow augmentation through the importation of water from outside the basin often accompany urbanization. Finally, one can add disruption of the aquatic ecosystem and general modification of the water quality, owing to municipal (sewage) as well as industrial pollution, to this list of a few of the many impacts associated with the term urbanization.

The last named activity, i.e., the alteration of water quality caused by pollution, is the final major impact discussed in the present paper. This topic has been the focus of a great increase in recent research activity as is witnessed by the numerous articles in all of the hydrologic journals.

WATER POLLUTION

The term water pollution signifies man's influence in the general deterioration of water quality through the direct input of matter or energy into the fluid stream or river channel. Thus pollution is simply one type of impact upon water quality.

One of the best review articles on water quality from the geographical point of view is Douglas' "The Geographical Interpretation of River Water Quality Data" (1972). Some additional first-rate sources of water quality information appear in the works of Powell (1964) and Velz (1970).

In order to investigate seriously the nature of man's impact upon the quality of the fluid within the river channel, it is necessary to have a detailed knowledge of the aquatic chemistry (its natural equilibrium and the specific cations, anions, nonionic constituents) and the other physical and chemical properties of water which man might influence. A recent basic source of information on this topic is the book, *Aquatic Chemistry*, by Strumm and Morgan (1970). In addition, information on the chemical nature of specific pollutants can be found in such encyclopedic works as *Water and Water Pollution Handbook*, volumes 1-4, edited by L. L. Ciaccio (1971) and in recent issues of the *Water Research*, journal of the International Association on Water Pollution Research, and also in the proceedings of the conferences of this organization. See, for example, Jenkins (ed.), *Advances in Water Pollution Research* (1969).

There is also important knowledge on man's impact on water quality at broader levels of generalization especially for scholars with a geographical perspective. Wolman (1971) has clearly stated that river quality consists of at least two broad spectra of attributes—those associated with the fluid transported through a stream channel and those associated with the physical channel itself.

Owing to their different spatial distributions, pollutants may be divided into natural and man-made categories, and the latter may be subdivided into municipal, industrial, and agricultural pollutants. Examples of each class are sediment, sewage, brine, and fertilizer, respectively. It is probably worth repeating that although all of these classes of pollutants may add the same chemical (for example sodium) to the stream flow, their spatial and temporal distributions are sufficiently different to justify recognition of man's impact at higher levels of generalization.

If water quality is defined to encompass more than the attributes of the fluid within the stream channel, then one must necessarily include investigation of man's impact upon the aquatic biota within a given channel reach. Basic information on this topic is available in several recent works, such as the *Ecology of Running Waters* by Hynes (1970); and *River Ecology and Man* edited by Oglesby, *et al.* (1972). It is this concern that has placed much recent interest in another form of physical (non-chemical) pollution, namely thermal pollution.

Like many other human impacts, thermal pollution may be the result of direct or indirect human action. Man may directly increase the temperature of the stream by injecting cooling water from an industrial plant back into the stream, or he may remove the riparian vegetation shading the channel, thus increasing the incidence of solar radiation received by the channel and therefore increasing the temperature of the stream indirectly (Pluhowski: 1970).

Man's impact on stream quality through the agency of natural pollution is simply his enhancement of the natural rates of sedimentation. This form of pollution is becoming increasingly important, especially in areas undergoing urbanization and, probably more significantly, suburbanization (Wolman: 1967*b*). Sedimentation is also an important indirect impact of deforestation, discussed previously under the heading of watershed alterations.

In a very informative article on the rivers of the United States, Wolman (1971) discusses several of the many problems which add to the complexity of the relationships involved in determining human impacts upon the river properties. Two of these complexities are the separation of long term effects from short term effects and the possible existence of natural thresholds within the hydrologic system. In addition Harris and Williams (1971) have discussed some of the problems of the statistical determination of man's impact upon stream characteristics with respect to watershed changes.

Rhoades and Bernstein (1971, pp. 208-214) also present a very informative description of several of the ways in which the pollution and degradation of water quality by agriculture can be minimized. Their discussion includes the reduction of erosional losses through better field management practices, and the placement of soil additives such as phosphorus fertilizers below the soil surface (Rhoades and Bernstein: 1971, pp. 213-214; see also the chapter by Schmid in the present volume).

ADDITIONAL HUMAN IMPACTS

In addition to augmentation of streamflow through manipulation of the storage components of the catchment, such as soil moisture storage (Green: 1970) and interception storage (Sopper and Lynch: 1970), streamflow can be increased by direct input from outside watersheds. One of the increasingly significant impacts of man upon streamflow is in the form of interbasin water transfers, especially in the southwestern United States. Examples of these interbasin transfer schemes include the California Water Plan, the North American Water and Power Alliance, the Colorado-Big Thompson project, the Texas Water Plan, and the Central Arizona Water Plan (Howe and Easter: 1971; and Beckinsale: 1969*b*). In the Soviet Union there is the proposed Kama-Vychegda-Pechora project (Micklin: 1969). And finally, there is even a plan to create a South American "Great Lakes" system (Panero: 1967).

In evaluating the impact of such schemes, it should be remembered that when two or more river basins are involved in water transfer, one basin's streamflow is diminished while the other's is being augmented.

In addition there are several methods of directly increasing the streamflow by importation of water other than from other streams, these include desalinization and distribution of ocean water, cloud seeding, pumping of ground water, deep pumping and desalinization of connate water and the prospect, now being considered, of hauling and melting icebergs for discharge at Los Angeles, California and Antofagasta, Chile.

CONCLUSION

As man's population pressures increase and man's technologies advance and spread throughout the world, his need for and influence upon the earth's waters will multiply. This review is merely an introduction to the rapidly expanding and complex array of human impacts upon streamflow and river quality. Understanding of the more rapid responses to man's actions within small watersheds will continue to progress in correspondence with the research effort expended on this problem. Owing to the inherent storages and greatly expanded complexity as the focus increases in size to national and global hydrologic systems, understanding of the human impact will continue to be achieved at a relatively slower pace. Although there are still many unknowns, there has been much progress in recent years, and research inspired by the cooperation of many scientists throughout the world during the International Hydrological Decade promises to advance greatly our understanding of the human-hydrologic interface.

REFERENCES

Anderson, D. G., 1970, *Effects of Urban Development on Floods in Northern Virginia*, Water-Supply Paper 2001-C. Washington, D.C.: U.S. Geological Survey.
ASCE Urban Hydrology Research Council, 1969, *An Analysis of National Basic Information Needs in Urban Hydrology*. New York: ASCE Urban Hydrology Research Council.
Beckinsale, R. P., 1969a, "River Regimes," in R. J. Chorley (ed.), *Water, Earth, and Man*, pp. 445-471.
———, 1969b, "Human Responses to River Regimes," in R. J. Chorley (ed.), *Water, Earth, and Man*, pp. 487-509.
Biswas, A. K., 1970, *History of Hydrology*. Amsterdam: North-Holland Publishing Co.
Bochkov, A. P., 1970, "Forest Influence on River Flows," *Nature and Resources*, Vol. 6, pp. 10-11.
Bowie, J. E. and W. Kam, (1968), *Use of Water by Riparian Vegetation, Cottonwood Wash, Arizona with a section on vegetation by F. A. Branson and R. S. Aro*. Washington, D.C.: U.S. Geological Survey.
Carter, R. W., 1961, "Magnitude and Frequency of Floods in Suburban Areas," *U.S. Geological Survey Professional Paper* 424-B, pp. B9-B11.
Changnon, Jr., S. A., 1968, "The La Porte Weather Anomaly—Fact or Fiction?," *Bulletin of the American Meteorological Society*, Vol. 49, pp. 4-11.
Chorley, R. J. (ed.), 1969, *Water, Earth, and Man*. London: Methuen.
Chorley, R. J. and B. A. Kennedy, 1971, *Physical Geography: A Systems Approach*. London: Prentice-Hall International.
Chow, Ven Te (ed.), 1964a, *Handbook of Applied Hydrology*, New York: McGraw-Hill.
———, 1964b, "Runoff," Section 14 in *Handbook of Applied Hydrology*, pp. 1-54.
Ciaccio, L. L. (ed.), 1971, *Water and Water Pollution Handbook*, New York: Marcel Dekker.
Cobb, E. D. and J. E. Biesecker, 1971, *The National Hydrologic Bench-Mark Network*, Circular 460-D. Washington, D.C.: U.S. Geological Survey.
Council on Environmental Quality, 1972, *Environmental Quality*. Washington, D.C.: U.S. Government Printing Office.

Crippen, J. R., 1965, "Changes in Character of Unit Hydrographs, Sharon Creek, California, After Suburban Development," *U.S. Geological Survey Professional Paper 525-D*, pp. D196-D198.

Dawdy, D. R., 1969, *Considerations Involved in Evaluating Mathematical Modeling of Urban Hydrologic Systems.* Water-Supply Paper 1591-D, Washington, D.C.: U.S. Geological Survey.

deVries, M., 1968, "River Bed Degradation Below Dams," *Proceedings American Society of Civil Engineers*, Hydraulics Division, Vol. 94 (HY2).

Douglas, I., 1972, "The Geographical Interpretation of River Quality Data," *Progress in Geography*, Vol. 4, pp. 1-81.

Franke, O. L. and N. E. McClymonds, 1972, *Summary of the Hydraulic Situation on Long Island, New York, as a Guide to Water-management Alternatives.* Professional Paper 627-F. Washington, D.C.: U.S. Geological Survey.

Gilbert, G. K., 1917, *Hydraulic Mining Debris in the Sierra Nevada*, Professional Paper 105. Washington, D.C.: U.S. Geological Survey.

Green, M. J., 1970, "Calibration of the Brenig Catchment and the Initial Effects of Afforestation," in *Symposium on the Results of Research on Representative and Experimental Basins*, Publication No. 96, International Association of Scientific Hydrology, pp. 329-345.

Hadley, R. F., 1972, "Hydrologic Impact of Land Use and Treatment Measures on Arid Lands," paper presented at 85th Annual Meeting of the Geological Society of America, Minneapolis, Nov. 14, 1972.

Hammer, T. R., 1972a, "Stream Channel Enlargement Due to Urbanization" Regional Science Research Institute, *Discussion Paper Series No. 55.*

_____, 1972b, "Empirical Estimation of Flood-detention Capacity Needed to Offset Effects of Urbanization" Regional Science Research Institute *Discussion Paper Series No. 57.*

Harris, E. E. and S. E. Rantz, 1964, *Effect of Urban Growth on Streamflow Regimen of Parmanente Creek, Santa Clara County California.* Water-Supply Paper 1591-B, Washington, D.C.: U.S. Geological Survey.

Harris, D. D. and R. C. Williams, 1971, *Streamflow, Sediment Transport, and Water-Temperature Characteristics of Three Small Watersheds in the Alsea River Basin, Oregon.* Circular 642, Washington, D.C.: U.S. Geological Survey.

Hockensmith, R. D. (ed.), 1960, *Water and Agriculture: A Symposium.* Washington, D.C.: American Association for Advancement of Science, Publication No. 62.

Howe, C. W. and K. W. Easter, 1971, *Interbasin Transfers of Water*, Baltimore: Johns Hopkins Press.

Hughes, E. E., 1968, "Phreatophytes: Problems and Perspectives," *Water Resources Bulletin*, Vol. 4, pp. 50-53.

Hynes, H. B. N., 1970, *The Ecology of Running Waters*, Toronto: University of Toronto Press.

IASH-UNESCO, 1970, *Symposium on the Results of Research on Representative and Experimental Basins.* Publication No. 96, International Association of Scientific Hydrology.

Ives, J. D., 1972, "Environmental Impact of Winter Cloud Seeding in Mountainous Terrain, A Case Study from the San Juan Mountains, Southwest Colorado," paper presented at 85th Annual Meeting Geological Society of America, Minneapolis, Nov. 14, 1972.

Jenkins, S. H. (ed.), 1969, *Advances in Water Pollution Research*, Oxford: Pergamon Press.

Jons, S. W. and M. B. McPherson, 1964, "Hydrology of Urban Areas," Section 20 in Van Te Chow (ed.), *Handbook of Applied Hydrology.* New York: McGraw-Hill, pp. 1-45.

Jones, Jr., D. E., 1971, "Where is Urban Hydrology Practice Today?" *Proceedings of the American Society of Civil Engineers*, Hydraulics Division, Vol. 97, pp. 257-264.

Komura, S. and D. B. Simons, 1967, "River-Bed Degradation Below Dams," *Proceedings of the American Society of Civil Engineers*, Hydraulics Division, Vol. 93, Proceedings Paper 5335.

_____, 1969, "River-Bed Degradation Below Dams—Closure," *Proceedings of the American Society of Civil Engineers*, Hydraulics Division, Vol. 95, pp. 1042-1048.

Lawler, E. A., 1964, "Hydrology of Flood Control, Part 2: Flood Routing," Section 25 in Van Te Chow (ed.), *Handbook of Applied Hydrology.* New York: McGraw-Hill, pp. 34-59.

Leopold, L. B., 1962, *The National Network of Hydrological Bench-Marks.* Circular 460-B, Washington, D.C.: U.S. Geological Survey.

_____, 1968, *Hydrology for Urban Land Planning—A Guidebook on the Hydrologic Effects of Urban Land Use.* Circular 554, Washington, D.C.: U.S. Geological Survey.

_____, 1972, "River Channel Change with Time: An Example," Presidential Address, 85th Annual Meeting, Geological Society America, Minneapolis, Nov. 13, 1972.

Leopold, L. B., and T. Maddock, Jr., 1954, *The Flood Control Controversy.* New York: Ronald Press.

Leopold, L. B., M. G. Wolman, and J. P. Miller, 1964, *Fluvial Processes in Geomorphology*, San Francisco: W. H. Freeman.

Linsley, R. K. and J. G. Franzini, 1972, *Water-Resources Engineering.* 2nd ed., New York: McGraw-Hill.

Lull, H. W. and K. G. Reinhart, 1972, *Forests and Floods in the Eastern United States.* U.S.D.A. Forest Service, Research Paper NE-226.

Martens, L. A., 1968, *Flood Inundation and Effects of Urbanization in Metropolitan Charlotte, North Carolina.* Water-Supply Paper 1591-C, Washington, D.C.: U.S. Geological Survey.

McDonald, C. C. and G. Hughes, 1968, *Studies of Consumptive Use of Water by Phreatophytes and Hydrophytes near Yuma, Arizona.* Professional Paper 486-F, Washington, D.C.: U.S. Geological Survey.

Micklin, P. P., 1969, "Soviet Plans to Reverse the Flow of Rivers: the Kama-Vychegda-Pechora Project," *Canadian Geographer*, Vol. 13, pp. 199-215.

Moore, W. L. and C. W. Morgan (eds.), 1969, *Effects of Watershed Changes on Streamflow.* Austin: University of Texas Press.

Moore, R. J., 1969, "The Basin Hydrological Cycle," in R. J. Chorley (ed.), *Water, Earth and Man*, pp. 67-76.

Muckel, D. C., 1966, "Phreatophytes—Water Use and Potential Water Savings," *Proceedings of the American Society of Civil Engineers, Irrigation Division*, Vol. 92, pp. 27-34.

Odum, E. P., 1971, *Fundamentals of Ecology*, 3rd ed., Philadelphia: W. B. Saunders.

Oglesby, R. T., C. A. Carlson, and J. A. McCann (eds.), 1972, *River Ecology and Man.* New York: Academic Press.

Orme, A. R. and R. G. Bailey, 1971, "Vegetation Conversion and Channel Geometry in Monroe Canyon, Southern California," *Yearbook*, Association Pacific Coast Geographers, Vol. 33, pp. 65-82.

Panero, R., 1967, *A South American "Great Lakes" System.* Groton-on-Hudson, New York: Hudson Institute.

Pierce, R. S., J. W. Hornbeck, G. E. Likens and F. H. Bermann, 1970, "Effect of Elimination of Vegetation on Stream Water Quantity and Quality," in *Symposium on the Results of Research on Representative and Experimental Basins*, Publication No. 96, International Association of Scientific Hydrology, pp. 311-328.

Pluhowski, E. J., 1970, *Urbanization and its Effect on the Temperature of the Streams on Long Island, New York.* Professional Paper 627-D, Washington, D.C.: U.S. Geological Survey.

Powell, S. T., 1964, "Quality of Water," Section 19 in Ven Te Chow (ed.), *Handbook of Applied Hydrology.* New York: McGraw-Hill, pp. 1-37.

Rantz, S. E., 1970, *Urban Sprawl and Flooding in Southern California*, Circular 601-B, Washington, D.C.: U.S. Geological Survey.

Rhoades, J. D. and L. Bernstein, 1971, "Chemical, Physical, and Biological Characteristics of Irrigation and Soil Water" in L. L. Ciaccio (ed.), *Water and Water Pollution Handbook.* Vol. 1, New York: Marcel Dekker, pp. 141-222.

Riggs, H. C., 1965, "Effect of Land Use on the Low Flow of Streams in Rappahannock County, Virginia," *U.S. Geological Survey Professional Paper 525-C*, pp. C196-198.

Rutter, E. J. and L. R. Engstrom, 1964, "Hydrology of Flood Control Part III Reservoir Regulation" Section 25 in Ven Te Chow (ed.), *Handbook of Applied Hydrology.* New York: McGraw-Hill, pp. 60-97.

Sartz, R. S., 1970, "Effect of Land Use on the Hydrology of Small Watersheds in Southwestern Wisconsin," in *Symposium on the Results of Research on Representative and Experimental Basins*, Publication No. 96, International Association of Scientific Hydrology, pp. 286-295.

Savini, J. and J. C. Kammerer, 1961, *Urban Growth and the Water Regimen.* Water-Supply Paper 1591-A, Washington, D.C.: U.S. Geological Survey.

Sawyer, R. M., 1963, "Effect of Urbanization on Storm Discharge and Ground-water Recharge in Nassau County, New York," Article 106, *U.S. Geological Survey Professional Paper 475-C*, pp. C185-C187.

Schaake, J. C., Jr., 1972, "Water and the City," in T. R. Detwyler and Melvin Marcus (eds.), *Urbanization and Environment*. Belmont, California: Duxbury Press, pp. 97-133.

Schneider, W. J., 1970, *Hydrologic Implications of Solid-waste Dispersal*. Circular 601-F, Washington, D.C.: U.S. Geological Survey.

Schneider, W. J. and A. M. Spieker, 1969, *Water for the Cities—the Outlook*. Circular 601-A, Washington, D.C.: U.S. Geological Survey.

Schumm, S. A., 1969, "River Metamorphosis," *Proceedings of the American Society of Civil Engineers*, Hydraulics Division, Vol. 95, pp. 255-273.

——, 1971, "Fluvial Geomorphology in River Mechanics," in S. A. Schumm (ed.), *River Morphology*. Stroudsburg, Pa.: Dowden, Hutchinson, and Rees, pp. 365-417.

Seaburn, G. E., 1970, *Preliminary Results of Hydrologic Studies of Two Recharge Basins on Long Island, New York*, Professional Paper 627-C. Washington, D.C.: U.S. Geological Survey.

——, 1969, *Effects of Urban Development on Direct Runoff to East Meadow Brook, Nassau County, Long Island, New York*. Professional Paper 627-B, Washington, D.C.: U.S. Geological Survey.

Sheaffer, J. R., D. W. Ellis, and A. M. Spieker, 1970, *Flood-Hazard Mapping in Metropolitan Chicago*. Circular 601-C, Washington, D.C.: U.S. Geological Survey.

Smith, N., 1971, *A History of Dams*, London: Peter Davies.

Society of American Foresters, Columbia River Section, 1963, *Symposium of Forest Watershed Management*.

Sopper, W. E. and H. W. Lull (eds.), 1967, *International Symposium on Forest Hydrology*. Oxford: Pergamon Press.

Sopper, W. E. and J. A. Lynch, 1970, "Changes in Water Yield Following Partial Forest Cover Removal on an Experimental Watershed," in *Symposium on the Results of Research on Representative and Experimental Basins*, Publication No. 96, International Association of Scientific Hydrology, pp. 386-399.

Spieker, A. M., 1970, *Water in Urban Planning*, Salt Creek Basin, Illinois. Water-Supply Paper 2002, Washington, D.C.: U.S. Geological Survey.

Stewart, O. C., 1956, "Fire as the First Great Force Employed by Man," in W. L. Thomas, Jr. (ed.), *Man's Role in Changing the Face of the Earth*. Chicago: University of Chicago Press, pp. 115-133.

Strumm, W. and J. J. Morgan, 1970, *Aquatic Chemistry*. New York: Wiley and Sons.

Swank, W. T. and J. D. Helvey, 1970, "Reduction of Streamflow Increases Following Regrowth of Clearcut Hardwood Forests," in *Symposium on the Results of Research on Representative and Experimental Basins*. Publication No. 96, International Association of Scientific Hydrology, pp. 346-360.

Task Force on the Effect of Urban Development on Flood Discharges, Committee on Flood Control, ASCE, 1969, "Effect of Urban Development on Flood Discharges—Current Knowledge and Future Needs," *Proceedings of the American Society of Civil Engineers*, Hydraulics Division, Vol. 95, pp. 287-309.

Thomas, H. E., 1954, *The First Fourteen Years of Lake Mead*. Circular 346, Washington, D.C.: U.S. Geological Survey.

——, 1956, "Changes in Quantities and Qualities of Ground and Surface Waters," in W. L. Thomas, Jr. (ed.), *Man's Role in Changing the Face of the Earth*. Chicago: University of Chicago Press, pp. 542-563.

——, 1965, "Water Problems," *Water Resources Research*, Vol. 1, pp. 435-445.

Thomas, H. E. and W. J. Schneider, 1970, *Water as an Urban Resource and Nuisance*. Circular 601-D, Washington, D.C.: U.S. Geological Survey.

Todd, D. K., 1970, *The Water Encyclopedia*, Port Washington, New York: Water Information Center.

Trefethen, P., 1972, "Man's Impact on the Columbia River," in R. T. Oglesby, C. A. Carlson, and J. A. McCann (eds.), *River Ecology and Man*. New York: Academic Press, pp. 77-98.

UNESCO, 1967, "IHD Co-ordinating Council and Working Groups," *Nature and Resources*, Vol. 3, pp. 12-15.

Vannote, R. L., 1972, "The Effects of Stream Channelization on the Productivity of Aquatic Ecosystems," paper presented at the 85th Annual Meeting of the Geological Society of America, Minneapolis, Nov. 14, 1972.

Velz, C. J., 1970, *Applied Stream Sanitation*, New York: John Wiley and Sons.

Vice, R. B., H. P. Guy and G. E. Fergusen, 1969, *Sediment Movement in an Area of*

Suburban Highway Construction, Scott Run Basin, Fairfax County, Virginia, 1961-64. Water-Supply Paper 1591-E, Washington, D.C.: U.S. Geological Survey.

Waananen, A. O., 1961, "Hydrologic Effects of Urban Growth—Some Characteristics of Urban Runoff," *U.S. Geological Survey Professional Paper 424-C*, pp. C353-C356.

Walling, D. E. and K. J. Gregory, 1970, "The Measurement of the Effects of Building Construction on Drainage Basin Dynamics," *Journal of Hydrology*, Vol. 11, pp. 129-144.

Ward, R. C., 1967, *Principles of Hydrology*, London: McGraw-Hill.

Willrich, T. L. and G. E. Smith ed., 1970, *Agricultural Practices and Water Quality*. Ames, Iowa: Iowa State University Press.

Wilson, K. U., 1967, "A Preliminary Study of the Effect of Urbanization on Floods in Jackson, Mississippi," *U.S. Geological Survey Professional Paper 575-D*, pp. D259-D261.

Wolman, M. G., 1971, "The Nation's Rivers," *Science* Vol. 174, pp. 905-918.

_____ , 1967a, "Two Problems Involving River Channel Changes and Background Observations," in W. L. Garrison and D. F. Marble (eds.), *Quantitative Geography, II: Physical and Cartographic Topics*, Northwestern University Studies in Geography, No. 14, pp. 67-107.

_____ , 1967b, "A Cycle of Sedimentation and Erosion in Urban River Channels," *Geografiska Annaler* Vol. 49A, pp. 385-395.

Wolman, M. G. and A. P. Schick, 1967, "Effects of Construction on Fluvial Sediment, Urban and Suburban Areas of Maryland," *Water Resources Research* Vol. 3, pp. 451-464.

Climatic Modification

Werner H. Terjung
University of California, Los Angeles

Man's presence on earth has necessitated a continuous struggle with climatic vicissitudes. Other life forms have survived the climatic changes of the past, but even with his modern technology, man is still vulnerable to such changes. The question is not merely whether man can survive, but also whether he will be able to retain present economic and cultural standards.

In recent years concern has been expressed that man, in addition to coping with natural changes in climate, may himself be partially responsible for such changes. Man's impact on climate began long before the modern period of intense interest in air pollution—in fact several thousand years ago, when irrigation was first practiced in arid regions and agriculture began to spread into the world's forests. His aspiration to control weather is also old. The uniqueness of the current situation is that for the first time this ambition may be realized. New capabilities present a complex set of problems requiring not only a scientific and technological competence but also new techniques in economic analysis, legal innovations, and political wisdom (Fleagle: 1969). The purpose of this chapter is to present an assessment of the different types of climatic modification and consider their probable effects on the earth's climatic patterns.

Weather and climate modification has recently been defined (National Academy of Sciences–National Research Council: 1966) as follows: "... any artificially produced changes in the composition, behavior, or dynamics of the atmosphere. Such changes may or may not be predictable, their production may be deliberate or inadvertent, they may be transient or permanent, and they may be manifested on any scale from the microclimate of plants to the macro-dynamics of the worldwide atmospheric circulation." According to this definition, climatic modification may range from strongly controlled climates inside buildings, the only partially controlled pollution of cities, to the completely uncontrolled effects of fossil fuel combustion on the atmosphere. The benefits of deliberate modification on a small scale may be kept under control, but we need to be cautious of the large and small scale effects of inadvertent modifications. Widespread changes have been created on the earth's surface by the agricultural, urban, and industrial revolutions. Forests of smoke stacks pour forth billions of tons of gases, particulates, and water vapor. These effects are still for the most part localized, but it is increasingly evident that this will not be true much longer (Sewell: 1969). The realization has been growing that the atmosphere is not a dump of infinite capacity.

The increasing ability of man to modify his environment has resulted in the last decade in a burgeoning area of research, the formulation of theoretical atmospheric models. This era of model building has been made possible by the use of high-speed computers to solve previously unfeasible numerical experiments and to simulate climatic features of the entire globe. A concomitant development has been the increasingly sophisticated measurement and observation of relevant atmospheric phenomena. The amount of scientific literature devoted to the study of man's impact on climate has increased at a similar pace. Some recent summaries of climatic modification studies have been made by National Academy of Sciences–National Research Council (1966), Singer (1970), Wilson and Matthews (1970, 1971), Matthews, Kellogg, and Robinson (1971), Landsberg (1971), and Hare (1971).

CLIMATES AND THE SOLAR ENERGY CASCADE

In order to understand the nature of inadvertently induced climatic changes, the main forcing and response functions that determine climate must be examined. Although the systems approach in climatology has arrived somewhat belatedly, energy balance climatology promises to give a new viability to this formerly tradition-bound discipline. The exchanges and conservation of *energy* (radiation, convection, conduction), *mass* (the amount of material in a body— e.g., particulates, gases, and the three phases of water), and *momentum* (mass multiplied by velocity involving direction and speed—e.g., the movement of air and its inclusions) under a tendency toward the steady state (achieved via complex feedback mechanisms) have become the new paradigm.

In this vein, one could interpret the climate of the earth-atmosphere system as being determined by the solar radiation incident on top of the atmosphere, the composition of the atmosphere, and the structure of the earth's surface. The motion of the atmosphere is one of the elements of climate and not an external causative factor (Budyko: 1969a). Thus, the earth-atmosphere system is an enormous heat engine driven by the sun's energy, influenced by topographical and thermal anomalies at the surface, which together with the effects of the planet's rotation, causes stretching and piling up of air in the various areas. The ensuing circulation transports heat, mass, and momentum from sources to sinks. Eventually this energy, via convection, advection, condensation, and finally reradiation, leaves the earth's surface, to be dissipated into the ultimate sink of space. Clearly, in order to understand climate one must study the entire system. This means the detailed interactions of energy, mass, and momentum between the oceans, polar ice, and land. Land is assumed to include the soil-vegetation subsystem (biosphere), as well as subsystems of inhabited places (Hare: 1971).

The development of numerical modeling experiments, made possible only with high-speed, large memory computers, has made it feasible for the climatologist to replace his previous passive role in paleoclimatological research. A common approach in atmospheric modeling consists of solving the time-dependent, nonlinear, partial differential equations of atmospheric dynamics that are subject to variable surface (boundary layer) conditions, beginning with arbitrary initial conditions (Manabe: 1969; Bryan: 1969).

To study the atmosphere, the climatologist must consider a fluid shell surrounding a spinning sphere. This heterogeneous fluid contains water which can exist in three stages. Versatility is further complicated by the inputs of radiant energy in amounts which vary daily, seasonally, and locationally. The absorptive and frictional differences between land and water surfaces also affect the motion of air. Various properties of the interface are not independent of the atmosphere. For example, the roughness of the ocean surface can be increased by wind-generated waves and the albedo of the land surface can be dramatically changed by snow cover. So we are dealing with a complex fluid shell bounded by the heterogeneous surface of the rotating globe that is exposed to disparate fluxes of energy. Figure 1 shows a generalized, schematic picture of the linked subsystems of the earth-atmosphere system that are unified by the solar energy cascade. Figure 2 shows the same concept in terms of a canonical structure (for an explanation of these and similar concepts see Chorley and Kennedy: 1971). In the latter graph, the decision regulators (controlling the operation of the system) are often those portions of the system where man could intervene and produce changes in the distribution of energy, mass, and momentum. In this cascade the output from one subsystem becomes the input of the neighboring system. Regulators operate either to divert a part of the input into storage, introducing a time lag in the subsequent flow, or to continue as throughput. Linkages between subsystems often involve negative feedback processes which are self-regulatory and promote steady states. Some feedbacks can be positive which, if unchecked, can result in a "snowballing" effect of increase or decrease away from the steady state situation.

The cascades are linked (by sharing certain variables) to morphological systems (not shown) which characterize the state or physical properties of systems. These are responses to the forcing input by the cascade (e.g., cloud formation and distribution, snow and ice cover, and ocean roughness from wind stress). The process-response system (stage) is thus the result of the interlocking of morphological structures (form) and cascades (process).

HUMAN ACTIVITIES INFLUENCING CLIMATE

The determination of whether man's activities have a significant effect on climate, be it global or local, is beset by two major problems. First, the exchanges of energy, mass, and momentum are so diverse and intertwined with many direct or looped feedbacks that it is extremely difficult to predict the effects of any natural or man-made change (Figure 2). The second major problem is the Herculean task of distinguishing between natural causes and man-made causes of climatic interference. This review traces systematically man's climatic interference at the earth's surface, in the troposphere, and in the stratosphere.

THE EARTH'S SURFACE

Even to define the influence of land or ocean surfaces on the exchanges of energy, mass and momentum with the atmosphere is not an easy task. These

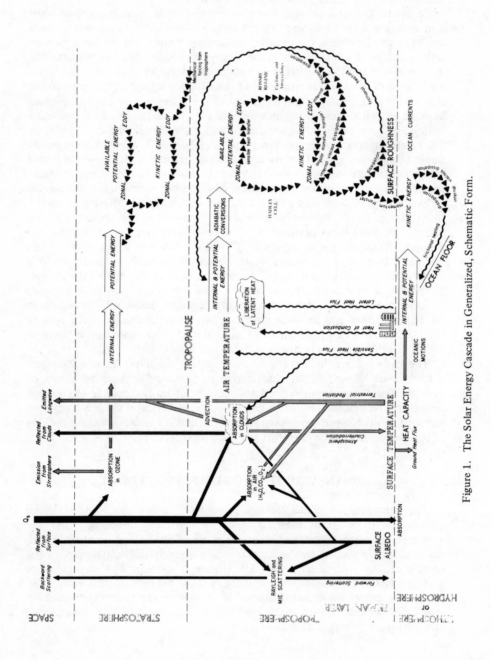

Figure 1.   The Solar Energy Cascade in Generalized, Schematic Form.

SOLAR ENERGY CASCADE

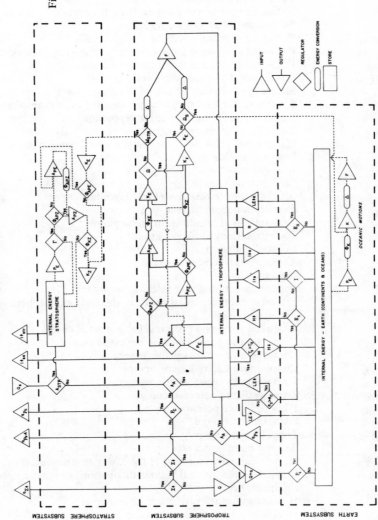

Figure 2. The Solar Energy Cascade Shown as a Canonical Structure (Simplified). All symbols are defined in Table 1. Dashed flow lines are uncertain. Many other linkages and feedbacks occur but are omitted for the sake of simplicity. For instance, Φ_{KE} and Φ_{KZ} are linked with Γ, but should also be linked to R. Also Q + q is linked to R. Storage units for P_E and K flows are also omitted. The sequence depicted in the stratosphere is highly speculative. For references see Lorenz: 1967; Newell, *et al.*: 1969; Hare: 1965; Rayner: 1967; Rayner: 1972; Bullock and Johnson: 1972; Murgatroyd: 1969.

TABLE 1—Notations for the Solar Energy Cascade

Symbol	Explanation
$\Sigma\uparrow$	Backscattering
$\Sigma\downarrow$	Forwardscattering
P_s	Reflection by earth surface
A_A	Absorption by atmosphere (H_2O, CO_2, O_2)
Q	Direct beam solar radiation
q	Diffuse solar radiation
q_{Ps}	Reflected shortwave radiation from the surface
$q_{\Sigma\uparrow}$	Backscattered shortwave radiation
P_C	Reflected shortwave radiation from clouds
q_{Ps-A}	Reflected shortwave radiation after absorption by atmosphere
q_{Pc}	Reflected shortwave radiation from clouds
A_{STR}	Absorption by stratosphere (O_3)
Q_s	Shortwave radiation on top of the atmosphere
$LE\uparrow$	Positive latent heat flux (energy used for evapotranspiration)
$LE\downarrow$	Negative latent heat flux (dew deposition)
e_s	Water vapor pressure at surface
e_a	Water vapor pressure in the atmospheric boundary layer
$H\uparrow$	Positive sensible heat flux (convection)
$H\downarrow$	Negative sensible heat flux
T_s	Surface temperature
T_a	Air temperature of atmospheric boundary layer
E_s	Evaporation from surface
E_a	Evaporation of raindrops in atmosphere
$I\uparrow_s$	Terrestrial (longwave) radiation
I	Infrared radiation
$I\downarrow_a$	Atmospheric counterradiation
R	Precipitation
$LE\uparrow_a$	Positive latent heat flux in the atmosphere
$I\uparrow_{sa}$	Effective outgoing radiation from the earth-atmosphere system
P_E	Potential energy
Γ	Adiabatic conversion to available potential energy
Φ_{APZ}	Conversion to zonal available potential energy
Φ_{APE}	Conversion to eddy available energy
Φ_{KE}	Conversion to eddy kinetic energy
Φ_{KZ}	Conversion to zonal kinetic energy
A_{PZ}	Zonal available potential energy
A_{PE}	Eddy available potential energy
K_E	Eddy kinetic energy
K_Z	Zonal kinetic energy
Ω	Angular momentum transfer
M_{STR}	Mechanical work (forcing) at the lower stratosphere
Δ	Dissipation (or internal viscous dissipation) of kinetic energy
F	Frictional heating
Ω_S	Momentum transfer to ocean surface
$I\uparrow_{str}$	Effective outgoing radiation from the stratosphere
a	Albedo of the surface
a_a	Albedo of the atmosphere
a_g	Planetary albedo

interactions are largely governed by the equilibrium surface temperature (e.g., land, water, ice, vegetation, man-made structures),[1] surface roughness (e.g., topography, vegetation, structures, the sea), soil moisture conditions, variability of albedo, aspects of slope and orientation, and man-made emissions of hygroscopic nuclei, gases, and water vapor at the surface.

Urban Effects

Among the climatic changes caused by man, urbanization has increasingly been responsible for the most radical of these changes. Modern cities have developed with little or no regard for climatic modification (Landsberg: 1970). As Schmid indicates elsewhere in this volume, the city's compact mass of buildings and pavement constitutes a profound alteration of the natural landscape, resulting in an almost infinite number of microclimates. This urban-atmospheric system is interdependent and sustained by a complex web of feedbacks. Therefore, the urban climate cannot be treated independently of the urban environment. As cities grow into megalopolises, man's effects on urban microclimates begin to reach beyond the urban confines and may assume mesoclimatic proportions (Landsberg: 1971).

The urban landscape contributes to climatic modification in several basic ways (Lowry: 1967): (1) The additional surface area of buildings with large vertical surfaces exposes a huge portion of the city to additional exchanges of energy, mass and momentum; (2) the surface materials are rocklike with high conductivities, heat capacities, and albedos; (3) the city generates artificial heat because of its traffic, industries, domestic heating, and the rejected heat of air-conditioning; (4) the city is a vast source of contaminants that are by-products of its daily activities; and (5) the impervious surfaces lead to a rapid disposal of rain and snow, fundamentally altering the moisture and heat budget. Contributions to urban climatology have recently been frequent and numerous. See, for example, McBoyle (1968), Peterson (1969), Chandler (1970), and Terjung (1972).

When comparing urban to rural environments, global radiation $(Q + q)$ decreases on the average between 15 and 20 percent ($\Sigma\uparrow$ and $\Sigma\downarrow$, Figure 2) and the duration of sunshine decreases between 5 to 15 percent (Landsberg: 1970). The reduction of global radiation in the ultraviolet portion of the spectrum can be much more severe. For instance, during October 1965, a moderate-to-heavy smog day in Los Angeles exhibited a peak attenuation of ultraviolet radiation of 58 percent and a mean reduction of 38 percent (Nader: 1967; Coulson, et al.: 1971). Mateer's (1961) results in Toronto showed that $Q + q$ was about 3 percent higher on Sundays than on the more polluted week days. From November to March, $Q + q$ in English cities was 25-55 percent less than at rural sites (Chandler: 1965). Monteith (1966) summarized observations on the relationship between particulate pollution and solar radiation in central London and discovered that, because of air pollution controls, smoke density had decreased whereas radiation had increased by 1 percent. In a comparison between Tucson and Mauna Loa, Heidel (1972) noticed that global radiation at Mauna Loa had returned to the volcanic pre-eruption level by 1970, but that Tucson's turbidity continued to increase. This appeared to be especially caused by nearby smelters which contributed to a decline of $Q + q$ by about 5-10 percent. During an eight-year period in Cincinnati, the vertical turbidity structure had hardly changed (Bach: 1971). In this case, a uniform dust dome appears to extend far over the surrounding countryside since only small differences could be detected between rural and urban sites. Apparently megalopolises have already begun to form vast pollution sheds. In the lowest 1000 meters on a polluted day, 65 percent of the solar radiation was attenuated, whereas on a clear day the attenuation amounted to about 30 percent. Bach found that the first 45 meters of the air layer can contribute up to 21 percent of total solar attenuation (Figure 3).

Horizontally, urban haze interferes with visibility and can result in reductions of 80-90 percent (Landsberg: 1971). This is further emphasized by the formation of water droplets around hygroscopic nuclei which are plentiful in urban air. As a result, fog occurs from two to five times more frequently in cities than at rural sites. Apparently the introduction of different fuels or heating practices can improve visibilities (Jenkins: 1969). Ludwig, et al. (1970), found a similar trend of slight reductions (7 percent) in particulates for 58 urban locations in the U.S., but warned that such aerosols constitute only one percent of the total mass of the six major gaseous pollutants typically found in the urban air.

It has often been surmised that the dust dome over a city contributes toward the heat island effect through the absorption of radiation by suspended particles and subsequent reradiation to the earth's surface as atmospheric counterradiation ($I\downarrow_a$). Oke and Fuggle (1972) questioned this assumption by conducting twelve climatic traverses during clear nights measuring $I\downarrow_a$. It appeared that higher counterradiation is part of the urban effect and not one of the causes of the urban heat island. The increase seems to be due to the increased warmth of the urban air rather than to changes in the radiation properties (e.g., aerosols) of the atmosphere. According to these authors, net radiation (R_s) showed only small urban-rural differences.[2]

The existence of urban heat islands has long been recognized and the study of these phenomena has become synonymous with urban climatology. Urban heat islands influence urban ecology in a variety of ways such as the alteration of the physiological comfort of man—excessive mortality appears to conform to the shape of the heat island (Buechley, et al.: 1972); cooling and heating require-

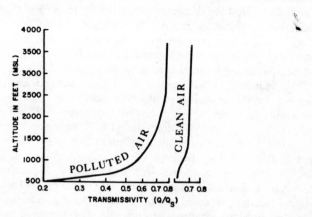

Figure 3.   Vertical Variation of Transmissivity Q/Q_s over Cincinnati (modified from Bach: 1971). The regression lines were fitted through the data of six vertical recordings (June and September 1969) from the city center and two airports in semi-rural settings.

ments; duration of snow cover; length of growing season; altered zoological habitats; convection cells created by turbulent heat flux and associated air pollution circulation and diffusion; and increased precipitation over cities. Traditionally, climatologists listed several major factors as contributing to the causation of heat islands; thermal heat capacity and conductivity of the urban interfaces, additions of heat from combustion and other artificial sources, the prevailing dryness of the city's surfaces (net radiation R_s is partitioned only between heat storage G and convection H↑), and a reduction of wind flow because of the frictional effects of city structures.

Is the heat island caused by man? The following evidence seems to support this contention:

(1) almost all cities, regardless of their size and topographic settings, have heat islands (Table 2);
(2) when air temperatures are arranged by day of the week, heating is weaker on Sundays than on other days (Table 3); and
(3) population density and size correlates with the intensity of the warming (Table 2).

In terms of air temperatures, the heat island phenomenon is mainly reflected in night minimum temperatures, when the maximum difference between city and country air temperatures seems to be about 5-8°C. Heat islands often exhibit strong temperature gradients at their periphery, while, internally, multicellular cores of hot and cold spots can also be observed (e.g., Oke and East: 1971). Landsberg and Maisel (1972) monitored a new town (Columbia, Md.) since 1967 and showed the expansion of the heat island as the town expanded. Even before the advent of internal heating of buildings and industrial emissions the urbanized area was warmer than the surrounding countryside (Table 4). In Paris, Dettwiller (1970) analyzed the measured temperature at a depth of 28 meters (cellar of Paris Observatory) from 1776 to the present. He found that the deep soil temperature matched closely the urban air temperature increase in that city during the same time span.

Because of its influence on air pollution, vertical temperature profiles over cities have been examined. For instance, Bornstein (1968) and Davidson (1967) used helicopters to measure the night profile over New York City. Both observed

TABLE 2—Rates of Urban Warming of Selected Cities

City	Period of Record	Growth Rate Index[a]	Urban Warming Rate (°F/100 yrs)			
			Winter	Spring	Summer	Fall
Cleveland, Ohio	1895-1941	12.9	1.8	3.8	5.1	2.7
Boston, Mass.	1895-1933	10.5	2.9	3.2	4.7	3.7
Washington, D.C.	1893-1954	9.9	b	1.5	4.3	2.7
Tampa, Fla.	1895-1931	6.6	4.8	2.6	2.9	3.4
Baltimore, Md.	1894-1954	6.0	b	2.0	3.0	2.7
Charlotte, N.C.	1897-1951	5.1	b	b	1.7	b
Nashville, Tenn.	1897-1948	3.0	b	b	b	b

Source: Mitchell: 1962. Excess over rural environs. a = rate of change of root population (units per year); b = not significantly different from zero.

TABLE 3–Excess Warmth of City Compared with Airport (°F)

Day of Week	Maximum Temperature	Minimum Temperature	Mean Daily Temperature
Sunday	0.1	1.2	0.6
Monday	0.0	2.0	1.0
Tuesday	0.2	2.4	1.3
Wednesday	0.0	2.1	1.1
Thursday	0.0	2.3	1.2
Friday	0.0	2.4	1.1
Saturday	0.0	2.1	1.0

Source: Mitchell: 1962. Data for New Haven, Conn., in four winter seasons 1939-1943.

multiple elevated inversions over the city. Thus, cities seem to have few surface inversions, but raised inversions of longer duration do occur. These inversions inhibit the escape of pollutants. A model for the radiation budget of a polluted air layer dealing only with radiative temperatures and pre-specified surface temperatures (non-advective stable cases), was developed by Atwater (1971). Accordingly, when the aerosol layer is absent, no elevated inversion forms. The maximum decrease in temperature was within the polluted layer whereas a more stable layer (inversion) formed above the polluted layer. The model predicted that the temperature decrease within the aerosol layer was proportional to the concentration of that stratum. The presence of pollutants increased counterradiation $(I\downarrow_a)$ and reduced solar radiation $(Q + q)$ at the surface (Figure 4). At night, this would increase the surface temperature, whereas during the day the net effect depended on the relative magnitude between the increased longwave radiation and decreased shortwave radiation.

TABLE 4–Elements of Heat Balance in Columbia Town Area

	T_a	T_s	$Q + q$	$I\downarrow_a$	$I\uparrow_s$	$LE\uparrow$	$H\uparrow$	G
				1200 hours				
Weed field	24.7	32.0	1.20	0.43	0.67	0.30	0.12	0.24
Parking lot	24.7	47.5	1.23	0.43	0.85	0.00	0.10	0.64
	T_a	T_s	R_s	$I\downarrow_a$	$I\uparrow_s$			G
				0000 hours				
Weed field	12.7	15.5	−0.10	0.41	0.54			−0.13
Parking lot	15.0	21.5	−0.12	0.41	0.61			−0.20
				0500 hours				
Weed field	12.2	11.0	−0.009	0.40	0.50			−0.10
Parking lot	12.7	18.0	−0.13	0.41	0.57			−0.16

Source: Landsberg and Maisel: 1972. Temperatures are in °C and energy units are in cal cm^{-1} min^{-1}. T_a = air temperature; T_s = surface temperature. All other symbols are defined in Table 1.

A simple energy budget model of a city consisting of a closed set of equations, has been used to simulate a variety of situations (Myrup: 1969). For instance, city temperatures were more sensitive to wind speed when air

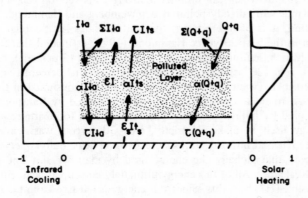

Figure 4. Changes in Radiation Caused by the Presence of a Polluted Layer (modified from Atwater: 1971). Σ = scattered, ϵ = emissivity, τ = transmissivity, α = absorptivity. All other symbols are defined in Table 1.

movement was rather low. Increasing winds decreased the maximum temperatures, but increased the minima. City temperatures were most sensitive to latent heat flux (LE↑) when the evaporating surfaces comprised about 20-30 percent of the entire city. An albedo change of 10 percent affected the temperature by 1.25°C. However, the computation of the amount of heat artificially generated in the city appeared to be erroneous (Myrup: 1970).

Using radiation theory, a generalized urban shortwave absorption model was developed which accounted for the solar input onto streets, buildings, and the multiple reflections and shading effects occurring at the urban interface (Terjung and Louie: 1973). Use was made of view factor algebra and multiple integrations which allowed for the interplay of shortwave energy between city surfaces ranging from 80-floor skyscrapers to level parking lots. The predictions of the model were subjected to a sensitivity analysis for a variety of typical building-street systems. The predictions were tested for the ratio of absorbed total solar radiation on a three-dimensional structure system to that of a two-dimensional horizontal system, $(Q + q)_{abs}/(Q + q)_h$. Thus, the ratio indicated to what degree a structure system would absorb more or less than a non-urban plain. Largest ratios occurred at lowest sun angles when street orientation was also most important. Systems that include skyscrapers can absorb more than six times the radiation of a non-urban level surface. The stronger the solar heat island effect, the weaker is the absorption at the street level. At all latitudes most daily ratios exceed unity.

A portion of the urban temperature rise can be ascribed to thermal pollution or waste heat created by combustion, air-conditioning and the metabolisms of urban dwellers. Based on a series of observations in Cincinnati, Bach and Patterson (1969) report that artificial heat comprises a sizable percentage of the urban energy budget. Similarly, Montreal's waste heat contributes about 22 percent of the heat island effect (Landsberg: 1971), and in 1952 Sheffield's waste heating contributed about 30 percent of net radiation (R_s) and 20 percent of solar radiation (Q + q) (Garnett and Bach: 1965). Thus, on the local scale the anthropogenic heat flux is of the same order of magnitude as natural radiation.

As urbanization increases, escaping heat plumes may combine to form larger regional heat islands which can produce a stronger convection cell and feed the local heat islands with already polluted air (Weinberg and Hammond: 1971). In this connection, it is of interest that the United States has doubled its energy consumption in the past 20 years. Hammond (1972) estimated that 96 percent of this energy is based on fossil fuels, i.e., petroleum (43 percent), natural gas (33 percent), coal (20 percent), hydro-electric power (3 percent), and nuclear power (1 percent). Twenty-five percent of the energy consumed in the U.S. in 1970 was used to make electricity, 25 percent was used by transportation, 30 percent was used by industry, and 20 percent was used for heating and cooling. Of the energy used to make electricity, only 30 percent was converted, the balance being released into the atmosphere as waste heat. Budyko, *et al.* (1971), have postulated that globally the energy used by man per unit land surface is about 0.02 Kcal cm^{-2}. All of this energy ultimately ends up as heat, either latent (LE↑) or sensible (H↑) heat flux. Since this energy is released from the storage of past ages of photosynthesis, it entails an addition of heat to the earth-atmosphere system. These authors estimated that energy consumption on a world-wide basis increases by 4 percent per year and doubles every 17 years. If the present rate is continued, in 200 years it will reach the magnitude of mean net radiation (R_s) on a global scale. If the rate were to increase by 10 percent, this event would occur 100 years earlier.

Budyko (1972) believes that consumption of this magnitude would greatly change the climate of the earth. However, considerable controversy exists as to the effects of such projected energy consumptions. Weinberg and Hammond (1970) have argued that at high world-wide consumption rates (20 kw/person), the increase in world temperature would be only about 0.5°C, and their view is supported by a numerical simulation of the NCAR general circulation model, which considered only thermal energy created by man without other urban climatic or aerosol effects (Washington: 1972). This model, which seemed to predict current world patterns rather well, used a consumption rate of 15 kw per person and an ultimate world population of 20 billion.[3] The energy was geographically distributed according to present population distribution (Figure 5). The author concluded that only small modifications of the earth-atmosphere heat balance would result and that they were of the same order as the natural fluctuations generated by the model. However, he admitted that a major shortcoming of the experiment was a fixed ocean temperature and no coupling between the atmosphere and the ocean.

When Sellers (1969) modeled Budyko's estimate of 50 Kcal cm^{-2} $year^{-1}$ of man-made waste heat, to occur in less than 200 years, he came to opposite conclusions. His model predicted that the mean global temperature would increase by about 15°C, ranging from 11°C near the equator to 27°C at the North Pole. This would result in the removal of all ice fields. If the negative feedback effect of added turbidity due to aerosols were included, probable increases would be only 1-2°C lower. The model did not include the thermal inertia of the ocean.

As a sequel to the urban heat island effect, gradients of temperature and pressure induce a local air circulation and increased convection (H↑) over built-up areas. Even at night, when inversions are common over rural sites, a positive temperature lapse rate will exist in the city's boundary layer. The energy differential between city and country sets a country breeze into motion. For instance, Findlay and Hirt (1969) reported that for Toronto during February the

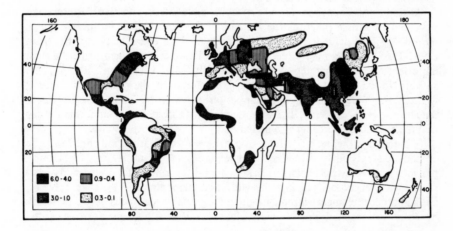

Figure 5.   Distribution of Expected Levels of Thermal Pollution (modified from Washington: 1972). Units are in millions of megawatts.

daytime heat island caused a pressure deficit which was sufficient to cause the development of a centripetal counterclockwise air circulation, centered on the downtown area. Since this country breeze is continuous (under anticyclonic conditions and weak macroscale winds), pollution emitted near the urban perimeter tends to drift in and concentrate near the city's core.

There seems to be a consensus regarding the general decrease of horizontal air movement in urban areas, although this is difficult to measure. Available data suggest a mean wind decrease of about 25 percent compared to rural sites (Landsberg: 1971). This can be misleading since the vertical wind speed (and even horizontal funneling and eddying caused by buildings) can increase considerably because of the much greater aerodynamic roughness of the urban landscape and the increased turbulent heat exchange (H↑). This vertical tendency is instrumental in creating the characteristic dust domes over urban regions. When regional winds are blowing, such domes are transformed into plumes which transport energy and mass downstream out of the city, affecting the rural energy budgets. Incidentally, this combined effect of increased convection (H↑) and advection, results in less pollens and molds (and possibly nuclear fall-out after an atomic blast) at the leeward side of a city than in the surrounding countryside (Heise and Heise: 1957).

Most climatologists agree that rainfall over cities has increased. The anthropogenic origin of such increases indicates a weekly cycle, with minimum precipitation on Sundays (Landsberg: 1971). The following are potential causes for urban-induced precipitation (Huff and Changnon: 1972): (1) the atmosphere becomes destabilized by the output of terrestrial radiation ($I\uparrow_s$) and sensible heat flux (H↑) from the heat island; (2) there is a modification of the microphysical and dynamical process in clouds via the addition of condensation and ice nuclei from industry; (3) there is an increase in low-level turbulence because of increased roughness of the urban landscape; and (4) there is a modification of the low-level humidity conditions because of emissions from industry (stacks and cooling towers) and changes in natural evapotranspiration as a result of the increased imperviousness of the city.

A study by Changnon (1969) of four midwestern and two eastern cities indicated an annual precipitation increase of 5-8 percent for the former and an increase of 7-16 percent for the latter (Table 5). In a recent analysis of St. Louis (1941-1968), the thermal effects of the heat island were judged to be the most important cause of altered precipitation (Huff and Changnon: 1972). These authors found that the mean seasonal precipitation increased 6-15 percent, whereas the mean wet season precipitation increased by 11-18 percent. Heavy rainstorms (+31 percent), hail-day frequency (+35 percent) and thunderday frequency (+20-25 percent) also increased.

In summary, the general effects of urban areas on weather and climate can be obvious, e.g., visibility, windiness, and temperature; or subtle, e.g., fog, clouds, precipitation, snowfall, solar radiation, humidity, atmospheric electricity, and severe weather events (Changnon, Huff and Semonin: 1971). (See Table 6.) Urban-induced changes, although intense on the megalopolis level, presently have not yet reached globally discernible magnitudes, but appear to be on the verge of producing regional changes.

TABLE 5—Summary of Urban Increases in Precipitation

	C	LP	SL	CU	T	DC	NY
Precipitation							
Annual	5	31	7	5	8	7	16
Warmer half-year	4	30	*	4	5	6	12
Colder half-year	6	33	*	8	11	9	20
All rain days							
Annual	6	0	*	7	*	*	*
Warmer half-year	8	0	*	3	*	*	*
Colder half-year	4	0	*	10	*	*	*
Moderate-heavy rain days							
Annual	10	34	*	5	*	*	*
Warmer half-year	15	54	*	9	*	*	*
Colder half-year	0	5	*	0	*	*	*
Thunderstorm days							
Annual	6	38	11	7	*	*	*
Summer	7	63	20	17	*	*	*

C=Chicago; LP=LaPorte; SL=St. Louis; CU=Champaign-Urbana; T=Tulsa; DC=Washington, D.C.; NY=New York.

Source: Changnon: 1969. Urban-rural difference (increase) expressed as a percent of rural values. * = insufficient data.

TABLE 6—Worldwide Mean Climatic Changes in Cities

	Annual	Cold Season	Warm Season
Contaminants	+1000	+2000	+500
Solar radiation	−22	−34	−20
Temperature (°F)*	+1.5	+2.0	+1.0
Humidity	−6	−2	−8
Visibility	−26	−34	−17
Fog	+60	+100	+30
Wind speed	−25	−20	−30
Cloudiness	+8	+5	+10
Rainfall	+11	+13	+11
Snowfall	+10	+10	–
Thunderstorms	+8	+5	+17

Source: Changnon, Huff and Semonin: 1971. Average changes expressed as percent of rural conditions. * = percentages not applicable.

Agricultural Effects

Man has been changing the landscape for thousands of years by converting natural vegetation into arable land and pastures. For cropped land, the soil often remains nearly bare for several months. This not only alters the energy budget but, because the CO_2 production of soil bacteria continues, results in a temporary increase of the amount of CO_2 released to the atmosphere. Other effects are changes in surface roughness, water budget, surface albedo, and the apportionment of the net radiation (R_s) into the energy used for evapotranspiration (LE↑) and convection (H↑). Via poor agricultural practices man also increases dust. Although little replacement of middle latitude forests by arable land is currently in progress (some areas are even reverting to forest because of their marginal value to agriculture), such conversion is widespread in tropical Africa, northeastern Brazil, some semi-arid regions of central America, and southeastern Asia. It is estimated that 18 to 20 percent of the total area of the continents has been changed by agricultural practices (Wilson and Matthews: 1971).

Deforestation causes increases in surface temperatures (T_s), decreases in evapotranspiration (LE↑), and increases in convection (H↑) and soil energy storage (G↓). On occasion, precipitation appears to increase on the windward side of forests and to decrease on the lee side. When most forests are eliminated in a large area, a general decrease in precipitation has been reported (Budyko, *et al.*: 1971). The most significant changes can be observed in the Bowen ratio β (Table 7).[4]

The local or regional influences of such changes seem to be more important over tropical continents. These areas are more sensitive because the water vapor transport decreases more rapidly with height due to the small vertical wind shear. The average residence time of water vapor molecules over Africa is only 8-9 days, as against a global average of 11 days. Thus if the natural vegetation is reduced, resulting in increased convection (H↑) and higher air temperatures, a decrease in precipitation will result unless additional water vapor sources are available (Flohn: 1963). Newell (1971) voices similar concern. He argued that most latent heat flux (LE↑) of the low latitudes is provided by the world's rainforest areas. A reduction in the volume of the water cycling between the forest and the air would alter the latent heat forcing function and lead to changes in the other terms of energy and momentum exchange. It is suspected that a decrease in the generation of zonal available potential energy (A_{PZ}) would result because of lessening of the release of the latent heat of vaporization (LR). This would have an effect on the generation and dissipation of easterly waves.

The dramatic change of the Bowen ratio β from about 0.3 over forests to about 2.0 to 6.0 when forests are replaced by man-made deserts was emphasized by a study of the results of overgrazing in western India. It appears that this area was altered by a combination of overcropping and overgrazing in the past (Bryson and Baerreis: 1967). This man-made desert causes a dense pall of dust which appears to contribute to increased atmospheric subsidence over the area. A positive feedback is in operation. The dust absorbs radiation and attenuates solar radiation, resulting in relatively lower surface temperatures. However, the tropospheric layer is heated by the absorbed radiation, inhibiting vertical motion and consequently the necessary mechanism for precipitation.

TABLE 7—Energy Budget Changes Upon Conversion from Forest to Agricultural Use

	Albedo	β	H*	LE*
Coniferous forest	0.12	0.50	33	66
Deciduous forest	0.18	0.33	25	75
Arable land—wet	0.20	0.19	16	84
Arable land—dry	0.20	0.41	30	70
Grassland	0.20	0.67	40	60

Source: Wilson and Matthews: 1971. β = H/LE (Bowen ratio); H = sensible heat flux; LE= latent heat flux; * = percentage of net radiation R_s.

Irrigation in arid or semi-arid regions causes increases in latent heat flux (LE↑), decreases in convection (H↑)—a lowering of the Bowen ratio H/LE—and decreases in surface temperatures (T_s) and albedos (a). Heat storage (G↓) and net radiation (R_s) is increased. Energy is often added to R_s by negative turbulent heat exchange (H↓) (when $T_s < T_a$, thus leading to negative Bowen ratios), because the air temperature (T_a) is higher than the surface temperature—the so-called oasis effect (Table 8). If irrigated areas are large enough, the overlying air mass could be altered (Budyko et al.: 1971). The direct influence of the energy used for evaporation of irrigation water (R_s and H↓) is to speed up the

TABLE 8—Annual Energy Budget of Tunisian Oases

	Albedo	β	H*	LE*
Oases (mean)	0.15	−0.26	−36	136
Semi-desert	0.20	5.60	84	16

Source: Wilson and Matthews: 1971. See Table 7 for explanations.

hydrological cycle. On a global scale, this could have an impact on changes in cloud cover and consequent changes in the energy budget. In spite of the reduction of local temperatures by irrigation, global temperatures are raised because of increased absorption of solar radiation $(Q + q)(1 - a)$. It has been calculated that present irrigation has resulted in an increase in average temperature near the earth's surface of about $0.07°C$ (Budyko, quoted in Wilson and Matthews: 1971). Estimates indicate that the irrigated area will double by A.D. 2000. However, swamp drainage will tend to offset the effects of irrigation.

Manipulations of the Earth's Surface

Aside from the urban and agricultural alterations of the natural landscape, man can drastically alter the surface of the planet by other means. It is quite certain that the number of artificial lakes or reservoirs will substantially increase in response to demands of agriculture, hydroelectric power, industry, and perhaps bureaucratic self-perpetuation. Some of the effects of reservoirs are similar to those of irrigated areas. Net radiation increases, albedo decreases, surface temperatures decrease, the Bowen ratio decreases, and because of less surface roughness wind speed will increase. This latter effect will be especially noticeable in the fall at middle and high latitudes when the water surface temperature is higher than the overlying air, resulting in increased turbulence $(H\uparrow)$. The opposite may occur in the spring when an ice cover outlasts the snow cover of the land (Budyko *et al.*: 1971). Over land, most of the absorbed energy is reradiated, evaporated or convected in a relatively short time, whereas water is capable of storing huge quantities of energy $(G\downarrow)$ which are given off $(G\uparrow)$ months later, or in the case of the ocean, even years later.

The Soviet Union has tentatively proposed to divert the major rivers of Asia (especially Pechora, Ob, and Yenesei) to transport extra water to the dry lands of Central Asia and regions near the Caspian and Aral seas (Lamb: 1971a). The tapping of water for irrigation has already caused a decline of water levels in the Caspian and Aral seas. The reduction of a fresh water supply to the Arctic ocean touches a sensitive spot in the climatic regime of the northern hemisphere. Since the existence of the surface layer of low salinity (100-200 meters of surface waters where ice regularly forms) partially depends on the supplies of these rivers, withdrawal of the fresh river water could raise the mean salinity of the Arctic ocean by several parts per thousand. The significance of such a change is that the low salinity (lesser density) layer remains on top of the Arctic ocean, isolated from convective overturnings of saltier waters beneath. This top layer (often only 100 meters) therefore remains largely unaffected by mixing with deeper waters (3000-4000 meters). Fresh water has a maximum density at $+4°C$. When the surface layer is cooled below this temperature, the coldest water tends to stay on top and will eventually freeze. On the other hand, sea water of normal salinity increases in density with cooling to the freezing point. Thus the cooling of the surface water (of normal salinity) in the high latitudes of the Atlantic sets up deep convection currents which mix the water to great depths. In the Arctic ocean (less surface salinity) this mixing is limited to about 200 m and the cooling initiated at the surface needs to spread only through this layer which freezes quickly. Once the sea ice is formed, a positive feedback process is in operation (high albedo, low $I\uparrow_s$, $G\downarrow$, and T_a) that tends to maintain the ice. The decrease of fresh water supply of the rivers would result in the penetration of more saline waters (especially from the Atlantic) into the regions of polar sea ice and result in a decrease or eventual disappearance of ice. Temperatures currently at about $-20°$ to $-25°C$ would increase to about $0°C$. According to a study by Drozdov (quoted in Lamb: 1971a), an ice-free Arctic would significantly affect circulation and precipitation in large portions of the northern hemisphere. Precipitation, for example, would increase over most of the Arctic and in low latitudes, whereas it would decrease in middle latitudes, areas that presently exhibit high population densities and industrial developments. This, incidentally, would include parts of Central Asia for which the irrigation diversion scheme was originally planned.

The polar ice pack plays a special role in the heat budget of the earth-atmosphere system, for there is a very real possibility that man could modify the global climate in a substantial way by dusting the ice, reversal of rivers, and increases in waste heat. The alteration of the ocean surface energy budget as a result of ice removal would involve a decrease in surface albedo, an increase in atmospheric moisture, an increase in clouds, an increase in terrestrial radiation ($I\uparrow_s$), changes in latent ($LE\uparrow$), and sensible ($H\uparrow$) heat fluxes, and a more poleward penetration of warm ocean currents. The large capacity of oceans for heat and chemicals has acted as a stabilizer against even stronger climatic variations that the planet might otherwise have experienced. Weyl (1968) proposed that the climatic changes of the Pleistocene arose primarily from variations in the extent of sea ice, i.e., sea ice is the cause, not the result of climatic change. He believes that the areal extent of sea ice is more closely coupled to the salinity patterns of oceans than the heat exchange between ocean and atmosphere. The great salinity contrasts between the northern Pacific and Atlantic oceans was postulated by this author to be the result of water vapor transport westward across Central America to the Pacific. If this transfer ceased for a few hundred years, significant changes in salinity distribution between the two oceans would result.

The distribution of ice is an important factor in amplifying the climatic effects of small changes in global heating (Fletcher: 1969). This influence is greatest during fall and winter, and an increase in the extent of ice distribution near Antarctica corresponds to an intensification of the zonal circulation in the southern hemisphere and an increased tendency for a similar circulation in the northern hemisphere. This trend is accompanied by a warming over most of the northern high latitudes. Therefore, a colder southern heat sink would increase the global circulation and warm the atmosphere over most of the planet.

In January the surface temperature of the Central Arctic is in the neighborhood of $-30°C$. The ice and snow cover are such good insulators, that only a few feet below the temperature is about $-2°C$. Thus, ice suppresses heat loss from the ocean in winter and reduces heat gain in summer (Figure 6). Under present (ice-in) conditions, about 10 Kcal cm^{-2} is gained in summer (melting about one-third of the ice's thickness). If the Arctic ocean were ice-free, about 40 Kcal cm^{-2} would be gained in summer. The atmospheric cooling during ice conditions in winter amounts to about 6-8 Kcal cm^{-2} month^{-1}, whereas the summer loss would be about one-third of this (total cooling 66 Kcal cm^{-2} year^{-1}). Over an ice-free Arctic the annual pattern (44 Kcal cm^{-2} year^{-1}) would be reversed with strongest cooling during summer (Fletcher: 1969).

This drastically different forcing pattern of heating and cooling would influence the atmospheric circulation. Under ice-free conditions, Fletcher suggested that the zonal and meridional circulation would decrease more in the

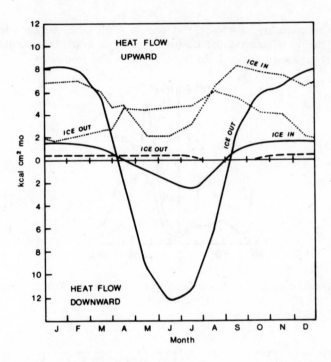

Figure 6. Heat Flow in Relation to the Arctic Ocean Surface and Atmospheric Cooling under Present (ice-in) and Possible (ice-out) Conditions (modified from Fletcher: 1969). Dotted curves = atmospheric cooling; dashed curves = sensible heat flux H↑; solid curves = heat flow to and from the surface.

winter than in the summer, resulting in smaller seasonal contrasts. An ice-free Arctic might remain ice-free. The variation in solar heating, amplified by the variable ice extent of Antarctica can influence (with lags and feedbacks) the northern hemisphere. In June, for instance, the potential energy (P_E) is slightly higher in the northern hemisphere, but the relatively higher air temperatures of the Arctic produce less available potential energy (A_{PE}) than in the southern hemisphere where a strong poleward gradient of temperature exists. Consequently, the kinetic energy (K_E) generated in the southern hemisphere is about 3.5 times greater than that of the northern hemisphere (Figure 7). This increased wind speed increases evaporation (LE↑) over the oceans. This moisture (some in sensible form via liberation of the latent heat of vaporization) will be transported toward the ITC, fueling the northern part of the Hadley Cell. Thus the greater amount of kinetic energy (K_E) produced by ice conditions in Antarctica, the stronger will be the circulation in the northern hemisphere with the reversed effect of warming in the Arctic. A 3 percent change in ice extent in Antarctica would mean a substantial change in thermal forcing for the opposite hemisphere (Fletcher: 1969).

Sellers (1969) developed a numerical model for steady-state conditions of the earth-atmosphere using a dependent variable of mean annual sea level temperature in 10° latitude belts. He showed that attempts to modify the climate of a small portion on the earth could eventually affect the entire globe. In a sensitivity analysis, Sellers tested the effect of different albedo combinations (expressed as plenatary albedos a_g) at one or both poles between latitudes 70-90° (Figure 8). Removing the ice from the Arctic would increase the mean temperature poleward of 70°N by about 7°C, in the tropics by 1°C, and in

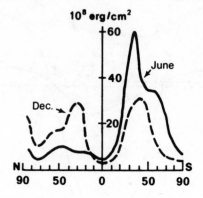

Figure 7. Global Distribution of Kinetic Energy K_E in Summer and Winter (modified from Fletcher: 1969).

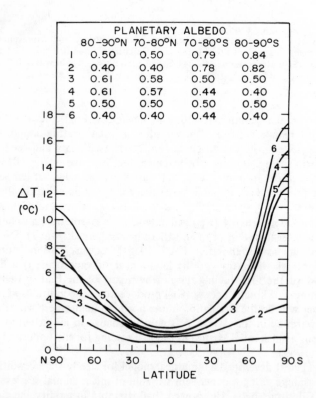

Figure 8. Predicted Latitudinal Distribution of the Mean Annual Temperature Rise ΔT (°C) Associated with Different Albedo Combinations at One or Both Poles (modified from Sellers: 1969).

Antarctica by 1-3°C. If the ice were removed from the Antarctic, temperatures would increase by 12-15°C and in the Arctic by 4°C. If the ice were removed from both polar regions, temperatures would increase 7-10°C in the Arctic, 13-17°C in the Antarctic, and 2°C in the tropics. Sellers concluded with Fletcher (1969), that the extent of sea ice in the southern hemisphere seems to have a greater potential effect on the global circulation than that of the northern hemisphere. Budyko (1969b) derived similar results, but believed that because of the present distribution of oceans and continents, there is a possibility for two climatic regimes to exist, ice-free and glacial. Both regimes were considered very unstable since small variations in solar radiation (Q + q) could change the system to either mode. Another model (Manabe and Wetherald: 1967) indicated that the larger the surface albedo, the colder the atmospheric temperatures and that this influence waned with increasing altitude (Figure 9).

Although Donn and Shaw (1966) postulated that an ice-free polar surface is stable and can be maintained if the ice is artificially removed, doubts have been voiced concerning the stability of present climatic patterns. For instance, new data from oxygen isotopic analyses of deep-sea cores show the unusualness of the present high temperatures within a basically glacial cycle. Emiliani (1972) has warned that the present episode of a temperate climate is coming to an end and that man's interference might disturb the present climatic balance, resulting in either a runaway glaciation or a runaway deglaciation. Faegre (1972) found that there is not one resultant temperature distribution consistent with present values of his model's parameters, but five (intransitivity).[5] One of these distributions corresponded to the present climate (Figure 10). For the present climate (curve 1), a 2 percent decrease of radiation or a 4 percent increase both resulted in instability. Faegre concluded that for a 2 percent decrease in radiation the only solution was a climate (curve 3) indicating glaciation of the entire planet. Also, upon reaching that state, the earth would remain ice-covered, even when the radiation was returned to pre-glaciation values. The author

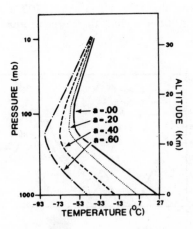

Figure 9. The Vertical Distribution of the Temperature of Radiative Convective Equilibrium for Selected Surface Albedos (modified from Manabe and Wetherald: 1967).

contended that the present system is oscillating back and forth between the present climate (curve 1) and a climate (curve 3) that corresponds to the glaciation of the Quaternary.

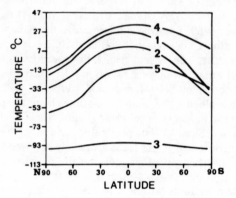

Figure 10. Five Climatic Solutions of an Intransitive Model (modified from Faegre: 1972). 1 = earth's present climate; 2 = climate similar to an ice age; 3 = ice-covered earth; 4 and 5 are asymmetric and difficult to account for physically.

THE TROPOSPHERE

The basic components which rule the circulation of the troposphere are the distributions and intensities of the sinks and sources of energy and the extent of the planet's rotational effects. Although the distribution of net radiation in the atmosphere (R_a) provides the initial energy source for atmospheric motions, subsequent interactions between motions and radiation proceed through a number of nonlinear processes (Figure 2).[6]

Observations have revealed systematic fluctuations of global climate in the last 100 years. Between the 1800's and the 1940's a mean net warming of approximately 0.6°C occurred, while thereafter a cooling (0.3°C) trend has developed (Figure 11).

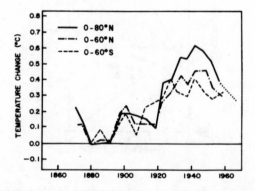

Figure 11. Changes of Mean Annual Temperatures for Selected Latitudes (modified from Mitchell: 1970).

One of the most dramatic impacts man has made on the environment is the direct contamination of the air. When the city heat and pollution plume fans out (Figure 12) beyond about 100 kilometers, it undergoes certain modifications (Munn and Bolin: 1971) because of: (1) the effect of the daily cycle of wind in the boundary layer (especially important near coasts and along slopes); (2) the daily fluctuation in thickness of the mixed layer because of alternating inversions and convections (Figure 13); and (3) the increasing probability that with time, the pollution plume will participate in atmospheric chemical reactions or be drawn into cloud or precipitation systems. As the plume meanders according to synoptic influences, the sources and sinks (e.g., precipitation scavenging, chemical reactions, depletion at the surface) will vary drastically along the way.

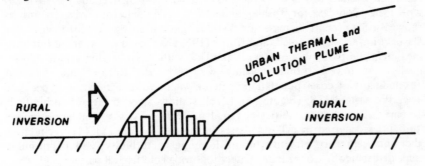

Figure 12. Extension of Urban Thermal and Pollution Plume Downwind of a City During Clear Nights (after Munn and Bolin: 1971).

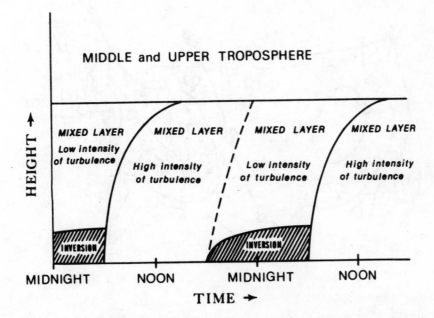

Figure 13. Schematic Representation of the Structure of the Lower Troposphere During a Period of Clear Weather (after Munn and Bolin: 1971).

Particulates

The effects and distributions of particulates are difficult to study because they encompass a large variety of sizes, optical properties, and atmospheric residence times. Aerosols usually scatter direct solar radiation (Q) in a forward direction ($\Sigma\downarrow$), resulting in diffuse haziness (q). Some of the incident radiation (Q) is backscattered ($\Sigma\uparrow$) toward space, resulting in an increased planetary albedo, $a_g = (q_{\Sigma\uparrow} + q_{Pa-A} + q_{Pc})/Q_s$. Some aerosols absorb radiation, warming the air (contributions to $I\downarrow_a$) layer. Particles are also involved in the initiation of condensation and freezing in clouds.

In 1967 McCormick and Ludwig compared the turbidity readings of Angstrom at Washington, D.C. (1903-1907) and Davos, Switzerland (1914-1926) with 1962-1966 data for Washington and 1957-1959 data for Davos. The results showed a 57 percent increase for Washington, and an 88 percent increase for Davos. Flowers, McCormick, and Kurfis (1969) examined five years of turbidity measurements (volz photometer) in the U.S. with the following results: (1) annually, the lowest turbidity values were over the Rockies and the west (excluding west coast population centers), whereas the highest values occurred over the eastern U.S. (Figure 14); (2) all stations showed highest turbidity in summer; (3) lowest turbidities occurred in cP air masses in winter and highest turbidities occurred in mT air masses in summer (Figure 15); (4) precipitation did not seem very effective in the lowering of turbidity; and (5) turbidity appeared somewhat lower immediately following cold frontal passage.

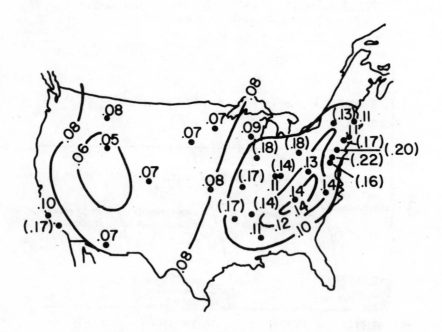

Figure 14.   Mean Annual Turbidity over the U.S. (after Flowers, McCormick and Kurfis: 1969). Urban stations are in parenthesis.

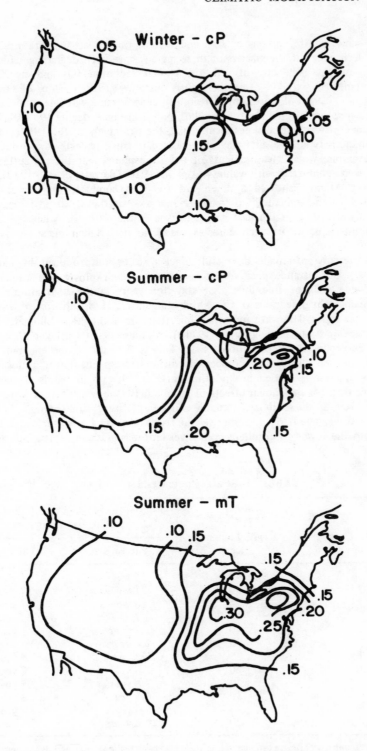

Figure 15. Mean Turbidity for Various Air Masses (after Flowers, McCormick and Kurfis: 1969.)

In some high mountains of Asia and eastern Europe air temperatures have been declining, but the glaciers of these regions have been degrading. This was caused by the high intensity of direct solar radiation (Q) and significant absorptance $(Q + q)(1 - a)$ by the slightly dusty ice surface (decline of albedo). Davitaya (1969) took dust samples from firn crevasses and was able to reveal the historical record of the industrial revolution. For instance, during 1952-1962 the dust content was several times greater than the firn layers of the 19th century.

Conductivity of the air is inversely related to small particle concentrations. For example, when measurements of the atmosphere near the sea surface in 1967 were compared with values taken in 1910 (Barrett, *et al.*: 1970), the northern Atlantic showed a downward trend in conductivity, whereas the southern Pacific indicated no trend. It appears that there was an increase in particulate loading in the past half-century over the northern Atlantic, but no significant transport of such aerosols seems to have taken place across the equator.

At present, man-made dust still appears to be outproduced by natural processes. For instance, great volcanic eruptions of the explosive type can create world-wide veils of fine dust that stay for years in the high atmosphere, accompanied by injections of CO_2, hydrogen sulfide H_2S, sulfur dioxide SO_2, and water vapor. The most important injections are to the 20-27 kilometer level in the lower stratosphere (Lamb: 1971*b*). At these heights a layer of sulfate particles produced by oxidation exists. This is a result of the encounter of atomic oxygen with sulfur compounds diffused from the lower atmosphere (Table 9). Dust is carried around the world by the upper winds. Typically, volcanic dust (or the similar effects of atomic blasts) may take from two to six weeks to circuit the earth in the middle and lower latitudes and from one to four months to become fairly uniform over the zones into which it was injected. Dust put into the lower stratosphere over lower latitudes gradually spreads over the

TABLE 9—Stratospheric Residence Times

Particle diameter μm	Initial height Km	Total times taken to fall through still air to tropopause	
		(a) at 17 Km	(b) at 12 Km
2	40	25 weeks	41 weeks
2	30	21 weeks	37 weeks
2	25	16 weeks	31 weeks
2	20	7 weeks	23 weeks
1	40	1.9 years	3.1 years
1	30	1.6 years	2.8 years
1	25	1.3 years	2.4 years
1	20	0.6 years	1.7 years
0.5	40	7.8 years	12.5 years
0.5	30	6.5 years	11.3 years
0.5	25	5.0 years	9.7 years
0.5	20	2.2 years	6.9 years

Source: Lamb: 1971*b*. (a) applies in latitudes between about 30° and 0°, where the tropopause is usually at a height of about 17 Km. (b) applies to all other latitudes, where the lower tropopause is about at 12 Km. μm = 1 micro-meter = 10^{-6} m.

entire earth. But dust originating in the high latitudes rarely spreads beyond latitude 30°. Reductions of direct solar radiation (Q) by 20-30 percent have been reported. This is accompanied by increases in diffuse solar radiation (q), so that there is a net decrease of global radiation by about 5 percent. Dust effect is greatest in the high latitudes because of lower solar altitudes and larger optical air masses.

Variation in the solar constant (S) is equivalent to variation in the contamination of the atmosphere by dust. Sellers (1969) modeled the effects when albedos were permitted to vary with temperature. A reduction of S by 2 percent initiated an ice age with the ice caps reaching latitude 50° (mean temperature −10°C) and winter snows existing to latitude 30°. Any further drop of S would have resulted in the rapid glaciation of the entire planet (Figure 16). An increase

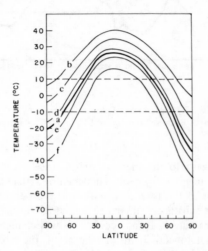

Figure 16. The Predicted Latitudinal Distribution of the Mean Annual Sea Level Temperature as a Function of Changing Solar Constants S (modified from Sellers: 1969). a = present conditions (S = 2.0 cal cm^{-2} min^{-1}); b = S(1.01); c = S(1.05); d = S(1.10); e = S(0.99); f = S(0.98).

of S by 3 percent would have melted all ice sheets. The model also indicated that small changes in the ability of the atmosphere and oceans to transport heat poleward could offset such changes in the solar constant. The results of Budyko's model (1969b) were similar to Sellers'. He claimed that the instability resulting from slight changes in energy input falls well within the possible effects of volcanic eruptions. He regarded the Milankovitch (1930) radiation cycles to be insufficient causes of major glaciations and that changes of energy (and resultant temperatures) are determined mainly by atmospheric transmissivity fluctuations (Figure 17).

Lettau and Lettau (1969) parameterized the shortwave radiation between the top and the bottom of the atmosphere in order to investigate possibilities of climatic modification. A comparison was made between the air of a polluted city and a desert station. They both had similar coefficients of total attenuation, but with different ratios of absorption (A_A) to scattering (Σ). The city's aerosols (industrial) were more efficient as absorbers, whereas desert aerosols (mineral dust) were more efficient as scatterers. This resulted in greater surface heating of the desert when the albedo or the aerosols were increased. The city's effect was a greater heating of the atmosphere. Similar conclusions were reached by Charlson

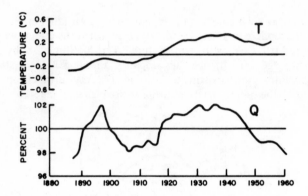

Figure 17. The Anomalies of Temperature T (averaged by moving 10-year periods) and Direct Solar Radiation Q Between Latitudes 17° and 90°N (modified from Budyko: 1969*b*).

and Pilat (1969) in regard to the increase or decrease of absorbed shortwave energy in the earth-atmosphere system. They believed that the backscattering ($\Sigma\uparrow$) is only 10 percent of the total attenuation. It is especially important what type of light absorbing substances appear in industrial smoke (e.g., carbon and iron oxides): the system may heat, not cool. This was challenged by Schneider (1971) who claimed that for an albedo of 10 percent, the effect of aerosols was always cooling via the reduction of absorbed solar radiation $(Q + q)(1 - a)$ and that this absorption for the combined surface-aerosol system far exceeded any reduction in outgoing longwave radiation to space. This was refuted because of the unrealistically low albedo employed by Schneider: heating would have commenced with an albedo of 30 percent (Charlson and Pilat: 1971).

Barrett *et al.* (1970) claimed that the earth's temperature is primarily affected by particulate scattering of radiation. The energy attenuation was modeled as a function of aerosol loading on the basis of Rayleigh and Mie scattering theory (Figure 18). A loading of 100 g hectare^{-1} corresponds to a total areosol loading of 5.2 million metric tons (present atmospheric estimate $\approx$2-4 million tons). Using 4 million tons, one observes that the global annual mean sea level temperature is 0.8°C below what it would be in the absence of any aerosol. Doubling of aerosols would result in a further reduction of 1°C. Since the aerosol doubling time is much shorter than that for CO_2, it was concluded that the net effect would be cooling.

The controversy continued. Atwater (1970) computed a warming trend for cities and a cooling trend for deserts. He emphasized that only small changes in the ratio of absorption to scattering of aerosols can reverse the heating or cooling trend. If the backscattering ($\Sigma\uparrow$) of the incoming shortwave radiation is more important than the decrease of the effective outgoing radiation from the earth-atmosphere system ($I\uparrow_{sa} + I\uparrow_{str}$), the planetary albedo (a_g) will increase faster than the warming effect of CO_2, with a resultant planetary cooling. Using a theory of multiple scattering, Rasool and Schneider (1971) determined that the effect of particulates on visible radiation was much more pronounced than

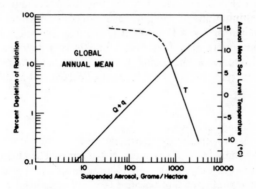

Figure 18. Percentage Depletion of Global Annual Mean Solar Radiation Q + q and Global Annual Mean Sea Level Temperature T as a Function of Particulate Loading (modified from Barrett, *et al.*: 1970).

was their effect on longwave radiation. The authors quoted studies indicating that the global dust content has increased during the last decades by a factor of 2 and warned that if this rate reaches a factor of 4 the global temperature could decline by about 3.5°C, thus triggering an ice age.

Mitchell (1971) used a "critical ratio" (the point at which the air temperature is neither cooling nor heating) which depends on the ratio of absorption of Q + q to backscattering of Q. Accordingly, stratospheric aerosols always cool the atmosphere near the surface, but tropospheric aerosols may either cool or warm the air, depending on the properties of the pollutant and on the properties of the earth's surface. Mitchell concluded that the recent world-wide cooling was not because of aerosol increases, but appeared to be a natural geophysical event.

Neumann and Cohen (1972) applied two models: one with a particulate layer near the surface or in the lower stratosphere and another with two particulate layers, one near the surface, one in the lower stratosphere. The first model indicated that the total gain for the earth-atmosphere system was almost always negative and that the atmospheric gain was almost always positive. A high surface albedo tended to increase the gain of the total system. The second model showed that atmospheric gain was greater than in the first model, that the earth gain was slightly negative, and that the gain to the total system can be positive, producing a general warming.

It appears that the controversy is destined to continue for some time until more realistic and exacting models can be constructed to test the effect of pollutants on global climate. Presently, and on a global scale, man's production of particulates is small compared to natural sources. Such sources include volcanic dust, sea spray and its particulate products, wind-raised dust from arid regions, particles of organic material formed from exudations of vegetation (e.g., terpenes in coniferous forests), microorganisms, pollens and spores, and smoke from forest fires. Man-made particulates include particles directly emitted (during combustion) and particles later formed in the air from gases emitted during combustion, domestic and agricultural burnings, and dust raised by plowing and overgrazing. Estimates of the percent of particulates created by man range from 5 to 45 (Table 10). The most important anthropogenic contributions are sulfate particles which have reached about 50 percent of those naturally produced. Continuation of present energy consumption rates will double particulate production by A.D. 2000. The average residence time of particles in the lower troposphere is a few days while it is a few weeks in the upper troposphere. Evidence is increasing that the northern hemisphere's turbidity coefficient has increased by about 50 percent (Wilson and Matthews: 1971).

Gases

The injection of man-made particulates into the atmosphere is usually accompanied by the release of gaseous contaminants. The chemically stable gases (e.g., carbon dioxide CO_2, hydrogen H_2, methane CH_4) add to the global gas components of the atmosphere because they are long-lived and diffuse widely. Those gases with limited lifetimes (e.g., sulfur dioxide SO_2, hydrogen sulfide H_2S, ammonia NH_3, unburned hydrocarbon, DDT) are soon transformed into particles or converted into other gases and tend to remain only in the latitudinal belts into which they were released. The short-lived or volatile gases thus eventually become part of the hydrosphere and biosphere. Since the ocean makes up the largest part of gaseous sinks, the majority of these gases and their end products will finally be deposited into marine environments. The gases

TABLE 10—Estimates of Particles of Less than 20-μ Radius

Source	10^6 metric tons year^{-1}
Natural	
Soil and rock debris*	100-500
Forest fires and slash-burning debris*	3-150
Sea salt	300
Volcanic debris	25-150
Particles formed from gaseous emissions:	
Sulfate from H_2S	130-200
Ammonium salts from NH_3	80-270
Nitrate from NO_x	60-430
Hydrocarbons from plant exudations	75-200
Total	773-2200
Man-Made	
Particles (direct emissions)	10-90
Particles formed from gaseous emissions:	
Sulfate from SO_2	130-200
Nitrate from NO_x	30-35
Hydrocarbons	15-90
Total	185-415

Source: Wilson and Matthews: 1971. * = includes unknown amounts of indirect man-made contributions. 1 μ = 10^{-6} m.

which especially influence the energy budget of the earth's atmosphere are CO_2, H_2O, NO_2, and SO_2.

Carbon dioxide is a product of fossil fuel combustion. In spite of a greater weight than the air, atmospheric circulation keeps it mixed at an almost constant mean concentration in the troposphere. Near the surface it is quite difficult to determine the average amount of CO_2, because of large daily and seasonal variations caused by photosynthesis. Urban CO_2 concentrations can also vary considerably from mean values (Figure 19).

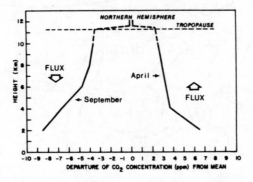

Figure 19.   Vertical Profile of CO_2 (ppm) in the Northern Hemisphere North of Latitude 30°N (after Bolin and Bischof: 1970).

Bolin and Bischof (1970) estimated the mean value of CO_2 for 1968 at 320 ppm. They determined that the annual range was 15 ppm in the lowest layer and about 7 ppm near the tropopause (Figure 20). Because of the vegetation sink during summer, CO_2 concentrations increased upward, whereas in winter the opposite occurred. These authors suggested a present annual increase of about 0.7 ppm year^{-1}. In predicting the future trend, one has to consider the amount of CO_2 being added to the atmosphere and the fraction that will remain airborne. It has been suggested that the world consumption of fossil fuels will continue to grow at the present 4 percent per year until 1980, then drop to 3.5 percent per year by A.D. 2000, because of the increased use of nuclear energy (Wilson and Matthews: 1970). The increase of CO_2 between 1860 and 1950 has been about 10 percent. Estimates vary as to the possible future concentrations (Table 11).

The quantity of atmospheric CO_2 is determined by sources and sinks such as the reservoirs of the ocean, rocks, and living organisms. Of these, the oceanic reservoir of CO_2 is more than 50 times the atmospheric reservoir (Plass: 1959). He suggested that a 50 percent decrease of CO_2 would result in a mean temperature decrease of 3.8°C. This would initiate glaciation, but since ice contains little CO_2, the shrunken oceans would accumulate the excess CO_2, eventually release it to the atmosphere, and temperatures would rise again (negative feedback). However, there is also a positive feedback in action, for a colder atmosphere holds less water vapor and therefore leads to reduced terrestrial radiation ($I\uparrow_s$) absorption. Also, cloudiness will increase (in spite of water vapor reduction), causing further diminution of solar radiation (Q + q) and temperature. Other complications exist. For instance, at lower water tempera-

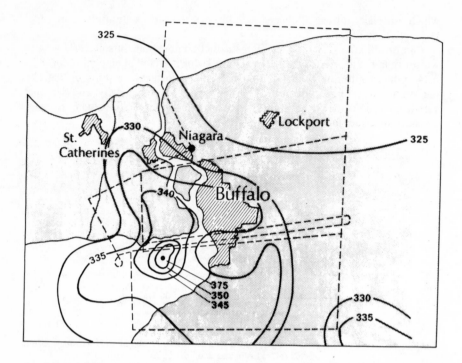

Figure 20. Isolines of CO_2 (ppm) Concentrations (about 1000 ft elevation) in the Vicinity of Buffalo, N.Y. on December 6, 1969 (after Barrett, *et al.*: 1970). Dashed lines are flight path of mission.

tures, more CO_2 is absorbed than at higher temperatures. This is partially coupled to the extent of mixing in the cold deeper waters of the ocean as compared with those near the surface. Surfactants (e.g., oil films) also influence the CO_2 exchange at the oceanic interface, since films decrease evaporation (LE↑) and change the albedo and turbidity characteristics of water. It has also been suggested that an enzyme-like carbonic anhydrase may partially control the absorption of CO_2 by sea water (Berger and Libby: 1970). Man not only adds

TABLE 11—Predicted Atmospheric CO_2 Concentrations (ppm)

Annual emission increase %	Year	Percentage of emissions remaining in atmosphere	
		35%	45%
4	1980	332	335
4	1990	348	355
4	2000	371	388
4	2010	403	430
5	1990	349	356
5	2000	378	395
5	2010	418	450

Source: Munn and Bolin: 1971.

CO_2 by fossil burning, but his agricultural activities also tend to increase the gas with cultivation, since this permits the CO_2 produced by soil bacteria to escape into the atmosphere.

Carbon dioxide has a strong absorption band near 15 μm (long-wave part of spectrum). This band emits infrared radiation downward ($I\downarrow_a$) and upward to space ($I\uparrow_{sa}$). In 1963 Möller argued that Plass' (1959) calculations were valid only for a dry atmosphere. Since there is an overlap of CO_2 and H_2O absorption bands near 15 μm, the temperature change due to CO_2 would diminish. Accordingly, a doubling (300 to 600 ppm) of CO_2 would increase temperatures only about 1.5°C. He also noted that the increase in atmospheric water vapor content concomitant with rising temperatures resulted in a positive feedback. For a constant relative humidity, the consequence was an increase of 10°C. Möller hypothesized that this would not happen, since a change in water vapor content of only 3 percent or by a change in cloudiness of 1 percent, would compensate for it (resulting in no temperature increase). Gebhart (1967) included the absorptance of shortwave radiation of CO_2. His results made the climatic influence of CO_2 (doubling the present amount) appear even smaller, resulting in an increase of 1.2°C. At the same time, Manabe and Wetherald (1967) found that a doubling of CO_2 increased the mean temperature near the surface by 2°C. The opposite is true for the stratosphere where temperatures would decline and be much more sensitive to CO_2 variations than the troposphere (Figure 21).

Rasool and Schneider (1971) computed the outgoing flux for every 10-cm^{-1} interval in the infrared (4-100 μm) for a 60-layer atmospheric model. Even by increasing CO_2 to eight times as much, the temperature increase near the surface was less than 2°C. It appeared that the rate of temperature increase diminished with increasing CO_2 (Figure 22), and there was no runaway "greenhouse" effect. Budyko (1972) also considered the feedback effects of polar ice in relation to CO_2 concentrations. His results far exceeded those of other investigators. For a complete melting of the polar ice, an increase in CO_2 by less than 50 percent of its present value would be sufficient, whereas a reduction by one-half would lead to a complete glaciation of the planet. Budyko suggested that CO_2 had been decreasing naturally for millions of years. Given this natural decline, the earth

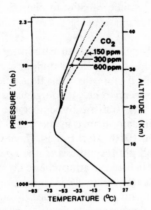

Figure 21. Vertical Distribution of Temperature in Radiative Convective Equilibrium for Selected CO_2 Concentrations (after Manabe and Wetherald: 1967).

would have been completely covered by ice in about a million years, but considering the Milankovitch energy cycles, this would have happened in only several hundred thousand years. The author postulated that only man's increase in production of CO_2 and waste heat will prevent future glaciations.

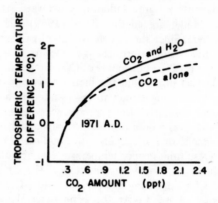

Figure 22. Change in Tropospheric Temperature (°C) as a Function of CO_2 (ppm) Concentration (after Rasool and Schneider: 1971). The dashed curve is for constant surface absolute humidity, whereas the solid curve is for the case in which surface relative humidity is kept constant. ppt = parts per thousand.

Nitric oxide (NO), a combustion product at high temperatures, easily oxidizes in the atmosphere to nitrogen dioxide (NO_2), a key constituent of photochemical smog, by reacting rapidly (absorbing ultraviolet radiation) with ozone (O_3). Nitrogen dioxide also absorbs solar radiation ($Q + q$) in the visible part of the spectrum. In cities it is a significant part of the atmospheric energy budget and may largely be responsible for the typically brownish urban haze. Because of its high reactivity it is not considered to be a problem on a global scale.

Sulfur dioxide SO_2 is another short-lived atmospheric constituent having a mean residence time of about 2.5 days (Matthews, Kellogg and Robinson: 1971). The oxidation to sulfuric acid and the formation of ammonia sulfate particles is the main importance of SO_2 to climatic impact. Presently over 30 million tons of SO_2 per year are being discharged into the atmosphere of the U.S. (Koide and Goldberg: 1971).

Man releases about 270 million tons of carbon monoxide (CO) per year into the atmosphere, and except for localized buildups, no problems are expected since natural sources produce more than ten times that amount (Maugh: 1972). The major sinks for CO appear to be microorganisms in the soil. Barrett, et al. (1970), could not find any statistically detectable trend of ozone (O_3) in Hawaii. Similarly, no significant change in the atmosphere's oxygen (O_2) could be detected since at least 1910 (Machta and Hughes: 1970). In fact, Ryther (1970) reasoned that if all photosynthesis in the oceans would stop, at least a million years would go by before the atmospheric O_2 would even decrease by 10 percent. According to Abeles, et al. (1971), soil acts as an important sink for ethylene (an air pollutant and plant hormone) through microbial degradation, and for SO_2 and NO_2 primarily through chemical action. For the latter two, the mechanism of degradation is large enough to accommodate all the SO_2 and NO_2 produced in the U.S. each year. Lovelock (1971) considered the atmosphere as a biological cybernetic system whose constituents are in a state of dynamic balance with the biosphere. Accordingly, SO_2 and H_2S (originating almost entirely from the biosphere) are the precursors of sulfuric acid (H_2SO_4). About ten times as much nitrogen oxides (NO_x), which are the precursors of nitric acid, are produced by natural processes (Table 12). Nitric acid can combine with biologically produced ammonia (NH_3), resulting in fine aerosols of ammonia salts. Thus there is much more widespread haze over tropical forests and deserts where turbidity is highest in summer. The author postulated that CO_2 stimulates vegetation growth, increasing the output of terpenes, ammonia, and hydrogen sulfide. All these are aerosol precursors. Lovelock suggested that there exists a regulatory response in the eocsystem to combustion emissions, neutralizing the CO_2 increase by increasing atmospheric haziness (declining transmissivity), a response to correct the warming effect.

Water Vapor and Clouds

Weather modification can be classified by the nature of the altered atmospheric process or component, the cause of modification, and the scale and dimension of the area where the modification occurs (U.S. Congress: 1966). Three scales can be considered. Microscale processes (horizontal dimensions less than 15 kilometers) contain the human microclimate, plant microclimates, frost protection, greenhouses, evaporation suppression, fog dissipation, cloud dissipation, hail prevention, seeding of individual cumulus clouds and orographic cap clouds, lightning suppression, and precipitation suppression. Mesoscale processes (horizontal dimensions between 15 and 200 kilometers) present higher orders of complexities and difficulties in the statistical evaluation of modification attempts. The precipitation of orographic cloud systems, the precipitation of non-orographic cumulus systems, and the modification of hurricanes and tornados are of primary concern. Macroscale processes would contain modifications of the global wind systems, the melting of sea ice, and the diversion of ocean currents. All these would be instrumental in the alteration of the energy, mass, and momentum budget of the earth-atmosphere system.

Small suspended particles affect the atmosphere by serving as cloud nuclei and also affect the radiation budget. The growth of precipitation particles in

TABLE 12—Concentration, Source, and Duration of Atmospheric Constituents

Gas	Concentration ppm	Combustion & Industrial Emission	Natural emission	Half-life
CO_2	320.0	14.0	140.0	2-5 yrs
CO	0.08	0.28	0.1	3 yrs
CH_4	1.5	—	2.0	16 yrs
Hydrocarbons	<0.001	0.1	0.1	—
H_2S	0.0002	0.003	0.1	2 days
SO_2	0.002	0.14	—	4 days
NO_x	0.001	0.05	0.5	5 days
N_2O	0.5	—	0.6	4 yrs
NH_3	0.01	—	1.2	7 days
O_2	2.1×10^5	−10.0	100.0	1000 yrs

Source: Lovelock: 1971. Emissions are in 10^9 tons year^{-1}.

clouds is a result of instabilities in their microstructure. In warm clouds predominantly consisting of liquid water, the larger drops may continue to increase by coalescence with smaller droplets, whereas in cold clouds which consist of supercooled droplets and ice crystals, ice crystals grow at the expense of droplets. The two processes are aided by the release of latent heat (LR), adding to the buoyancy of the cloud and increasing its vertical development. An increase in cloud condensation nuclei over tropical oceans leads to greater cloud stability and reduced precipitation, whereas an increase in the number of ice-nucleating particles tends to increase precipitation in the middle and high latitude continental areas (Barrett, et al.: 1970). Twomey and Wojciechowski (1969) claimed that observations did not support the idea of industrial or other man-made pollution as the major source of cloud nuclei. They observed that nuclei levels were higher over Australia and Africa than over North America.

There is, at this time, no general agreement as to the effects of deliberate weather modification. The scientific basis for artificial cloud modification developed in the 1930's. In the 1940's the effects of dry ice (solid CO_2) and silver iodide on supercooled clouds were demonstrated. This led to the federally sponsored "Project Cirrus." Many others were to follow, but numerous scientists remained skeptical for statistical reasons since the proper randomization of cloud seeding trials had not been achieved. Opinions became strongly divided between commercial cloud seeding interests, federal agencies, and the scientific community (Fleagle: 1969). Area experiments in seeding in some regions seem to have produced precipitation increases of 10 to 20 percent (Wilson and Matthews: 1971).

Cloud cover can be modified in two ways. In the first approach, clouds containing many droplets will (because of their small size) not produce rain as readily as a cloud containing fewer but larger droplets. Thus in this kind of cloud an increase in nuclei will lead to decreased efficiency, especially warm clouds, in the rain-making process, resulting in increased cloud cover or depth. In the second approach, if large effective ice nuclei are added, precipitation may be stimulated, resulting in cloud dissipation and a reduction in cloud cover (Wilson and Matthews: 1971).

Man may be inadvertently seeding clouds by the emissions of ice nuclei from steel plants. Barrett, et al. (1970) showed evidence of the ice-nucleating effect downwind of urban-industrial aerosols (Figure 23). Inadvertent cloud seeding by jet aircraft, leading to the formation of a persistent contrail, is believed to be introducing nuclei in numbers equivalent to ground-based generators (Murcray: 1970). Murcray suggested that routine airline operations are affecting precipitation to a much greater extent than are present deliberate seeding operations.

A 500-meter thick contrail sheet increased counterradiation ($I\downarrow_a$) from the sheet by 18 percent, but decreased solar radiation ($Q + q$) by 15 percent (Barrett, et al.: 1970). The increased $I\downarrow_a$ could not make up for the loss of $Q + q$, resulting in a net depletion of incoming energy at the surface (Figure 24). Machta and Carpenter (1971) concluded that high cloudiness has increased over the U.S. since 1965. They argued that since most commercial jets fly just below the tropopause where air is coldest and can hold only small amounts of moisture, cloud formation is most readily accomplished in this part of the atmosphere.

The albedo of cloud tops is a function of height, thickness, and characteristic properties of the cloud. Cloud albedos can range from 0.2 (high cirrus) to 0.7 (cumulus). Clouds constitute a major contribution to the planetary albedo and

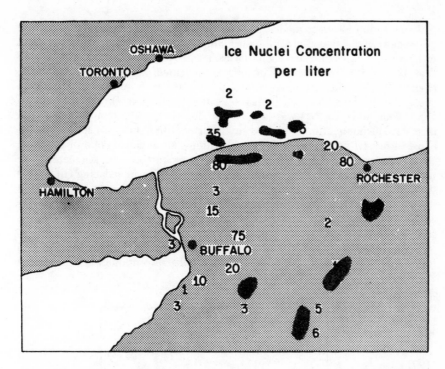

Figure 23. Measurements of Ice Nucleus Concentrations over Western New York State on November 25, 1968 (after Barrett, *et al.*: 1970). Note plumes of high nucleus concentrations and their correlation with positions of snow showers (hatched areas).

are sensitive components in climate control. In addition to reflecting, attenuating, absorbing, and scattering solar radiation, clouds also reradiate longwave radiation. This infrared radiation to space in cloudy areas is proportional to the cloud-top temperature, effectively replacing the earth's surface as a longwave radiator.

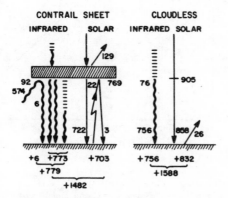

Figure 24. Tropical Radiation Budget for Cloudless Sky and Beneath a Contrail Sheet, measured at 19°N, 53°W on June 9, 1969 (after Barrett, *et al.*: 1970). Values are in cal cm^{-2} day^{-1}.

Using a global-average model, an attempt was made to simulate the effective outgoing longwave radiation for the earth-atmosphere ($I\uparrow_{sa} + I\uparrow_{str}$) in response to different cloud covers and heights (Wilson and Matthews: 1971). They found that $I\uparrow_{sa} + I\uparrow_{str}$ decreased with increasing cloud height and cloud cover (Figure 25). For the temperature near the surface to be unaltered, shortwave absorption in the system must equal longwave reradiation, $Q_s(1 - a_g) = I\uparrow_{sa} + I\uparrow_{str}$. Thus, if $Q_s(1 - a_g)$ was larger than $I\uparrow_{sa} + I\uparrow_{str}$, the temperature would increase. The intersection of various cloud curves with $Q_s(1 - a_g)$ determines the locus of several possible equilibrium conditions. Mean global conditions (cloud cover = 50 percent) indicate this compensation point to be 5.5 kilometers. The finding that increasing cloud cover was more effective in reducing $Q_s(1 - a_g)$ than $I\uparrow_{sa} + I\uparrow_{str}$, was in agreement with results modeled by Manabe and Wetherald (1967), who also indicated that the influence of cloudiness on the equilibrium temperature was more pronounced in the troposphere than in the stratosphere.

Sellers (1964) modeled the energy balance of an atmospheric column and found that the warming of the atmosphere via the absorption of $Q + q$ averaged

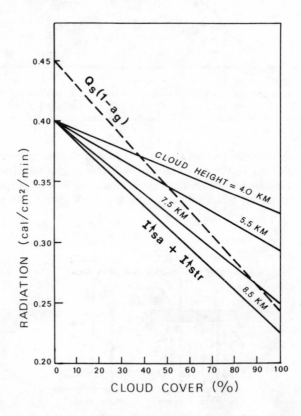

Figure 25. Effective Outgoing Longwave Radiation $I\uparrow_{sa} + I\uparrow_{str}$ by the Earth-Atmosphere System as a Function of Cloud Cover and Cloud Height (after Wilson and Matthews: 1971). $Q_s(1 - a_g)$ = absorbed solar radiation. The temperature profile was held constant ($T_s = 15°C$). Surface albedo = 0.1; mean global cloud albedo = 0.5. Symbols are defined in Table 1.

about $0.5°C$ day^{-1}. Infrared cooling averaged about $1.3°C$ day^{-1}. In order to maintain equilibrium, the difference was made up by convection (H↑), advection, or the liberated heat of vaporization (LR). The ultimate source of all this heat came from a zone between latitude $0°$ and $10°N$, which cooled $0.6°C$ day^{-1} as a result of the exportation of one-half of LR within the zone to higher latitudes. Sellers suggested that most of the atmospheric warming between latitude $60°N$ and $60°S$ was a result of the release of LR, and the climates of higher latitudes were mainly determined by atmospheric processes near the equator. A decrease in equatorial precipitation could lead to a temperature decrease in poleward areas. Consequently, any deliberate or inadvertent change in tropical cloud or humidity conditions could have global repercussions.

Neiburger (1971) saw other fundamental and ecological effects as a result of precipitation modification. For instance, the distribution of natural vegetation could be affected if temperature changes (as feedbacks to increased clouds and LE↑) accompanied the alteration. This could also create changes in animal life, and present balances between insects, plant pathogens, and their hosts might be disturbed. Climatic modification could create synergistic responses in ecosystems. Also, the very methods of weather modification could introduce toxic substances into the environment (e.g., silver or lead iodide).

THE STRATOSPHERE

For the first time in human history man has the ability to deposit material directly into the stratosphere. A supersonic transport fleet could deposit exhaust products such as CO_2, H_2O, CO, NO_x, SO_2 and the associated sulfate, and soot. The stratosphere is sensitive to changes due to long pollutant residence times (a result of the great thermal stability of the stratosphere) and processes creating and destroying ozone (O_3) from ultraviolet radiation. Ozone is instrumental in exercising temperature control over the stratosphere and in providing an effective umbrella against ultraviolet radiation harmful to life. In most spectral bands the surface "sees" either only the lower troposphere or the entire atmosphere, except in the atmospheric window (8-13 μm band), where the surface can radiatively interact with space on clear days. Here a narrow O_3 band (9.6 μm) provides a direct radiative linkage between the earth's surface and the lower stratosphere which is in a very delicate radiative balance (Munn and Bolin: 1971).

The tropopause is a rather effective barrier to the exchange of air between the troposphere and the stratosphere, but several exchange mechanisms have been proposed (Wilson and Matthews: 1971). The stratosphere represents a strong inversion (via absorptance of Q by O_3). The lowest part of the stratosphere is mechanically stirred (M_{STR}) by the tropospheric circulation below. Here the contaminant half-life residence is about six months. At 20 kilometers (SST cruising height) the half-life is one to five years (Johnston: 1971).

With regard to the SST, concern was expressed that the quantity of water vapor added could become comparable to that naturally present (Harrison: 1970). With the projected water vapor input of the SST's, ozone was predicted to decline 3.8 percent, solar transmission was predicted to increase by 0.07 percent, and the temperature near the surface (northern hemisphere) was to increase by $0.04°C$. Manabe and Wetherald (1967) determined that the higher the stratospheric humidity, the warmer the tropospheric temperature, whereas the opposite applied to the stratosphere. The dependence of the stratospheric equilibrium temperature on water vapor was much greater than the tropospheric.

Singer (1971) believes that methane (CH_4) production was more important in the increase of water vapor into the stratosphere than that coming from the SST's exhaust. Methane is produced from the decomposition of organic matter, swamps, rice paddies, coal fields, natural gas and petroleum wells, and industry. Close to 50 percent of the CH_4 production has been identified as cultural, increasing by 2-3 percent per year. Singer was concerned at the rate of CH_4 oxidation and conversion to water vapor in the stratosphere. The water vapor introduced into the stratosphere by this process was twice the rate of a possible SST fleet (Table 13). Johnston (1971) also discounted the role of water vapor

TABLE 13—Water Vapor Injections into the Stratosphere

Process	g sec^{-1}
CH_4 oxidation	3.4×10^6
Human-related portion	1.7×10^6
Injected by SST fleet	1.5×10^6
Injected by Hadley Cell circulation	5.0×10^6

Source: Singer: 1971.

from SST exhaust as being less important than oxides of nitrogen NO_x emitted from the SST. The NO_x increment from the SST was considered more destructive of O_3 than the entire natural background of H_2O. Johnston argued that the importance of stratospheric H_2O was its role in removing NO_x rather than its direct reaction with O_3. The model predicted a great sensitivity of O_3 when NO_x was added to about 20 Km (cruise height). If concentrations of NO and NO_2 were increased by the amounts accepted by Wilson and Matthews (1970) and government agencies, the ozone shield would experience a major reduction. Van Valin (1971) attempted to summarize the possible effects of the SST (Table 14). He concluded, considering the rather small effects produced by the more massive injections of volcanic eruptions, that SST emissions will have an insignificant effect on the environment. However, he warned that a great deal of our knowledge concerning the processes and components in the stratosphere is limited.

TABLE 14—Emission Concentrations as a Fraction of Natural Concentrations*

Constituent	Average	Maximum
CO_2	0.0018	0.0036
H_2O	0.01-0.25	0.02-0.5
NO_2	0.5	1.0
SO_2	0.25-0.5	0.5-1.0
Unburned hydrocarbons	>0.0016	>0.0032
Soot	0.5	1.0

Source: Van Valin: 1971. * = northern hemisphere.

From 1963 to 1970 a new series of seven volcanic eruptions in seven years occurred. Cronin (1971) reported that at least three of these eruptions introduced significant amounts of water vapor into the stratosphere and that all eruptions appeared to have penetrated the tropopause. Two belts (56°N to 65°N and 8°S to 15°N) were the primary sources of volcanic ejecta and gaseous effluent to the stratosphere. The high latitude belt was believed to be the more significant since the tropopause is considerably lower at these latitudes. Because of this, the northern hemisphere is probably more turbid than the southern hemisphere. Ellis and Pueschel (1971) reexamined the turbidity at Mauna Loa for 13 years and found no evidence that human activities affected transmissivity on a global scale, and that short term fluctuations were associated with volcanic eruptions. The authors concluded that Peterson and Bryson (1968) were erroneous in their analysis of the data for Mauna Loa.

CONCLUDING REMARKS

For centuries, man's value structure was preoccupied with making a living. The side effects were taken in stride and generally ignored until recently. Despite the utter massiveness of the earth-atmosphere system, man's deliberate or inadvertent modification of climate is a problem that must be dealt with if making a living and the quality of life as we know it are to continue. The exponential growth of population is not only creating havoc with the world's finite resources, but the increased use of energy sources with deleterious by-products may upset the current balance of energy, mass, and momentum of the global climate. This is especially true on a long term basis and under current rates of "progress." There is little doubt that if the industrial revolution continues, it will only be a question of time before climate changes on a global scale.

The atmosphere is one of mankind's major resources. It determines areas of cultivation, types of plants, and environmental limits to agricultural productivity. Climatic factors also influence mortality, diseases, comfort, and general well-being. Ecologists have become increasingly conscious of the central role of climate when considering the flow of energy and mass between the physical systems of the earth-atmosphere and ecosystems.

The assessment of planned or inadvertent anthropogenic alterations in the earth-atmosphere system is made difficult by the large range and number of natural fluctuations. These natural oscillations, common throughout the planet's history, constitute a strong source of "noise" that masks man-made contributions to climatic changes. Most students of climatic change will agree that man has definitely produced local climatic modifications, and the feeling is growing that we are on the brink of accomplishing regional changes.

There is great uncertainty as to what is in store for us on a short term basis, e.g., 50 years hence. One basic question deals with the dilemma of simultaneous increases in turbidity and carbon dioxide concentrations in the atmosphere. Turbidity is instrumental in cooling the earth-atmosphere system, whereas the CO_2 propagates a warming trend. Conclusions are divided, but many believe that the doubling time for aerosols is considerably shorter than carbon dioxide. With this outcome one would expect several decades of planetary cooling. This trend may be further strengthened by a world-wide natural cooling already in progress since the 1940's. Increasing air contamination will not only affect thermal events, but cloud and precipitation processes as well. Because of multiple feedbacks, alterations are extremely difficult to predict. Changes in solar radiation, ultimately caused by the increased aerosol loading of the air, will change the source of available potential energy and resultant kinetic energy that drives the global circulation as a direct heat engine. Feedback to changes in cloudiness and the transport of heat, water vapor, and dust, will add further nonlinearity to the complexity of atmospheric circulation.

A second basic question arises from the sensitivity of the planetary system to changes in surface albedo. The polar sea ice distribution and extent is viewed by many as one of the most unstable parts of the global climate where man's interference could cause large-scale consequences. This instability could be compounded further by what appears to be an inherent climatic instability of the entire system (intransitivity). Albedo changes often influence the ratio of turbulent heat exchange to the energy used for evapotranspiration (Bowen ratio). Sensible heat is directly available to drive atmospheric motions, but latent heat, upon condensation, is often released large distances away from the original place of evaporation.

Third, because of the great sensitivity of the stratosphere to small intrusions and the long residence time of foreign objects, many investigators are concerned about the future effect of many SST's cruising at stratospheric heights. This is of great importance to the possible alteration of the ozone shield which protects us from biologically harmful radiation. At this point, a considerable controversy rages over this possible danger.

Finally, man is doubling his energy conversion rate every 17.5 years. On a long-term basis, this large artificial heat addition to the global system is predicted to reach magnitudes equal to the present absorptance of solar radiation in only about two hundred years. It has been hypothesized that this input of waste heat would terminate the present cooling trend and drastically change the world's climate.

When reflecting on the infinitely complex mechanisms and awesome consequences of environmental alteration it becomes apparent how preliminary and yet sophisticated our comprehension still is. It is far beyond the scope of one person, one discipline, or one world organization to deal with such an explosion of knowledge. The geographer may still be a climatologist but this is no longer a mutually exclusive field. Indeed, the advancement of frontiers in climatology requires a multidisciplinary approach. It is perhaps still the geographer who seeks the total picture of things and can synthesize such a body of knowledge and apply it to man-land relationships. This writer discovered that out of over 100 references used in this review dealing with climatic modification, only a handful originated from geographers. In these days of increasing public concern and interest regarding the changing nature of the physical and biological geography of our planet, one would expect and hope that in the future geographers will take this unique and demanding opportunity to play a larger role in research from which mankind is sure to benefit.

ACKNOWLEDGMENT

Thanks are due to Professor John N. Rayner, Department of Geography, Ohio State University, for examining a draft of Figure 2 and for making valuable comments.

FOOTNOTES

[1] Since the energy processes shown in Figure 2 occur simultaneously, the final equilibrium temperature of a surface, object, or parcel of air accounts for all possible processes. This is a passive result of the constant dynamic interactions among all the energy fluxes and the equilibrium temperature is merely a response to all of the synchronous forcing and response functions.

[2] $R_s = (Q + q)(1 - a) - (I\uparrow_s - I\downarrow_a)$ cal cm^{-2}

[3] If we divide 20 billion persons by the surface area of the planet and multiply by 20 kw/person, the result is about one magnitude lower than Budyko's estimate of energy production per cm^2.

[4] $\beta = H/LE$, the ratio of sensible heat flux to latent heat flux. Taking soil heat flux G into account, β indicates the proportion of available energy (net radiation R_s) used for evaporation or used to heat the air. The ratio can also be viewed as an index of dryness.

[5] According to ergodic theory, for the case of nonlinear equations, the uniqueness of long-term statistics is not assured. If a system of deterministic equations, extended indefinitely into the future, results in a time-dependent solution which is independent of the choice of the initial conditions, the system is considered *transitive*. That is, the physical laws (often expressed by variations and parameterization of the "primitive equations") which govern the atmosphere are responsible for the determination of a unique planetary climate. However, the equations governing the atmosphere are highly non-linear. The process mostly responsible for this nonlinearity is advection by the means of the field of motion itself. This field of motion is continually being distorted, resulting in an infinite variety of shapes which need not repeat themselves. Thus, if there are several possible sets of long term statistics ("climate" here defined as long term statistics of the flow of the circulation), based on different initial inputs, the system is termed *intransitive* and physical laws do not uniquely determine the climate. Lorenz (1968) believes that the real atmosphere may be of an *almost-intransitive* type. Here statistics taken over infinitely long time intervals are dependent upon initial conditions, but statistics taken over very long but finite intervals will have solutions that differ from one such interval of averaging to another. That is, such finite intervals do depend upon initial conditions. If this theory is substantiated, almost-intransitivity could be a major cause of climatic changes, a result of inherently unstable circulation patterns and not of environmental changes. In fact, environmental changes could be concealed by a free internal fluctuation going in the opposite direction (Lorenz: 1968).

[6] $R_a = [Q_s + (Q + q)a] (1 - a_a) - I\uparrow_{sa}$ cal cm^{-2}

REFERENCES

Abeles, F. B., L. E. Craker, L. E. Forrence, and G. R. Leather, 1971, "Fate of Air Pollutants: Removal of Ethylene, Sulfur Dioxide, and Nitrogen Dioxide by Soil," *Science*, Vol. 173, pp. 914-916.

Atwater, M. A., 1970, "Planetary Albedo Changes Due to Aerosols," *Science*, Vol. 170, pp. 64-66.

——, 1971, "The Radiation Budget for Polluted Layers of the Urban Environment," *Journal of Applied Meteorology*, Vol. 10, pp. 205-214.

Bach, W., 1971, "Variation of Solar Radiation with Height over an Urbanized Area," *Journal of the Air Pollution Control Association*, Vol. 21, pp. 621-628.

Bach, W. and W. Patterson, 1969, "Heat Budget Studies in Greater Cincinnati," *Proceedings of the Association of American Geographers*, Vol. 1, pp. 7-11.

Barrett, E. W., R. F. Pueschel, H. K. Weikmann, and P. M. Kuhn, 1970, *Inadvertent Modification of Weather and Climate by Atmospheric Pollutants*, ESSA Technical Report ERL 185-APCL 15. Washington, D.C.: Government Printing Office.

Berger, R. and W. F. Libby, 1970, "Exchange of CO_2 Between Atmosphere and Sea Water: Possible Enzymatic Control of Rate," in S. F. Singer, (ed.), *Global Effects of Environmental Pollution*. New York and Dordrecht, Holland: Springer-Verlag and D. Reidel Publishing Co., pp. 30-33.

Bolin, B. and W. Bischof, 1970, "Variations of the Carbon Dioxide Content of the Atmosphere of the Northern Hemisphere," *Tellus*, pp. 431-442.

Bornstein, R. O., 1968, "Observation of the Urban Heat Island Effect in New York City," *Journal of Applied Meteorology*, Vol. 7, pp. 575-582.

Bryan, K., 1969, "Climate and the Ocean Circulation: III. The Ocean Model," *Monthly Weather Review*, Vol. 97, pp. 806-827.

Bryson, R. A. and D. A. Baerreis, 1967, "Possibilities of Major Climatic Modification and their Implications: Northwest India, a Case for Study," *Bulletin of the American Meteorological Society*, Vol. 48, pp. 136-142.

Budyko, M. I., 1969a, "Climatic Change," *Soviet Geography: Review and Translation*, Vol. 10, pp. 429-457.

———, 1969b, "The Effect of Solar Radiation Variations on the Climate of the Earth," *Tellus*, Vol. 21, pp. 611-619.

———, 1972, "The Future Climate," *EOS, Transactions of the American Geophysical Union*, Vol. 53, pp. 868-874.

Budyko, M. I., O. A. Drozdov and M. I. Yudin, 1971, "The Impact of Economic Activity on Climate," *Soviet Geography: Review and Translation*, Vol. 12, pp. 666-679.

Buechley, R. W., J. Van Bruggen and L. E. Truppi, 1972, "Heat Island = Death Island?" *Environmental Research*, Vol. 5, pp. 85-92.

Bullock, B. R. and D. R. Johnson, 1972, "The Generation of Available Potential Energy by Sensible Heating in Southern Ocean Cyclones," *Quarterly Journal of the Royal Meteorological Society*, Vol. 98, pp. 495-518.

Chandler, T. J., 1965, *The Climate of London*. London: Hutchinson.

———, 1970, *Selected Bibliography on Urban Climate*. Geneva: World Meteorological Organization.

Changnon, Jr., S. A., 1969, "Recent Studies of Urban Effects on Precipitation in the United States," *Bulletin of the American Meteorological Society*, Vol. 50, pp. 411-421.

Changnon, Jr., S. A., F. A. Huff and R. G. Semonin, 1971, "Metromex: An Investigation of Inadvertent Weather Modification," *Bulletin of the American Meteorological Society*, Vol. 52, pp. 958-967.

Charlson, R. J. and M. J. Pilat, 1969, "Climate: The Influence of Aerosols," *Journal of Applied Meteorology*, Vol. 8, pp. 1001-1002.

———, 1971, "Reply," *Journal of Applied Meteorology*, Vol. 10, pp. 841-842.

Chorley, R. J. and B. A. Kennedy, 1971, *Physical Geography: A Systems Approach*. London: Prentice-Hall.

Coulson, K. L., T. K. Cummings, and D. W. Reynolds, 1971, *On Radiative Effects of Atmospheric Turbidity*. Davis, Calif.: Department of Agricultural Engineering, University of California.

Cronin, J. F., 1971, "Recent Volcanism and the Stratosphere," *Science*, Vol. 172, pp. 847-849.

Davidson, B., 1967, "A Summary of the New York Urban Air Pollution Dynamics Research Program," *Journal of the Air Pollution Control Association*, Vol. 17, pp. 154-158.

Davitaya, F. F., 1969, "Atmospheric Dust Content as a Factor Affecting Glaciation and Climatic Change," *Annals of the Association of American Geographers*, Vol. 59, pp. 552-560.

Dettwiller, J., 1970, "Deep Soil Temperature Trends and Urban Effects at Paris," *Journal of Applied Meteorology*, Vol. 9, pp. 178-180.

Donn, W. L. and D. M. Shaw, 1966, "The Heat Budget of an Ice-Free and an Ice-Covered Arctic Ocean," *Journal of Geophysical Research*, Vol. 71, pp. 1087-1093.

Ellis, H. T. and R. F. Pueschel, 1971, "Solar Radiation: Absence of Air Pollution Trends at Mauna Loa," *Science*, Vol. 172, pp. 845-846.

Emiliani, C., 1972, "Quaternary Paleotemperatures and the Duration of the High-Temperature Intervals," *Science*, Vol. 178, pp. 398-401.

Faegre, A., 1972, "An Intransitive Model of the Earth-Atmosphere-Ocean System," *Journal of Applied Meteorology*, Vol. 11, pp. 4-6.

Findlay, B. F. and M. S. Hirt, 1969, "An Urban-Induced Meso-Circulation," *Atmospheric Environment*, Vol. 3, pp. 537-542.

Fleagle, R. G., 1969, "Background and Present Status of Weather Modification," in R. G. Fleagle, (ed.), *Weather Modification: Science and Public Policy*. Seattle: University of Washington Press, pp. 3-17.

Fletcher, J. O., 1969, *Ice Extent on the Southern Ocean and Its Relationship to World Climate*. Santa Monica: The Rand Corporation.

Flohn, H., 1963, "Theories of Climatic Change from the Viewpoint of the Global Energy Budget," in UNESCO, *Arid Zone Research* XX, pp. 339-344.

———, 1971, "Saharization: Natural or Management?" in World Meteorological Organization, *Special Environmental Report No. 2*, Selected Papers on Meteorology as Related to the Human Environment. Geneva: WMO, pp. 101-106.

Flowers, E. C., R. A. McCormick and K. R. Kurfis, 1969, "Atmospheric Turbidity over the United States, 1961-1966," *Journal of Applied Meteorology*, Vol. 8, pp. 955-962.

Garnett, A. and W. Bach, 1965, "An Estimate of the Ratio of Artificial Heat Generation to Natural Radiation Heat in Sheffield," *Monthly Weather Review*, Vol. 93, pp. 383-385.

Gebhart, R., 1967, "On the Significance of the Shortwave CO_2-Absorption in Investigations Concerning the CO_2-Theory of Climatic Change," *Archiv für Meteorologie und Bioklimatologie*, Vol. 15, pp. 52-61.

Hammond, A. L., 1972, "Energy Options: Challenge for the Future," *Science*, Vol. 177, pp. 875-876.

Hare, F. K., 1965, "Energy Exchanges and the General Circulation," *Geography*, Vol. 50, pp. 229-241.

———, 1971, "Future Climates and Future Environments," *Bulletin of the American Meteorological Society*, Vol. 52, pp. 451-456.

Harrison, H., 1970, "Stratospheric Ozone with Added Water Vapor: Influence of High-Altitude Aircraft," *Science*, Vol. 170, pp. 734-736.

Heidel, K., 1972, "Turbidity Trends at Tucson, Arizona," *Science*, Vol. 177, pp. 882-883.

Heise, H. A. and E. R. Heise, 1957, "Effect of a City on the Fall-Out of Pollens and Molds," *Journal of the American Medical Association*, Vol. 163, pp. 803-804.

Huff, F. A. and S. A. Changnon, Jr., 1972, "Climatological Assessment of Urban Effects on Precipitation at St. Louis," *Journal of Applied Meteorology*, Vol. 11, pp. 823-842.

Jenkins, L., 1969, "Increases in Averages of Sunshine in Greater London," *Weather*, Vol. 24, pp. 52-54.

Johnston, H., 1971, "Reduction of Stratospheric Ozone by Nitrogen Oxide Catalysts from Supersonic Transport Exhaust," *Science*, Vol. 173, pp, 517-522.

Koide, M. and E. D. Goldberg, 1971, "Atmospheric Sulfur and Fossil Fuel Combustion," *Journal of Geophysical Research*, Vol. 76, pp. 6589-6596.

Lamb, H. H., 1971*a*, "Climate-Engineering Schemes to Meet a Climatic Emergency," *Earth-Science Reviews*, Vol. 7, pp. 87-95.

———, 1971*b*, "Volcanic Activity and Climate," *Palaeogeography, Palaeoclimatology, Palaeoecology*, Vol. 10, pp. 203-230.

Landsberg, H. E., 1970, "Climates and Urban Planning," in World Meteorological Organization, *Urban Climates*. Geneva: WMO, pp. 364-374.

———, 1971, *Man-Made Climatic Changes*. College Park, Md.: University of Maryland, Technical Note BN-705.

Landsberg, H. E. and T. N. Maisel, 1972, "Micrometeorological Observations in an Area of Urban Growth," *Boundary-Layer Meteorology*, Vol. 2, pp. 365-370.

Lettau, H. and K. Lettau, 1969, "Shortwave Radiation Climatonomy," *Tellus*, Vol. 21, pp. 208-222.

Lorenz, E. N., 1967, *The Nature and Theory of the General Circulation of the Atmosphere*. Geneva: World Meteorological Organization.

———, 1968, "Climatic Determinism," *Meteorological Monographs*, Vol. 8, No. 30, pp. 1-8.

Lovelock, J. E., 1971, "Air Pollution and Climatic Change," *Atmospheric Environment*, Vol. 5, pp. 403-411.

Lowry, W. P., 1967, "The Climate of Cities," *Scientific American*, Vol. 217, pp. 15-23.

Ludwig, J. H., G. B. Morgan and T. B. McMullen, 1970, "Trends in Urban Air Quality," *EOS, Transactions of the American Geophysical Union*, Vol. 51, pp. 468-475.

Machta, L. and E. Hughes, 1970, "Atmospheric Oxygen in 1967-1970," *Science*, Vol. 168, pp. 1582-1583.

Machta, L. and T. Carpenter, 1971, "Trends in High Cloudiness at Denver and Salt Lake City," in W. H. Matthews, W. W. Kellogg, and G. D. Robinson, (eds.), *Man's Impact on the Climate*. Cambridge, Mass.: MIT Press, pp. 410-415.

Manabe, S., 1969, "Climate and the Ocean Circulation: I. The Atmospheric Circulation and the Hydrology of the Earth's Surface, II. The Atmospheric Circulation and the Effect of Heat Transfer by Ocean Currents," *Monthly Weather Review*, Vol. 97, pp. 739-805.

Manabe, S., and R. T. Wetherald, 1967, "Thermal Equilibrium of the Atmosphere with a Given Distribution of Relative Humidity," *Journal of the Atmospheric Sciences*, Vol. 24, pp. 241-259.

Mateer, C. L., 1961, "Note on the Effect of the Weekly Cycle of Air Pollution on Solar Radiation at Toronto," *International Journal of Air and Water Pollution*, Vol. 4, pp. 52-54.

Matthews, W. H., W. W. Kellogg and G. D. Robinson (eds.), 1971, *Man's Impact on the Climate*. Cambridge, Mass.: MIT Press.

Maugh, T. H., 1972, "Carbon Monoxide: Natural Sources Dwarf Man's Output," *Science*, Vol. 177, pp. 338-339.

McBoyle, G. R., 1968, "A Review of Urban Climatology," *Earth Science Journal*, Vol. 2, pp. 88-95.

McCormick, R. A. and J. H. Ludwig, 1967, "Climate Modification by Atmospheric Aerosols," *Science*, Vol. 156, pp. 1358-1359.

Milankovitch, M., 1930, "Mathematische Klimalehre und Astronomische Theorie der Klimschwankungen," in W. Köppen and R. Geiger (eds.), *Handbuch der Klimatologie*. Berlin: Gebrüder Borntraeger, Band 1, Teil A.

Mitchell, Jr., J. M., 1962, "The Thermal Climate of Cities," *Symposium: Air Over Cities*, SEC Technical Report A62-5. Cincinnati: Taft Sanitary Engineering Center, pp. 131-145.

―――, 1970, "A Preliminary Evaluation of Atmospheric Pollution as a Cause of Global Temperature Fluctuation of the Past Century," in S. F. Singer (ed.), *Global Effects of Environmental Pollution*. New York and Dordrecht, Holland: Springer-Verlag and D. Reidel Publishing Co., pp. 140-155.

―――, 1971, "The Effect of Atmospheric Aerosols on Climate with Special Reference to Temperature near the Earth's Surface," *Journal of Applied Meteorology*, Vol. 10, pp. 703-714.

Möller, F., 1963, "On the Influence of Changes in the CO_2 Concentration in Air on the Radiation Balance of the Earth's Surface and on the Climate," *Journal of Geophysical Research*, Vol. 68, pp. 3877-3886.

Monteith, J. L., 1966, "Local Differences in the Attenuation of Solar Radiation over Britain," *Quarterly Journal of the Royal Meteorological Society*, Vol. 92, pp. 354-362.

Munn, R. E. and B. Bolin, 1971, "Global Air Pollution—Meteorological Aspects," *Atmospheric Environment*, Vol. 5, pp. 363-402.

Murcray, W. B., 1970, "On the Possibility of Weather Modification by Aircraft Contrails," *Monthly Weather Review*, Vol. 98, pp. 745-748.

Murgatroyd, R. J., 1969, "The Structure and Dynamics of the Stratosphere," in G. A. Corby (ed.), *The Global Circulation of the Atmosphere*. London: Royal Meteorological Society, pp. 159-195.

Myrup, L. O., 1969, "A Numerical Model of the Urban Heat Island," *Journal of Applied Meteorology*, Vol. 8, pp. 908-918.

―――, 1970, "Corrigendum," *Journal of Applied Meteorology*, Vol. 9, p. 541.

Nader, J. S., 1967, *Pilot Study of Ultraviolet Radiation in Los Angeles, October 1965*. Durham, N. C.: U.S. Department of Health, Education, and Welfare.

National Academy of Sciences—National Research Council, 1966, *Weather and Climate Modification—Problems and Prospects*, 2 vols., Publication No. 1350. Washington: Printing and Publishing Office, NAS.

Neiburger, M., 1971, "Implications on Intentional Weather and Climate Modification on the Human Environment," in World Meteorological Organization, *Special Environmental Report No. 2*, Selected Papers on Meteorology as Related to the Human Environment. Geneva: WMO, pp. 55-61.

Neumann, J. and A. Cohen, 1972, "Climatic Effects of Aerosol Layers in Relation to Solar Radiation," *Journal of Applied Meteorology*, Vol. 11, pp. 651-657.

Newell, R. E., D. G. Vincent, T. G. Dopplick, D. Ferruzza, and J. W. Kidson, 1969, "The Energy Balance of the Global Atmosphere," in G. A. Corby (ed.), *The Global Circulation of the Atmosphere*. London: Royal Meteorological Society, pp. 42-90.

Newell, R. E., 1971, "The Amazon Forest and Atmospheric General Circulation," in W. H. Matthews, W. W. Kellogg and D. G. Robinson (eds.), *Man's Impact on the Climate*. Cambridge, Mass.: MIT Press, pp. 457-459.

Oke, T. R. and C. East, 1971, "The Urban Boundary Layer in Montreal," *Boundary-Layer Meteorology*, Vol. 1, pp. 411-437.

Oke, T. R. and R. F. Fuggle, 1972, "Comparison of Urban/Rural Counter and Net Radiation at Night," *Boundary-Layer Meteorology*, Vol. 2, pp. 290-308.

Peterson, J. T., 1969, *The Climate of Cities: A Survey of Recent Literature*. Washington: Government Printing Office.

Peterson, J. T. and R. A. Bryson, 1968, "Atmospheric Aerosols: Increased Concentrations During the Last Decade," *Science*, Vol. 162, pp. 120-121.

Plass, G. N., 1959, "Carbon Dioxide and Climate," *Scientific American*, Vol. 201, pp. 41-47.

Rasool, S. I. and S. H. Schneider, 1971, "Atmospheric Carbon Dioxide and Aerosols: Effects of Large Increases on Global Climate," *Science*, Vol. 173, pp. 138-141.

Rayner, J. N., 1967, "A Statistical Model for the Explanatory Description of Large-Scale Time and Spatial Climate," *Canadian Geographer*, Vol. 11, pp. 67-86.

_____, 1972, *Conservation, Equilibrium, and Feedback Applied to Atmospheric and Fluvial Processes*, Commission on College Geography, Resource Paper No. 15. Washington, D.C.: Association of American Geographers.

Ryther, J. H., 1970, "Is the World's Oxygen Supply Threatened?" *Nature*, Vol. 227, pp. 374-375.

Schneider, S. H., 1971, "A Comment on 'Climate: The Influence of Aerosols,' " *Journal of Applied Meteorology*, Vol. 10, pp. 840-841.

Sellers, W. D., 1964, "The Energy Balance of the Atmosphere and Climatic Change," *Journal of Applied Meteorology*, Vol. 3, pp. 337-339.

_____, 1969, "A Global Climatic Model Based on the Energy Balance of the Earth-Atmosphere System," *Journal of Applied Meteorology*, Vol. 8, pp. 392-400.

Sewell, W. R. D., 1969, "Weather Modification: When Should We Do It and How Far Should We Go?" in R. G. Fleagle (ed.), *Weather Modification: Science and Public Policy*. Seattle: University of Washington Press, pp. 94-104.

Shaw, D. M. and W. L. Donn, 1968, "Milankovitch Radiation Variations: A Quantitative Evaluation," *Science*, Vol. 162, pp. 1270-1272.

Singer, S. F. (ed.), 1970, *Global Effects of Environmental Pollution*. New York and Dordrecht, Holland: Springer-Verlag and D. Reidel Publishing Co.

_____, 1971, "Stratospheric Water Vapour Increase due to Human Activities," *Nature*, Vol. 233, pp. 543-545.

Terjung, W. H., 1972, "Urban Climatology," in S. W. Tromp, (ed.), *Progress in Biometeorology*, Division A, Progress in Human Biometeorology, Part I. Amsterdam: Swets and Zeitlinger, forthcoming.

Terjung, W. H. and S. S-F. Louie, 1973, "Solar Radiation and Urban Heat Islands," *Annals of the Association of American Geographers*, Vol. 63, pp. 181-207.

Twomey, S. and T. A. Wojciechowski, 1969, "Observations of the Geographical Variation of Cloud Nuclei," *Journal of the Atmospheric Sciences*, Vol. 26, pp. 684-688.

U.S. Congress, 1966, *Weather Modification and Control*. Washington, D.C.: Government Printing Office.

Van Valin, C. C., 1971, *Effects on the Stratosphere of SST Operation*, NOAA Technical Report ERL 208-APCL 21. Washington, D.C.: Government Printing Office.

Washington, W. M., 1972, "Numerical Climatic-Change Experiment: The Effect of Man's Production of Thermal Energy," *Journal of Applied Meteorology*, Vol. 11, pp. 768-772.

Weinberg, A. M. and R. P. Hammond, 1970, "Limits to the Use of Energy," *American Scientist*, Vol. 58, pp. 412-418.

_____, 1971, "Global Effects on Increased Use of Energy," Paper presented before the Fourth International Conference on the Peaceful Uses of Atomic Energy, Geneva, September 7.

Weyl, P. K., 1968, "The Role of the Oceans in Climatic Change: A Theory of the Ice Ages," *Meteorological Monographs*, Vol. 8, No. 30, pp. 37-62.

Wilson, C. M. and W. H. Matthews, 1970, *Man's Impact on the Global Environment*. Cambridge, Mass.: MIT Press.

_____, 1971, *Inadvertent Climate Modification*. Cambridge, Mass.: MIT Press.

The Human Predator:
A Survey

Robin W. Doughty
University of Texas

An essay written the greater part of a century ago provides an interesting historical dimension to current concern and pessimism about man's impact upon wildlife. The account, related by the sportsman's weekly, *Forest and Stream* (17 September, 1885), prophesied the pauperization of wildlife in the United States. The story begins as an aging father takes his son on a river outing in the future year 1950. He points out scenes of devastation that his own generation has wrought upon the landscape and its wild creatures. Songbirds such as orioles have almost disappeared, consumed by the "stomachs of men and bonnets of women." Gourmets have "tickled their maws" with succulent buntings. "Skin hunters" have invaded all parts of the land, carrying away any bird of shapely form or handsome plumage. Wild game has been virtually hunted out. Raccoons and opossums have vanished. Mountains denuded of trees have been transformed into piles of rock "not giving so much as a home to the eagle." Marshland has been drained, and herons and kingfishers no longer frequent relict water bodies.

This sorry tale carries the tone of contemporary conservation parlance. There is today the same concern that by his unrestrained greed mankind has beggared the American scene. The modern news media have given electronic consecration to messages of environmental Jeremiahs who speak of the ultimate costs of overpopulation and of a polluted planet, yet the ecocrisis which these sooth-sayers depict cannot be dismissed as entirely illusory (O'Riordan: 1971; Opie: 1971; Rakestraw: 1972).

This chapter describes facets of a past and present concern for wildlife. Secondly, it exemplifies changes in the numbers and distributions of animal populations resulting from human actions. Such actions range from the direct killing of animals for subsistence and commercial purposes to the use of chemical pesticides that through diffusion and concentration in the environment may contribute indirectly to the destruction of wildlife. Innovations in com-munication, in travel, and in the multiplication and intensification of such networks, have similarly contributed to fluctuations in wildlife numbers. Indirect ways of bringing pressures to bear on animals and birds must also

152

include habitat alteration which has both created new niches for fauna and obliterated niches already in existence. A last means of affecting fauna, either by accident or by design, is the dissemination of agricultural crops and livestock, game and ornamental species, each with its peculiar complement of parasites, from one continent to another. Finally, this chapter notices actions taken to protect and rehabilitate a variety of wildlife.

It is recognized that mankind has altered the distribution and abundance of a large number of invertebrate phyla, particularly classes of insects, of crustacea (crabs, shrimps, and barnacles), and of mollusks (slugs and shellfish) (Bishop: 1951; Mead: 1961; Elton: 1958). However, due to limitations of space, most attention will be focussed upon the phylum of vertebrates (*Chordata*), notably placental mammals and birds. Invertebrates and micro-organisms fall largely beyond the scope of this essay, although geographers will be familiar with a treatment of invertebrates and micro-organisms as they pertain to human health (May: 1950, 1959, 1961; Zinsser: 1934; Dubos: 1968).

CURRENT ATTITUDES TOWARD WILDLIFE

In recent discussions about animals exploited for use in fashionable dress, history has repeated itself. In the first years of this century, a discussion about the propriety of wearing the nuptial garb of egrets, known as aigrettes, appeared in the pages of popular and scientific journals on both sides of the Atlantic. Scientists argued that many plumiferous birds were useful to agriculturalists and were integral to the balance of nature. In their arguments for bird protection, ornithologists and nature writers repeated cherished themes about man and birds and about man's duties to lower creatures. Other people, appalled by the cruel methods of killing birds and by the scale of wildlife destruction, appealed for laws to stamp out the feather trade (Welker: 1955; Nicholson: 1970; Doughty: 1972). Similar concerns have surfaced in the 1960's and organizations such as the Audubon Society, which were founded to promote bird protection and nature study, now focus public attention on threats to more exotic wildlife populations, for example, the decline in African and Asian leopard and cheetah populations and in Latin American jaguars and ocelots at the hands of skin-dealers (Regenstein: 1971; Buchheister and Graham: 1973). Some newspapers and fashion journals have argued recently that "leopard skin coats look better on leopards." The World Wildlife Fund, an organization founded in 1961 to promote wildlife protection, has discouraged numbers of "beautiful people" from donning apparel manufactured from skins of animals in short supply. However, it does not oppose fur products *per se* nor articles made up from fur-bearers bred in captivity for their pelts. The Fund has made awards to fashion houses unwilling to stock high-priced "spotted cat" products. It supported a Manhattan show entitled "No Skin Off Their Backs" to demonstrate to fashion interests that fake furs were chic and elegant. Furriers, as the feather merchants before them, have been contacted by international agencies such as the International Union for the Conservation of Nature and Natural Resources (IUCN) to place an embargo on trade in endangered species (Crimmins: 1970; King: 1971; Paradiso: 1972).

In a complementary vein, the clubbing of Canadian harp seal (*Pagophilus groenlandicus*) pups on ice floes in the Gulf of Saint Lawrence has brought the problem of cruelty to animals into the pages of coffee-table magazines and onto evening television screens. Investigations by groups committed to the prevention of cruelty to animals revealed that some newly born "white coat" seals have been skinned alive (Davies: 1970). Films of the annual Saint Lawrence seal hunt created an outcry in both Western Europe and the United States and stimulated demands for more humane methods of killing. This sensitivity to animal welfare evokes memories of Henry Bergh, founder of the American Society for the Prevention of Cruelty to Animals, who last century pioneered campaigns in this country against horse whipping and "sparrow" shoots (Turner: 1965).

Further sophistication in man's relationship to fauna is exemplified by federally sponsored research programs directed towards determining the economic and ecological value of eagles, coyotes and other predators to livestock operations (Leopold: 1964; Spofford: 1964; National Research Council: 1970). A recent report to the Council on Environmental Quality stated that "control decisions are still based on the assumption of benefit rather than on proof of need" (University of Michigan: 1972, p. 12). Most predator control programs, the report concluded, were based largely on subjective judgments as to the damage inflicted by wild animals. The Advisory Committee on Predator Control, which was responsible for this report, also criticized the methods of predator and rodent control, stating that there was overwhelming evidence that the widespread use of highly toxic chemical pesticides such as sodium fluoroacetate (1080), thallium and strychnine (sometimes applied to bait materials and indiscriminately broadcast from aircraft) in control programs resulted in frequent losses of non-target species through direct and secondary poisoning (see also Atzert: 1971). The committee recommended immediate congressional action to remove all existing toxic chemicals from registration and use in predator control programs. In an Executive Order issued in February 1972, President Nixon ordered a halt to the use of such poisons on federal lands while the Environmental Protection Agency has since prohibited the shipment of strychnine and 1080 in interstate commerce (Rathlesberger: 1972).

Customary distrust of carnivorous animals and birds, born out of entrenched prejudice against such "varmints," is being dispelled. Labels of "good" and "bad" animals are becoming redundant as urban dwellers seeking outdoor contacts find predators of aesthetic value and derive pleasure from hunting them with a camera as well as with a gun. More people in this country and in Europe are questioning the values of those who promote the wearing of expensive skins of endangered species. They are also voicing objections to inhumane and wasteful practices of killing wildlife to alleviate damage to crops and livestock and are prepared to categorize such killing as shortsighted, simplistic, perhaps cavalier. In this sense, western society is chipping away at compulsive anthropocentrism towards nature, albeit on a full stomach.

ENDANGERED WILDLIFE

A recurrent theme in the conservation movement is the considerable attention given to the plight of rare and endangered species. Some ecologists argue that we must protect wildlife gene-pools from becoming irrevocably lost because they may be needed to improve domestic stock. They point out that a multiplicity of species is integral to full community development and to the stability of ecosystems. Richness connotes structural stability, soundness of organization and increased system effectiveness through specialization, division of labor, and regulating pathways (Margalef: 1963; Odum: 1971). Other scientists will state that the idea of a balance in nature is a biological absurdity. From this viewpoint, conservationists who protest man's "destructive" practices, flout rules of change, adjustment and response governing every organisms's link with its environment. Constant flux, with extinction, constitutes the essence of nature. Organic diversity is molded by environmental selectivity. Accordingly, conservation remains an economic and moral imperative, not a biological truth (Fleischman: 1969).

Reflection upon the element of finality which characterizes the idea of extinction implies an irrevocable limitation in the gamut of experiences open to each individual. Nobody will ever again witness the spectacle of a passenger pigeon flight or be awed by the thunder of wings of this "biological storm" (Schorger: 1955).

Other experts point out that preserving the California condor (*Gymnogyps californianus*), or a wilderness area, provides us with a benchmark to our continuous rearrangement of nature—a biological record for further study (Allen: 1966; Houston: 1971). As Rush indicates, "When man obliterates wilderness, he repudiates the evolutionary force that put him on this planet. In a deeply terrifying sense, man is on his own" (McCloskey: 1972, p. 352). Attention is being given especially to wildlife, particularly endangered species, as indicators of environmental quality and of the effectiveness of resource management programs. The Smithsonian has recommended that certain species of fish, mammals, birds and plants be monitored regularly as indices of the health of the environment (Table 1).

Recreationists eager for novel experiences and vistas are captivated by the exotic qualities and appeal of a number of vanishing animals and birds and take pride from encounters with them. To have glimpsed the ivory-billed woodpecker (*Campephilus principalis*) is on a par with winning a trophy in a big game competition sponsored by the Boone and Crockett Club. More and more people are supporting efforts to protect big game in Africa and India simply for the satisfaction of knowing that they are there, not because they will ever see them. To brag about the killing of the last bear or deer in a township, reputedly a frontier attitude, is no longer perceived as an act of heroism (Yarborough: 1969). To those people with a craving for variety in nature, the impressive evolutionary history of wildlife guarantees them as much of a right to survival as man (Fosberg: 1966).

It should be noted, however, that the destruction and extinction of animals as a result of human actions has a long tradition. Paul Martin, for example, has produced evidence of a number of animal extinctions in prehistoric times that point to the substantial effects of late Pleistocene hunting groups upon megafauna (Martin and Wright: 1967). Habitat change through the conquest of fire lies at least fifty times further removed in prehistory. The possibility of a humanly induced "pleistocene overkill" illustrates the degree and the pace of faunal change under the hand of man. According to one estimate, over the past two millennia humans have exterminated at least three percent of the world's 4,000 species of aquatic and terrestrial mammals. Moreover, the tempo has quickened dramatically of late. Over half the total extinctions have occurred this century (Talbot: 1970; Fisher, Simon and Vincent: 1969).

Conservation-oriented societies are going to considerable lengths to document and to publicize the plight of dwindling fauna. With United Nations support, the IUCN in liaison with the International Council for Bird Preservation (founded in

TABLE 1—Indicator Species of Wildlife

Species:	Environmental aspects of which species is indicative
California condor	Aesthetic quality, endangered species management.
Golden eagle	Chemical contamination, aesthetic quality.
Bald eagle	Chemical contamination, aesthetic quality.
Osprey	Chemical contamination.
Herring gull	Chemical contamination, garbage and filth contamination.
Robin	Chemical contamination, aesthetic quality.
Bluebird	Aesthetic quality.
Cardinal	Aesthetic quality.
Mockingbird	Aesthetic quality.
Starling	Garbage and filth contamination, crop damage, urban degradation.
Red-winged blackbird	Crop damage.
Cowbird	Crop damage.
Common grackle	Crop damage.
Domestic pigeon	Garbage and filth contamination, urban degradation.
Mallard duck	Recreation, wildlife management effectiveness.
Redhead duck	Recreation, wildlife management effectiveness.
Canvasback duck	Recreation, wildlife management effectiveness.
Canada goose	Recreation, wildlife management effectiveness.
Mourning dove	Chemical contamination, recreation, wildlife management effectiveness.
Woodcock	Chemical contamination, recreation, wildlife management effectiveness.
Polar bear	Aesthetic quality, endangered species management.
Norway rat	Garbage and filth contamination, crop damage, urban degradation.
Cave bats	Chemical contamination.
Prong horned antelope	Aesthetic quality, recreation, wildlife management.
Northern fur seal	Wildlife management effectiveness, endangered species management.
Sea otter	Aesthetic quality, wildlife management effectiveness.
Beaver	Aesthetic quality, wildlife management effectiveness.
Alligator	Aesthetic quality, endangered species management.

Source: Smithsonian Institution, 1972, *Development of a Continuing Program to Provide Indicators and Indices of Wildlife and the Natural Environment*, Washington, D.C.

1922) works through six commissions to compile information about the human exploitation of resources, particularly of rare and endangered creatures (Table 2). The five volume IUCN *Red Data Book* is a catchall for information about threatened fauna. In 1971, it listed in its pages 376 species or subspecies of birds and nearly eight percent of the world's mammals. Current entries include reptiles, amphibians, flowering plants, and fishes. More species are being added to the *Red Data Book* as information about them expands. At present 1,000 mammals and birds, 170 reptiles and amphibians, and 60 fish are to be found in the IUCN publication.

Thirteen of the 19 orders of mammals have at least one representative officially recognized as endangered in some area of the world. Clusters of certain animals occur. Forty marsupials in Australia, 24 primates in the Malagasy Republic, and 17 rodents in North America are threatened by hunting, collecting, and habitat alteration. The sweep of land and water of the Palaearctic and Oriental regions hold endangered felids such as the clouded leopard (*Neofelis nebulosa*), Asiatic lion (*Panthera leo persica*) and Bengal tiger (*Panthera t. tigris*). Africa, south of the Sahara, contains depleted numbers of primates, including lemurs (Lemuridae), Colobus monkeys (*Colobus* spp.) and the mountain gorilla (*Gorilla gorilla beringei*). South America's only bruin, the spectacled bear

TABLE 2—International Union for the Conservation of Nature
Classification of Rare and Endangered Species

Category 1	*Endangered*	In immediate danger of extinction; continued survival unlikely without the implementation of special protective measures.
Category 2	*Rare*	Not under immediate threat of extinction, but occurring in such small numbers and/or in such a restricted or specialized habitat that it could quickly disappear. Requires careful watching. [Note: this does not include the large number of forms which, for the reasons given in the Introduction, have been placed on the Supplementary List.]
Category 3	*Depleted*	Although still occurring in numbers adequate for survival, the species has been heavily depleted and continues to decline at a rate which gives cause for serious concern.
Category 4	*Indeterminate*	Apparently in danger, but insufficient data currently available on which to base a reliable assessment of states. Needs further study.

(*Tremarctos ornatus*) is now becoming largely restricted to Ecuador and northern Peru. In sum, the future survival of more than 300 species and subspecies of mammals is in doubt (Fitter: 1968).

The United States enjoys the dubious distinction of having 15 percent of its 395 native mammals listed in its own *Red Book of Rare and Endangered Fish and Wildlife of the United States*. Personnel in the Department of the Interior's Office of Endangered Species believe that 14 mammals, seven reptiles and amphibians, 30 fishes and 50 birds are endangered. All entries are open to constant review and changes have occurred in lists of animals. Compared with 1966, for example, the 1968 edition of the *Red Book* dropped two birds from its listings, added ten others, changed the status of two more from rare to endangered and added to that class three others which had previously been thought extinct (U.S. Department of the Interior: 1966).

WILDLIFE FLUCTUATIONS AS A RESULT OF KILLING FOR SUBSISTENCE AND COMMERCIAL PURPOSES

The path to the brink of oblivion has broadened with pressures from both an increase in the numbers of people and innovations in technology. Hunting for purposes of subsistence, sport, commerce and collection, has led to the demise in the last 150 years of more bird species in North America than on any other similar-sized landmass (Greenway: 1958). Specialized creatures such as the flightless great auk (*Pinguinus impennis*), found on offshore islets of the North Atlantic seaboard, the enormously gregarious passenger pigeon (*Ectopistes migratorius*), itinerant bird of eastern and central states, and the conspicuous Carolina parakeet (*Conuropsis carolinensis*) of southern hardwood forests, fell to our grandparents' clubs, nets and guns. A swiftly-flying shorebird, the eskimo curlew (*Numenius borealis*), hovered about wounded members of its flocks and was shot by the cartload on Kansas prairies during spring migration in the 1880's. A non-breeding migrant in this country, the bird avoids an extinct label due to occasional sightings of solitary individuals about Galveston, Texas, in spring. Plovers, godwits, sandpipers, and an assortment of waterfowl and upland game birds, shot by market hunters and nimrods, hung from meatvending stalls and graced family tables in cities from Chicago to Boston in the 1880's and 1890's (Parmalee: 1969; Mackey: 1965; Matthiessen: 1959; Trefethen: 1961).

At that time expressions of outrage about the parlous state of wildlife on both sides of the Atlantic rang from the pages of sportsmen's journals, scientific periodicals and the daily press. George P. Marsh believed that destruction of wildlife in Western Europe was, in part, a consequence of the overturning of restrictive game laws, particularly in France. He cited Arthur Young's story written in 1789, that "every rusty firelock in all Provence was at work in the indiscriminate destruction of all the birds" (Marsh: 1864, p. 91).

In the United States, numbers had been declining for a long time. In 1898, William T. Hornaday, ardent preservationist, calculated that over the previous 15 years bird life in 30 states had decreased by an average 43 percent. He launched a hard-hitting campaign for insectivorous birds, deer, elk, and antelope. He ridiculed "sportsmen" who were photographed amid spoils of their marksmanship and backed federal legislation to outlaw the possession and transportation of wildlife for commercial purposes. Boys who collected eggs and shot small birds did not escape the wrath of this energetic and outspoken protagonist of dwindling fauna (Hornaday: 1898, 1913, 1931; Clepper: 1971, p. 171).

Joel Asaph Allen, ornithologist and conservationist, recognized too that declines in the abundance of wildlife in the United States had been spectacular. "The wave of destruction, which of late years has moved on in ever-increasing volume, has at last reached its limit of extension," he declared (in 1886) and predicted that vigorous enforcement of existing laws for wildlife would be complemented by federal action once society realized the value and significance of birds and animals (Allen: 1886, p. 191; 1876). The destruction of scores of different birds for food, millinery, sport, and scientific purposes received a deluge of criticism at this time (Brewer: 1869; Flagg: 1875; Drury, Fisher et al.: 1886; Shufeldt: 1887; Abbott: 1895; Oldys: 1902). Allen and a number of others, among whom were nature writers such as John Burroughs and Neltje Blanchan and scientists such as William Brewster and Frank M. Chapman, worked in professional and popular circles to promote appreciation for wildlife, especially for song and insectivorous birds (Chapman: 1933; Pearson: 1933, 1937; Schmitt: 1969; Clepper: 1971; Hicks: 1924).

The fortunes of professional killers of waterfowl and upland game birds followed buffalo and hide hunters. Wildlife carnage in the final quarter of the last century proved irrefutably that ducks, geese, rails and grouse had finite numbers. It took breech-loading shotguns, repeating and automatic weapons in the hands of shore gunners and "game hogs" to prove that massive kills of these birds would be short-lived. However, commercial interests and the belief of hunters in "the existence far north of our borders of a sort of mysterious duck and snipe factory which could turn out the required supply practically forever" (Phillips: 1934, p. 5), hampered legislation in this country until the second decade of the twentieth century when Congress moved to protect game, song and insectivorous species (Lawyer: 1918; Hayden: 1942; Leedy: 1961).

In an extensive work on bird extinction, James C. Greenway, ornithologist of the American Museum of Natural History, has compiled a record of declines for North America paralleled only by vulnerable avifauna of islands (Greenway: 1958). Indigenous creatures of coral atolls have been similarly hard hit over the past two centuries. Early this century, plume hunters and egg gatherers decimated seabirds on Pacific Islands to equal and surpass exploits on the mainland of North America. As a consequence of the abandonment of these activities in the past half century, however, native fauna has made a slow comeback. The diminutive duck (Anas laysanensis) of Laysan Island has recovered substantially in the last twenty years, as has a shorebird, the hudsonian godwit (Limosa haemastica) which survived remorseless shooting early this century along the central and eastern flyways of the United States. A tiny population of short-tailed albatrosses (Diomedea albatrus) on Japan's Torishima Island has survived catastrophic raids on its nesting colonies. The present population is similar in numbers to the sixty whooping cranes (Grus americana) in North America which are also staging a comeback (Figure 1). These large cranes have built up their numbers in the isolated Sass River region of the Canadian north, and undertake a hazardous 2,500 mile annual migration to wintering grounds on the Blackjack Peninsula near Rockport, Texas (Ziswiler: 1967; Fisher, Simon and Vincent: 1969; Sanger: 1972).

Marine fauna have been subjected to great pressure from commercial enterprises. Maritime nations have depleted stocks of fish and sea mammals at an unprecedented rate (Bardach: 1968; United States House of Representatives:

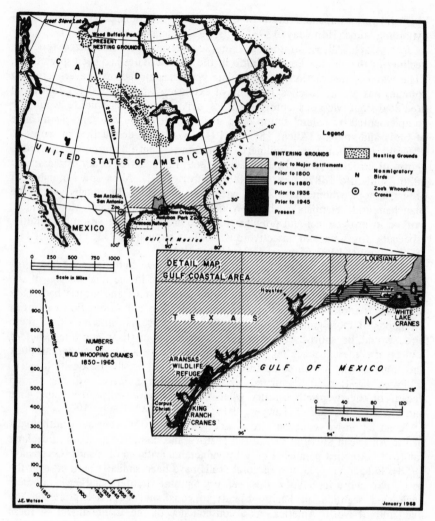

Figure 1. Whooping Crane Distribution, 1800 to Present. Data from Allen: 1952; McNulty: 1966.

1971). The Pacific sardine (*Sardinops caerulea*) fishery was ruined in North America by the late 1940's through poor management. Overfishing with the numbers removed from the total stock exceeding the rate of replacement now threatens the future of the North Sea herring (*Clupea harengus*) industry. Very recently the Atlantic salmon (*Salmo salar*) has suffered a catastrophic decline in numbers due to commercial operations in its feeding grounds off southwest Greenland (Ricker: 1969; Graham: 1956; Dorst: 1970).

The story of cetaceans provides interesting documentation of direct and exploitative use. George Small has noted that accurate information governing the life history of blue whales (*Balaenoptera musculus*) was assembled only after the bulk of the species had vanished and was no longer commercially viable (Small: 1971). Limits on catches were proposed as early as 1931 during the League of

Nations Convention for the Regulation of Whaling, but the International Whaling Commission (established in 1946) has been ineffective in enforcing internationally agreed upon limits. Again, the expression of overall limits in terms of "Blue whale units" (1 blue = 2 fin = 6 sei) encouraged whaling nations to concentrate for simple economic reasons on the larger blue whales. As a result, the blue whale is nearly extinct despite the fact that the symptoms of overhunting, including a diminishing catch per unit effort and a decrease in the size and percentage of pregnant females taken, were clearly evident to the regulatory agency (Ehrenfeld: 1970; McVay: 1966, 1973).

Whales and fishes have been subjected to innovations in technology that have produced larger and speedier catches; so, too, have terrestrial organisms. Innovations in transportation, communication, and in ways of spending leisure time directly affect fauna. The use of the internal combustion engine has opened up previously remote and inaccessible areas. Machines carry more people into back country every year. Hunting from maneuverable and high-speed vehicles has brought about declines in several animal populations. The Arabian oryx (*Oryx leucoryx*), for example, ranged throughout much of Saudi Arabia until unrestricted use of firearms coupled with their use from automobiles, brought about the disappearance of this desert ungulate from most parts of its range. At times scores of cars, trucks, and jeeps have moved in concert to hunt desert fauna (Talbot: 1960).

In an equally extreme environment, the Arctic wilderness, until recently more than one thousand polar bears (*Thalarctos maritimus*) annually became trophies of wealthy sportsmen who hunt by airplane. Flying in tandem, pilots in two aircraft locate and follow bear tracks on sea ice in Alaska and elsewhere. When a beast is discovered and a hunter landed in a favorable position, the second plane can herd the animal towards the hunter (IUCN: 1970; Klein: 1972).

WILDLIFE DECLINE THROUGH INDIRECT MEANS

The technological revolution of the twentieth century has not only provided us with more efficient means of hunting wildlife, but together with the pressures generated by population growth, by land clearance and urbanization, and by changes in recreational activities, has contributed to changes in the nature and quality of habitats and thereby, indirectly, to wildlife decline.

Vehicle speed, noise and mobility upset remote and sensitive wildlife populations. Recent proliferation of snowmobiles in off-road areas of midwestern states has led to reports of deer, coyotes, and foxes being hounded to death. All-terrain vehicles have become a novel stress factor to these animals at a difficult time in their seasonal cycle. Users of trail bikes and dune buggies may unwittingly disturb eagle eyries and beach nesting terns, while opportunities for vandalism abound (Baldwin: 1970; Hickey: 1969, pp. 350, 493-95). Federal Aviation Agency officials and federal biologists have long been aware that birds pose hazards to aircraft and airport facilities but the threat has been reinforced by the advent of high-speed, jet-powered airplanes. Jet engines can ingest flocks of gulls, shorebirds, starlings, swallows, and other birds, especially on take-off or landing. Most bird strikes to USAF planes in 1971, for example, occurred below 2,000 feet and showed an increase over previous years. An estimate of over a thousand bird strikes to USAF equipment per year must be multiplied many times when calculations are made for civil carriers and privately owned aircraft (United States Air Force: 1972; Murton and Wright: 1968).

Casualties from automobile and railroad operations exceed aircraft strikes. One study in the United Kingdom suggests that every year two and a half million birds became traffic victims on British roads. Eighty-eight species of birds have been identified in roadside collisions. Fledglings and adult birds nesting beside roads are frequently killed by automobiles. However, only one species, the English sparrow (*Passer domesticus*), suffered enough fatalities for collision with vehicles to be a significant mortality factor (Hodson and Snow: 1965).

High buildings, towers, radio beacons and lighthouses are other indirect ways affecting the abundance of fauna. In the first edition of *Man and Nature* (1864), George P. Marsh noted the negative effects of such "new circumstances" as a lighthouse on Cape Cod which cut down birds passing in the night. The problem of migrant warblers "piling up" about dazzling beacons in the manner of moths has become exacerbated during this century with the massive growth of communications systems. The problem of large numbers of birds killed about lighthouses was tackled at the turn of the century when authorities in Europe constructed perches and platforms upon which disoriented nocturnal migrants could rest without dropping into the sea or succumbing to ground scavengers (Royal Society for the Protection of Birds: 1913). The Empire State Building and Washington Monument take a toll of species following the Atlantic flyway each year. Florida towers, however, cause injury and death to larger numbers of migrants. One study reported kills of 15,000 individual birds of about 150 species in six years ending 1961. Spectacular losses continue to occur elsewhere. A ceilometer on an Air Force Base in Macon, Georgia, apparently destroyed 50,000 birds in October, 1954 (Howell *et al*: 1954). Another 10,000 small birds piled into a high tower at Eau Claire, Wisconsin, on two nights in September, 1963 (Drury: 1966). On Midway Island in the Pacific, a "hot spot" in the early 1960's for bird collisions, the military base and airfield occupy a traditional nesting ground of albatrosses. In the past, aircraft collided with birds almost daily, entailing costly repairs and endangering lives of crew members. Station personnel have killed several thousand birds (11,000 in 1957 and 1958) in an effort to reduce the hazard problem. They have experimented with noise and odor producing devices as bird scarers. No measures have been particularly successful. Extensive bulldozing operations to flatten dunes in order to make them less attractive for nesting and soaring birds have proven most effective (Robbins: 1966; Fisher: 1966).

"Wirescapes," tall buildings, and towers can become to birds what dams, locks, canals and irrigation ditches are to the passage of fish. Schemes to extend irrigated cropland, to provide energy and recreational facilities to metropolitan areas, and to facilitate the flow of goods can alter, sometimes almost overnight, the complexion of aquatic communities in an area. The California Water Plan, for example, has become a politically charged and acrimonious conservation issue over the past decade. Opponents of this engineering accomplishment point out that canalization and the impoundment of rivers in Northern California will result in a general deterioration in quality and quantity of water which flows into the Sacramento-San Joaquin delta. Such projects increase incursions of saline water upstream and could nullify plans to conserve runs of anadromous shad (*Alosa sapidissima*), steelhead trout (*Salmo gairdnerii gairdnerii*), and king salmon (*Oncorhynchus tshawytscha*), already reduced in numbers along the

Pacific Coast (Dasmann: 1965; Stead: 1968; California, Department of Fish and Game: 1966, 1967; Crutchfield and Pontecorvo: 1969).

The Welland Canal, linking Lakes Ontario and Erie, opened up the Midwest heartland to settlement and trade. The Canal bypassed the Niagara Falls, a barrier to fish migration, and provided a means, albeit a difficult one, for two species, the sea lamprey (*Petromyzon marinus*) and alewife (*Alosa pseudoharengus*), to pass from Lake Ontario to progressively colonize lakes to the west. Both fish had become abundant in Lakes Huron and Michigan in the 1950's and 1960's and have significantly impoverished local fisheries (Smith: 1968). Fishes, crustaceans and mollusks have spread with the construction of the Panama Canal, so have grassland species and those favoring second growth vegetation along its banks. They can be expected to proliferate as work continues on and about the Panama Canal, and upon its equivalent in the Old World, the Suez Canal (Rubinoff and Rubinoff: 1968; Rubinoff: 1968; Briggs: 1969; Bennett: 1968; Ben-Tuvia: 1966).

The topic of habitat change is also crucial to the theme of man's impact on fauna by indirect means. Through forest clearance, land drainage schemes, the creation of pastures for domesticated animals, agriculturalists, and others have created new niches for birds and animals. Even the expanding urban and suburban environment has provided a new habitat for certain adaptable species as discussed by James Schmid elsewhere in this volume. Human activities have therefore favored the expansion of range of some creatures and hastened the contraction in range of others (Allee and Schmidt: 1951).

Small birds in particular, are mobile, adaptable, and able to seek out suitable niches as they become available (Moreau: 1961). A diminutive member of the wood warblers (*Parulidae*), Kirtland's warbler (*Dendroica kirtlandii*), discovered breeding in Peninsula Michigan in 1903, provides an excellent illustration of the impact of human induced habitat change on the range and numbers of particular species. The warbler nests in thickets of fire-adapted Jack Pine which were spread last century by logging operations and forest fires. This summer migrant continues to inhabit stands of young pine trees with open space nearby. State officials have conducted prescribed burns in recent years to insure that requisite habitat is available to the warbler. Reproduction has declined, however, due to parasitism from cowbirds (*Molothrus ater*) which have spread into the warbler's range as a result of expansion of fields and pastures. The number of singing male warblers has dropped 60 percent in the past decade. Conditions that man prompted in the past by clearance and fire and promotes today by prescribed burns are being nullified by humanly induced interspecific competition. The cowbird is likely to cost Kirtland's warbler a place in posterity (Mayfield: 1960, 1963, 1972).

The abundance of fish and game cheered immigrants and adventurers to America's eastern shores. Several commentators apparently enjoyed the sight of skies blackened by wildfowl but were disturbed by seemingly endless vistas of forests and mountains and by a desolation of a wilderness so unlike and so far removed from England's tamer shires. Colonists set about altering the land with religious fervor and zeal born of daily need. They planted natural openings and fields abandoned by Indians. They grew maize and imported cereals, grasses, and fodder crops. They set in motion a process of landscape change that has had enduring effects on native wildlife. Removal of trees by girdling, felling, burning and rooting, created clearings for field animals. Splitting rails for fences, digging ditches to relieve the soil of moisture, turning the sod, and hoeing and weeding grains and vegetables, were marks of good husbandry (Nash: 1967; Huth: 1957; Graham: 1947).

Forest clearance and the development of open landscapes, as the assault on European woodlands before it, benefited seed and insect-eating birds and browsing animals at the expense of arboreal creatures and others intolerant of human disturbance or perceived as a threat to civilization. The timber wolf (*Canis lupus*), cougar (*Felis concolor*), beaver (*Castor canadensis*), marten (*Martes americana*), bison (*Bison bison*), elk (*Cervus canadensis*), and moose (*Alces alces*) had been banished by the plough, axe, rifle, and trap from eastern states by the mid-nineteenth century. Blackbirds and orioles (Icteridae), flycatchers (Tyrannidae), raccoons (*Procyon lotor*) and the red fox (*Vulpes fulva*) adapted well to human settlement as dense stands of oak, hickory, walnut, and pines became beams, posts, wagons, and agricultural implements (Allen: 1962; Graham: 1947; Gabrielson: 1959; Matthiessen: 1959).

Mechanized and highly intensive methods of crop production characteristic of recent trends in agriculture have enlarged the average size of fields with a resultant loss of vegetation along fence rows preferred by cottontails and quail. Since 1950, however, farmers have achieved increased yields despite an overall decline (of 34 million acres) in the area under cultivation. Marginal land has been returned to woodland to which creatures adapted to forest succession have responded. The white-tailed deer (*Odocoileus virginianus*) hard hit by logging, forest fires, and meat and hide hunters, has made a spectacular comeback from an estimated low of 300,000 in the United States and Canada in 1890. In the late 1960's hunters culled one and a half million whitetails in this country, barely 20 percent of the total population. Tighter game laws, restoration programs, but especially fire suppression and marginal farmland turned back to woodland, have made this recovery possible (Trefethen: 1970; Hosley: 1968). Farmers continue to reclaim alluvial soils capable of sustaining high crop yields. At least one-third of all natural wetlands in the 48 contiguous states have been drained for agricultural purposes, while a further half million acres of estuarine habitat have been developed in the past two decades. Species which are unable to adjust to such drainage and fill schemes, or forestry practices of clear-cutting and replanting with even age "super trees," have been labeled "relict." Woodpeckers (the ivory-billed and red-cockaded [*Dendrocopos borealis*]), alligators, some raptors and marsh birds, the manatee (*Trichechus manatus*), and the Texas red wolf (*Canis rufus*) surviving only in the Big Thicket, fall into this category (National Research Council: 1970; Lay and Russell: 1970; Paradiso and Nowak: 1971; Stieglitz and Thompson: 1967).

Changes in land use elsewhere, especially in tropical countries continue to have dramatic effects on fauna. Energetic forest clearance and the formation of "artificial pastures" planted to African grasses (Parsons: 1970, 1972) continue to cause serious disruptions to endemic species of birds and mammals in tropical America. Central America is biologically wealthy, yet now the less desirable, more remote wet and rain forest life zones are being subjected to increasing disturbance. Viewed largely as a function of population pressure, experts predict that the natural vegetation and resident avifauna of northern Latin America will soon be seriously threatened (Bennett: 1968; Corzo: 1970; Daugherty: 1972; Holdridge: 1970).

To the south, Chile, Argentina, and Brazil have a history of timberlands set ablaze almost annually. Locomotives, metal smelting, charcoal, and domestic fuel needs chip away at Brazilian forests. In the state of Parana, half the area under Araucaria woodland has been cleared and the rate of tree removal is quickening. This type of habitat change affects a broad spectrum of forest creatures. Moreover, areas opened up by the Belem-Brasilia highway and the Trans-Amazonian road (under construction) permit an influx of agriculturalists, hunters, and collectors who make short work of animals useful for their pelts, meat, and aesthetic qualities (Sternberg: 1968; Johnson: 1972).

The shrinkage of wetlands in Europe, oil operations on Alaska's North Slope, man-made lakes in Africa, the California water plan, tourism to the Galapagos and Antarctica, and London's third airport, are tributes to the energy, skill, and resourcefulness of Western culture. However, conservation professionals view with misgiving the disruptions to the land and wildlife that accompany them.

Some species, however, have taken advantage of dramatic changes in habitat attendant upon advances in technology (Figures 2 and 3). The fulmar (*Fulmarus*

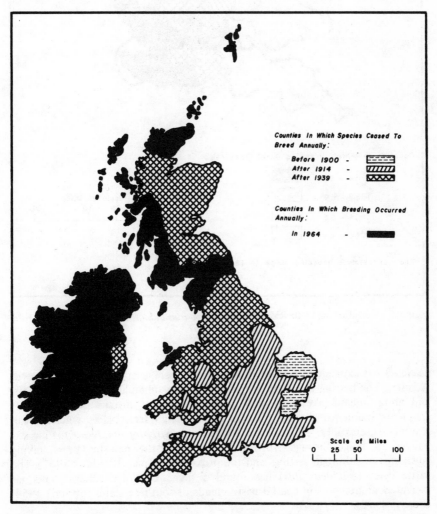

Figure 2. Contraction of the Range of the Corncrake (*Crex crex*) in the British Isles. Adapted from Parslow: 1967.

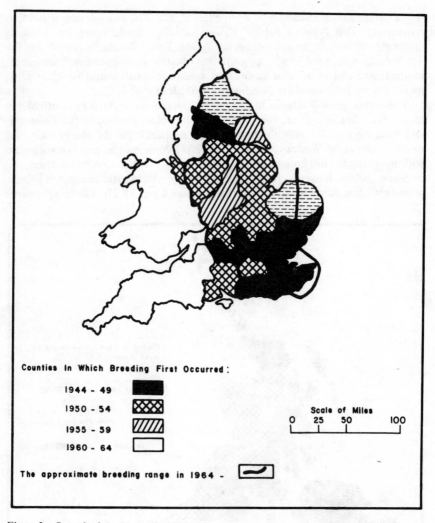

Figure 3.   Spread of the Little Ringed Plover (*Charadrius dubius*) in England. Adapted from Parslow: 1967.

glacialis) has expanded its range in response to fishing procedures in the North Atlantic. The herring gull (*Larus argentatus*) nests on buildings, on inland cliffs, and about inland lakes in several counties of Great Britain and Ireland. It frequents municipal dumps, harbors and fishing piers, places where it can scavenge successfully. The collared turtle dove (*Streptopelia decaocto*) has expanded its range through Northwest Europe in the past ten years, taking advantage of suburban settings and the proximity of man (Parslow: 1967). The cattle egret (*Bubulcus ibis*) has found a niche in North America and has increased its numbers in coastal pasturelands of southern states (Sprunt: 1954; Crosby: 1972).

On the other hand, certain industrial practices give little or no room for wildlife adaptation or adjustment. The trend in numbers of pelagic seabirds, namely alcids, is particularly poignant. The fate of many breeding colonies of holarctic murres (or guillemots), puffins, and razorbills, highly vulnerable to oil spills in coastal waters and deep-sea shipping lanes, is in balance. Estimates of 100,000 auks and other seabirds lost to oil contamination off the British Isles in the winter of 1951-52 are matched by the estimates of 30,000 birds killed following the wreck of the tanker *Torrey Canyon* in March, 1967 (Smith: 1968; Beer: 1968). Alcids have a low rate of replacement. Other diving species such as loons, cormorants, grebes, and sea ducks, which pass much time in coastal waters, are also particularly hard hit by oil spills and have a low survival rate even if cleansed and cared for through a molt state (Aldrich: 1970; Holcomb: 1969; Holmes: 1969).

Joel Allen was aware of the hazards of telegraph wires to birds migrating at night in the 1890's; naturally, he could not foresee the effects of the cargo of chemical pesticides unleashed on the environment since World War II. As described elsewhere in this volume by Manners, seabirds, raptors, and mammals at the tops of food chains have been particularly hard hit. Eggshell thinning and reproductive failures ascribed to persistent pesticides have resulted in a collapse of numbers of brown pelicans (*Pelecanus occidentalis*) along the Gulf Coast and threaten the Pacific Coast populations (Keith, Woods, and Hunt: 1970). Waterfowl are poisoned from lead which they pick up during feeding about ponds and sloughs where spent shot has accumulated. Recognition of the phenomenon of lead poisoning is more than a century old, but conditions have deteriorated with an increase in hunting activity and a decrease in wetlands. The Planning Committee of the Mississippi Flyway Council reported (in 1964) that lead ingestion "kills more mallards than are being produced on all our management areas," and concluded that lead ingestion is a serious problem, accounting for the death of hundreds of thousands of ducks, geese, and swans per year in North America (Mississippi Flyway Council: 1964, p. 14; Bellrose: 1959). Botulism is another agent most destructive to waterfowl and shorebirds crowded into wetland habitats while on spring migration in western states (Kalmbach: 1968; Hunter: 1970).

By his constant shuffling of organisms in space and time mankind has encouraged or permitted certain creatures to dwell in his presence. However, the introduction both deliberately and inadvertently of alien species into new habitats can have unforeseen repercussions. The English sparrow is an outstanding case of a bird introduced into North America through misguided zeal clouded with sentiment and backed by a poor understanding of the bird's life history. With a certain pageantry and promises of what it could do for horticulturalists, hundreds of sparrows were released in different urban places between 1852 and 1869. By the 1880's the bird had become a menace to other denizens of home and garden. It proved quarrelsome and noisy. With its "ruffian ways" it ousted wrens, swallows and bluebirds from cavities suitable for nesting. Its predilection for grain helped little to abate the "insect nuisance" it was supposed to eradicate (Barrows: 1889). Other exotic birds followed the sparrow into the United States. Larks never did very well, other "minstrels of the year" such as thrushes, finches and the nightingale (*Luscinia megarhynchos*) disappeared after a season or two. The European starling (*Sturnus vulgaris*) however, did as well as the sparrow and has become a bane to feedlot operations in the mid-west and western states.

In his classic work on the introduction of plants and animals, Charles Elton discussed in detail the fate of fauna subjected to disease, competition and predation from introduced birds and animals. New Zealand, he recognized, as containing 29 "problem animals" introduced through European colonization, while populations of 23 species of alien insects had become well established in the two decades ending 1949 (Elton: 1958; Howard: 1967). In a similar way, Hawaii has become a "melting pot" for organisms carried there through European contacts with little regulation and selectivity. Approximately 420 insects are considered indigenous to the chain of islands and perhaps one-third of the native species have disappeared. At least 76 species of game birds and another 60 non-game species are known to have been introduced by 1967. The unique forest birds (the Drepaniidae) have been largely destroyed, in part by Asian malaria whose mosquito vector was introduced to Maui in 1826 (Warner: 1968). Europeans brought in big game animals such as the axis deer (*Axis axis*) from India, blacktailed deer (*Odocoileus hemionus columbianus*), and pronghorn antelope (*Antilocapra americana*) from North America, the feral goat (*Capra hircus*), and mouflon sheep (*Ovis musimon*), since the eighteenth century. A further animal not currently open to hunting, is the Australian brush-tailed rock wallaby (*Petrogale pencillata*) first introduced in 1916 (Berger: 1972; Walker: 1967).

Since Colonial times the United States has been used to test thousands of animals from abroad (Phillips: 1928; Gottschalk: 1967). California and Texas compare with Hawaii in species and numbers of exotics established within their confines. Texas has 13 ungulates of African and Asian origin which total 30,000 individuals distributed in approximately 50 counties (Craighead and Dasmann: 1966; Ramsey: 1968*a*). There are more species of game animals in the Longhorn State in greater numbers than anywhere in North America (Ramsey: 1968*b*).

Modern man, by moving wildlife from place to place, is breaking down the concept of distinct "Faunal Realms," patterns of wildlife distribution which have evolved through geological time. The six faunal realms, developed in the nineteenth century by Alfred R. Wallace, naturalist and explorer, have been likened to great tanks of different chemical mixtures. According to Charles Elton (1958, p. 51) each tank is connected to another by narrow tubes controlled by taps.

> The tanks are the continents, the tubes represent human transport along the lines of commerce; but it has not proved possible to turn off the taps completely, even though we might often wish to do so. And although there is a Law of the Conservation of Matter, there is no Law of the Conservation of Species.

The rate of intermingling of fauna from one continent to another has increased dramatically over the past century. Man has broken down the barriers of isolation and has altered the process of selection in dissimilar environments upon which the nature of each realm was founded, thereby enabling species to spread to limits set only by their genetic characteristics. Highly adaptable and dispersive forms spread, perhaps at the expense of more specialized organisms. Worldwide, the diversity of species is thereby reduced.

WILDLIFE IN THE 1970's

The values that society attributes to wildlife will determine the status of animals in decades to come. Cave paintings by late paleolithic hunters indicate that they prized the physical qualities of animals and attempted to capture their spirit on wall motifs. We continue to admire the strength, endurance, agility and graceful movements of wild beasts. We fear the leopard's stealth, the buffalo's unpredictability, and the wolf's howl. We are intrigued by the homing instincts of birds and the mystery of their migrations. We hold animals in pastures to feed us, we make pets of them, and place them in menageries for curiosity and amusement. We tell tales about birds and beasts to our children. Everyday metaphors remind us of their "virtues," while folktales and allegories are full of lessons from the animal kingdom.

Tied by affection to wild creatures, we regard fauna as important in the myths, superstitions, symbols and ornaments that our culture has created; they are important enough for scientists, writers, and prominent people to have reminded us of our duties to the natural order of things in the first conservation rumblings last century. They argued for care in the disposal of resources and especially for the avoidance of any irrevocable loss of wildlife. Organizations founded to popularize bird study, to protect dwindling game, and to end the callous treatment of household animals, made a basic plea for the importance of wildlife to society. People argued that wild birds and mammals had inspired us to celebrate in song, painting, and prose the beauties of creation. Animals had instructed us about the secrets of nature and about ourselves. The Appendix at the end of this chapter documents important events and legislation affecting wildlife conservation in the United States and reflects the changes in attitude towards wildlife that have occurred in the last century.

The first American conservation movement which placed constraints on exploitation and set up a system of reserves for wildlife restoration became tied to carefully conceived management techniques. Fauna was perceived as not merely something to be saved but as a renewable resource to be harvested with care and selectivity. Game-cropping schemes in southern and eastern Africa have demonstrated that many ungulates contain higher proportions of protein than cattle. Such beasts thrive in places unsuitable to European livestock, and are resistant to endemic diseases. Wild ungulates spread the grazing load over the whole plant biomass (Dasmann: 1964; Bourliere: 1963; Talbot: 1963; Riney: 1967). Census techniques, including air photography, have enabled biologists to manipulate habitat and hunting in North America so that deer, quail, doves, and waterfowl can be taken on a sustained basis (within certain political and economic limits) by the growing cadre of outdoorsmen (MacDonald and Martin: 1971).

Planners anticipate that non-consumptive uses of wildlife will increase as recreationists press for chances to observe and study wild creatures at close quarters. However, outdoor visitation tied to a shorter workweek, recreational vehicles, and increases in mobility, pose certain threats to parks, natural areas and their associations of biota. Campers, hikers, and picnickers can disturb and destroy animals and habitat.

One response to the proliferation of motorized outdoorsmen is to make them more responsible in their contacts with nature. The National Park Service has begun a program to provide study areas in which school-age children can learn about ecological principles. They are encouraged to look for relationships between organisms and themselves and are encouraged to be responsible in recreational pursuits. Educational programs within the Park Service and Wildlife Refuge system are being expanded. As described by Butler and Nelson in a separate chapter in this volume, areas are zoned for different types and intensities of use and a reservation system in parks will head off the scramble to pack more and more people into parks at the expense of the fabric of areas themselves (Cahn: 1968; Darling and Eichorn: 1967; Conservation Foundation: 1972).

"Ornitholidays" for bird enthusiasts, safaris for camera-wielding animal buffs, and cruises to places off-the-beaten-track to view "untouched" animal populations, have become popular over the past decade and provide a rationale for wildlife protection. Ten years ago experts at the Arusha Conference on natural resource conservation in Africa predicted that urban American and European tourists "with an almost pathological attachment to animals" would come in large numbers to enjoy the sight of herds of big game (Grzimek: 1963). Their beliefs have been borne out. In Kenya upwards of 200,000 tourists spent $32 million in 1970 compared with 12,000 visitors in 1960. No other facet of the nation's economy is growing as rapidly as tourism. Hotel and lodge accommodations in African national parks are considered a sound investment (Thresher: 1972; Myers: 1972). *The World Wildlife Guide*, published in association with the World Wildlife Fund, lists 649 sites throughout the world where travelers can view animals. The guide contains details about fauna to be found in each country and lists available accommodations and travel arrangements for each park and refuge. Visitors to refuges help create a climate for further areas to be set aside for wildlife (Ross-Macdonald: 1971).

Legislation that enables information to be collected about numbers of animals also promises to curtail wildlife exploitation and to aid rare and endangered species. Two laws passed recently in the United States are important in helping to lay the foundations for international cooperation for world fauna. The Fish and Wildlife Conservation Act of 1966 (PL89-669;80 Stat. 926) provided the Department of the Interior with funding to preserve and propagate fish and wildlife native to North America which are threatened with extinction. It authorized the drawing up of a list of threatened animals and prohibited the possession of any listed animal without authorization from Interior officials (Goodwin and Denson: 1970). One hundred and one species or subspecies of indigenous fauna appear on the 1971 edition of the list provided for under this act.

A second law, The Endangered Species Conservation Act of 1969 (PL91-135;83 Stat. 275) extended the intent of the 1966 Act to prohibit the importation into this country of any wildlife designated officially as endangered. In this way commerce in threatened species and their parts could be terminated. A total of 396 species or subspecies occurs on the list under the 1969 Act which was first published in 1970.

Despite conservationists' criticisms of the way the 1969 Act has been interpreted, this piece of legislation is a milestone for animals (Conway: 1970; Rathlesberger: 1972). Efforts are being made to tighten controls on wildlife ingress into the United States, particularly of pets and laboratory animals. For example, U.S. Fish and Wildlife Service agents discovered that between January, 1971 and May, 1972 certain New York furriers purchased and/or sold illegally 102,000 animal pelts worth five million dollars. Prosecution was made under the 1969 Act (*Washington Post*: Feb. 22, 1973).

Allied to a push for more stringent legislation are programs for animal propagation. Biologists at the Patuxent Wildlife Research Center, Maryland, are engaged in breeding certain endangered birds in captivity. For instance, more than a dozen whooping cranes, raised from eggs collected in Canada and rendered permanently flightless, provide the "seed" stock from which other cranes can hopefully be raised and eventually released into the wild. Zoological gardens and animal collectors continue to follow the trend of breeding rare animals in captivity. They exchange information about different birds and mammals and keep a record of blood lines. To date the buildup in captivity (in the United Kingdom and the United States) and release of several hundred nene or Hawaiian geese (*Branta sandvicensis*) onto the volcanic uplands of the islands of Hawaii and Maui speak well of such propagation ventures (Erickson: 1968).

National and regional plans to integrate wildlife into the broader spectrum of outdoor recreation and resources management proceed apace. Experts of the Bureau of Outdoor Recreation (in the Interior Department) project a 70 percent increase in nature walks between 1960 and 1980, and a further 168 percent by 2000. This direct interest in wild creatures ranks eleventh in major outdoor summer activities in the United States. Fishing (ranked 8th), sightseeing (ranked 6th), walking and driving for pleasure (ranked 1st and 3rd) are, in various ways, concerned with animals (United States Department of Interior: 1967).

The National Environmental Policy Act of 1969 sets out "to promote efforts which will prevent or eliminate damage to the environment . . . stimulate the health and welfare of man . . . enrich the understanding of the ecological systems and national resources important to the Nation." The same act established a Council on Environmental Quality which among other activities has promoted investigations of predator control programs, of whales and whale products, and has an active interest in rare and threatened species. The United States is working to set up an Endangered Species Convention, endorsed by the Conference on the Human Environment, Stockholm, June, 1972, which will impose strict controls on trade in endangered wildlife (Council on Environmental Quality: 1972). For example, delegates from some 100 nations met in February, 1973, in Washington, D.C., to draw up regulations for international commerce in rare and threatened wildlife.

The White House in environmental messages to Congress (in 1971 and 1972) has made commitments to a land use policy for America and has supported the concept of a World Heritage Trust in which areas of unique historical, cultural and ecological significance can be placed. It supports proposals for states to protect fauna on the federal endangered list.

In commenting on the passenger pigeon, Aldo Leopold remarked that for one species to mourn the death of another was something new under the sun (Leopold: 1949). The old man's prophesy in *Forest and Stream* was not limited to the pigeon. It was an epitaph for wildlife in the United States. Yet the "abomination of desolation" he perceived in 1950 did not come to pass. Raccoons and opossums have adapted well to suburban environments. Many waterbirds have rebounded in numbers. On the other hand, on a worldwide basis the downward trend in species has continued, while the scale of declines has broadened and accelerated over the last hundred years. Pressures on animals have increased from growth in human numbers and from the means available to man to disrupt ecosystems, especially to simplify them. The path to the brink of extinction has broadened.

Man can live with wildlife if he so chooses. The British public has been encouraged to view the nesting ospreys (*Pandion haliaetus*) which have returned to Loch Garten. People can visit the nests of the ruff (*Philomachus pugnax*) and a godwit (*Limosa limosa*) in England again. Risks have been taken to recruit widespread sentiment for rare creatures on a national basis. It was done in a limited way in this country for the whooping crane. Should it not be tried for the tiger, gorilla, wolf or polar bear? Attitudes of the frontiersman are scarcely consonant with current exponential demands upon a spatially finite planet.

APPENDIX

Important Events for Wildlife Conservation
in the United States

1616– First New World wildlife protection: The government of Bermuda issues
to   proclamations protecting the cahow and the green turtle.
1622

1630– First New World bounty system: Massachusetts Bay Colony authorizes payment of one penny per wolf.

1639– Newport, Rhode Island, prohibits deer hunting for six months of the year.

1647– Massachusetts Bay Colonial Ordinance provisions for the right to hunt.

1677– Game law to cover seasons and export of game, hides and skins passed by Connecticut.

1678– New Jersey Concessions of Agreements provisions for the right to hunt.

1694– First closed season (on deer), in Massachusetts.

1708– First closed season on birds: in certain New York counties, on heath hen, grouse, quail, turkey.

1710– Massachusetts prohibits use of camouflaged canoes, or boats equipped with sails, in pursuit of waterfowl.

1739– First wardens (of deer) in Massachusetts.

1776– First federal game law: closed seasons on deer established in all colonies, except Georgia.

1797– Vermont places a closed season on a fur-bearer, the muskrat (repealed 1801).

1818– First law protecting non-game birds, establishing a closed season on larks and robins in Massachusetts.

1838– First law against use of batteries, or multiple guns, on waterfowl; later repealed (New York).

1846– First law against spring shooting (wood duck, black duck, woodcock, snipe); later repealed (Rhode Island).

1849– U.S. Department of the Interior established.

1851– English sparrow liberated in New York (failed, but succeeded in 1853).

1864– Yosemite Valley, California, reserved as a state park.

1869– First wild pigeon protection, in Michigan and later Pennsylvania (1878): no firearms to be discharged within half mile of roosts. New York prohibits swivel or punt guns and shooting wildfowl from stream or sailboats.

1871– Establishment of the Federal Commission of Fish and Fisheries (later Bureau of Fisheries).

1872– Yellowstone National Park established.

1874– A Bill "to prevent the useless slaughter of buffaloes within the Territories of the United States" is passed by Congress but is pigeonholed by President Grant.

1877– Florida passes a plume-bird law prohibiting wanton destruction of eggs and young; not enforced.

1878– First state game departments and commissions set up in California and New Hampshire.

1881– The successful introduction of the Chinese ring-necked pheasant (*Phasianus colchicus*) into Oregon.

1885—Boone and Crockett Club founded.

1886—Audubon Society formed by *Forest and Stream*, New York. Establishment of federal Division of Economic Ornithology and Mammalogy (later Division of Biological Survey).

1891—Forest Reserve Act permits the President to establish forest reserves (later National Forests) on the public domain.

1891—Yosemite National Park established.

1894—Park Protection Act provides protection for wildlife in national parks of the United States.

1896—The Supreme Court (Geer vs. Connecticut) decrees that game is the property of the state rather than the landowner. Revival of the Audubon movement in Massachusetts and Pennsylvania.

1900—Lacey Bill becomes first federal law forbidding importation of foreign creatures without a permit; also interstate traffic in creatures killed in violation of state laws. Organization of the North American Fish and Game Protective Association.

1902—Reclamation (Newlands) Act establishes Bureau of Reclamation in the Department of the Interior and launches a federal reclamation program. Organization of the National Association of Game and Fish Wardens.

1903—First federal wildlife refuge established, at Pelican Island, Florida, by Executive Order of President Roosevelt.

1905—National Association of Audubon Societies incorporated. American Bison Society formed.

1905—Forest reserves transferred from the Department of the Interior to the Forest Service within Department of Agriculture.

1910—New York establishes law prohibiting sale of wild game (Bayne Bill), also the possession for sale, offering for sale, or sale of wild bird plumage.

1911—"Seal Treaty" controlling the take of fur seals and sea otters signed by United States, Great Britain, Russia, and Japan. American Game Protective and Propagation Association founded.

1913—Federal Tariff Act bars importation into United States of wild bird plumage. Weeks-McLean Act awards responsibility for migratory game birds to the Biological Survey.

1914—Act of Congress authorizes funds for the control of wolves, prairie dogs, and other injurious animals.

1916—Ratification of Convention between United States and Great Britain for the Protection of the Migratory Game Birds in the United States and Canada, including full protection for band-tailed pigeons, cranes, swans, most shore birds (administered after 1918 by the Biological Survey).

1918—Federal Migratory Bird Treaty Act prohibits spring shooting, awards to the government the right to prescribe bag limits of migratory birds. United States and Canada give full protection to wood duck (until 1941).

1922—Izaak Walton League organized.

1929—Norbeck-Andresen Migratory Bird Conservation Act provides for further acquisition of waterfowl refuge land.

1934—Migratory Bird Hunting Stamp Act establishes federal hunting license in form of "duck stamp." Fish and game sanctuaries authorized in suitable National Forest areas.

1935—The American Wildlife Management Institute founded.

1936—National Wildlife Federation formed.

1937—Pittman-Robertson Federal Aid in Wildlife Restoration Act established excise taxes on guns, ammunition, for use in wildlife projects in United States. Treaty with Mexico for protection of migratory birds and mammals. The Wildlife Society organized.

1939—Reorganization Act transfers Bureau of Biological Survey and Bureau of
  to   Fisheries from Department of Agriculture and Department of Commerce,

1940 respectively, merges them under Department of Interior as Fish and Wildlife Service.
1940—Convention on Nature Protection and Wildlife Preservation in the Western Hemisphere (ratified by United States in 1942). President empowered by Executive Order to set aside refuges for fish and game in the National Forests.
1946—U.S. Bureau of Land Management established to consolidate the administration of the public domain.
1950—Dingell-Johnson Fish Restoration Act (equivalent of Pittman-Robertson wildlife act of 1937).
1954—International Convention for the Prevention of Pollution of the Sea by Oil (ratified by United States in 1961).
1957—Coordination Act separates Fish and Wildlife Service into Bureau of Commercial Fisheries and Bureau of Sports Fisheries and Wildlife.
1963—The Bureau of Outdoor Recreation established within the Department of the Interior to coordinate federal efforts.
1964—Wilderness Act establishes a National Wilderness Preservation System.
1966—Endangered Species Preservation Act offers protection to threatened wildlife of the United States.
1969—Endangered Species Conservation Act limits importation of threatened wildlife into the United States.
1970—National Environmental Policy Act has broad scale intent of improving environmental quality and creates Council on Environmental Quality.

Sources: Graham: 1947; Matthiessen: 1959; Nash: 1967; Palmer: 1912.

REFERENCES

Abbott, Charles C., 1895. *The Birds about Us.* 2nd edition, Philadelphia: Lippincott.
Aldrich, John W., 1970, *Review of the Problem of Birds Contaminated by Oil and Their Rehabilitation*, United States Department of Interior, Bureau of Sport Fisheries and Wildlife, Division of Wildlife Research, Resource Publication No. 87. Washington, D.C.: Government Printing Office.
Allee, W. C. and Karl P. Schmidt, 1951, *Ecological Animal Geography.* 2nd edition, New York: Wiley.
Allen, Durward L., 1966, "The Preservation of Endangered Habitats and Vertebrates of North America," in F. Fraser Darling and John P. Milton (eds.), *Future Environments of North America.* Washington, D.C.: Conservation Foundation, pp. 22-37.
_____, 1962, *Our Wildlife Legacy.* Revised Edition, New York: Funk and Wagnalls.
Allen, Joel A., 1886, "The Present Wholesale Destruction of Bird-Life in the United States," *Science*, Vol. 7, pp. 191-95.
_____, 1876, "On the Decrease of Birds in the United States," *The Penn Monthly*, Vol. 7, pp. 931-44.
Allen, Robert P., 1952, *The Whooping Crane*, National Audubon Society Research Report No. 3. New York: National Audubon Society.
Atzert, Stephen P., 1971, *A Review of Sodium Monofluoroacetate (Compound 1080), Its Properties . . .*, United States Department of Interior, Bureau of Sport Fisheries and Wildlife, Special Scientific Report—Wildlife, No. 146. Washington, D.C.: Government Printing Office.
Baldwin, Malcolm F., 1970, *The Off-Road Vehicle and Environmental Quality.* Washington, D.C.: Conservation Foundation.
Bardach, John E., 1968, *Harvest of the Sea.* New York: Harper.
Barrows, Walter B., 1889, *The English Sparrow (Passer domesticus) in North America*, United States Department of Agriculture, Division of Economic Ornithology and Mammalogy, Bulletin I. Washington, D.C.: Government Printing Office.
Beer, J. V., 1968, "The Attempted Rehabilitation of Oiled Sea Birds," *Wildfowl*, Vol. 19, pp. 120-24.
Bellrose, Frank C., 1959, "Lead Poisoning as a Mortality Factor in Waterfowl Populations," *Illinois Natural History Survey Bulletin*, No. 27, pp. 235-88.

Ben-Tuvia, Adam, 1966, "Red Sea fishes recently found in the Mediterranean," *Copeia*, Vol. 2, pp. 254-75.

Bennett, Charles F., 1968, "Human Influences on the Zoogeography of Panama," *Ibero-Americana*, No. 51.

Berger, Andrew J., 1972, "Hawaiian Birds 1972," *Wilson Bulletin*, Vol. 84, pp. 212-22.

Bishop, M. W. H., 1951, "Distribution of Barnacles by Ships," *Nature*, Vol. 167, p. 531.

Bourliere, F., 1963, "Conservation and Management of Game Stock," in UNESCO, International Documents Service, *A Review of the Natural Resources of the African Continent*. New York: Columbia University Press, pp. 395-407.

Brewer, T. M., 1869, "Sea-Side Ornithology," *The American Naturalist*, Vol. 3, pp. 225-35.

Briggs, John C., 1969, "The Sea-Level Panama Canal: Potential Biological Catastrophe," *BioScience*, Vol. 19, pp. 44-47.

Buchheister, Carl W. and Frank Graham Jr., 1973, "From the Swamps and Back: A Concise and Candid History of the Audubon Movement," *Audubon*, Vol. 75, pp. 5-45.

Cahn, Robert, 1968, "Will Success Spoil the National Parks?" *Christian Science Monitor* (Reprint of 16 articles).

California, Department of Fish and Game, 1966, *California Fish and Wildlife Plan*. Sacramento: Resources Agency.

California, Department of Fish and Game and Department of Water Resources, 1967, *Water Development and the Delta Environment*, Summary Progress Report, Delta Fish and Wildlife Protection Study, Report No. 7. Sacramento: Resources Agency.

Chapman, Frank M., 1933, *Autobiography of a Bird-Lover*. New York: Appleton.

Clepper, Henry E. (ed.), 1971, *Leaders in American Conservation*. New York: Ronald Press.

Conservation Foundation, 1972, *National Parks for the Future*. Washington, D.C.: Conservation Foundation.

Conway, William G., 1970, "What's 'Endangered'?" *Animal Kingdom*, October, pp. 2-9.

Corzo, Rodolfo H., 1970, "Mexico: Avifauna and Modification of Habitat," in Helmut K. and Jimmie H. Buechner (eds.), *The Avifauna of Northern Latin America*. Smithsonian Contributions to Zoology No. 26. Washington, D.C.: Smithsonian, pp. 63-68.

Council on Environmental Quality, 1972, *Environmental Quality*. Washington, D.C.: Government Printing Office.

Craighead, Frank C. and Raymond F. Dasmann, 1966, *Exotic Big Game on Public Lands*, United States Bureau of Land Management. Washington, D.C.: Government Printing Office.

Crimmins, Margaret, 1970, "Is Furor over Furs only Fashionable . . . ," *The Washington Post*, June 28.

Crosby, Gilbert T., 1972, "Spread of the Cattle Egret in the Western Hemisphere," *Bird-Banding*, Vol. 43, pp. 205-12.

Crutchfield, James A. and Giulio Pontecorvo, 1969, *Pacific Salmon Fisheries: A Study of Irrational Conservation*. Baltimore: Johns Hopkins Press.

Darling, F. Fraser and Noel D. Eichorn, 1967, *Man and Nature in the National Parks*. Washington, D.C.: Conservation Foundation.

Dasmann, Raymond F., 1965, *The Destruction of California*. New York: Macmillan.

———, 1964, *African Game Ranching*. Oxford: Pergamon Press.

Daugherty, Howard E., 1972, "The Impact of Man on the Zoogeography of El Salvador," *Biological Conservation*, Vol. 4, pp. 273-78.

Davies, Brian, 1970, *Savage Luxury*. New York: Ballantine.

Dorst, Jean, 1970, *Before Nature Dies*, translated by Constance D. Sherman. Baltimore: Penguin.

Doughty, Robin W., 1972, "Concern for Fashionable Feathers," *Forest History*, Vol. 16, pp. 4-11.

Drury, Charles, William H. Fisher, *et al.*, 1886, "Papers on the Destruction of Native Birds," *Journal of the Cincinnati Society of Natural History*, Vol. 9, pp. 163-224.

Drury, William H., 1966, "Birds at Airports," in Alfred A. Stefferud (ed.), *Birds in Our Lives*. Washington, D.C.: Government Printing Office, pp. 384-89.

Dubos, René, 1968, *Man, Medicine, and Environment*. New York: Praeger.

Ehrenfeld, David W., 1970, *Biological Conservation*. New York: Holt, Rinehart, Winston.

Elton, Charles S., 1958, *The Ecology of Invasions by Animals and Plants*. London: Methuen.

Erickson, Ray C., 1968, "A Federal Research Program for Endangered Wildlife," *Transactions of the 33rd North American Wildlife and Natural Resources Conference*, Vol. 33, pp. 418-33.

Fisher, Harvey I., 1966, "Airplane—Albatross Collisions on Midway Atoll," *The Condor*, Vol. 68, pp. 229-42.

Fisher, James, Noel Simon and Jack Vincent, 1969, *Wildlife in Danger*. New York: Viking.

Fitter, Richard S. R., 1968, *Vanishing Wild Animals of the World*. New York: Franklin Watts.

Flagg, Wilson, 1875, *The Birds and Seasons of New England*. Boston: Osgood.

Fleischman, Paul, 1969, "Conservation: The Biological Fallacy," *Landscape*, Vol. 18, pp. 23-26.

Fosberg, F. Raymond, 1966, "Restoration of Lost and Degraded Habitats," in F. Fraser Darling and John P. Milton (eds.), *Future Environments of North America*. Washington, D.C.: Conservation Foundation, pp. 503-15.

Gabrielson, Ira N., 1959, *Wildlife Conservation*. 2nd edition. New York: Macmillan.

Goodwin, Harry A. and Eley P. Denson, 1970, "A Report on the National Effort to Save Endangered Species," United States Department of Interior, Bureau of Sport Fisheries and Wildlife, Office of Endangered Species. Mimeographed.

Gottschalk, John S., 1967, "The Introduction of Exotic Animals into the United States," in *Towards a New Relationship of Man and Nature in Temperate Lands*. Morges: International Union for the Conservation of Nature and Natural Resources, pp. 124-40.

Graham, Edward H., 1947, *The Land and Wildlife*. New York: Oxford University Press.

Graham, Michael, 1956, "Harvests of the Seas," in William L. Thomas (ed.), *Man's Role in Changing the Face of the Earth*. Chicago: University of Chicago Press, pp. 487-503.

Greenway, James C. Jr., 1958, *Extinct and Vanishing Birds of the World* (American Committee for International Wild Life Protection, Special Publication No. 13). New York: American Committee for International Wild Life Protection.

Grzimek, B., 1963, "Value of the Tourist Industry," *Conservation of Nature and Natural Resources in Modern African States*. Morges: International Union for the Conservation of Nature and Natural Resources, pp. 189-92.

Hayden, Sherman Strong, 1942, *The International Protection of Wild Life*. New York: Columbia University Press.

Hickey, Joseph J. (ed.), 1969, *Peregrine Falcon Populations: Their Biology and Decline*. Madison: University of Wisconsin Press.

Hicks, Philip M., 1924, *The Development of the Natural History Essay in American Literature*. Philadelphia.

Hodson, N. L. and D. W. Snow, 1965, "The Road Deaths' Enquiry, 1960-61," *Bird Study*, Vol. 12, pp. 90-99.

Holcomb, R. W., 1969, "Oil in the Ecosystem," *Science*, Vol. 166, pp. 204-206.

Holdridge, L. R., 1970, "Natural Vegetation and Reservation Prospects in Northern Latin America," in Helmut K. and Jimmie H. Buechner (eds.), *The Avifauna of Northern Latin America*, Smithsonian Contributions to Zoology, No. 26. Washington, D.C.: Smithsonian, pp. 27-33.

Holmes, R. W., 1969, "Oil on the Sea," in D. P. Hoult (ed.), *Oil on the Sea*. New York: Plenum, pp. 15-27.

Hornaday, William T., 1931, *Thirty Years War for Wild Life*. Stanford, Conn.: Permanent Wild Life Protection Fund.

——, 1913, *Our Vanishing Wildlife, Its Extermination and Preservation*. New York: New York Zoological Society.

——, 1898, "The Destruction of Our Birds and Mammals: A Report of the Results of an Inquiry," *Second Annual Report of the New York Zoological Society*, pp. 77-107.

Hosley, N. W., 1968, *Selected References on Management of White-tailed Deer, 1910 to 1966*, United States Department of Interior, Bureau of Sport Fisheries and Wildlife, Special Scientific Report—Wildlife, No. 112. Washington, D.C.: Government Printing Office.

Houston, Douglas B., 1971, "Ecosystems of National Parks," *Science*, Vol. 172, pp. 648-51.

Howard, W. E., 1967, "Ecological Changes in New Zealand due to Introduced Animals," *Towards a New Relationship of Man and Nature in Temperate Lands*. Morges: International Union for the Conservation of Nature and Natural Resources, pp. 219-40.

Howell, J. C., A. R. Laskey, and J. T. Tanner, 1954, "Bird Mortality at Airport Ceilometers," *Wilson Bulletin*, Vol. 66, pp. 207-15.

Hunter, Brian F., 1970, "Ecology of Waterfowl Botulism Toxin Production," *Transactions of the 35th North American Wildlife and Natural Resources Conference*, Vol. 35, pp. 64-72.

Huth, Hans, 1957, *Nature and the American: Three Centuries of Changing Attitudes.* Berkeley: University of California Press.

International Union for the Conservation of Nature and Natural Resources, Survival Service Commission, 1970, *Polar Bears* (Supplementary Paper, No. 29). Morges: International Union for the Conservation of Nature and Natural Resources.

Johnson, Stanley, 1972, "Burnt in the Name of Progress," *New Scientist*, pp. 344-45.

Kalmbach, E. R., 1968, *Type C Botulism among Wild Birds–A Historical Sketch*, United States Department of Interior, Bureau of Sport Fisheries and Wildlife, Special Scientific Report–Wildlife, No. 110. Washington, D.C.: Government Printing Office.

Keith, James O., Leon A. Woods Jr., and Eldridge G. Hunt, 1970, "Reproductive Failure in Brown Pelicans on the Pacific Coast," *Transactions of the 35th North American Wildlife and Natural Resources Conference*, Vol. 35, pp. 56-63.

King, F. Wayne, 1971, "Adventures in the Skin Trade," *Natural History*, Vol. 80, pp. 8-10, 12, 14, 16.

Klein, David R., 1972, "Problems in Conservation of Mammals in the North," *Biological Conservation*, Vol. 4, pp. 97-101.

Lawyer, George A., 1918, "Federal Protection of Migratory Birds," in United States Department of Agriculture, *Yearbook*. Washington, D.C.: Government Printing Office, pp. 303-16.

Lay, Daniel W. and Dennis N. Russell, 1970, "Notes on the Redcockaded Woodpecker in Texas," *The Auk*, Vol. 87, pp. 781-86.

Leedy, Daniel L., 1961, "Some Federal Contributions to Bird Conservation During the Period 1885 to 1960," *The Auk*, Vol. 78, pp. 167-75.

Leopold, Aldo, 1949, *A Sand County Almanac.* New York: Oxford University Press.

Leopold, A. S., 1964, "Predator and Rodent Control in the United States," *Transactions of the North American Wildlife and Natural Resources Conference*, Vol. 29, pp. 27-49.

MacDonald, Duncan and Elwood Martin, 1971, *Trends in Harvest of Migratory Game Birds . . .* , United States Department of Interior, Bureau of Sport Fisheries and Wildlife, Special Scientific Report–Wildlife, No. 142. Washington, D.C.: Government Printing Office.

Mackey, William J., 1965, *American Bird Decoys.* New York: Dutton.

Margalef, R., 1963, "On Certain Unifying Principles in Ecology," *American Naturalist*, Vol. 97, pp. 357-74.

Marsh, George Perkins, 1864, *Man and Nature; or, Physical Geography as Modified by Human Action.* New York: Scribner.

Martin, Paul S. and H. E. Wright Jr. (eds.), 1967, *Pleistocene Extinctions: the Search for a Cause.* New Haven: Yale.

Matthiessen, Peter, 1959, *Wildlife in America.* New York: Viking Press.

May, Jacques M. (ed.), 1961, *Studies in Disease Ecology.* New York: Hafner.

———, 1959, *Ecology of Human Disease.* New York: MD Publications.

———, 1950, "Medical Geography: Its Methods and Objectives," *Geographical Review*, Vol. 40, pp. 9-41.

Mayfield, Harold F., 1972, "Third Decennial Census of Kirtland's Warbler," *The Auk*, Vol. 89, pp. 263-68.

———, 1963, "Establishment of Preserves for the Kirtland's Warbler in the State and National Forests of Michigan," *Wilson Bulletin*, Vol. 75, pp. 208-15.

———, 1960, *The Kirtland's Warbler.* Cranbrook Institute of Science.

McCloskey, Michael, 1972, "Wilderness Movement at the Crossroads, 1945-1970," *Pacific Historical Review*, Vol. 41, pp. 346-61.

McNulty, Faith, 1966, *The Whooping Crane.* New York: Dutton.

McVay, Scott, 1973, "Stalking the Arctic Whale," *American Scientist*, Vol. 61, pp. 24-37.

———, 1966, "The Last of the Great Whales," *Scientific American*, Vol. 215, pp. 13-21.

Mead, A. R., 1961, *The Giant African Snail.* Chicago: University Press.

Mississippi Flyway Council, Planning Committee, 1964, "Wasted Waterfowl." Mimeographed.

Moreau, R. E., 1961, "Problems of Mediterranean-Saharan Migration," *Ibis*, Vol. 103, pp. 373-427, 580-623.

Murton, R. K. and E. N. Wright (eds.), 1968, *The Problems of Birds as Pests.* London: Academic Press.

Myers, Norman, 1972, *The Long African Day.* New York: Macmillan.

Nash, Roderick, 1967, *Wilderness and the American Mind.* New Haven: Yale University Press.

National Research Council, Committee on Agricultural Land Use and Wildlife Resources, 1970, *Land Use and Wildlife Resources.* Washington, D.C.: National Academy of Sciences.

Nicholson, Max, 1970, *The Environmental Revolution.* New York: McGraw-Hill.

Odum, Howard T., 1971, *Environment, Power, and Society.* New York: Wiley.

Oldys, Henry, 1902, "Audubon Societies in Relation to the Farmer," in United States Department of Agriculture, *Yearbook.* Washington, D.C.: Government Printing Office, pp. 205-18.

Opie, John (ed.), 1971, *Americans and Environment: The Controversy Over Ecology.* Lexington: Heath.

O'Riordan, Timothy, 1971, "The Third American Conservation Movement: New Implications for Public Policy," *Journal of American Studies*, Vol. 5, pp. 155-71.

Palmer, Theodore S., 1912, *Chronology and Index of the More Important Events in American Game Protection, 1776-1911*, United States Department of Agriculture, Bureau of Biological Survey, Bulletin, No. 41. Washington, D.C.: Government Printing Office.

Paradiso, John L. and Ronald M. Nowak, 1971, *A Report on the Taxonomic Status and Distribution of the Red Wolf*, United States Department of Interior, Bureau of Sport Fisheries and Wildlife, Special Scientific Report–Wildlife, No. 145. Washington, D.C.: Government Printing Office.

Paradiso, John L., 1972, *Status Report on Cats (Felidae) of the World, 1971*, United States Department of Interior, Bureau of Sport Fisheries and Wildlife, Special Scientific Report–Wildlife, No. 157. Washington, D.C.: Government Printing Office.

Parmalee, Paul W., 1969, *Decoys and Decoy Carvers of Illinois.* DeKalb: Northern Illinois University Press.

Parslow, J. L. F., 1967, "Changes in the Status Among Breeding Birds in Britain and Ireland," *British Birds*, Vol. 60, pp. 181-82.

Parsons, James J., 1972, "Spread of African Pasture Grasses to the American Tropics," *Journal of Range Management*, Vol. 25, pp. 12-17.

———, 1970, "The 'Africanization' of the New World Tropical Grasslands," Beiträge zur Geographie der Tropen und Subtropen (Festschrift für Herbert Wilhelmy), *Tübinger Geographische Studien*, Vol. 34, pp. 141-53.

Pearson, T. Gilbert, 1937, *Adventures in Bird Protection.* New York: Appleton-Century.

———, 1933, "Fifty Years of Bird Protection in the United States," *Fifty Years' Progress of American Ornithology, 1883-1933.* Lancaster: American Ornithologists' Union, pp. 199-213.

Phillips, John C., 1934, *Migratory Bird Protection in North America*, Special Publication of the American Committee for International Wild Life Protection, Vol. 1. Cambridge, Mass.: Museum of Comparative Zoology.

———, 1928, *Wild Birds Introduced or Transplanted in North America*, United States Department of Agriculture, Technical Bulletin, No. 61. Washington, D.C.: Government Printing Office.

Rakestraw, Lawrence, 1972, "Conservation Historiography: An Assessment," *Pacific Historical Review*, Vol. 41, pp. 271-88.

Ramsey, Charles W., 1968a, *Texotics*, Texas Department of Parks and Wildlife, Bulletin, No. 49. Austin.

———, 1968b, "State Views of Governmental and Private Programs of Introductions of Exotic Animals," in Wildlife Society (Texas Chapter), *Introduction of Exotic Animals: Ecologic and Socio-Economic Considerations.* College Station: Caesar Kleberg Research Program, pp. 9-10.

Rathlesberger, James (ed.), 1972, *Nixon and the Environment.* New York: Taurus.

Regenstein, Lewis, 1971, "Can Spotted Cats Survive Despite the Fur Industry?" *The Washington Post*, August 9.

Ricker, William E., 1969, "Food from the Sea," in National Research Council, National Academy of Sciences, *Resources and Man.* San Francisco: Freeman, pp. 87-108.

Riney, T., 1967, *Conservation and Management of African Wildlife.* Rome: F. A. O.

Robbins, Chandler S., 1966, *Birds and Aircraft on Midway Islands, 1959-63 Investigations*, United States Department of Interior, Bureau of Sport Fisheries and Wildlife, Special Scientific Report–Wildlife, No. 85. Washington, D.C.: Government Printing Office.

Ross-Macdonald, Malcolm (ed.), 1971, *The World Wildlife Guide.* New York: Viking.

Royal Society for the Protection of Birds, 1913, "Birds at Lighthouses," *Bird Notes and News*, Vol. 5, pp. 65-67.

Rubinoff, Ira, 1968, "Central American Sea-Level Canal: Possible Biological Effects," *Science*, Vol. 161, pp. 857-61.

Rubinoff, Roberta W. and Ira Rubinoff, 1968, "Interoceanic Colonization of a Marine Goby through the Panama Canal," *Nature*, Vol. 217, pp. 476-78.

Sanger, Gerald A., 1972, "The Recent Pelagic Status of the Short-tailed Albatross (*Diomedea albatrus*)," *Biological Conservation*, Vol. 4, pp. 189-93.

Schmitt, Peter J., 1969, *Back to Nature: The Arcadian Myth in Urban America*. New York: Oxford University Press.

Schorger, Arlie W., 1955, *The Passenger Pigeon*. Madison: University of Wisconsin Press.

Shufeldt, R. W., 1887, "The Wanton Destruction of the Florida Heronries," *Science*, Vol. 10, pp. 47-48.

Small, George L., 1971, *The Blue Whale*. New York: Columbia University Press.

Smith, J. E., 1968, *Torrey Canyon Pollution and Marine Life*. Cambridge: Cambridge University Press.

Smith, Stanford H., 1968, "Species Succession and Fishery Exploitation in the Great Lakes," *Journal Fisheries Research Board of Canada*, Vol. 25, pp. 667-93.

Smithsonian Institution, 1972, *Development of a Continuing Program to Provide Indicators and Indices of Wildlife and the Natural Environment*. Washington, D.C.

Spofford, Walter R., 1964, *The Golden Eagle in the Trans-Pecos and Edwards Plateau of Texas*, Audubon Conservation Report, No. 1. New York: National Audubon Society.

Sprunt, A. Jr., 1954, "The Spread of the Cattle Egret," *Smithsonian Institution Annual Report*, pp. 259-76.

Stead, Frank M., 1968, "Losing the Water Battle," *Cry California*, Vol. 3, pp. 15-21.

Sternberg, Hilgard O., 1968, "Man and Environmental Change in South America," in E. J. Fittau *et al.* (eds.), *Biogeography and Ecology of South America*. The Hague: Junk, pp. 413-45.

Stieglitz, Walter O. and Richard L. Thompson, 1967, *Status and Life History of the Everglade Kite in the United States*, United States Department of Interior, Bureau of Sport Fisheries and Wildlife, Special Scientific Report—Wildlife, No. 109. Washington, D.C.: Government Printing Office.

Talbot, Lee M., 1970, "Endangered Species," *BioScience*, Vol. 20, p. 331.

_____, 1963, "Comparison of the Efficiency of Wild Animals and Domestic Livestock in Utilization of East African Rangelands," *Conservation of Nature and Natural Resources in Modern African States*. Morges: International Union for Conservation of Nature and Natural Resources, pp. 329-33.

_____, 1960, *A Look at Threatened Species*. London: Fauna Preservation Society and International Union for the Conservation of Nature and Natural Resources.

Thresher, Philip, 1972, "African National Parks and Tourism—an Interlinked Future," *Biological Conservation*, Vol. 4, pp. 279-84.

Trefethen, James B., 1970, "The Return of the White-tailed Deer," *American Heritage*, Vol. 21, pp. 97-103.

_____, 1961, *Crusade for Wildlife*. Harrisburg: Stackpole.

Turner, Ernest E., 1965, *All Heaven in a Rage*. New York: St. Martin's.

U.S. Air Force, Directorate of Aerospace Safety, 1972, "Bird Strike Summary, 1971," Norton A.F.B.: Inspection and Safety Center. Mimeographed.

U.S. Department of the Interior, 1966, *Rare and Endangered Fish and Wildlife of the United States*. Washington, D.C.: U.S. Government Printing Office.

U.S. Department of the Interior, Bureau of Outdoor Recreation, 1967, *Outdoor Recreation Trends*. Washington, D.C.: U.S. Government Printing Office.

U.S. House of Representatives, 1971, *Marine Mammals*, Hearings before the Subcommittee on Fisheries and Wildlife Conservation of the Committee on Merchant Marine and Fisheries, 92nd Congress, First Session. Washington, D.C.: U.S. Government Printing Office.

University of Michigan, Institute for Environmental Quality, Advisory Committee on Predator Control, 1972, *Predator Control 1971*, Report to the Council on Environmental Quality and the Department of the Interior. Ann Arbor.

Walker, Ronald L., 1967, "A Brief History of Exotic Game Bird and Mammal Introductions into Hawaii with a Look to the Future," *The Elepaio*, Vol. 28, pp. 29-32, 39-43.

Warner, Richard E., 1968, "The Role of Introduced Diseases in the Extinction of the Endemic Hawaiian Avifauna," *The Condor*, Vol. 70, pp. 101-20.

Welker, Robert H., 1955, *Birds and Men*. Cambridge, Mass.: Harvard University Press.

Yarborough, Ralph W., 1969, [Statement] in U.S. Congress-Senate, *Endangered Species*,

Hearings before the Subcommittee on Energy, Natural Resources, and the Environment, Committee on Commerce, 91st Congress, First Session. Washington, D.C.: U.S. Government Printing Office.

Zinsser, Hans, 1934, *Rats, Lice and History*. Boston: Little, Brown.

Ziswiler, Vinzenz, 1967, *Extinct and Vanishing Animals*. Revised English edition by Fred and Pille Bunnell. New York: Springer-Verlag.

The Environmental Impact of
Modern Agricultural
Technologies

Ian R. Manners
University of Texas

The second half of the twentieth century has seen a significant shift in the attitude of the American public towards the environment. The evidence of environmental deterioration, particularly in large metropolitan areas where problems of living space, noise, air pollution, and waste disposal produced a growing assault upon the senses, together with the publication of such books as Rachel Carson's *Silent Spring* generated widespread concern over human management of the environment (O'Riordan: 1971). This concern found expression in public demands for an improvement in environmental quality. Such a concept, intimately related to individual tastes and desires, is not easily defined yet it reflects a general feeling that much greater emphasis must be placed upon such intangible values as clean air, clean water, the appearance of the landscape, and the preservation of natural communities. The growing concern for environmental quality has produced a challenge to traditional strategies of resource management. The demand is for a more realistic appraisal of the social and ecological costs associated with environmental degradation. In part, at least, this approach reflects one of the major themes of the environmental movement, namely the need for the human population to view itself as an integral part of nature rather than as a force apart from nature (Bates: 1969). The writings of such scientists as Paul Ehrlich and Barry Commoner have helped to popularize the ecological approach which recognizes that the natural environment comprises a complex system of interacting processes and interdependent components in a state of dynamic equilibrium, an equilibrium which human intrusion has all too frequently disrupted (Commoner: 1966, 1971; Ehrlich: 1968, 1972).

The management of the agricultural resource base has not been exempt from this challenge. Modern agricultural systems, no less than urban systems, can be regarded as artificial ecosystems that continue to function only as a result of extensive human manipulation. The magnitude of the indirect costs (in the form of polluted water bodies and health hazards) associated with the technologies designed to maintain and increase the productivity of agricultural systems has become a subject of considerable controversy. The present paper is intended to

181

provide a geographical appraisal of agricultural activities and environmental stress. The first part of the paper focusses on changes in the structure, functioning, and equilibrium of agricultural systems, suggesting as have other anthropologists and geographers, that the application of ecological concepts offers both a research methodology and a conceptual framework for the analysis of agricultural activities (Geertz: 1963; Harris: 1969a, 1969b; Rappaport: 1971; Stoddart: 1965; Wolf: 1966). The second part of the paper reviews some of the problems associated with the widespread use of commercial fertilizers and chemical pesticides in modern agricultural systems. Implicit in this ecological approach is the recognition that problems of environmental degradation cannot be analyzed, let alone resolved, without a holistic approach that involves the social scientist as well as the natural scientist. Any consideration of the pesticide problem, for example, requires not only an understanding of the processes that have resulted in the diffusion and concentration of persistent pesticides throughout the environment, but consideration of the human needs for sustained agricultural growth and of the economic pressures that have forced farmers to depend upon this particular form of pest control.

THE ECOLOGY OF AGRICULTURAL SYSTEMS

Increases in agricultural output have traditionally been achieved through an expansion of the cultivated area. As is evident from Figure 1, however, the last century has witnessed a rapid adoption of technologies designed to increase the productivity of lands already under cultivation. Mechanization, the use of artificial fertilizers and chemical methods of pest control, the adoption of improved irrigation techniques, the breeding of new crop varieties that are more responsive to fertilizer, more resistant to drought, more rapidly maturing and less vulnerable to disease than their natural ancestors, have combined to produce rapid and continuing increases in output per acre—a yield "take-off"—in mid-latitude farming regions (Brown: 1963, 1965, 1967).

The Nature of Modern Agricultural Ecosystems

The human population has been engaged in manipulating natural ecological systems for many thousands of years, yet there remain marked variations in terms of the intensity of such intervention. Agricultural systems, for example, range from solar based, subsistence systems to highly productive systems that are heavily dependent upon auxiliary energy and nutrient sources (Odum: 1967, 1971). Wolf has distinguished between what he terms traditional "palaeotechnic" agricultural systems in which human and animal labor predominate, and modern "neotechnic" systems of farming in which high productivity is linked to advanced scientific skills and to an energy subsidy (Wolf: 1966). The impact of an energy subsidy on both the productivity and the functioning and maintenance of modern agricultural systems is indicated in Figure 2. In a natural ecological system, as described by David Watts in a previous chapter, the system is maintained through a network of food chains and mineral recycling routeways that are directly dependent upon the input of solar energy. In traditional agricultural systems, human actions are designed to increase the proportion of the total energy fixed in plant photosynthesis that is channelled to the direct

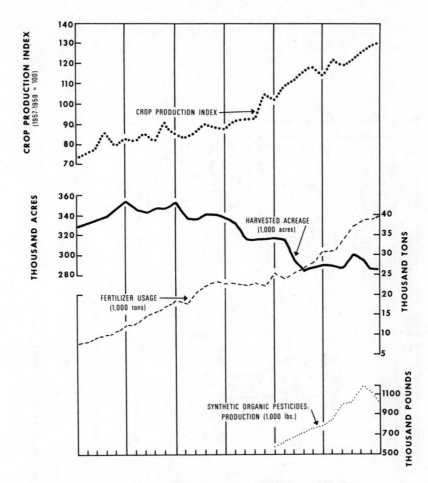

Figure 1. Agricultural Change in the United States, 1939-1970.

support of the human population. In effect, a larger proportion of the energy budget of the system is controlled through the selection and management of the producer and consumer (crop and livestock) components of the system. But, as in a natural system, the human population is supported entirely by solar energy, the processes necessary to the continued functioning of the system being performed directly by human labor or indirectly by the producer, consumer, and decomposer populations with energy supplied from the system's own resources (Figure 2a). In modern agricultural systems, however, the use of mechanization in place of human and animal labor, the manufacture and distribution of fertilizers, the discovery and preparation of chemical pesticides, and the development through genetic manipulation of new plant varieties all represent agricultural inputs that involve the expenditure of additional energy derived from fossil fuels (Figure 2b).

The introduction of an energy subsidy has not only resulted in vastly increased yields in mid-latitude farming regions but has produced far-reaching changes in agricultural practices and in functionally related sectors of the

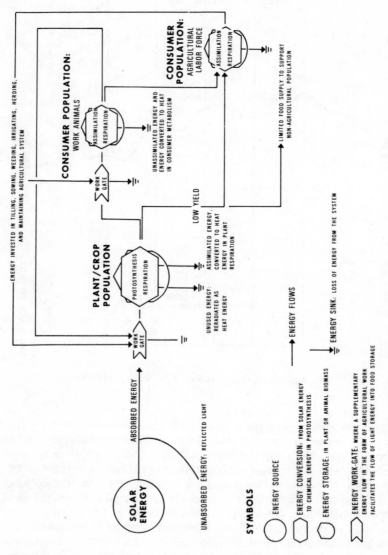

Figure 2a.   "Palaeotechnic" Agricultural System. Adapted from Odum: 1971.

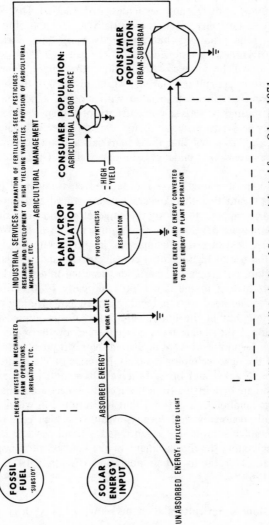

Figure 2b. "Neotechnic" Agricultural System. Adapted from Odum: 1971.

economy, freeing some of man's own energy for pursuits other than food production and enabling developed countries to be fed, with only 5 percent of the population directly employed in agriculture. As Odum has pointed out, however, "the bulk of the persons who work to support the farming process are in cities far away from the farm but they are just as necessary to the farm as the man riding the tractor" (Odum: 1967, p. 60). The full costs of developing and maintaining modern agricultural systems have been substantial. Achieving continued increases in yield, for example, requires disproportionate increases in inputs, particularly of fertilizers and pesticides (FAO: 1970). The expenditure of fossil fuel energy is not only often substantially greater than the energy yield embodied in the food produced, but represents energy that was fixed in the process of photosynthesis in previous ages (Brown: 1970a). As fossil fuels become scarcer, it will be necessary to develop other energy sources or face a significant decrease in agricultural output. Again, disposal of the organic wastes, pesticides and excess fertilizers associated with modern agricultural systems is dependent upon natural processes, the capacity of the environment to absorb, degrade, and recycle waste materials being available free of charge. However, many ecologists are concerned that these materials are now accumulating in the environment at a rate which endangers human welfare (Institute of Ecology: 1972).

It is ironic, to say the least, that the delayed environmental expression of these dangers has meant that this concern is being voiced at a time when many developing countries appear to be on the verge of a yield breakthrough, using techniques and principles developed in the farming regions of the Western world. In India and West Pakistan, for example, as in other countries in South and Southeast Asia, the use of high-yielding cereal varieties and associated inputs of controlled irrigation, fertilizers, and pesticides resulted in a remarkable increase in agricultural production in the late 1960's and early 1970's (Brown: 1970b; Dalrymple: 1972). The need for rapid and sustained agricultural growth in these countries is obvious but in the initial euphoria that surrounded the so-called "Green Revolution," the longer-term consequences of the rapid transfer and diffusion of these technologies were neglected. Nor is it possible to consider the consequences of the new technologies solely in terms of their potential impact on the biosphere. Frankel and other observers have noted, for example, that those farmers who are benefitting from the recent changes are mainly those with medium and large landholdings, a trend that has resulted in wider disparities in farm income both regionally and locally. Again, the high cost of the inputs necessary to maximize returns has accentuated a trend towards larger, mechanized farms, accelerating the displacement of the landless rural population and increasing the rate of rural to urban migration (Frankel: 1971; Ladejinsky: 1970; Wharton: 1969).

The Stability of Modern Agricultural Systems

Human actions in replacing the natural flora and fauna by more "useful" plant and animal species have altered the balance of the earth's plant and animal populations. Frequently, this process of biotic modification has involved changes in the global distribution of plant and animal species with the introduction both deliberately and accidentally of new varieties into new environments (Elton: 1958). In the process of biotic modification, however, man has essentially *simplified* the structure of the environment over vast areas, substituting for the diversity of the natural environment a relatively small number of cultivated plants and domesticated animals. This process of simplification reaches its most extreme form in the case of a monoculture. But all modern agricultural systems are simpler, less diverse in terms of their structure, than the natural systems that they have replaced. The objective, of course, is to increase the proportion of solar energy fixed by the plant communities that is directly available to man, but the net result is a man-designed agricultural ecosystem. Commercial preparation and mechanized planting replace natural methods of seed dispersal; chemical pesticides replace natural controls on population numbers in an attempt to remove unwanted plants (weeds) and to reduce direct competitors among the insect and vertebrate populations (pests); and genetic manipulation replaces natural processes of plant evolution and selection. Even the decomposer element is altered since plant growth is harvested and soil fertility maintained not through the natural recycling of nutrients but through the application of fertilizers. By and large, such artificial systems have proved capable of supporting a growing population, but there is considerable evidence that the equilibrium in such highly specialized systems is much more delicately poised.

The explanation for this potential instability must be sought in terms of changes in the organization and functioning of ecological systems that follow human intervention in the biosphere. In the absence of such intervention, the long-term trend of evolution appears to be towards creating complex, stable ecosystems (Margalef: 1963, 1968; Odum: 1969) although the contrasts between, for example, tropical rainforest and tundra ecosystems in terms of structure and complexity should be noted. The process of ecological succession has been the subject of extensive research by ecologists, ranging from the descriptive studies of Frederick Clements to the early work on community energetics by Raymond Lindeman and the more recent studies of the structural and functional characteristics of a developing ecosystem by Eugene Odum and others (Clements: 1916; Johnston and Odum: 1956; Lindeman: 1942; Odum: 1969; Woodwell: 1970). A detailed appraisal of this literature is to be found in Eugene Odum's *Fundamentals of Ecology* (1971, pp. 251-275).

Odum's studies have indicated that the process of succession involves a number of significant shifts in the way in which an ecological system functions, shifts that affect both the pattern of energy flow and mineral cycling. Nutrient cycles, for example, become very much "tighter" as succession proceeds; climax communities retain nutrients for recycling within the system in contrast to successional communities where much larger amounts of nutrients are lost from the system (Odum: 1969, p. 267). Studies by Bormann and Likens of the nutrient budget of a forest ecosystem in New Hampshire have strikingly documented the loss of nutrients and the decreased resistance to soil erosion that follow a reversal of the process of ecological succession, in this instance through deforestation (Bormann and Likens: 1967, 1970; Likens, Bormann *et al.*: 1970). Nitrogen *lost* during the first year after cutting, for example, was equivalent to the amount annually turned over in the undisturbed system (Bormann, Likens, Fisher and Pierce: 1968). In terms of the energetics of succession, the rate of gross primary production (i.e., the total amount of energy fixed in the process of photosynthesis) in the early stages of ecological succession *exceeds* the rate of community respiration, so that organic matter and biomass accumulate within the system. As an ecosystem approaches maturity, however, an increasing amount of fixed energy is appropriated to maintain the system; in other words, the energy fixed in photosynthesis is balanced by total community respiration. Changes in the pattern of energy flow during succession are parallelled by changes in ecosystem structure, characterized by an increase in the *variety* of species to be found within the community. The net result of these subtle changes is the creation of a large and complex organic structure; the routeways whereby energy and nutrients are transferred through the system are extraordinarily intricate, while the relationships between species are characterized by increased interdependency.

It is this complexity that appears to provide a mature ecosystem with a measure of stability in a fluctuating environment (Woodwell and Smith: 1969). Severe stresses in the *external* physical environment, for example, (such as a change in moisture, temperature or light conditions) are less likely to adversely affect the entire system for, in the presence of a highly diversified biota, numerous alternatives exist for the transfer of energy and nutrients through the system. Hence, the system is capable of adjusting and continuing to function with little if any detectable disruption. Similarly, *internal* biotic controls (such as predator-prey relationships) prevent destructive oscillations in population numbers further promoting the overall stability of the system. The practical significance of such considerations as far as resource management is concerned has been discussed by Watt (1968).

With regard to human intervention in the biosphere, Margalef, Odum, Rappaport and others have emphasized the extent to which modern agricultural systems resemble immature ecosystems (Margalef: 1968; Odum: 1969; Rappaport: 1971). Odum has suggested a basic conflict between the strategies of man and of nature, contrasting the process of ecological succession with its goal of "maximum protection" and homeostasis with mankind's desire to achieve as much *production* as possible in the form of harvestable products. In relation to human needs, therefore, the human strategy can be viewed as a reversal of the successional sequence, creating and maintaining early successional types of ecosystem where gross production exceeds community respiration. Such agricultural ecosystems, despite their high yield to mankind, carry with them the disadvantages of all immature ecosystems, in particular they lack the ability to perform essentially protective functions in terms of nutrient cycling, soil conservation and population regulation. The functioning of the system is thus dependent upon continued human intervention. Even the crops that are selected for cultivation are frequently incapable of reproducing themselves without assistance or of competing against natural species without constant protection, a consequence of the process of domestication and of consciously picking and breeding plants that possess desirable traits. As Odum (1971, p. 267) has pointed out:

> Many essential life-cycle resources, not to mention recreational and esthetic needs, are best provided for man by the less "productive" landscapes. . . . Until recently mankind has more or less taken for granted the gas-exchange, water-purification nutrient cycling, and other protective functions of self-maintaining ecosystems, that is, until his numbers and his environmental manipulations became great enough to affect regional and global balances.

The problems that arise from human attempts to maintain highly simplified agricultural ecosystems, in particular the use of commercial fertilizers and chemical pesticides to replace natural processes of nutrient recycling and population regulation, will be discussed in detail in the following sections, but the overall vulnerability of a highly simplified agricultural ecosystem is well illustrated by the "Dust Bowl" incident. In this instance, the desired crops proved ill-adapted to the short term climatic fluctuations that characterize the Great Plains. Years of continuous wheat monoculture, resulting in a gradual deterioration in soil structure and fertility, the practice of bare fallowing, and the failure to plant windbreaks or to interplant grass strips that would have provided a greater degree of protection to the soil, all contributed to the intensification of soil erosion.

The epidemic of southern corn leaf blight that devastated the corn crop in the United States in 1970 provides a further example of the dangers of uniformity. The blight attacked only a single type of corn, a high-yielding variety known as Texas cytoplasm, but this variety accounted for over 80% of the total acreage under corn (Tatum: 1971). An alarming picture emerges from a recent report prepared by the National Research Council of the National Academy of Sciences on the extent to which many staple crops have become genetically uniform and vulnerable to epidemics (National Academy of Sciences: 1972). This trend towards uniformity is apparent, for example, in the "Green Revolution" where many farmers now plant a single high-yielding variety in place of several different traditional varieties (Frankel, Agble, Harlan, and Bennett: 1969). The potential consequences of some sort of corn-blight incident affecting a staple food crop can best be appreciated by recalling the Irish famine of the 1850's where the population was essentially dependent upon a single crop, the potato. As the NRC report warns, the methods and technologies of production that have evolved in the United States and that are now being transferred to the developing world are increasing the probability of major crop epidemics. The crux of the problem is to be found in the economic pressures that encourage uniformity. The farmer, for example, is confronted with a situation where production costs are at least partially dependent upon the degree of diversification and where uniform crops are easier to sow, easier to harvest and easier to market. Thus the farmer is forced to choose between the low production costs and economic advantages of a monoculture and the high-cost but low-risk strategy of diversification. All too frequently, the short-term advantages of the former course of action are more immediately apparent.

THE IMPACT OF COMMERCIAL FERTILIZER USAGE ON BIOGEOCHEMICAL CYCLES

The harvesting of plant growth for human consumption inevitably disrupts natural nutrient recycling mechanisms. At the same time, the displacement of the natural vegetation community by a crop cover that provides less protection to the soil results in increased surface runoff and accelerated rates of soil erosion and nutrient loss. Without any compensating increase in the rate of weathering, the available pool of nutrients in the soil-humus complex would be gradually depleted. Over the centuries, a number of strategies have evolved designed to replace natural recycling mechanisms and to compensate for nutrient loss. The practice of using animal manures, for example, dates back to pre-Classical times. The agricultural history of manure and the continued importance of manure in many agricultural economies have been reviewed by Mather and Hart (1956). In the last century, however, advances in chemical fertilizer technology affecting the production of the primary soil macronutrients—nitrogen, phosphorus and potassium—and the realization that intensive fertilizer application could triple or even quadruple soil productivity, have resulted in a growing dependency on artificial fertilizers (Pratt: 1965; Sauchelli: 1960). The potential impact of this strategy to maintain and increase the productivity of agricultural systems on the cycling of nitrogen and phosphorus has now become a subject of considerable controversy.

Human Activities and the Nitrogen Cycle

Human intervention in the nitrogen cycle probably exceeds all other interventions in terms of magnitude. As discussed by David Watts in an earlier chapter, only a few highly specialized organisms are capable of "fixing" free atmospheric nitrogen into a form that can be utilized by other plants. However, a variety of industrial processes have been developed whereby atmospheric nitrogen can be cheaply incorporated into such inorganic compounds as ammonium sulfate and ammonium phosphate. It has been estimated that the amount of nitrogen "fixed" in industrial processes each year now equals the amount that was biologically fixed by all terrestrial ecosystems prior to the development of modern agriculture (Delwiche: 1970).

This rapid increase in the mobilization of nitrogen for use in the biosphere has alarmed many ecologists. They have pointed to the high nitrate content of many water sources and to high nitrate concentrations in certain foods as causes for real concern (Commoner: 1968a, 1968b). Commoner in his address to the American Association for the Advancement of Science suggested that the magnitude of these hazards will eventually require restrictions on the usage of nitrogen fertilizers (Commoner: 1970). These claims have not gone unchallenged. Byerly, for example, while recognizing the desirability of reducing the entry of nitrates from fertilizers into ground and surface waters states that: "The degree of control compatible with essential crop production will depend on the improvement of technology through research and the application of that technology. This we can and should do. I do not share Dr. Commoner's alarm. I see no clear and present danger" (Byerly: 1970, p. 105). Viets and Hageman, in a review of the factors affecting the accumulation of nitrate in soil, water, and plants (1971), conclude (p. 53) that

> the available information on nitrate in soil, water, foods and feeds is that the potential for nitrate accumulation does not pose a threat of an environmental crisis. There is no indication of widespread upward trends of nitrate concentrations in foods, feeds, surface or groundwater.

Viets and Hageman go even further (p. 54) in challenging Commoner:

> Since much of our farmland has already lost much of its native organic N, thereby impairing its capacity to produce unless fertilized, we must use increasing amounts of fertilizer to utilize the full potential of our better varieties and water resources. The "balance of nature" can be better restored by using higher rates of N fertilizer than by using less.

In view of our imperfect knowledge of the functioning of the nitrogen cycle, assessing these conflicting claims on the impact of man's intervention in the cycle becomes a major problem. It does appear, however, that before the large-scale industrial fixation of nitrogen, the amount of nitrogen removed from the atmosphere by natural fixation processes was closely balanced by the amount returned to the atmosphere through denitrification. This steady-state situation at the global level was maintained by the various self-regulating, feedback mechanisms already described by David Watts. However, with the rapid increase in the rate at which fixed nitrogen is being introduced into the biosphere by industrial fixation and through the cultivation of legumes, many ecologists express the concern that denitrification may not be keeping pace with fixation processes (Delwiche: 1970; Institute of Ecology: 1972). A substantial body of research provides some indication as to the rate at which fixed nitrogen may be building up in the biosphere: in the soil, in groundwater reservoirs, in rivers, and lakes. Harmeson and Larson, for example, have shown an average increase of over 50 percent in the nitrate levels of the surface waters of four major Illinois rivers (Harmeson and Larson: 1970). Similarly studies of the agricultural and urban areas of the Fresno-Clovis region in California and of the Grover City-Arroya Grande Basin in California, both reveal a trend of increasing nitrate concentrations in the ground water reservoirs (Nightingale: 1970; Stout and Bureau: 1967). Nor are such trends restricted to the United States. The research of Gruener and Shuval indicates increasing nitrification of ground water in the coastal plain of Israel (Gruener and Shuval: 1970).

One of the main concerns regarding the buildup of nitrates in natural water bodies is eutrophication. The basic processes involved in eutrophication have been well reviewed (Sawyer: 1966; Hasler: 1970). There exist several excellent case studies of eutrophication, in particular of Lake Washington by Edmondson and of the Great Lakes by Beeton (Edmondson, Anderson and Peterson: 1956; Beeton: 1965; Edmondson: 1968, 1970). Limited eutrophication benefits a surface water body in that the increased input of nutrients promotes algal growth, providing an increased food supply for the herbivorous animals higher up the food chain. Excessive nutrient enrichment, however, supports large growths of algae, the "algae blooms" that choke waterways and intakes and hinder navigation. At the same time, the higher levels of community respiration resulting from the decomposition of the increased mass of organic matter leads to severe O_2 depletion with disastrous impacts on the fish population. In those portions of the water body where biochemical oxygen demand (BOD) exceeds the available dissolved oxygen (DO), decomposition continues under anaerobic conditions which leads to the generation of foul smells and odors that further reduce the aesthetic and recreational value of the water body. Recent research has shown that it is the availability of phosphates rather than of nitrates that is the key to the control of eutrophication in water bodies. In particular, it appears that many nuisance species of blue-green algae are capable of fixing atmospheric nitrogen and can therefore exist independently of other sources of nitrogen (Oglesby and Edmondson: 1966; Institute of Ecology: 1972).

In addition to eutrophication, ecologists are concerned that nitrate concentrations in foodstuffs, feeds and water supplies present a growing health hazard. The U.S. Public Health Service has established a standard of 10 ppm of nitrate nitrogen as a level that should not be exceeded in drinking water. In many areas (for example, in parts of Illinois, Missouri, and Iowa) nitrate levels in well and ground waters exceed this limit (Keller and Smith: 1967). Nitrates are also a natural constituent of plants but occur in particularly high concentrations in such vegetables as spinach. A high intake of nitrates, however, only represents a hazard where circumstances are favorable for their conversion to toxic substances. In the gastrointestinal tracts of infants, for example, nitrate may be reduced to nitrite which can cause the physiological disorder, methemoglobinemia, the nitrite combining with hemoglobin to reduce the blood's oxygen carrying capacity. Numerous infant deaths from this disorder have been recorded although careful monitoring of water supplies have substantially reduced the number in the United States in the last two decades (Bosch, Rosenfeld, Huston, Shipman and Woodward: 1950; Lenain: 1970; Gruener and Shuval: 1970). The possible reaction of nitrite with amines to form toxic compounds and the possible carcinogenic effect of nitrosamines is also a subject of growing concern (Wolff and Wasserman: 1972). Wolff and Wasserman (1972) provide an excellent review of the current status of research in this area. It is their conclusion (p. 18) that while further research is still required, the health hazard presented by nitrites and nitrosamines does not appear to be sufficiently great to cause alarm.

A general trend of increased nitrate concentrations in the environment has been established, yet the precise nature and magnitude of the threat contained in this build-up is the subject of considerable debate. In a similar vein there is disagreement as to the precise role of commercial fertilizers in the build-up of nitrate. Critics of commercial fertilizers point to the inefficiency of crops in making use of the nitrogen that is applied. About 90 percent of the commercial nitrogen fertilizer used on American farms is in the form of ammonia, ammonium salts or urea. Ammonium is retained against leaching in all soils except the most sandy, but if the soil is moist and the temperature above 45°F it is quickly nitrified to nitrate. Nitrate, however, being negatively charged is only weakly held on ion exchange surfaces in the soil (the negatively charged soil particles that act as exchange sites tightly retaining only positively charged nutrient ions). Nitrate is therefore likely to be rapidly leached out of the soil. Allison's detailed studies of the recovery of nitrogen by plants indicate that usually less than 50 percent of the nitrogen applied or mineralized from organic matter is recovered in harvested crops (Allison: 1965, 1966). Commoner summarizes (1968b, p. 12) the critics' argument as follows: "We must look for some of the six million tons of nitrogen added to U.S. soils during the last year not in the soil or in the harvested crops, but in the nation's lakes and rivers, and in the rain and snow that falls on the land." A recent study of nitrate concentration in the Sangamon watershed of Illinois concluded that a minimum of 55 to 60 percent of the nitrate in the surface waters of the catchment originated from fertilizer nitrogen (Kohl, Shearer, and Commoner: 1971), although the accuracy of the data collection method, based on differences in the natural isotopic composition of soil nitrogen, fertilizer nitrogen and atmospheric nitrogen has been challenged (Hauck et al.: 1972). It is in this context that the disadvantages inherent in man's efforts to maintain the productivity of agricultural ecosystems become apparent. Under natural conditions, as already noted, not only is the nitrogen cycle balanced at the global level, but at the local level there is a very conservative use of nutrients. Most of the nitrogen in the soil is in the form of organic substances bound up in the humus complex. The nitrogen incorporated in organic matter is slowly released in the form of ammonium nitrogen which is either taken up directly by plants or oxidized by other soil bacteria to nitrate which is immediately taken up by the plants. As a result, the natural concentration of nitrate in the soil is low and comparatively little is leached out of the soil.

In modern agricultural ecosystems the tendency of many farmers to rely solely on commercial nitrogen fertilizers that are rapidly converted to nitrate results in the leakage of nitrates into groundwater, rivers and lakes. At the same time, the efficiency of nutrient recovery is reduced since the failure to maintain the organic structure of the soil means that soil porosity, and hence the supply of oxygen that is essential to the process of nutrient absorption, is reduced.

Problems of nitrate loss are further compounded by excessive usage of nitrogen fertilizers at rates far in excess of crop needs. Ward (1970), for example, cites a report of the California Department of Water Resources indicating that the average annual application of nitrogen for certain vegetable crops in the Grover City area was as much as 290 lbs. per acre—not surprisingly, this area now reveals high concentrations of nitrate in the shallow water table.

The defenders of commercial fertilizers, however, point to the array of alternative mechanisms that can lead to the concentration of nitrate in the environment, including sewage treatment plants, livestock and poultry feeding operations as well as natural biological and geological processes (Viets and Hageman: 1971, pp. 12-21). Smith (1967) has shown that natural water supplies in a number of areas of the United States contain concentrations of nitrate that are of concern to sanitary engineers—yet such supplies can have received only small amounts of nitrate from fertilizers. Spring waters in the Ozarks, for example, contain significant levels of nitrate nitrogen, yet the catchment area is largely forested with little use of fertilizer and sparse population of both humans and livestock. Smith's analysis of rural water supplies in Missouri (1965) also indicates that animal wastes and septic tank seepage rather than commercial fertilizers are the most significant sources of nitrate contamination of the shallow wells and surface reservoirs that are the main source of domestic water supplies. His conclusions that organic wastes are frequently a major causal factor of high nitrate levels in groundwater have been supported by other researchers (Stout and Bureau: 1967; Stewart, Viets and Hutchinson: 1968).

Human Activities and the Phosphorus Cycle

The effect of human intervention on the phosphorus cycle is similarly a source of growing concern to ecologists—however the nature of these concerns is rather different from those expressed in relation to the disruption of the nitrogen cycle and reflects significant differences in the dynamics of these two cycles. Of particular significance is that, in contrast to nitrogen, the phosphorus cycle lacks a gaseous phase; hence the pool of phosphorus immediately available to man cannot be replenished by interaction between the atmosphere and living systems. In the natural cycle, as described by David Watts earlier in this volume, phosphates are leached or eroded from the land surface and transported to streams, lakes and, ultimately, to the ocean. The return of phosphorus to the land is almost entirely dependent upon the geologic uplift of ocean sediments, a rate of return that in human terms is virtually non-existent. Hence the concern over human intervention in the phosphorus cycle is focussed on the functioning of the cycle at the global level. As far as the human population is concerned, phosphorus, unlike nitrogen, is essentially a non-renewable resource. Yet the natural rate of phosphate mobilization has been increased through mining phosphate rock and the down-hill movement of phosphorus to deep ocean sediments has been accelerated through poor management. Various estimates have suggested that (assuming unchanging levels of technology and projecting current growth rates in the use of phosphate fertilizers) available reserves of phosphorus will be exhausted well before the end of the twenty-first century (Institute of Ecology: 1972, pp. 53-56).

In other respects, however, human intervention in the phosphorus cycle has repercussions more comparable to those evident in the nitrogen cycle. The greater part of the phosphorus applied to the soil in the form of fertilizers is rapidly immobilized in the form of phosphate salts (calcium phosphate; aluminum phosphate) that are not readily soluble in water, hence crops are unable to make a very efficient use of added amounts of phosphorus. While the relative insolubility of phosphates limits the amount of leaching that occurs, surface run-off and erosion transports phosphorus from heavily fertilized farm lands to rivers and lakes, contributing to the problem of eutrophication. As in the case of nitrogen, part of the phosphate fertilizer is removed in the form of harvested crops. In the processing and consumption of these crops, however, these macronutrients are released in the form of waste products, urine and feces. In urban areas, sewerage systems concentrate wastes for treatment, but even with secondary treatment about 70 percent of the phosphorus passes through into the effluent (American Chemical Society: 1969, p. 108). Similar concentrations of phosphorus and nitrogen occur at feedlots, contributing again to the nutrient enrichment of natural water bodies. Here again, however, there is disagreement as to the relative contribution of agricultural sources to the process of eutrophication. Verduin, for example, has concluded that the contribution of phosphorus from agricultural sources is substantially less than from municipal sources, and that in the municipal sewage fraction detergents contribute about three times more phosphate than is contributed by domestic organic matter (Verduin: 1967). A recent study of agricultural pollution in the Great Lakes has estimated that less than 2½ percent of the phosphorus entering Lake Erie and Lake Ontario is attributable to fertilizer use (Cywin and Ward: 1971, p. 30).

It is now possible to summarize briefly the rather contrasting ways in which man's attempts to maintain and increase the productivity of his agricultural systems have altered the phasing of two major biogeochemical cycles. In the first place, human needs have accelerated the rate at which phosphorus and nitrogen are being introduced into the biosphere. Ultimately, following man's use, these elements are circulated through the environment but *en route* secondary concentrations may occur either through human processes (as in the case of waste water treatment plants), or through natural processes (as in the case of eutrophication). It is in these areas of secondary concentration that the major problems of environmental quality occur at a predominantly local level. Analysis of these environmental problems therefore frequently involves consideration of locational and spatial relationships, relationships that are of particular concern to the geographer. It should be evident that spatial distributions lie at the heart of many environmental problems. The concentration of organic wastes for sewage treatment and the concentration of animals in feedlots are dictated by economies of scale, yet both processes result in the large and concentrated discharge of nutrients at a single point.

THE IMPACT OF CHEMICAL PESTICIDES
ON THE STRUCTURE AND FUNCTIONING OF ECOSYSTEMS

The intensity of debate over the benefits and risks associated with commercial fertilizers has been surpassed by the controversy surrounding the use of chemical pesticides to control the population size of unwanted species. In reviewing this controversy, it is necessary to bear in mind (1) that there exists a vast range of insecticides, herbicides, miticides and fungicides; (2) that these various pesticides differ greatly in their mode of action, in the length of time they remain in the biosphere, and in their toxicity (see Appendix at end of this chapter), and (3) that the use of chemical pesticides represents only one of a wide range of possible methods of pest control. Williams (1967) has described what he terms the "three generations of pesticides," namely (1) a first generation exemplified by inorganic salts such as lead arsenate and copper sulfate, (2) the DDT generation of persistent, broad-spectrum chemical pesticides that have dominated pest control since the second world war, and (3) a future generation consisting of insect hormones and biological controls that aim at specific control of particular species.

As the Appendix to this chapter suggests, chemical pesticides are designed and valued for their deadly effect on living organisms. Inevitably, therefore, there must be concern over the ultimate fate of these substances. All pesticides in common use produce residues that survive for varying periods of time on plant foliage or in soils, a characteristic that in conjunction with the toxicity of the residue is important in determining how soon crops can be harvested and consumed after a pesticide has been applied. Some pesticides (for example, insecticides of the organic phosphorus group and herbicides such as 2,4-D) produce residues that survive for only a few days. In the case of the chlorinated hydrocarbons, sizable amounts of the original application survive in the environment in unaltered form for years—in one experiment, for example, 39 percent of the DDT applied still remained in the soil in its original form seventeen years later (Nash and Woolson: 1967). Persistence of pesticides is an advantage to the farmer insofar as the residual activity of the pesticide against pest species reduces the need for frequent applications, *but* the longer the pesticide remains in the environment the greater the potential for its dispersal through the environment with obvious dangers for other species. The chemical processes involved in the ultimate breakdown of toxic residues in the soil into nontoxic compounds have been the subject of numerous symposia and reviews (Alexander: 1967; American Chemical Society: 1969; Rosen and Kraybill: 1966). Since the greatest concern is usually directed towards the surviving residue of the parent chemical, it is perhaps worth noting that under certain circumstances the derivative products can be more toxic than the parent residue. For example, in the breakdown of aldrin, widely used in the past in fire ant control programs, the more persistent and toxic compound dieldrin may be formed (Rudd: 1964*b*).

The Chlorinated Hydrocarbon Group

Much of the recent criticism of pesticide practices has been directed against the widespread use of the chlorinated hydrocarbon group of insecticides. These insecticides are non-specific (i.e., they are toxic not only to the targeted pest but also to other insects) and they are highly persistent. Once a persistent, broad-spectrum pesticide has been introduced into the environment it becomes subject to normal ecological processes (Wurster: 1969). As a result, residues are likely to be found in non-target organisms and in areas far removed from sources of direct contamination. Significant levels of DDT (averaging 6.4 parts per million) have been found in the eggs and young of the Bermuda Petrel, a rare oceanic bird whose feeding habits are wholly pelagic and whose breeding grounds have never been treated with DDT (Wurster and Wingate: 1968). Again, high levels of DDT have been found in the tissues of Adelie penguins and Skua gulls in the Antarctic, an area remote from the nearest point of pesticide application (Sladen, Menzie and Reichel: 1966; Tatton and Ruzicka: 1967). The physical and biological processes responsible for the dispersal and concentration of pesticide residues have been well reviewed by Wurster (1969). Biological mechanisms include the transfer of residues through food chains, a process that has been studied in some detail in relation to the southern shore of Long Island (Woodwell, Wurster and Isaacson: 1967). Physical mechanisms include the dispersal of residues through both atmospheric and fluvial processes. There is increasing evidence that atmospheric dispersal—as a result of drift, vaporization and codistillation with water—is a major disseminator of pesticide residues (Cohen and Pinkerton: 1966; Frost: 1969; Risebrough, Huggett, Griffin and Goldberg: 1968; Woodwell: 1967). The dispersal and accumulation of chlorinated hydrocarbon residues has been greatly aggravated by the use of aerial spraying techniques. According to the National Agricultural Aviation Association, aircraft applied 65 percent of all pesticides used by farmers in 1970 (U.S. Department of Agriculture: 1972a), yet as Woodwell (1961) has suggested less than half of an insecticide sprayed from a plane is likely to reach the target on the ground. The ineffectiveness of the campaign to eradicate the imported fire ant, which was based on mass aerial spraying of entire landscapes, has been well documented by Brown (1961). As he points out, better results could probably have been achieved with less expenditure of federal funds and less destruction of beneficial species through more controlled applications.

Effects on the Animal Population

It has already been noted that the environmental stress associated with the use of commercial fertilizers is greatest following secondary concentration of the primary nutrients. In a similar manner, the dangers inherent in the global dispersal and accumulation of persistent pesticides are intensified as a result of the biological concentration of residues. Thus, while residual values as measured in soil, air and water may appear to be low and insignificant, residues in organisms further up the food chain may be approaching levels that are catastrophic for those populations. This process of biological magnification has been well documented (Rudd: 1964a; Hickey, Keith and Coon: 1966; Woodwell, Wurster and Isaacson: 1967; Woodwell: 1967). The Woodwell, Wurster and Isaacson study revealed that the birds at the top of the food chain had concentrations of DDT a million times greater than those occurring in the estuary waters (Figure 3). In this instance, the process of biological magnification resulted mainly from the trophic concentration of residues, i.e., as organic matter is consumed by the predator, stored residues are also transferred from prey to predator. In contrast to organic matter, however, the losses of pesticide residues along the food chain are small in proportion to the amount that is transferred, a process that results in the highest concentrations in the higher order carnivores. This process is compounded by the physiological concentration of residues in the lipid or fatty fractions of body tissues and in organs such as the liver and kidneys.

While direct kills of birds and animals as a result of the magnification of residues to toxic levels have been recorded, of increasing concern to ecologists is the evidence that DDT and other chlorinated hydrocarbon residues may be affecting species numbers in much more subtle ways. Peakall and others, for example, have shown that the chlorinated hydrocarbons interfere with calcium metabolism in bird populations by inducing a breakdown in steroid hormones.

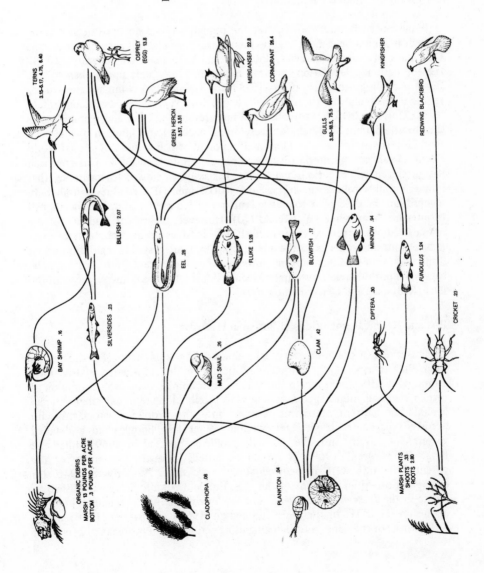

Figure 3. Concentration of DDT in a Long Island Estuary Food Web. Numbers indicate residues of DDT and its derivatives (in parts per million, wet-weight, whole body basis) found in each kind of organism. (From Woodwell, George M., "Toxic Substances and Ecological Cycles" copyright © 1967 by Scientific American, Inc. All rights reserved.)

Aberrant calcium metabolism has been linked both to a decrease in clutch size and to a reduction in the size and thickness of eggshells, eggs being produced with shells so thin that the chances of embryo mortality or breakage are greatly increased (Peakall: 1967, 1970; Bitman, Cecil, Harris and Fries: 1969). It would appear that DDT and its metabolites have had adverse effects on the reproduction rates of a wide range of bird species including the Bermuda Petrel, the brown pelican, the peregrine falcon and the sparrow hawk (Ames: 1966; Wurster and Wingate: 1968; Hickey and Anderson: 1968; Anderson, Hickey, Risebrough, Hughes and Christensen: 1969; Porter and Wiemeyer: 1969; Heath, Spann and Kreitzer: 1969), although it should be noted that polychlorinated biphenyls (PCB's), mercury and lead may be influencing reproduction rates in a similar manner (Institute of Ecology: 1972, p. 142).

Effects on the Human Population

While no such direct effects on the human population have been demonstrated, it should be evident that no human can have escaped accumulating some DDT in body tissues (Davies, Edmundson, Schneider and Cassady: 1968). Present pesticide legislation and the monitoring programs undertaken by the Food and Drug Administration (FDA) are designed to eliminate the risk of residues accumulating to hazardous levels by establishing acceptable safety levels. Thus the FDA has established 5 ppm residue of DDT and metabolites as the threshold limit for such fish as salmon, mackerel and kingfish on the basis that daily consumption of a quarter of a pound of fish would not exceed World Health Organization criteria for acceptable daily intake of DDT. This approach has produced some curious paradoxes. It has been shown, for example, that mother's milk contains on average 0.1 to 0.2 ppm DDT residue, considerably higher than the 0.05 ppm tolerance limit permitted by the FDA in milk shipped in interstate commerce (Wurster: 1970). However, the recent evidence of the rather insidious effects of comparatively low residues on bird populations must raise serious questions as to the adequacy of present pesticide legislation which in no way protects humans from contamination. One recent study, for example, suggests a possible relationshhip between residual DDT levels and cirrhosis of the liver (Radomski and Deichmann: 1969).

Past and Recent Recognitions of Potential Hazards

Thus much of the controversy surrounding the use of chemical pesticides has been directed against the persistent pesticides of the chlorinated hydrocarbon group, with critics pointing to the reduction in numbers and even extinction of certain bird and animal species as well as to possible long-term dangers to human health. The current status of research into the problems associated with persistent pesticides is well reviewed in Miller and Berg, while a detailed government inquiry into the pesticide problem appeared in 1969 (Miller and Berg: 1969; Mrak: 1969). It should be noted, however, that many of the potential hazards were recognized at an early stage. As early as 1946, for example, Cottam and Higgins of the U.S. Fish and Wildlife Service published an article in the *Journal of Economic Entomology* warning of the dangers inherent in the use of DDT. In the 1950's, Soloman (1953) and Ripper (1956) among others wrote of the dangers of inducing more serious pest outbreaks as a result of the growing dependency on chemical controls. However, it was the publication of *Silent Spring* by Rachel Carson in 1962 that alerted public opinion to the hazards of chemical methods of pest control. In the ensuing decade, the development of more sophisticated methods of residue detection together with extensive research into the mode of action of the most widely used pesticides, have not only confirmed the scientific validity of Rachel Carson's observations but have encouraged a reappraisal of pesticide policies and practices. In the United States, for example, the registration of DDT under the *Federal Insecticide, Fungicide and Rodenticide Act* was cancelled in January 1971 by the Environmental Protection Agency. Accordingly, the insecticide cannot presently be offered for shipment in interstate commerce. Within the past few years, the registration of several pesticides has been suspended. These include certain mercury fungicides used for seed treatment, and liquid formulations of the weed killer 2,4,5-T registered for use on lakes and ponds, one of the constituent compounds of 2,4,5-T having been shown to be teratogenic (or fetus-deforming) at extremely low concentrations (Nelson: 1969; Gruchow: 1970). Under the *Federal Environmental Pesticide Control Act* of 1972, pesticide products will continue to be registered for particular uses on a product by product basis without any special provision for particular groups of pesticides such as chlorinated hydrocarbons. However, the act does require that all pesticides must now be classified for either restricted or general use and that restricted pesticides can be employed only by certified persons. There remain, however, remarkable variations in pesticide legislation. Japan, for example, has totally banned use of the organophosphate TEPP, yet this product remains registered for a wide variety of uses in the United States (Rudd: 1971). Today, few proponents of continued usage of chemical pesticides would subscribe to the hysterical outcry that followed the publication of *Silent Spring* (Graham: 1970, pp. 59-86). However, defenders of chemical pesticides point to the potential loss of control over many vector borne diseases should usage of chlorinated hydrocarbons be severely restricted on a global basis. The World Health Organization has estimated, for example, that well over 1,000 million persons were freed from the risk of malaria during the decade 1959-1970 largely through the use of DDT (World Health Organization: 1971).

Ecological Effects of Chemical Control

As the benefits and risks involved in the use of persistent chemical pesticides have become more apparent, so the argument over pesticide practices has tended to focus on whether or not particular pesticides or groups of pesticides should be restricted or banned. In the process, the broader dimensions of pest control practices have been largely obscured. In particular, it is not always appreciated that chemical methods of control, far from offering a permanent solution to the problem of pest control, serve only to intensify the problem.

In this context it should be evident that when large areas are planted with a limited number of crops, the organisms that thrive on those crops are likely to increase their numbers and their range, particularly as many of the natural predators are unlikely to find the altered habitat to their liking. In this respect, a pest may represent a man-made hazard. The complexity of a natural ecosystem provides an array of regulating mechanisms that contribute to the stability of population members. Biotic controls, such as prey-predator relationships, regulate population size by producing changes in numbers that are density-dependent, i.e., mortality rates increase as population density increases and vice versa. In the simplified ecosystems created by humans, however, the agents that would normally begin to operate following an increase in the numbers of any population are no longer present. The human strategy is to deal with this situation by substituting chemical methods of control for natural regulatory mechanisms. Such a strategy cannot provide a long-term solution for it fails to provide for the *permanent* regulation of population numbers. Repeated pesticide applications are required, timed to hit the target species whenever it begins to re-establish itself, a procedure that is extremely costly in terms of materials, time and manpower, and that places a premium on the use of broad-spectrum persistent pesticides. In the long term, the human strategy leads to the destruction of beneficial species, to the resurgence of pests to population levels much higher and more damaging than those recorded prior to pesticide use, and to the development of resistance in certain target populations (Figure 4).

Of particular significance is the further decrease in the efficiency with which natural regulatory mechanisms will operate as a result of the elimination of parasites and predators capable of containing a resurgence of pest numbers (Conway: 1969, 1971). In a similar manner, nonselective pesticides may kill off the natural predators of a hitherto harmless species that may then build up to pest status. The increase in numbers of mites and scale insects, for example, can be attributed to the reduction in numbers of their natural, insecticide-susceptible, predators. In England, the red spider mite has become a serious pest in fruit orchards following intensive pesticide use that eliminated ladybirds and other predators (Massee: 1958). Resistance to pesticides is not a new phenomenon but since the introduction of organic pesticides the number of resistant species has increased dramatically. In the early 1940's some ten pest species showed resistance, principally to the older inorganic insecticides such as lead arsenate. By 1967, however, over 200 species exhibited resistance to one or more pesticides (Conway: 1971). In order to counteract growing resistance farmers frequently resort to increased applications of different pesticides, but as a number of ecologists have pointed out, the effectiveness of this response is open to question due to the phenomenon of cross-resistance, i.e., a species that acquires resistance to one specific insecticide will also possess a degree of resistance to other insecticides (Institute of Ecology: 1972, p. 121).

Benefits, Risks, and Alternatives

Clearly there are both benefits and risks involved in the use of chemical pesticides. It is important to recognize, however, that dependency upon chemical pesticides offers, at best, a temporary stop-gap solution to the overall problem of pest control. A recognition of the dangers of massive applications of chemical pesticides appears to be particularly important in those developing countries which, as noted earlier, appear to be on the verge of a yield breakthrough. Unless alternative solutions are available, it is inevitable that farmers in these countries will adopt the strategies of pest control used in developed countries. A good deal of research and field experimentation has already gone into the development of alternative methods of pest control. The problems and potentialities of these various methods have been discussed in several excellent reviews (Kilgore and Doutt: 1967; Conway: 1971). Biological controls, that seek to simulate nature's

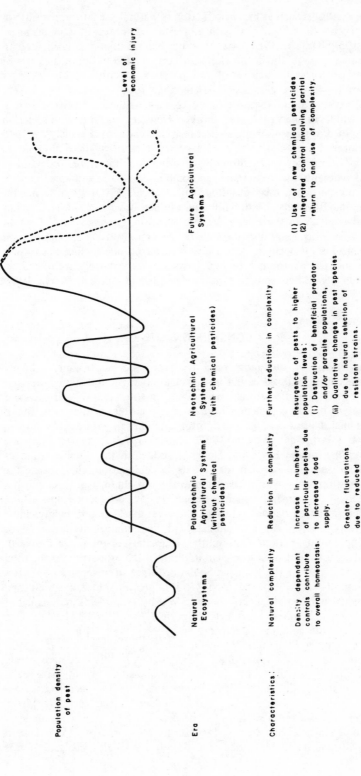

Figure 4. The Historical Development of Pest Control and Pest Fluctuations. Adapted from Moore, 1967.

own control methods, such as the introduction of natural predatory, parasitic or pathogenic species, have been used with a measure of success in some instances (Huffaker: 1959; Ordish: 1967). Another mechanism that has been used to control the screw worm fly in the United States and the mosquito in parts of Southeast Asia involves the release of vast numbers of either sterile males or incompatible strains of a pest species (Knipling: 1960, 1964, 1965; Laven: 1967). Clearly these alternatives are likely to vary in their effectiveness from pest to pest and from one situation to another. However, together with selection and breeding of crops for disease and pest resistance rather than solely for yield and with improved crop and habitat management practices, these alternatives offer the opportunity for what entomologists refer to as integrated programs of pest control whereby the techniques or combinations of techniques can be adjusted to the particular local situation (Chant: 1966; FAO: 1966; Kennedy: 1968; Smith and Reynolds: 1966; Smith and van den Bosch: 1967). The success of integrated controls in the Canete Valley, a cotton growing area of Peru, in retrieving a near crisis situation, characterized by rapidly rising expenditure on chemical pesticides yet declining yields due to the continued resurgence of pest populations and the appearance of new pests, has been vividly recounted by Smith and van den Bosch and by Conway (Smith and van den Bosch: 1967; Conway: 1971).

CONCLUSION

The management of the agricultural resource base has become a highly complex science. As discussed earlier in this chapter, the human population has been engaged in altering the natural environment for thousands of years. Even as primitive hunters, human groups may have been responsible for the extinction of numerous animal species through overhunting, habitat alteration and competition for food (Martin and Wright: 1967; Martin: 1973), a subject discussed elsewhere in this volume by Robin Doughty. But with the domestication of animals and the selection of particular plants for cultivation, there began the process of more direct human intervention in the biosphere, a process that has culminated in the intensively managed and highly productive agricultural systems of industrialized nations. Through the careful selection of high-yielding species and strains of plants and animals and the removal of unwanted or competing populations, natural communities, characterized by a high degree of diversity and stability but by a low yield in terms of the proportion of the total biomass that is useful to the human population, have been replaced by a less diverse community in which the food yield is greater. Modern agricultural systems in industrialized nations are characterized by crop yields undreamed of by farmers even a hundred years ago, this yield breakthrough having been achieved through the coupling of nutrient and energy flows within the system with external "auxiliary" sources. While the overall goal has been to maximize food production to meet the needs of a rapidly growing population, many of the strategies adopted, particularly by farmers in the western world, have been dictated by social attitudes and economic pressures. Thus the need to ensure a high net return on capital invested in agricultural operations encourages both uniformity and the adoption of those modern technologies, such as chemical methods of pest control, that promise (at least in the short term) an increase in the productivity and profitability of farming operations. Farm amalgamation is encouraged by economic pressures to achieve economies of scale. Commercial fertilizer costs, relative to the resultant increase in crop productivity, are lower than for any other economic input (Commoner: 1971, 1972). The benefits to the farmer and to the community in terms of increased food production are very clear, but, given the decrease in efficiency with which crops respond to higher and higher applications of fertilizer, a disproportionate increase in fertilizer input is required to achieve the final few bushels of increased yield, much of the extra fertilizer being leached or otherwise lost from the soil.

But the "costs" of disposing of this surplus fertilizer—together with the other chemical by-products, pesticide residues and organic wastes generated in modern agricultural systems—are allocated to the environment and borne by the community as a whole in the form of a decline in environmental quality. In a similar manner, chemical methods of pest control (specifically the use of broad spectrum, persistent pesticides) represent a cheap and effective way of achieving an immediate reduction in the population density of target organisms. In the long term, however, the accompanying destruction of the natural predators of the target species, the development of resistance and the reduced intra-species competition negate the short-term benefits. Thus despite the fact that expenditure on chemical pesticides has risen steadily, the threat of strong pest resurgences has increased.

As a recent Institute of Ecology task force has emphasized, "intense management of ecosystems as we know it today can never be dependable without a remarkably comprehensive understanding of the workings of the whole ecosystem" (Institute of Ecology: 1972, p. 98). The basic question that must be addressed with regard to the management of modern agricultural systems is whether the strategies employed to achieve the desired goal of high productivity are consistent with other, equally critical considerations, namely (1) the need to ensure the long-term stability of agricultural systems, and (2) the need to prevent long-term degradation of the productive capacity of the biosphere. A number of problems that arise from human attempts to maintain the productivity of highly simplified agricultural systems have been identified in this chapter; to these may be added the problem of accelerated soil erosion discussed by Butzer elsewhere in this volume.

In *Conserving Life on Earth*, David Ehrenfeld suggests that loss of diversity represents by far the most serious of the many environmental problems stemming from man's alteration of the biosphere (1972, p. 49). The potential instability of agricultural ecosystems in which species diversity has been reduced and in which the selection and breeding of desirable strains has produced genetic uniformity is a subject of growing concern to many ecologists (Institute of Ecology: 1972, pp. 91-162; Watt: 1973). As Ehrenfeld points out, the breeding and development of high-yielding varieties, as exemplified in the "Green Revolution," was made possible only by a pre-existing diversity of plant types, yet the manner in which the "Green Revolution" is being pursued contributes to the destruction of that diversity. It is an effective reminder of the constraints that human dependency upon natural ecological processes imposes upon the degree and manner in which ecosystems may be altered. Many of these problems are resolvable through the adoption of alternative management strategies. For example, the recovery and recycling of nutrients released to the environment in agricultural wastes and sewage effluent would not only ease the potential constraints imposed by available phosphorus reserves but help to resolve some of the problems stemming from current management practices. Alternative pest control practices, including crop rotation, biological controls and more specific pesticides, would prevent the accumulation of toxic substances hazardous to human welfare. Other management strategies, frequently unperceived by farmers, include the possibility of raising native strains of plants and animals that are likely to be capable of using incoming solar radiation more efficiently than imported species. (Talbot: 1963; Talbot and Talbot: 1963).

The future challenge is therefore to manage agricultural ecosystems in a manner that will (1) avoid the build-up of substances that are either directly hazardous to human health or damaging to the structure and functioning of ecosystems; (2) ensure the effective recycling of essential plant nutrients; and (3) preserve wherever possible, both species diversity and spatial heterogeneity in the agricultural landscape. This challenge is critical at a time when it is frequently suggested that the best hope for increasing the world's food supply lies in the future intensification of agriculture, particularly through the diffusion of modern agricultural practices to less intensively managed parts of the biosphere.

APPENDIX

CHARACTERISTICS AND MODE OF ACTION OF COMMON PESTICIDES[1]

INSECTICIDES[2]

Common Name		Mammalian Toxicity[3]

Inorganic:

Arsenicals	Sodium Arsenate	AO 10	
	Lead Arsenate	AO 825	

Arsenic pesticides (and other inorganic pesticides such as copper sulfate and various mercuric compounds) used extensively prior to development of synthetic organic pesticides. Extremely persistent; arsenic residues (avr. 304 ppm) found in soils last treated with Lead Arsenate twenty years previously (Kearney, Nash and Isensee, 1969).

Copper and zinc sulfate widely used, primarily as fungicides. Mercury compounds still used extensively as a fungicide but use in seed treatment almost eliminated in 1970 following withdrawal of registration of most products containing mercury compounds.

Organic (Synthetic):

Chlorinated	Endrin	AO 3-45;	AD 12-19
Hydrocarbon	Aldrin	AO 39-60;	AD 80-200
compounds	Dieldrin	AO 40-100;	AD 52-117
	Toxaphene	AO 40-283;	AD 60-1613
	Lindane	AO 76-200;	AD 50-1200
	DDT	AO 87-500;	AD 1931-3263
	Chlordane	AO 283-590;	AD 580-1600
	DDD	AO 400-3400;	
	Benzene Hexachloride	AO 600-1250;	
	Methoxychlor	AO 5000-7000;	AD 2800

Broad spectrum pesticides affecting a wide range of organisms in numerous different ways. Greater toxicity to insects due to the ease with which pesticides are absorbed through insect cuticles. Rate of degradation of parent compound will depend on the particular environmental conditions to which it is subjected, but in general extremely stable persisting in the environment for extended periods of time. Nash and Woolson (1967) suggest possible upper limits for persistence in soils.

Mode of action not perfectly understood but act primarily on the central nervous system. Fat soluble and residues may be stored and concentrated in fatty tissues to be released gradually after exposure ceases or more rapidly if stored fat is drawn upon as an energy source.

Organic	Tetraethyl Pyro-		
Phosphorus	phosphate (TEPP)	AO 0.5-2;	AD 2-30
compounds	Parathion	AO 3-30;	AD 4-200
	Methyl		
	Parathion	AO 9-42;	AD 63-72
	Malathion	AO 885-2800;	AD 4000

Broad spectrum insecticide. Note lower order toxicity of Malathion to mammals which is due to the production in mammals of an enzyme, carboxyesterase, that breaks down Malathion. Chemically unstable and breakdown rapidly into nontoxic materials. As a result, frequently used on fruit and vegetable crops close to harvest.

Developed from chemical warfare nerve gases. Act as inhibitors of a nerval enzyme, cholinesterase, which breaks down acetylcholine. Accumulation of this substance at nerve junctions impedes transmission of impulses to muscles etc.

Carbamates	Baygon (Trade		
	name)	AO 95-175;	AD 100
	Carbaryl	AO 307-986;	AD 500

Broad spectrum insecticide. Like organophosphates, primary mode of action is an inhibitor of cholinesterase. Non persistent. Carbaryl has a half-life in the soil of about eight days.

Organic (Botanicals):

Nicotine	Nicotine		
Alkaloids	Sulfate	AO 50-91;	AD 140
Rotenoids	Rotenone	AO 132	
Pyrethroids	Pyrethrum	AO 200-2600;	AD 1800

Naturally occurring substances derived from plant products, e.g., Pyrethroids from pyrethrum grown mainly in East Africa and Ecuador, Rotenone from leguminous plants grown in East Indies. Rotenone is particularly important in controlling cattle grubs on dairy farms as tolerances have not been established for residues of other chemicals in milk.

HERBICIDES

Chloraphenoxy			
compounds	2,4,D		
	2,4,5-T		
	Picloram		

Selective herbicides, differential effect on broadleaved plants as opposed to narrowleaved grasses. 2,4,D is rapidly broken down by soil bacteria but 2,4,5-T and Picloram are persistent and remain active for longer periods.

Chemically similar to plant hormone, indolacetic acid, that regulates plant growth. Act by inducing uncontrolled growth leading to death or leaf drop. No direct effect on soil microorganisms as indolacetic acid does not function as a growth hormone but registration for most agricultural uses of 2,4,5-T withdrawn in 1970 due to evidence that it may be teratogenic.

Symmetrical	Simazine
Triazines and	Fenuron
Substituted	Diuron
Ureas	Monuron

Interfere with the process of photosynthesis resulting in plant 'starvation.' Stable to oxidation and hydrolysis; only slowly broken down by soil microorganisms and may remain active for several seasons.

FUNGICIDES

Dithiocarbamate compounds	Nabam
	Febam
	Maneb
	Thiram
	Zineb
	Ziram

Synthetic organic compounds that are highly toxic to fungi. Extremely stable, persisting in the environment for considerable periods of time.

Dicarboximide compounds	Captan
	Folpet

Non persistent, subject to rapid breakdown by soil microorganisms. Recent experiments with animals show high incidence of birth defects following exposure to captan whose chemical structure is similar to that of thalidomide.

RODENTICIDES

(Approx. values)

Anti-coagulants	Warfarin	AO 200
	Pival	
"Immediate Action"	Strychnine alkaloid	AO 16
	Thallium	AO 17
	Sodium fluoro-acetate ('1080').	AO 3

Traditionally, rodenticides have been chemicals of high toxicity (strychnine, '1080', thallium) applied to bait materials. Toxic to all mammals and capable of producing "secondary" poisoning. Anti-coagulants have replaced traditional rodenticides particularly in domestic and urban rodent control programs, although evidence from England that some rodent populations have developed resistance to Warfarin.

NOTES TO APPENDIX

[1] Data adapted from Rudd (1964*b*), Kearney, Nash and Isensee (1969), Ehrlich (1972), U.S. Department of Agriculture (1972*a*).

[2] Certain pesticides may be directed against more than one target group.

[3] Mammalian toxicity as judged by experiments on rat populations. Toxicity is based on LD_{50} i.e. the lethal dose for 50 percent of the test population. Dosages are in milligrams per Kilogram of body weight (mg/kg); AO = acute oral toxicity, AD = Acute dermal toxicity. For example, Aldrin killed 50 percent of the test population given oral doses of 39-60 mg/kg. Applied to the skin, LD_{50} occurred in one test population with a dosage of 80 mg/kg but in another test a skin dosage of 200 mg/kg did not produce LD_{50}. Pesticides in each group are arranged in decreasing order of acute oral toxicity.

It should be emphasized that these values do not provide comparisons of differential effects deriving from age, sex, species, etc., nor can they indicate possible long-term effects, for example, the possible effects of trace amounts of chlorinated hydrocarbons on hormonal balances of mammals. There is, however, a rough correlation between other mammals and humans in the relative acute oral toxicity of these pesticides. Thus TEPP is exceedingly toxic to humans and most of the deaths attributed to pesticides (169 in the United States in 1969) are due to the mishandling of the highly toxic organophosphate pesticides.

REFERENCES

Alexander, Martin, 1967, "The Breakdown of Pesticides in Soils," in Nyle C. Brady (ed.) *Agriculture and the Quality of Our Environment*, (AAAS Publication No. 85), Washington, D.C.: American Association for the Advancement of Science, pp. 331-342.

Allison, F. E., 1965, "Evaluation of Incoming and Outgoing Processes that Affect Soil Nitrogen," in W. V. Bartholomew and F. E. Clark (eds.), *Soil Nitrogen*. Madison, Wisconsin: American Society of Agronomists, pp. 573-606.

_____, 1966, "The Fate of Nitrogen Applied to Soils," *Advanced Agronomy*, Vol. 18, pp. 219-258.

American Chemical Society, 1969, *Cleaning Our Environment: The Chemical Basis for Action*. Washington, D.C.: American Chemical Society.

Ames, Peter L., 1966, "DDT residues in the eggs of the Osprey in the northeastern United States and their relation to nesting success," *Journal of Applied Ecology*, Vol. 3, pp. 87-97.

Anderson, D. W., J. J. Hickey, R. W. Risebrough, D. F. Hughes and R. E. Christensen, 1969, "Significance of chlorinated hydrocarbon residues to breeding pelicans and cormorants," *Canadian Field-Nature*, Vol. 83, pp. 91-112.

Bates, Marston, 1969, "The Human Ecosystem" in National Academy of Sciences–National Research Council, *Resources and Man*. San Francisco: Freeman, pp. 21-30.

Beeton, Alfred M., 1965, "Eutrophication of the St. Lawrence Great Lakes," *Limnology and Oceanography*, Vol. 10, pp. 240-254.

Bitman, J., H. C. Cecil, J. J. Harris and G. F. Fries, 1969, "DDT induces a decrease in eggshell calcium" *Nature*, Vol. 224, pp. 44-46.

Bormann, F. Herbert and Gene E. Likens, 1967, "Nutrient Cycling," *Science*, Vol. 155, pp. 424-429.

_____, 1970, "The Nutrient Cycles of an Ecosystem," *Scientific American*, Vol. 223, pp. 92-101.

Bormann, F. Herbert, Gene E. Likens, D. W. Fisher and R. S. Pierce, 1968, "Nutrient Loss Accelerated by Clear-Cutting of a Forest Ecosystem," *Science*, Vol. 159, pp. 882-884.

Bosch, H. M., A. B. Rosenfeld, R. Huston, H. R. Shipman and R. L. Woodward, 1950, "Methemoglobinemia and Minnesota Well Supplies," *Journal of the American Water Works Association*, Vol. 42, pp. 161-170.

Brady, Nyle C. (ed.), 1967, *Agriculture and the Quality of Our Environment*, (AAAS Publication No. 85). Washington, D.C.: American Association for the Advancement of Science.

Brown, Lester R., 1963, *Man, Land and Food*, (Foreign Agriculture Economic Reprint No. 11). Washington, D.C.: U.S. Department of Agriculture.

———, 1965, *Increasing World Food Output*, (Foreign Agriculture Economic Reprint No. 25). Washington, D.C.: U.S. Department of Agriculture.

———, 1967, "The world outlook for conventional agriculture," *Science*, Vol. 158, pp. 604-611.

———, 1970*a*, "Human Food Production as a Process in the Biosphere," *Scientific American*, Vol. 223, pp. 161-170.

———, 1970*b*, *Seeds of Change: The Green Revolution and Development in the 1970's*. New York: Praeger.

Brown, William L., 1961, "Mass insect control programs: four case histories," *Psyche*, Vol. 68, pp. 75-109.

Byerly, T. C., 1970, "Nitrogen compounds used in crop production," in S. S. Singer (ed.), *Global Effects of Environmental Pollution*. New York: Springer-Verlag, pp. 104-109.

Carson, Rachel, 1962, *Silent Spring*. New York: Houghton-Mifflin.

Chant, D. A., 1966, "Integrated control systems," in National Academy of Sciences, *Scientific Aspects of Pest Control*. Washington, D.C.: National Academy of Sciences, pp. 193-218.

Clements, F. E., 1916, "Plant succession: analysis of the development of vegetation," *Publications of the Carnegie Institute of Washington*, Vol. 242, pp. 1-512.

Cohen, Jesse M. and Cecil Pinkerton, 1966, "Widespread Translocation of Pesticides by Air Transport and Rain-Out," in Aaron A. Rosen and H. F. Kraybill (eds.), *Organic Pesticides in the Environment*. Washington, D.C.: American Chemical Society, pp. 163-176.

Commoner, Barry, 1966, *Science and Survival*. New York: Viking Press.

———, 1968*a*, "The Balance of Nature," in W. W. Kinkle (ed.), *Providing Quality Environment in Our Communities*. Washington, D.C.: U.S. Department of Agriculture, pp. 37-62.

———, 1968*b*, "Nature Unbalanced: How Man Interferes with the Nitrogen Cycle," *Scientist and Citizen*, Vol. 10, pp. 9-19.

———, 1970, "Threats to the Integrity of the Nitrogen Cycle: Nitrogen Compounds in Soil, Water, Atmosphere and Precipitation," in S. S. Singer (ed.), *Global Effects of Environmental Pollution*. New York: Springer-Verlag, pp. 70-95.

———, 1971, *The Closing Circle: Nature, Man and Technology*. New York: Alfred A. Knopf.

———, 1972, "The Environmental Costs of Economic Growth," in Ronald G. Ridker (ed.), *Population, Resources, and The Environment*, Volume 3 of Commission Research Reports, U.S. Commission on Population Growth and the American Future. Washington, D.C.: Government Printing Office, pp. 343-362.

Conway, Gordon R., 1969, "A consequence of insecticides; Pests follow the chemicals in the cocoa of Malaysia," in M. T. Farvar and John Milton (eds.), *The Unforeseen International Boomerang*, (Special Supplement to Natural History Magazine), pp. 46-51.

———, 1971, "Better Methods of Pest Control," in William W. Murdoch (ed.), *Environment: Resources, Pollution and Society*. Stamford, Connecticut: Sinauer Associates, pp. 302-325.

Cottam, Clarence and Elmer Higgins, 1946, "DDT and Its Effect on Fish and Wildlife," *Journal of Economic Entomology*, Vol. 39, pp. 44-52.

Cywin, Allen and David Ward (eds.), 1971, *Agricultural Pollution of the Great Lakes Basin*, (Combined Report by the Environmental Protection Agency and the Water Quality Office). Washington, D.C.: U.S. Government Printing Office.

Dalrymple, Dana G., 1972, *Imports and Plantings of High Yielding Varieties of Wheat and Rice in the Less Developed Nations*, (Foreign Economic Development Report No. 14). Washington, D.C.: U.S. Department of Agriculture.

Davies, J. E., W. F. Edmundson, N. J. Schneider and J. C. Cassady, 1968, "Problems of prevalence of pesticide residues in humans," *Pesticide Monitoring Journal*, Vol. 2, pp. 80-85.

Delwiche, C. C., 1970, "The Nitrogen Cycle," *Scientific American*, Vol. 225, pp. 71-80.

Edmondson, W. T., 1968, "Water-quality management and lake eutrophication: the Lake Washington case," in T. H. Campbell and R. O. Sylvester (eds.), *Water Resources Management and Public Policy*. Seattle: University of Washington Press, pp. 139-178.

———, 1970, "Phosphorus, nitrogen and algae in Lake Washington after diversion of sewage." *Science*, Vol. 169, pp. 690-691.

Edmondson, W. T., G. C. Anderson and D. R. Peterson, 1956, "Artificial eutrophication of Lake Washington," *Limnology and Oceanography*, Vol. 1, pp. 47-53.

Ehrenfeld, David, 1972, *Conserving Life on Earth*. New York: Oxford University Press.

Ehrlich, Paul R., 1968, *The Population Bomb.* New York: Ballantine.

———, 1972, *Population, Resources, Environment: Issues in Human Ecology.* 2nd edition, San Francisco: Freeman.

Elton, Charles S., 1958, *The Ecology of Invasions by Animals and Plants.* London: Methuen.

Food and Agricultural Organization, 1966, *Proceedings of the F.A.O. Symposium on Integrated Pest Control, October, 1965.* Rome: FAO.

———, 1970, *A Strategy for Plenty.* Rome: FAO.

———, 1972, *The State of Food and Agriculture, 1971.* Rome: FAO.

Frankel, Francine, 1971, *India's Green Revolution: Economic Gains and Political Losses.* Princeton, N.J.: Princeton University Press.

Frankel, O. H., W. K. Agble, J. B. Harlan and Erna Bennett, 1969, "Genetic dangers in the Green Revolution," *Ceres,* Vol. 2, pp. 35-37.

Frost, J., 1969, "Earth, Air and Water," *Environment,* Vol. 11, pp. 14-28, 31-33.

Geertz, Clifford, 1963, *Agricultural Involution: the process of ecological change in Indonesia.* Chicago: University of Chicago Press.

Graham, Frank, 1970, *Since Silent Spring.* New York: Houghton Mifflin.

Gruchow, N., 1970, "Curbs on 2,4,5-T Use Imposed," *Science,* Vol. 168, p. 453.

Gruener, N. and H. I. Shuval, 1970, "Health Aspects of Nitrogen in Drinking Water," in H. I. Shuval (ed.), *Developments in Water Quality Research.* Ann Arbor: Humphrey Science Publications, pp. 89-106.

Harmeson, R. H. and T. E. Larson, 1970, "Existing Levels of Nitrates in Waters—The Illinois Situation," *Nitrates and Water Supply: Source and Control,* (Proceedings 12th Sanitary Engineers Conference). Urbana: University of Illinois Press, pp. 27-39.

Harris, David R., 1969a, "Agricultural systems, ecosystems and the origins of agriculture," in P. J. Ucko and G. W. Dimbleby (eds.), *The Domestication and Exploitation of Plants and Animals.* London: Duckworth, pp. 3-15.

———, 1969b, "The Ecology of Agricultural Systems," in Ronald U. Cooke and James H. Johnson (eds.), *Trends in Geography.* Oxford: Pergamon Press, pp. 133-142.

Hasler, A. D., 1970, "Man-Induced eutrophication of Lakes," in S. F. Springer (ed.), *Global Effects of Environmental Pollution.* New York: Springer-Verlag, pp. 110-125.

Hauck, R. D., W. V. Bartholomew, J. M. Bremmer, F. E. Broadbent, H. H. Cheng, A. P. Edwards, D. R. Keeney, J. O. Legg, S. R. Olsen and L. K. Porter, 1972, "Use of Variations in Natural Nitrogen Isotope Abundance for Environmental Studies: A Questionable Approach," *Science,* Vol. 177, pp. 453-454.

Heath, Robert G., James W. Spann and J. F. Kreitzer, 1969, "Marked DDE Impairment of Mallard Reproduction in Controlled Studies," *Nature,* Vol. 224, pp. 47-48.

Hickey, J. J., J. A. Keith and F. B. Coon, 1966, "An exploration of pesticides in a Lake Michigan ecosystem," *Journal of Applied Ecology,* Vol. 3, pp. 141-145.

Hickey, J. J. and D. W. Anderson, 1968, "Chlorinated hydrocarbons and eggshell changes in raptorial and fish eating birds," *Science,* Vol. 162, pp. 271-273.

Huffaker, C. B., 1959, "Biological control of weeds with insects," *Annual Review of Entomology,* Vol. 4, pp. 251-276.

Institute of Ecology, 1972, *Man in the Living Environment: A Report on Global Ecological Problems.* Madison: University of Wisconsin Press.

Johnston, David W. and Eugene P. Odum, 1956, "Breeding bird populations in relation to plant succession on the Piedmont of Georgia," *Ecology,* Vol. 37, pp. 50-62.

Kearney, P. C., R. G. Nash and A. R. Isensee, 1969, "Persistence of Pesticide Residues in Soils," in Morton W. Miller and George G. Berg (eds.), *Chemical Fallout: Current Research on Persistent Pesticides.* Springfield, Illinois: Charles C Thomas, pp. 54-67.

Keller, W. D. and G. E. Smith, 1967, "Ground Water Contamination by Dissolved Nitrate," *Geological Society of America Special Paper No. 90.* Washington, D.C.

Kennedy, J. S., 1968, "The motivation of integrated control," *Journal of Applied Ecology,* Vol. 4, pp. 492-499.

Kilgore, W. W. and R. L. Doutt (eds.), 1967, *Pest Control: Biological, Physical and Selected Chemical Methods.* New York: Academic Press.

Knipling, E. F., 1960, "The Eradication of the Screw-worm Fly," *Scientific American,* Vol. 203, pp. 54-61.

———, 1964, *The Potential Role of the Sterility Method for Insect Population Control with Special Reference to Combining this Method with Conventional Methods,* (Agricultural Research Service Publication 33-98). Washington, D.C.: U.S. Department of Agriculture.

———, 1965, "The sterility method of pest population control," in G. O. Chichester (ed.), *Research in Pesticides.* New York: Academic Press, pp. 233-249.

Kohl, Daniel H., Georgia B. Shearer and Barry Commoner, 1971, "Fertilizer Nitrogen: Contribution to Nitrate in Surface Water in a Corn Belt Watershed," *Science*, Vol. 74, pp. 1331-1335.

Ladejinsky, Wolf, 1970, "Ironies of India's Green Revolution," *Foreign Affairs*, July, pp. 758-768.

Laven, H., 1967, "Eradication of *Cluex pipiens fatigans* through cytoplasmic incompatibility," *Nature*, Vol. 216, p. 383.

Lenain, A. F., 1970, "The Impact of Nitrates on Water Use," *Journal of the American Water Works Association*, Vol. 59, pp. 1049-1054.

Likens, Gene E., F. Herbert Bormann, Noye M. Johnson, D. W. Fisher and Robert S. Pierce, 1970, "Effects of Forest Cutting and Herbicide Treatment on Nutrient Budgets in the Hubbard Brook Watershed-Ecosystem," *Ecological Monographs*, Vol. 40, pp. 23-47.

Lindeman, Raymond L., 1942, "The Trophic-Dynamic Aspect of Ecology," *Ecology*, Vol. 23, pp. 399-418.

Margalef, Ramon, 1963, "On certain unifying principles in ecology," *American Naturalist*, Vol. 97, pp. 357-374.

———, 1968, *Perspectives in Ecological Theory.* Chicago: University of Chicago Press.

Martin, Paul S., 1973, "The Discovery of America," *Science*, Vol. 179, pp. 969-975.

Martin, Paul S. and H. E. Wright Jr. (eds.), 1967, *Pleistocene Extinctions: the Search for a Cause.* New Haven: Yale University Press.

Massee, A. M., 1958, "The effect on the balance of arthropod populations in orchards arising from unrestricted use of chemicals," *Proceedings 10th International Congress of Entomologists*, Vol. 3, pp. 163-168.

Mather, Eugene and John Fraser Hart, 1956, "The Geography of Manure," *Land Economics*, Vol. 32, pp. 25-38.

Miller, Morton W. and George G. Berg (eds.), 1969, *Chemical Fallout: Current Research on Persistent Pesticides.* Springfield, Illinois: Charles C. Thomas.

Moore, Norman W., 1967, "A synopsis of the Pesticide Problem," in J. B. Cragg (ed.), *Advances in Ecological Research.* New York: Academic Press, pp. 75-129.

Mrak, Emil M. (ed.), 1969, *Report of the Secretary's Commission on Pesticides and their Relationship to Environmental Health.* Washington, D.C.: U.S. Department of Health, Education, and Welfare.

Nash, R. G. and C. A. Woolson, 1967, "Persistence of chlorinated hydrocarbon insecticides in soils," *Science*, Vol. 157, pp. 924-927.

National Academy of Sciences, 1972, *Genetic Vulnerability of Major Crops.* Washington, D.C.: NAS.

Nelson, B., 1969, "Herbicides: Order on 2,4,5-T issued at unusually high level," *Science*, Vol. 166, pp. 977-979.

Nightingale, H. L., 1970, "Statistical Evaluation of Salinity and Nitrate Content and Trends Beneath Urban and Agricultural Areas—Fresno, California," *California Groundwater*, Vol. 8, pp. 22-28.

Odum, Eugene P., 1969, "The Strategy of Ecosystem Development," *Science*, Vol. 164, pp. 262-270.

———, 1971, *Fundamentals of Ecology.* 3rd edition, Philadelphia: W. B. Saunders.

Odum, Howard T., 1967, "Energetics of World Food Production," in the *World Food Problem* (Report of the President's Science Advisory Committee: Panel on World Food Supply). Washington, D.C.: Government Printing Office, Vol. 3, pp. 55-94.

———, 1971, *Environment, Power and Society.* New York: Wiley Interscience.

Oglesby, R. T. and W. T. Edmondson, 1966, "Control of Eutrophication," *Journal of Water Pollution Control Federation*, Vol. 38, pp. 1452-1460.

Ordish, G., 1967, *Biological Methods in Crop Pest Control.* London: Constable.

O'Riordan, Timothy, 1971, "The Third American Conservation Movement: New Implications for Public Policy," *Journal of American Studies*, Vol. 5, pp. 155-171.

Peakall, D. B., 1967, "Pesticide-induced enzyme breakdown of steroids in birds," *Nature*, Vol. 216, pp. 505-506.

———, 1970, "Pesticides and the reproduction of birds," *Scientific American*, Vol. 222, pp. 72-78.

Porter, R. D. and S. N. Wiemeyer, 1969, "Dieldrin and DDT: Effects on sparrowhawk eggshells and reproduction," *Science*, Vol. 165, pp. 199-200.

Pratt, Christopher, 1965, "Chemical Fertilizers," *Scientific American*, Vol. 212, pp. 67-72.

Radomski, J. L. and W. B. Deichmann, 1969, "Pesticide Levels in Humans in a Variety of Natural and Experimental Conditions," in Morton W. Miller and George G. Berg (eds.), *Chemical Fallout: Current Research on Persistent Pesticides*. Springfield, Illinois: Charles C. Thomas, pp. 297-310.

Rappaport, Roy A., 1971, "The Flow of Energy in an Agricultural Society," *Scientific American*, Vol. 225, pp. 117-132.

Ripper, W. E., 1956, "Effects of pesticides on the balance of arthropod populations," *Annual Review of Entomology*, Vol. 1, pp. 403-438.

Risebrough, R. W., R. J. Huggett, T. J. Griffin, and E. D. Goldberg, 1968, "Pesticides: Transatlantic movements in the north-east trades," *Science*, Vol. 159, pp. 1233-1236.

Rosen, Aaron A. and H. F. Kraybill (eds.), 1966, *Organic Pesticides in the Environment*. Washington, D.C.: American Chemical Society.

Rudd, Robert L., 1964a, *Pesticides and the Living Landscape*. Madison, Wisconsin: University of Wisconsin Press.

——, 1964b, "The Long-Range Damage of Pesticides," *Audobon Magazine*, Vol. 66, pp. 361-366.

——, 1971, "Pesticides," in William W. Murdoch (ed.), *Environment: Resources, Pollution and Society*. Stamford, Connecticut: Sinaver Associates, pp. 279-301.

Sauchelli, Vincent, 1960, *The Chemistry and Technology of Fertilizers*. New York: Reinhold.

Sawyer, Claire N., 1966, "Basic concepts of eutrophication," *Journal Water Pollution Control Federation*, Vol. 38, pp. 737-744.

Sladen, William J. L., C. M. Menzie and W. L. Reichel, 1966, "DDT Residues in Adelie Penguins and a Crabeater Seal from Antarctica," *Nature*, Vol. 210, pp. 670-673.

Smith, George E., 1965, "Nitrate problems in water as related to soils, plants and water," *Missouri Agricultural Experimental Station Special Report*, Vol. 55, pp. 42-52.

——, 1967, "Fertilizer Nutrients as Contaminants in Water Supplies," in Nyle C. Brady (ed.), *Agriculture and the Quality of Our Environment*. Washington, D.C.: American Association for the Advancement of Science, pp. 173-187.

Smith, Ray F. and H. T. Reynolds, 1966, "Principles, definition and scope of integrated pest control," in *Proceedings of the FAO Symposium on Integrated Pest Control*, Vol. 1, pp. 11-17.

Smith, Ray F. and R. van den Bosch, 1967, "Integrated control," in W. W. Kilgore and R. L. Doutt (eds.), *Pest Control: Biological, Physical and Selected Chemical Methods*. New York: Academic Press, pp. 295-340.

Soloman, M. E., 1953, "Insect population balance and chemical control of pests. Pest outbreaks induced by spraying," *Chemical Industry*, Vol. 43, pp. 1143-1147.

Stewart, B. A., F. G. Viets and G. L. Hutchinson, 1968, "Agriculture's Effect on Nitrate Pollution of Ground Water," *Journal of Soil and Water Conservation*, Vol. 23, pp. 13-15.

Stoddart, David R., 1965, "Geography and the ecological approach: the ecosystem as a geographic principle and method," *Geography*, Vol. 50, pp. 242-251.

Stout, P. R. and R. G. Bureau, 1967, "The Extent and Significance of Fertilizer Build-Up in Soils as Revealed by Vertical Distribution of Nitrogenous Matter between Soils and Underlying Water Reservoirs," in Nyle C. Brady (ed.), *Agriculture and the Quality of Our Environment*. Washington, D.C.: American Association for the Advancement of Science, pp. 283-310.

Talbot, L. M., 1963, "Comparison of the Efficiency of Wild Animals and Domestic Livestock in Utilization of East African Rangelands," in *The Conference Papers* (Arusha Conference). Morges: International Union for the Conservation of Nature and Natural Resources, pp. 329-335.

Talbot, L. M. and M. H. Talbot, 1963, "The High Biomass of Wild Ungulates on East African Savanna," *Transactions of the 28th North American Wildlife and Natural Resources Conference*, pp. 465-476.

Tatton, J. O'G. and J. H. A. Ruzicka, 1967, "Organochlorine pesticides in Antarctica," *Nature*, Vol. 215, pp. 346-348.

Tatum, L. A., 1971, "The Southern Corn Leaf Blight Epidemic," *Science*, Vol. 171, pp. 1113-1116.

United States Department of Agriculture, 1971, *Commercial Fertilizers: Consumption of Commercial Fertilizers, Primary Plant Nutrients and Micronutrients*, (Statistical Bulletin No. 472 Crop Reporting Board, Statistical Reporting Service). Washington, D.C.: Government Printing Office.

——, 1972a, *The Pesticide Review: 1971*. Washington, D.C.: Government Printing Office.

―――, 1972*b*, *Agricultural Statistics, 1971*. Washington, D.C.: Government Printing Office.

United States Tariff Commission, 1970, *Synthetic Organic Chemicals: United States Production and Sales of Pesticides and Related Products, 1970*. Washington, D.C.: Government Printing Office.

Verduin, Jacob, 1967, "Eutrophication and Agriculture in the United States," in Nyle C. Brady (ed.), *Agriculture and the Quality of Our Environment*. Washington, D.C.: American Association for the Advancement of Science, pp. 163-172.

Viets, Frank G. and Richard H. Hageman, 1971, *Factors Affecting the Accumulation of Nitrate in Soil, Water and Plants*, (Agricultural Research Service Handbook No. 413). Washington, D.C.: U.S. Department of Agriculture.

Ward, P. C., 1970, "Existing Levels of Nitrates in Waters—The California Situation," in *Nitrate and Water Supply: Source and Control*, (Proceedings 12th Sanitary Engineers Conference). Urbana: University of Illinois Press, pp. 14-26.

Watt, Kenneth E. F., 1968, *Ecology and Resource Management*. New York: McGraw-Hill.

―――, 1973, *Principles of Environmental Science*. New York: McGraw-Hill.

Wharton, Clifton R., 1969, "The Green Revolution: Cornucopia or Pandora's Box," *Foreign Affairs*, Vol. 47, pp. 464-476.

Williams, Carroll M., 1967, "Third-Generation Pesticides," *Scientific American*, Vol. 217, pp. 13-17.

Wolf, Eric R., 1966, *Peasants*. Englewood Cliffs, N.J.: Prentice-Hall.

Wolff, I. A. and A. E. Wasserman, 1972, "Nitrates, Nitrites, and Nitrosamines," *Science*, Vol. 177, pp. 15-19.

Woodwell, George M., 1961, "The persistence of DDT in a forest soil," *Forest Science*, Vol. 7, pp. 194-196.

―――, 1967, "Toxic Substances and Ecological Cycles," *Scientific American*, Vol. 216, pp. 24-31.

―――, 1970, "The Energy Cycle of the Biosphere," *Scientific American*, Vol. 223, pp. 64-97.

Woodwell, George M. and H. H. Smith (eds.), 1969, *Diversity and Stability in Ecological Systems*, (Brookhaven Laboratory Publication No. 22). Upton, New York: Brookhaven Laboratory.

Woodwell, George M., Charles F. Wurster, Jr. and Peter Isaacson, 1967, "DDT Residues in an East Coast Estuary: A Case of Biological Concentration of a Persistent Insecticide," *Science*, Vol. 156, pp 821-824.

World Health Organization, 1971, *The Place of DDT in operations against malaria and other vector borne diseases*. Geneva: WHO.

Wurster, Charles F., Jr. and David B. Wingate, 1968, "DDT Residues and Declining Reproduction in the Bermuda Petrel," *Science*, Vol. 159, pp. 979-981.

Wurster, Charles F., Jr., 1969, "Chlorinated hydrocarbon insecticides and the world ecosystem," *Biological Conservation*, Vol. 1, pp. 123-129.

―――, 1970, "DDT in Mother's Milk," *Saturday Review*, Vol. 53, pp. 58-59.

The Environmental Impact of Urbanization

James A. Schmid

*Jack McCormick and Associates, Inc., Ecological Consultants,
Devon, Pennsylvania*

Urban and environmental problems at present enjoy the limelight of public and scholarly attention. Dissatisfaction with one's environment is characteristic of the modern human condition: the perfect environment, the perfect city, will never be attained, although much effort will be expended in the attempt. The great increase in numbers of people, together with the even more spectacular rise in the proportion inhabiting urban places, generates grave problems of environmental disruption never before encountered on such a massive scale (Table 1). Twentieth-century men possess the technical capability and the incentive to transform vast segments of the earth's surface. Natural cycles of geochemistry and biology, which provided raw materials and dispersed wastes so long as men lived in small, scattered settlements, no longer function without massive human intervention. Early in this century conservationists worried chiefly about the supply of raw materials and energy; now their primary concerns are the disposal of waste and the preservation of species. The natural cycles man inherited contained a great deal of buffering; early men soon eliminated many of the more fragile components of ecosystems (Martin and Wright, eds.: 1967; Krantz: 1970). But at present urban people demonstrate both their technical capacity and their willingness to destroy even the toughest of inherited environments. At the same time, consistent efforts have rarely been made to assure the fitness of the new urban environments for human habitation. The present review is devoted to an appraisal of geographical aspects of urban environments as interacting systems of men and natural elements, both living and non-living.

Urban man is a specialist. City life permits, and successful city life requires, the concentration of a person's energy and attention on a small selection from the activities potentially open to him, and the confinement of his personal acquaintance and active social interaction to a tiny fraction of the people found nearby. Milgram has summarized the behavioral consequences of city life from the viewpoint of a psychologist (1970). City dwellers devote little time to subsistence activity: others grow, distribute and at least partially prepare their food; build, heat, and light their dwellings; attempt to create awareness of and

213

TABLE 1—World Trends in Population Growth
(in millions)

Area and Kind	1950	1960	1970	1980	1990	2000
World Total	2486	2982	3635	4467	5456	6515
Urban	704	935	1352	1854	2517	3329
Rural	1782	1997	2283	2614	2939	3186
More Developed Regions	858	976	1091	1210	1337	1454
Urban	439	582	717	864	1021	1174
Rural	418	394	374	347	316	280
Less Developed Regions	1628	2005	2545	3257	4120	5061
Urban	265	403	635	990	1496	2155
Rural	1363	1603	1910	2267	2623	2906

Source: Ciborowski: 1972, from United Nations: 1971.

supply their every "need." So long as the system functions smoothly, the urbanite commanding adequate purchasing power has the opportunity to ignore virtually all save the man-made environment. Nature is rearranged into useful patterns; myriad insulators spring up, from galoshes to earplugs to air conditioners. Major environmental interruptions, such as massive snows or rainstorms, are rare enough to become news items in the mass media, serving to point up the everyday adequate functioning of urban systems. Yet urban society has only haltingly begun to evolve specialists in environment. The very notion is paradoxical: today everyone knows the message of "ecology," that everything is connected to everything else. But there are still sanitation administrators filling marshes, housing administrators demolishing cherished homes, park directors presiding helplessly while highways are paved through unique areas they are by law charged to preserve (Cunningham: 1970), not to mention the expected self-serving actions of private persons and corporations. Holistic thinking has proved a difficult reality for a society of specialists with limited perspectives.

Urban regions are the most intensively transformed segments of the earth's surface, although their tributary mine and factory landscapes run a close second (Hibbard: 1968; U.S. Department of the Interior: 1967), along with labor-intensive cropland devoted to horticulture and wet rice. In this paper current knowledge about urban landscapes is organized under five subsystems of the terrestrial environment: (1) Landforms and Geological Substructure; (2) Soils and Substrates; (3) Climate; (4) Vegetation; and (5) Animal Life.

LANDFORMS AND GEOLOGICAL SUBSTRUCTURE

Cities exist in a variety of topographic settings; their inhabitants interact with these settings in myriad ways. From the earth people seek resources of structural support and of building materials, and they expose themselves and their handiwork to environmental hazards. The kinds of risks are not all new; urban societies have only slowly adjusted to their topographic settings, and the process is by no means complete. A number of scholars have examined the dissimilar patterns of landscape which urbanites of different cultures have imposed on street patterns and the functional organization of urban space (Tuan: 1971;

Wheatley: 1971; Stanislawski: 1946). Yet certain regularities of landform utilization appear over and over.

Geomorphological problems have troubled cities for as long as cities have existed. Clusters of dwellings whose inhabitants did not produce their own food have been present in some parts of the world for at least five millennia. The circumstances under which early cities arose remain dim, and provide much scope for controversy among prehistorians. Organized religion is intimately connected with early urbanism, both in producing the temple complex as a functional nucleus for city life and in the forms of streets and structures imposed to govern spatial organization. Particular landforms have been regularly viewed as appropriate to shrines in both town and countryside (for Greek examples, see Scully: 1962), and religious criteria apparently determined early urban location to a considerable extent. Defense needs have recommended elevated sites for citadels from time immemorial; they have prompted urbanites to seek the protection offered by rivers, moats, and marshes, preferring the less obvious attacks by other organisms to attacks by their own species. From ancient times cities have been linked to watercourses, for seacoasts and stream valleys are loci where lie vital transport nets without which cities are inconceivable. Water supply, too, has continuously been a vital consideration governing the siting of urban centers; only in recent years has industrial technology provided through expensive desalinization the potential for water supply where urban wealth exists far from potable waters (e.g., Kuwait). Thus cities are most often found in lowlands, and their problems include sedimentation and poor ventilation, discussed in later sections of this paper. Continuous material progress in the organization of environmental functions has not marked urban history (Mumford: 1961, p. 75):

> at an early date rural ways of disposing of rubbish and excrement became a menace in crowded urban quarters, without apparently spurring sufficient efforts for the improvement of urban sanitation and hygiene. . . . For thousands of years city dwellers put up with defective, often quite vile sanitary arrangements, wallowing in rubbish and filth they certainly had the power to remove, for the occasional task of removal could hardly have been more loathsome than walking and breathing in the constant presence of such ordure. If one had any sufficient explanation of this indifference to dirt and odor that are repulsive to many animals, even pigs, who take pains to keep themselves and their lairs clean, one might have a clue to the slow and fitful nature of technological improvement itself, in the five millennia that followed the birth of the city.

In the United States, recent federal legislation requiring "environmental impact" studies for new construction in which the federal government is involved may herald a new era to the extent that the measure can be enforced and other units of government follow suit (White: 1972). It is surprising that such measures were not taken long ago, but sufficient reason is found in the ideology of laissez-faire set in an enormous frontier continent of few people and vast, practically free resources. As the loci of enormous investments of capital, labor, and sentiment, cities display great inertia: their physical structures change only slowly to incorporate new technical knowledge and new demands of their inhabitants. This is true in spite of the fact that cities have been, from the outset, centers of innovation (Jacobs: 1961) and despite the fact that the pace of technical innovation has increased immensely in the post-medieval city of European influence (Mumford: 1961; Bobek: 1962; Murphey: 1954).

Economic motivation lies behind activity in modern cities, for even administrative capitals require distribution systems for goods, people, energy, and information. Favorable geographic location and a vigorous populace combine to generate pressures for urban expansion in thriving metropolitan areas. Eschman and Marcus have distinguished "levels of resistance" in the environs of several centers, which can be read directly in the outlines of a city's map (Eschman and Marcus: 1972). Universally the initial settlements are made on the most favorable sites of the moment; latecomers must pay costs of overcoming distance or of transforming marshes, steep hillsides, or otherwise hazardous or defenseless places into safe, usable space. There appear to be no obstacles which cannot be overcome, or to which satisfactory adjustments cannot be made, given sufficient economic motivation. But both the economic cost and the risks to people and to natural systems increase over time with disappearance of choice urban land favorably located. The federal government has spent vast sums for fifty years to reduce flood losses, but damage totals increase each year as ever more buildings are erected in flood plains without structural adaptation to their hazardous locations (Sheaffer: 1960). Each winter's rains cause foundations to fail on the steep, muddy hillsides of southern California, where wealthy homeowners spend unstintingly for decoration but neglect proper siting and the adequate underpinning of foundations. One might expect ordinary property insurance rates to reflect topographical differences in flood risk (as they reflect spatial variations in risk from theft and fire); that they do not is one of the institutional irrationalities of man-land interactions in the United States. Geographers have been prominent among scholars studying human behavior in the face of such hazards (Mitchell and Saarinen elsewhere in this volume).

The most comprehensive discussion of local geological transformations by urbanites remains that by Sherlock (1922) for London, a city whose rearranged rivers are the subject of an entire book (Barton: 1962). During the half-century since Sherlock wrote, the rate of such transformations and the area affected by them have increased rapidly, with many unfavorable side effects. A recent attempt to describe geological transformations by urban and industrial society is a detailed case study of Austin, Texas (Flawn: 1970). To illustrate contemporary interactions of cities and their geological substructure, two examples are discussed below. The first of these is subsidence of the land surface as fluids are withdrawn; the second is the provision of building material, which both gives landscape character to an urban center and creates its own set of environmental problems.

Possibly the most spectacular instance of substructure modification to date has been the subsidence of land as oil has been withdrawn from beneath the harbor at Long Beach and adjoining parts of Los Angeles, California (Poland and Davis: 1969). The subsidence was first noticed in 1940; by 1962 the affected areas covered twenty-five heavily urbanized square miles, and at its center the ground surface had dropped twenty-seven feet. Vertical movement was accompanied by horizontal displacements of as much as nine feet. More than $100 million were spent to alleviate the resulting damage—for levees, retaining walls and fills, and the raising of individual structures—before any money was spent to attack the cause. Not until the late 1950's was repressuring of the field with seawater begun, following intensive work on legal, economic, and engineering problems. The surface has begun to rebound at a cost of some $30 million. Other areas of California, Texas oil fields and regions of ground-water withdrawal (including those around Galveston and Houston), Venezuela's Lake

Maracaibo, gas fields in the Po delta in Italy and at Niigata, Japan, and Mexico City are all experiencing subsidence (see the review by Poland and Davis: 1969). For cities at sea level (or like Mexico City, built over old lakebeds underlain by compressible volcanic sediments) the subsidence problem is most serious. Even along coasts where subsidence is attributed chiefly to natural causes, economic activity contributes to urban problems, as in Venice, Taipei, and Holland.

One of the newer methods advocated for the disposal of liquid wastes involves pumping them into deep rock strata—as much as 12,000 feet at Denver, twice the depth of the Wilmington oil field at Long Beach. Injections at Rocky Mountain Arsenal during the 1960's coincided with a striking rise in earthquake frequency in an area which had known no earthquake for eighty years (Healy *et al.*: 1968; Evans: 1966). Much needs to be learned about the potential increase of seismic activity by fluid injections. To the extent that numerous small crustal movements replace infrequent massive ones, great human benefits may result. Human rearrangements of fluids may influence earthquakes at Los Angeles and Long Beach because they lie astride the San Andreas fault system, a part of the active circum-Pacific zone of earthquake activity (Hamilton and Meehan: 1971). Little is known of earthquake likelihood along historically more stable corridors of extensive urbanization such as the northeastern seacoast of the United States (Sullivan: 1973).

Cities are given character not only by their topographic settings but also by the rock which is utilized for their construction. Perhaps no one has examined the building stone of a city in such elaborate detail as has Arkell for Oxford (Arkell: 1947). The history of local economic life and transportation development may be read in the kinds of stone; in their decay, a commentary may be made on atmospheric quality. Mumford has proposed a strong linkage between cities and their underlying rock (Mumford: 1938, pp. 318-319):

> Because of its close, if not abject dependence upon local building materials and local qualities of site, the city epitomizes the surrounding country and gives a special character to the natural setting. At no moment in its existence is the divorce between the man-made environment and the earth complete. The red sandstone of Strasbourg, the yellow clay of London, the red brick of Bremen, the grey limestone of post-medieval Paris, the brown sandstone of old Frankfurt-am-Main—the very bricks and stones symbolize that underlying partnership between man and nature which is accepted and furthered, even while it is transformed, in the structure of the city.
>
> The immediate geological formations remain an important attribute of urban individuality; they seep into the consciousness in all sorts of indirect ways. The very infant at play, digging in the earth of his dooryard, is conscious of the ubiquitous sand if he lives in Rotterdam, or of the oily shale if in Pittsburgh, or of the tantalizing gleam of mica in the schist of Manhattan.

Sand and gravel for aggregate in concrete are indispensable requirements of urban-industrial society in the mid-twentieth century. Many cities are fortunate in their coastal or riverine location, for these materials often occur in waterlaid deposits; even so, transportation makes up a large part of the cost of sand and gravel in cities, and producers of aggregate try to locate as close to the market as possible. In 1913 British use of gravel amounted to less than 3.5 million tons per annum; by 1950 the yearly figure had grown to 50 million tons (Jennings: 1965). In Los Angeles, recent consumption of aggregate for highways alone has averaged roughly 7.5 million tons per annum (Flawn: 1970). Given the importance of sand and gravel as a natural resource in urban-industrial society, it is illustrative to consider the fate of these materials in the Soviet Union, where they create characteristic environmental problems.

The economist Goldman recently set out to examine conservation problems in the USSR on the premise that environmental decision making should be exemplary in an economy which ostentatiously rejects market-place valuations of goods and services, and which vests the ownership of both natural resources and enterprise itself in the general public rather than in private parties. In fact, the record of the Russians is even worse than that of the United States in environmental protection (Goldman: 1972). Along the Black Sea coast, beaches are composed chiefly of pebbles and shingle. These have been mined for decades as aggregate, while the rivers which replenished them have been dammed for power, irrigation, and transport. As the beaches vanished, the tourist industry of coastal towns lost a prime attraction, in this warmest of internal Soviet vacation spots. Storm erosion is posing an ever-greater threat to the new seaside hotels at Yalta, Sochi, Adler, and the intervening coastline. Goldman notes ironically that even strongly worded laws passed by a totalitarian state requiring the protection of environmental values frequently give rise years later only to other laws saying the same thing—equally strong in language, equally ineffective in reality. Traditional industrial development, not private ownership of the means of production, generates the most severe modern environmental disruption. Modern technology may help solve many environmental problems that it has heretofore created—if the reward system for corporate and bureaucratic executives is altered. However, in the long run, only education can succeed in showing the ecological disaster inherent in public expectations of ever-increasing materials and energy supplies and constant environmental "tinkering that is malignant in that each act of repair generates a need for further repairs to avert problems generated at compound interest" (Woodwell: 1970). Jennings has assembled references to studies of human disturbance of Australian beaches, as well as a number of other landforms on several continents (Jennings: 1965). Man's geomorphic activities clearly are not confined to one part of the globe.

One final point must be made in closing this section on topographic and geological interactions of urbanites and their surroundings. The direct costs of environmental hazards are most likely to fall on those urbanites at the bottom of the socioeconomic hierarchy, because the poor are most likely to live in hazardous locations where rents are lowest. Although examples are plentiful in the developed nations of the world, this point may be illustrated most starkly from the underdeveloped nations, which are unable to house their exploding urban populations adequately. The result is that one-third of the urbanites in the developing countries (some 210 million people) now live in shanty-towns (Table 2). The urban immigrants come in enormous numbers. They are characteristically penniless (Ciborowski: 1972, pp. 10-11):

> without professional training or skills, they are mostly illiterate, and, as a rule, hungry. They bring to the city only their eagerness to work, to improve their own lives and, if possible, those of their families, left behind and perhaps starving. From such a socioeconomic background, the process of 'urbanization' develops. Unable to meet the challenge in a straight-forward manner, both major participants, the city administration and new settlers, try to avoid direct confrontation. This results in spreading slums, barriadas, bidonvilles, favelas and shanty towns. They grow in an almost

TABLE 2—Selected Shanty-Town Populations
(in thousands)

| City | Year of Data | City Population | Shanty-Town Population | |
			Total	% of City Pop.
Africa				
Dakar	1969	500	150	30
Dar es Salaam	1967	273	93	34
Asia				
Calcutta	1961	6700	2220	33
Karachi	1968	2700	600	27
Manila	1968	3000	1100	35
Ankara	1970	1250	750	60
Latin America				
Rio de Janeiro	1961	3326	900	27
Brasilia	1962	148	60	41
Guyaquil	1968	730	360	49
Mexico City	1966	3287	1500	46
Lima	1969	2800	1000	36
Caracas	1964	1590	556	35

Source: Ciborowski: 1972, from United Nations: 1970.

clandestine way: they occupy land illegally, their land-use usually ignored in every development plan. If another land-use is proposed in such a plan, no provision is made for resettling present occupants. To protect themselves against expulsion by city authorities or offended landlords, the newcomers choose the less favorable and most unattractive areas: lagoons (Calcutta, Lagos), swamps (Djkarta, Maracaibo), inaccessible hillsides (Ankara, Caracas), or areas under the direct impact of noxious industries (Chimbote). This makes for the worst possible natural environmental conditions, which are further aggravated by lack of water and waste-disposal facilities, by overcrowding and lack of any social services. In addition, the technical quality of building is mostly below any reasonable standards, due to shortage of building materials and skills, and also the inhibition of capital investment by the owner's insecure tenure of 'his' piece of land.

SOILS AND SUBSTRATES

How does urban-industrial civilization interact with the thin upper layer of earth mantle which is even more easily manipulated than the underlying rock strata and landforms? The uppermost feet of the earth's surface are often composed of unconsolidated material, particularly in the lowland sites favored for urban location. Insofar as this material is viewed as a foundation for structures or as an obstacle to be removed from bedrock, as is the common practice of engineers and geologists, it is here discussed as "substrate." In accord with pedologic, agricultural, and biological usage, the term "soil" is reserved for that part of the earth-air interface where biogeochemical processes are in evidence, and are themselves of particular concern. In temperate latitudes soils are characteristically shallower than substrates, as where thick glacial till deposits have been weathered to a depth of only two or three feet. Urbanites have in the past been more concerned with substrates than with the complex ecology of soils.

Erosion and sedimentation are major processes affecting the earth's surface in urban as well as rural areas. In the hinterlands of cities, urban demands for food, timber, and mineral resources have long encouraged the exposure of land to accelerated erosion. Perhaps the best documented case is that of the Greek city states (Butzer in this volume). Grain farming bares the land to soil-removing forces of wind and water. Both Adams (1965) and Flannery (1969) have argued that it was not mere coincidence that the earliest known great cities were plagued by sediment in the lower Tigris and Euphrates valleys, because upstream the foothills of those same valleys supported the earliest known seed agriculture. The course of deforestation on Mount Lebanon, beginning with timber trade from earliest historic times, has been fully documented by Mikesell (1969). All around the Mediterranean, and to a slightly lesser degree in the more recently inhabited lands of northern Europe, coastlines have grown as a result of erosion speeded by human action, leaving historic seaports landlocked, e.g., Ephesus, Miletus, Ravenna, Pisa, Bruges (Sestini: 1962; Davis: 1956). When Europeans spread over the globe, they took agricultural erosion with them, but little incentive for traditional conservation practices. Sugar cane farming silted the harbor at Bridgetown, Barbados within twenty years of its introduction (Watts: 1968). In the venerable civilizations of East Asia, moist climate and artificial irrigation permitted wet-rice cultivation and intensive horticulture approximating closed systems on lowlands and terraced hillsides, but dry farming at the arid margins has provided vast loads of sediment to the great rivers even here since ancient times. Further discussion of man's influence on stream regimen and quality may be found in the chapter by Mrowka in this volume.

Within urban areas themselves, erosion under modern conditions peaks at the time construction is effecting the change from rural to urban land uses. Scheidt (1967) reports normal sediment in Maryland rivers at less than 200 tons per square mile of watershed per year; under urban development erosion increases ten to fifty times, and may reach 121,000 tons per square mile annually (see also Wolman and Schick: 1967). This is not so much a matter of deficient technical knowledge, but rather the result of great reluctance on the part of homebuilders and highway contractors to utilize known methods of protecting exposed land and trapping silt—a reluctance which stems from both the added costs of the measures and sheer indifference. Once the initial building is done, the presence of hard surfaces and pipes to carry runoff slows erosion over the city proper, while suburbanites protect their soil with lawns.

Rearranging the physical geography of the city to reflect human values requires enormous expenditures of human, animal, and now inanimate energy. The technical requirements for cutting and filling under myriad local conditions are today, by and large, systematically understood, as a great number of books in civil engineering and landscape architecture testify. But in the short run it is often cheaper for particular entrepreneurs or bureaucrats to increase slopes and compact fills insufficiently, taking quick profits (or praise for administrative accomplishment) whatever the total social cost. A sizeable literature on surficial geologic resources exists around urban centers in the developed countries. In the United States modern soil surveys contain engineering specifications for series whose users are much more concerned with bearing-load strengths beneath buildings or highway foundations, and with infiltration rates affecting spacing for septic-tank fields, than with yields of crops. Although published at smaller scale, soil maps are often locally available at 1:15,000 on "blue-line" sheets compiled from air photographs and checked in the field. Such information can be of great use to planners seeking to enourage wise development of the less hazardous sites available for urban expansion.

Drawing on their hinterlands, cities also accumulate material which slowly raises the land surface. Ancient tell mounds in Southwestern Asia are well known products of this process. Sherlock estimated the average rise of the surface in London to be about one foot per century (Sherlock: 1922). As late as the mid-nineteenth century, New Yorkers permitted vast quantities of refuse and excrement to accumulate in their streets, with severe repercussions on public health (Rosenberg: 1962). Most modern cities now transport their wastes to the urban fringe and dump it, in whatever sites are thought convenient. Occasionally, excavations bring to light the fascinating debris which ordinarily lies hidden beneath everyday pavements (Iglauer: 1972; Barton: 1962).

Swamps and marshes have long been favorite dumping sites, whose gradual filling-in has always been heralded as the reclamation of new urban space. If properly prepared, the sites of such landfills can in fact become additions to the available substrate of an urban area. Only in recent years have some urbanites begun to realize that wetlands *before* filling possess positive value for people. The list of such values cannot be elaborated here, but it includes at the least aesthetic value from the plants, wildlife, and waterfowl maintained close to densely inhabited sites; educational value for those who would study the complex biotic interaction of marshes; flood control value as sites for temporary water storage; resource value as spawning and feeding grounds for commercial fish; and sewage treatment value highly expensive to duplicate technologically. In recent testimony before a federal court in New York, Dr. E. H. Buckley of the Boyce Thompson Institute for Plant Research argued in favor of preserving a small marsh on the Hudson River (for details of the case, see Ehrenfeld: 1972, p. 244.):

> To the extent that the river cleans itself the governments of the municipalities, the state and the nation do not have to devote tax dollars for tertiary sewerage treatment. I have estimated on the basis of my detailed studies that an acre of tidal marsh, if thought of as tertiary sewerage treatment system is worth between $10,000 and $30,000 annually.

So long as rates and values of such benefits are unquantified, their loss to society must go unmeasured, defended only on the grounds of general aesthetic amenity against tangible benefits from made-land development in terms of private profits or public tax savings.

One may note in passing that useful data on the location and nature of surface installations of pipes, sewers, and associated underground paraphernalia are, surprisingly, often discarded by urban bureaucracies. The resulting ignorance of, for example, sanitary and storm sewer outfalls, presents a formidable obstacle to students of water pollution control. In New York the Interstate Sanitary Commission had to send its own staff members to compile a map of drains entering the Hudson from the city, because the city itself had never collected such information; fortunately, the commission possessed the statutory power to gain access to the appropriate scattered files. In environmental studies, as in other realms of academic concern, human behavior sometimes makes it easier to obtain information about contemporary nature directly than to identify the past works of man. In urban environments, neither kind of information is alone sufficient.

Soil scientists have not yet studied pedogenesis in urban areas, either in the United States or in the Soviet Union where this science was first developed (Mamaev: 1970). It is obvious that sulphuric acid and other airborne wastes rain down upon soils extending far beyond the edge of urban regions. Despite assurances from the electric power industry that airborne sulphur is always beneficial to crop growth (Ross: 1971), Scandinavian investigators in particular have begun to catalog the consequences of acid rain in their soils, concluding that rates of tree growth and nutrient cycling are retarded (Likens, Bormann, and Johnson: 1972). Plaster, miscellaneous rubbish, and excrement from pets may be added in large quantities to city soils left uncovered by hard pavements or re-exposed where buildings have been demolished. Lutz has had no followers in the systematic study of trampling on urban soils (Lutz: 1945), even though much research is underway concerning trampling effects on vegetation in parks of urban and non-urban areas. Road de-icing salt is now banned in some Massachusetts towns where it has not only killed roadside trees, but also contaminated groundwater (Huling and Hollocher: 1972). Salt damage to plants has also been recorded in Washington, D.C. (Wester and Cohen: 1968). But the first comprehensive paper on urban soils has yet to appear.

Urban water managers in the United States have begun to make use of nearby soils for the disposal of liquid wastes. The return of "night soil" to fields was an ancient practice in Eastern Asia (King: 1911), complete with its own complex of associated diseases, but American sanitary engineers have opposed land disposal for urban waste (e.g., Wolman: 1956). Private septic tanks for domestic sewage have long been in use; they, incidentally, return water and nutrients to use by ornamental plants in many suburbs. Eschman and Marcus (1972) point out the lack of suburban development in large, well-situated tracts surrounding Ann Arbor, Michigan. The tracts are still inaccessible to major sewers save via costly uphill pumping over the watershed divide; septic tanks are unsuitable on their heavy soils, and construction awaits the subsidy of local development costs by the larger polity. The latter nineteenth century saw technological innovation in sewerage engineeering expand London outward onto previously intractable sites (Clayton: 1964; Dancer and Hardy: 1969). In the humid lands where green plants are closely spaced, undisturbed soils have always been deemed excellent natural covers of watershed lands, for their porous structure permits maximum infiltration of rainfall with minimum loss of structural material or nutrients by erosion. As the necessity to remove chemical compounds which permit excessive growth of undesirable aquatic organisms has become recognized by Americans in recent years, along with a growing realization of the cost of technological tertiary treatment facilities, interest has once more developed in land-irrigation of soils for liquid waste treatment.

Land disposal of waste is not new, as two recent bibliographies indicate (Commonwealth Bureau of Pastures and Field Crops: 1969; Law: 1968). Possibly the oldest explicit use of town effluent for its nutrient and irrigation benefits in the eastern United States occurred in Pullman, Illinois, where treated sewage was applied to vegetables and a profit of eight percent was realized in 1885 (Buder: 1967). In eastern North America land disposal of large quantities of waste water was first practiced by industrial firms no longer allowed to dump their effluent into streams (Little, Lull, and Remson: 1959; Sopper: 1971). No effort was made to adjust the water application to pre-existing vegetation; full reliance was placed on the sizeable ion-exchange capacity of soil particles to capture such elements as phosphates, dyestuffs, and other organic compounds. Several of these projects are still functioning decades after they began (Jackson, Bastian, and Marks: 1972).

More carefully designed is the system at University Park, Pennsylvania, whose effects are studied by various scholars at Pennsylvania State University. Here optimum rates of application for secondary treatment-plant effluent have been derived empirically from a decade of experimentation (Parizek et al.: 1967; Kardos: 1970, 1971). As might be expected, application of effluent by overhead sprinklers increased growth rates of trees for pulping and gave high yields of hay. Effluent-irrigated plots produce bumper crops of maize every year, equalled by local farmers using commercial fertilizers only when rainfall is abundant. To date, however, farmers in the humid east have shown little interest in urban effluent; spray irrigation remains very much an innovation promoted by urban water managers. This situation is reversed in the arid West of the United States, where irrigators have long paid for urban effluent on the basis of its water value alone, and waste nutrients were present as a bonus. Geographers might well take note of the distribution and diffusion of these practices. Where is the line between "East" and "West" in the United States on the basis of irrigation practices?

Many questions remain to be settled regarding spray irrigation as a mode of processing great quantities of urban-industrial liquid waste. The role of heavy metals needs close attention, and the fate of nitrates must also be watched, because effluent nitrates, like those of commercial fertilizer, are captured only by vegetation or denitrifying bacteria, not by the inorganic soil matrix. Chlorides pass rapidly through soils, and may be phytotoxic. Application rates, storage technology, and cover crops must be determined empirically for various soils and climatic regimes. A major system for combined urban and paper mill waste is being constructed at Muskegon, Michigan, without benefit of local experience in a pilot plant. It remains to be seen whether the long-term flow of nutrients via groundwater through the sandy soils to Lake Michigan will be cut significantly by the crop-filter scheme adopted there. If the Muskegon project is successful, other such systems may be encouraged. The project at Pennsylvania State University adjoins an elegant new condominium-apartment complex, and to date has encountered no adverse criticism on aesthetic amenity grounds; it is slated for expansion, and is already credited with raising local groundwater levels depleted by pumping during the drought of the early 1960's.

If the "living filter" system proves widely adaptable, there will be many problems of geographical interest to consider in each local situation, such as the size and location of spray plots, optimum networks of pipelines to hold down pumping costs, and tradeoffs between scattered land filtration plots and either scattered or consolidated tertiary treatment operations. Under Pennsylvania conditions, effluent is applied at the rate of two inches per week; the soil is allowed to dry out in the interim. One million gallons of effluent per day require 129 acres; the ten-million-gallon daily discharge from a city of 100,000 would require 1290 acres for land filtration. Possibly the most striking contribution of sludge and liquid effluent concerns the revegetation of plant-toxic strip-mine spoil, a medium often highly resistant to plant colonization (Sopper et al.: 1970). By virtue of their structure and their protective cover of living and dead organic material, forest soils of the northern United States have a greater capacity for effluent absorption than do cultivated soils, particularly in winter. To what extent effluent filtration can be combined with other land uses in urban and peri-urban areas remains to be investigated.

CLIMATE

The following discussion concentrates on landscape consequences of urban climate. Elsewhere in this volume Terjung discusses the underlying causes of characteristic urban climate modifications.

A substantial climatological literature has developed over the past twenty years at the geographical scale of the urbanized region, over which characteristic differences occur in mesoclimate—the intermediate climate of atmosphere above the ground interface but below weather-shelter height. The standard works from which one begins study of urban climate are the general summaries of Kratzer (1956), Landsberg (1956, 1970c), Peterson (1969), and Tyson (1970); the bibliographies of Brooks (1952) and Chandler (1970); and a major book on London (Chandler: 1965). Alongside this literature there has developed a parallel body of investigation into the indoor climatology of buildings (Olgyay: 1963; WMO, 1970b, 1973). But micrometeorological studies have been dominated by agronomic and ecological questions in non-urban settings (Geiger: 1965). Long-term records of climatic phenomena across urban areas are available only for a very sparse network of points, and many anomalies may be expected to arise as data accumulate for individual cities. The La Porte anomaly is an early example: industrial dust causes excess precipitation in the lee of the Chicago metropolitan area, although neither the existence of the effect nor its causative mechanisms have been accepted without controversy (Changnon: 1968; Holzman and Thom: 1970; Changnon: 1970). It is necessary to consider here first the characteristic urban heat-water balance, and second the presence of air pollution in urban atmospheres.

Cities are warmer and less humid than their rural surroundings. Focal points for combustion and characterized by great expanses of stone and asphalt surface, cities stand out as "islands" of higher temperature on isothermal maps. As urban air is warmed and rises, a local breeze is generated in the lower atmosphere which blows inward from all compass directions. This heat-island effect can be observed at the scale of individual buildings (Landsberg: 1970b); it becomes more intense with (to a first approximation) the increasing size of the urban region, as measured by the minimum geostrophic (regional) wind speed necessary to overcome its effects (Oke: 1969). Warmer winter minimum and annual average temperatures mean that mid-latitude urbanites spend less fuel for winter heating than their suburban cousins, but more for summer cooling. The concentration of tall buildings increases aerodynamic roughness and slows regional wind to greater altitudes than can rural trees; but buildings channel wind down unprotected streets, giving higher velocities at the ground surface than occur beneath plant canopies. The higher rainfall measured in cities appears to be more than offset by rapid runoff from pavements through artificial drains. Incoming radiation is sharply attenuated in the shorter wavelengths by urban smog, but snow covers the ground for a shorter period than in the countryside because of higher temperatures and the accumulation of soot. The physiological consequences of such changes are better known for humans (Tromp, ed.: 1962) than for plants and animals, but the net effect is greater stress as judged by the smaller number of species able to survive in cities than in nearby rural areas. Some birds profit by urban warmth, utilizing grates and open waterways in winter; some species breed earlier and longer each season in town than in nearby rural areas (Bonnett: 1971). The effect of longer urban frost-free seasons appears not to have been systematically investigated with respect to plants, although it was long ago noticed that tree branches immediately next to street lights retained their leaves a few days longer in autumn than did other branches (Dansereau: 1957). Interest in phenology has slowed once again in the United States with the termination of the International Biological Program project (Stearns: 1972b). However, in two German studies the earlier blooming of conspicuous trees and shrubs in urban centers as contrasted with outlying suburbs has been mapped: forsythia (*Forsythia* sp.) in Hamburg (Franken: 1955) and fruit trees in Cologne (Kalb: 1962). In addition, Lindsey has attempted to predict empirically the blooming time of cherries (*Prunus* spp.) in Washington, D.C. where extensive meteorologic and phenologic records are available, but he has made no maps of blooming time across the Washington area (Lindsey: 1963).

Atmospheric composition, under the label air pollution, is the dismal glamor subject in urban climatology. Air pollution is a consequence not only of the unbridled emissions from combustion and industrial processes, but also of limited air supplies. On days when ventilation is adequate, there is little local harm done by all the air pollutants any city can muster, and visibility is not restricted; unfortunately, such days are rarer than Sir Launfal's day in June. Poor ventilation occurs in areas affected by large-scale subsidence of stable air masses generated by the global atmospheric circulation; frequency maps have been published for stagnant air in the United States by Pack (1964) and Leighton (1966). Severe episodes of stagnant air have marked major air pollution disasters, such as occurred in the Meuse Valley (1930), Donora, Pennsylvania (1948), and London (1952), when spectacular losses of human and animal life were recorded. Such conditions are now predictable a few days in advance, and urban emissions could be temporarily reduced for their duration in the interest of public health.

Local topographic conditions may encourage poor ventilation on a smaller geographic scale. The valley bottom which attracts urban settlement may be protected from ready air movement by mountain barriers, as in the well-known case of Los Angeles. Early-rising urbanites are accustomed to the poor visibility characterizing morning radiation inversions whenever skies are clear and wind speeds low, for heat-island convection is insufficient to break up inversions aloft. Moreover, large water bodies warm slowly by comparison with the land, producing diurnal inversions in cities adjacent to large lakes and oceans. Thus flat, windswept Chicago experiences pollution conditions typical of smog-ridden Los Angeles over a narrow zone along Lake Michigan on half the days of the average summer (Lyons: 1971; Cole and Lyons: 1972; Lyons and Olsson: 1972). Within that narrow zone lie the central business district and numerous residential blocks. One might expect that geographers could take the initiative in constructing visual models of air pollution frequency for urban areas, because each city is topographically unique. Such information would have wide application to a host of problems. Maps giving isopleths either of expected pollutant-concentration frequencies or of biological damage are rare indeed for American cities. Geographers have developed sophisticated cartographic techniques (Muehrcke:

1972; Peucker: 1972); here is a splendid place to apply them for general social benefit.

The literature on pollutants released into urban air is enormous and growing rapidly. Useful guides are the short book by Bach (1972*a*) and the collection of reviews edited by Stern (1968). Teachers at all levels will find resource material in the proceedings of a recent Pennsylvania conference (Center for Air Environment Studies: 1970). Current research appears in the *Journal of the Air Pollution Control Association* and in the proceedings of the annual Clean Air Congresses sponsored by that organization, as well as in general journals such as *Science.* Many comparative data on several American cities appeared in a paper on surveillance systems by Morgan (Morgan, Ozolins, and Tabor: 1970). In general, particulate matter and smoke have been remarkably lessened in coal-burning cities such as London and Pittsburgh over the past twenty years, and some improvement is claimed in sulphur dioxide levels from the increasing use of low-sulphur fuels (Simon and Ferrand: 1971). But oxidizing pollutants, notably ozone and peroxyacyl nitrates (PANs) characteristic of Los Angeles smog, have been increasing in most cities with the growth in numbers of internal combustion engines.

Urban dust plumes can easily extend downwind for distances of 150 miles and more, adding to unwelcome imports of neighboring states and countries. For example, Hong Kong receives the dust channeled for seventy miles from Canton down the Pearl River Valley (Bryson and Ross: 1972). Swedish forests are damaged by airborne wastes from English and German factories to the south and west (Engström: 1971). International losses from the power-plant and smelter emissions at Trail, British Columbia stimulated one of the first major studies of air-pollution damage and distribution in North America (Katz *et al.*: 1939). Air pollution has also been suggested as the most likely cause of decreasing tree growth measured by annual ring increments in stands of white oak (*Quercus alba*) south and east of Chicago (Ashby and Fritts: 1972), but few comparable studies have yet appeared.

Urbanites have good reason to be concerned with air-pollution-caused agricultural losses, for they must pay the bill in higher food prices. Such losses are being recognized and recorded with increasing precision (Weidensaul and Lacasse: 1970; Millecan: 1971; Feliciano: 1972). Nationwide, direct losses in the United States now mount into the hundreds of millions of dollars. But such economic consequences are not yet charged to pollution producers, as economic rationality would require. Yet pollutants in city air are receiving increasing scrutiny as medical attention is directed more and more toward the respiratory and degenerative diseases in which atmospheric contaminants are implicated (Stokinger and Coffin: 1968; Dubos: 1966; Chow and Earl: 1970).

VEGETATION

The vegetation of urban areas has been little studied. A recent brief discussion of plant life in cities has been published by Detwyler (1972); the present treatment derives from a longer study by Schmid (1974). From the outset one must bear in mind that plants occupy "open space," land for some reason not built upon. The quantity of green acreage decreases as one approaches the central business district of a modern city, and one seldom finds a sharp break between town and countryside in regions of megalopolitan sprawl. In American suburbia the great bulk of vegetation is privately owned, but in central cities most vegetation occurs in public open spaces. These often constitute major anomalies in the urban space-economy. They derive from the political action of bygone generations, and have accumulated human sentiment as "sacred" territory (Firey: 1946). It is therefore not surprising that vegetation occurs in sharply different quantities and arrangements across urban regions, and is managed for quite unlike goals even within a single city.

Both native and cultivated plants suffer displacement as land use intensifies and rents increase upon the arrival of urban commercial or residential activity. Native *ecosystems*, whether involving grassland, desert flora, or forest-understory shrubs and herbs, virtually never survive into modern American landscapes—with the exception of sacrosanct forest preserves, watersheds, or tiny residual bits of land between plots in outer suburbia, all frequently characterized by some environmental hazard. Native *trees*, however, are sometimes valued in private residential and public park tracts, and consequently are left standing rather than bulldozed outright. Yet even when trees are kept, mortality is greater than intended, as a visit to any new suburb will reveal. Old individuals grown in closed stands have little capacity to adjust to suddenly increased moisture stress and wind throw attendant upon the opening of streets and house sites. Accelerated drainage and disturbance of soil structure and level disrupt the ability of tree roots to supply moisture. Leveling the surface of a homesite is just as disastrous as parking construction equipment or automobiles over trees' rooting areas. New species, such as the Eurasian "Kentucky" bluegrass (*Poa pratensis*), serve as the homeowner's standards for measurement of water and fertilizers added, for the amount of shade to be tolerated, and for the need to rake away leaves. New trees planted after settlement suffer less from these conditions, to which they can adjust over a long period; besides, the new species planted are those known to coexist with people. Shagbark hickory (*Carya ovata*) and white oak are seldom found on the sales floors of nurseries in eastern North America among faster growing, less demanding species of maple (*Acer* spp.), willow (*Salix* spp.), and locust (*Gleditsia* spp.).

The results of such changes in microclimate, soil conditions, and species replacement are readily observable in any urban area; the results of air pollution are less clearly visible in contemporary cities. When present in low enough concentrations, several gaseous air pollutants can provide plants with nutrients in available form, which are sometimes in quite short supply locally: carbon dioxide, sulphur compounds (Ross: 1971), various forms of nitrogen (Malo and Purvis: 1963; Porter *et al*.: 1972; Hutchinson *et al*.: 1972). Unfortunately, urban-industrial wastes are often found in atmospheric concentrations far greater than optimum for plant physiology. The resulting damage to plants has been reviewed by Hepting (1963, 1968, 1971a) and by Heggestad (1968, 1971). Striking correlations of plant disappearance and increasing severity of air pollution were demonstrated in Leeds early in the twentieth century (Crowther and Ruston: 1911; Cohen and Ruston: 1925) and were mapped in South Chicago by Bakke (Bakke: 1913). Such obvious damage to vegetation may persist for many decades after the industrial activity ceases, as at Copper Hill, Tennessee (Hursh: 1948). It is still occurring in mining districts (e.g., Gorham and Gordon: 1960a, 1960b; Lihnell: 1969). But within cities air-pollution effects are no longer so obvious, as McCool and Johnson discovered in the Philadelphia and St. Louis areas thirty-five years ago (McCool and Johnson: 1938). Pollution damage assessment requires the services of plant pathologists trained in pollutant effects and experienced in a local area, because symptoms of different pollutants differ in subtle ways from one another and must be distinguished from plant responses to other habitat factors (see the recent atlas of APCA: 1970; Hindawi: 1970; Lacasse and Moroz: 1969). Indirectly, air-pollutant damage affects plant populations through changing interrelations with other organisms: sulphur may prevent the growth of mildew on Brooklyn lilacs (Hibben and Walker: 1966) and alter leaf microbiota in other ways (Saunders: 1971; Basile, Slade and Corpe: 1969; Parmeter and Cobb: 1972); photochemical smog from Los Angeles is helping beetles destroy the ponderosa pine (*Pinus ponderosa*) of the San Bernardino Mountains (Stark *et al.*: 1968; Cobb and Stark: 1970; Miller and Millecan: 1971). Air pollution has possibly its most striking effect on lichens, and the urban "lichen desert" has been well studied and mapped for several European and American cities (Barkman: 1958, 1969; Gilbert: 1965, 1968, 1969, 1970*a* 1970*b*; Skye: 1968; Brodo: 1966; Le Blanc and de Sloover: 1970; Vareschi: 1953). As Le Blanc has demonstrated in the Sudbury mining district of Ontario, maps of lichen response are virtually identical to maps based on continuous monitoring of SO_2; data gathering for the lichen map required two weeks, but for the SO_2 required ten years (Le Blanc, 1971). Because maps of damage to higher plants are virtually non-existent for cities, opportunities are great for geographers to work on questions seldom raised by plant pathologists, and interdisciplinary cooperation would be mutually profitable.

Turning from the growing edges of the urban fringe, the discussion now focuses on two basic features of cities as plant habitat. First, cities are classic examples of the biological instability derived from low species diversity and ecosystem simplification resulting from human activity. The most striking result in eastern North America is the disappearance of the American elm (*Ulmus americana*) as the primary street and shade tree. Second, cities are prime sites for observing the interaction of people and ruderal plants—that curious assortment of successfully colonizing species lumped together as "weeds."

Species diversity is a little-studied aspect of urban vegetation; data are not easily obtained except by one's own observation. Potential diversity is very great, for it is the business of breeders and nurserymen to create and introduce ornamental plant material from all over the world. Lists of plants grown in parks and arboreta can be extensive (Department of Public Parks: 1873; Eickhorst, Schulenberg and Swink: 1972). Yet the kinds of plants commonly grown across urban areas are far less diverse than those *able* to grow in any region, and the resulting plant communities are extremely simplified by comparison with natural communities. Departments of urban forestry today are very conservative when authorizing or approving more than a very few well-known kinds of trees—those which have been demonstrated to survive under the difficult growing conditions of city streets, to leave pipes and sidewalks undisturbed by roots, to be easily propagated, but not so easily as to become nuisances. Other species are banished to private property, and thus appear more characteristic of suburban than inner-city neighborhoods. The bureaucratically simple practice of planting entire blocks or streets to a single species has been reinforced by aesthetic arguments of landscape designers, who long supported unity in the view on a single avenue even when praising the differentiation of streets by contrasting species (Solotaroff: 1912; Kom: 1959). This generalization appears to hold for all American cities, even though climatic permissiveness renders ornamental species diversity greater in megalopolitan

California than in midwestern or northeastern cities. Floristic diversity bears no necessary connection with ideals of landscape beauty.

Over the past forty years Dutch elm disease has spread across the United States from the Atlantic to the Rockies, and its progress has been mapped by Holmes (1956, 1957, 1958, 1961, 1962). Native to floodplains where it infrequently formed pure stands, as well as to upland communities, American elm grows quickly into majestic, long-lived specimens. Since colonial times its attractiveness and light shade have encouraged its preservation in rural pastures and its planting along lanes and city streets, often to the virtual exclusion of other species. In the early years of this century a small European bark beetle (*Scolytus multistriatus*) spread across eastern North America, attracting little attention as it joined larger native bark beetles (*Hylurgopinus* spp.) in their ordinary habitats. In 1930 the first deaths of elm attributable to a fungus, *Ceratocystis ulmi*, were recorded in Ohio, where it had been introduced accidentally via a single shipment of European elm veneer logs which had not been de-barked. In a syndrome already well-known in 1930 from its previous ravages among the elms of Western Europe (Clinton and McCormick: 1936), the fungus is introduced into a tree by twig-feeding beetles or by root grafts underground. Once in the vascular system, the fungus multiplies rapidly, choking the tree's pipelines for water and food. By the present time, Dutch elm disease has spread from Nova Scotia to Texas, North Dakota to Georgia, and is even known in the cities of Idaho and Colorado, beyond the native range of *Ulmus americana* (La Perriere and Howard: 1971). To date no simple remedy for the disease has been found. Ruthless immediate cutting of infected individuals, their quick disposal by burning or burial (unless de-barked, the wood must not be kept for firewood, because it is ideal habitat for bark beetles), spraying to control the beetle vectors, and poisoning of root grafts around infected individuals must be combined in a comprehensive attack in order to save any elms at all (Carter: 1967). Such control measures are not merely expensive, but they must be carried out over wide areas of fragmented jurisdiction; they contribute to ambient pesticide levels (Carson: 1962), and increase air pollution (Cusumano and Wasser: 1965). Methoxychlor, more expensive but less persistent than DDT (Wurster *et al.*: 1965), is now used for aerial spraying. Preventive injections of systemic insecticides (e.g., Bidrin) into elms have to date proven nearly as likely to cause tree mortality as the disease itself, if they are concentrated enough to kill the beetles (English and Hartstirn: 1962). Recent work on systemic fungicides gives a little more cause for hope (Smalley: 1971; Gregory, Jones and McWain: 1971; Hart: 1972). Benomyl can be injected tree by tree, or it can be sprayed on soil or foliage. At the moment it appears to have far fewer deleterious consequences in urban ecosystems than the insect-directed pesticides it may replace; yet the history of Dutch elm disease provides little expectation of any panacea.

Outside Wisconsin and parts of Massachusetts and Illinois, the record of American cities in combatting the disease is pathetic. Midwestern cities without public control programs lost ninety-five percent and more of street elm populations within ten years of the disease's arrival (Neely: 1963, 1967, 1971, 1972). Northeastern cities have replaced their American elms with less majestic English and Scots species (*U. procera, U. glabra*) which (like related genera *Zelkova* and *Planera*) are less susceptible, though not immune to Dutch elm disease. Costs of removing dead elms are eventually borne by towns and individuals, because risk to persons and property increases as standing trees decay. Little or no salvage value attaches to the fungus-infected wood, which is simply left standing in the rural midwest and southern Ontario.

Dutch elm disease is but one of many blights which attack ornamental trees (Hepting: 1971b), although no other disease would be capable of causing equal economic or aesthetic damage in American cities. Phloem necrosis, a virus disease spread by leafhoppers (*Scaphoideus luteolus*), ravaged elms in the midwest in the late 1940's and 1950's, before its effects were overshadowed by Dutch elm disease farther north (Baker: 1949). Early in the present century an introduced blight eradicated American chestnut (*Castanea dentata*), an important species in eastern forests which in 1900 made up half the standing trees of Connecticut. Henry Wadsworth Longfellow notwithstanding, there is no evidence that the disappearance of chestnut caused much change in the appearance of eastern cities after the manner of the elm; its place in the forests has been taken by oaks (*Quercus* spp.). A fungus wilt disease of oaks involves only native beetles, squirrels, and fungus: at present it has spread south and east from the upper Mississippi valley, but it has not yet eliminated oak populations of midcontinent cities (Himelick and Fox: 1961). All ecosystems are potentially subject to explosions of one organism at the expense of others whenever the right combination of weather and other factors occurs (SCEP: 1971, p. 11):

> for each species of terrestrial plant there are about 100 species of animals capable of eating it, yet most of the time, most of the plant production falls to the ground uneaten. For many insects able to defoliate trees the population density rarely rises as high as one per tree.

Details of the ordinary complex equilibrium which prevails in nature are little understood; no one can predict what the next disastrous outbreak will be. But the simplified, species-poor ecosystems in cities are at least as vulnerable as the biologically impoverished croplands that feed urban consumers. Street trees can be diversified, and Detwyler sees evidence that this has in fact occurred in Ann Arbor (Detwyler: 1972). In any event, the investigations of diversity in urban vegetation, of why certain plants are introduced at certain times, of how a vernacular landscape style developed in North America, or of what purposes people may expect vegetation to fill in their urban environments, is left entirely to geographers by botanists, ecologists, and historians of art and landscape architecture.

Before this discussion of urban vegetation is concluded with a review of the purposes desired plants might serve, notice must be taken of the inadvertent, weedy flora of urban areas. Serious study of urban weeds has not yet begun in North America, although a sizeable European literature has been reviewed by American scholars (King: 1966; Frenkel: 1970). Information on the distribution and ecology of non-agricultural weeds in the United States must be gleaned from local floras, town by town and species by species; not all compilers of floras deem weeds worth mentioning. To date one can point to no monographs on weeds as indicators of culture history in North America along European models (e.g., Saarisalo-Taubert: 1963), despite recent interest in the genetics of colonizing species (Baker and Stebbins, eds.: 1965; Bradshaw: 1970, 1971) and work in plant hybridization as a result of human activity (Anderson: 1949, 1952, 1956; Heiser: 1949, 1951). Some contemporary weeds are imported exotics initially cherished for ornamental purposes: *Ailanthus altissima*, the Tree-of-Heaven that "grows in Brooklyn" and most other American cities from coast to coast as *the* city tree nonpareil; *Kochia scoparia*, a rank herb which forms dense stands across vacant lots in lower Manhattan and in the desolate highway and urban renewal sites of Chicago. Why such plants undergo shifts in cultural appraisal is a question not yet tackled by students of environmental perception, whose work is reviewed by Saarinen elsewhere in this volume.

Krieger has raised the interesting question "what's wrong with plastic trees?" (Krieger: 1973). Unfortunately, Krieger had no idea of the answer. In the ensuing paragraphs an attempt is made to outline some of the benefits which living plants provide (or could provide) in urban areas. It is difficult to see how artificial vegetation could perform any of these functions. One may note in passing that different demands are made on "open space" by different groups in American society (Gold: 1972; Clark *et al*.: 1971). An extended discussion of class differences in aesthetic preferences for urban vegetation, however, lies beyond the scope of the present paper.

Vegetation could be managed for economic return. Many European cities have long found timber production within the city limits a profitable enterprise. Thus almost one quarter of Zürich is forested: annual timber production yields about 1.5 million board feet, and the annual income of $80,000 in the 1960's was enough to maintain the forests for both production and recreation in addition to yielding a surplus to the municipal budget. Holscher (1971) has discussed other European cities besides Zürich, and Ruppert (1960) has described the management of the city forest in Frankfurt-am-Main. In North America the absence of timber scarcity eliminates this direct source of benefit from urban forestry. Yet an indirect economic rationale could be constructed. Trees are universally found in cities, and must be constantly removed for a variety of reasons. This produces waste material that must be disposed of at ever-greater expense, unless investment is made in chipping equipment and use is found for the chips. To the extent that some return is realized from the surplus wood, the physical waste problem should be diminished and its net costs reduced. Thornton has calculated that the half million board feet of sawlogs and 3000 cords of pulpwood which had to be carted away by Philadelphia in 1969 would have kept a small sawmill in operation all year. Aside from any consideration of growth rates in urban conditions, harvesting would be complex (Thornton: 1971, p. 131):

> the material to be removed ranges from small-diameter stems and limbs to extremely large trees that are likely to be defective. Typically there is a wide range of species, but most city trees are low in commercial value. Volumes are low and are scattered over large areas. Opportunities to salvage high-quality sawlogs are rare. And almost every tree to be cut presents an individual problem to removal crews. Protecting turf, structures, utilities, or other elements of the micro-environment can be most difficult.

Thornton concludes that the central benefit to be derived from urban forestry in North America is an educational demonstration of resource-management potential, spatially proximate and highly visible to urbanites (as rural state and national forests are not) and designed to inculcate values of environmental stewardship rather than the simple economic rationality of cost-benefit analysis.

A number of essentially engineering benefits can be derived from urban vegetation as part of the planned fabric of cities. Here notice may be taken of the potential role of vegetation in noise reduction, in environmental monitoring, and in climatic amelioration of the human habitat. The existence of such benefits was a basic tenet of environmental thinking in the mid-nineteenth century, when both public health measures and urban parks were first advocated in North America. Yet only recently has research been conducted to specify the means of environmental improvement, and to quantify the effect of plants. For the most part, such research is revealing a greater benefit from small quantities of plants than was thought likely by most planners. This knowledge, along with aerial photography for gathering and computer methods for analyzing and displaying large batches of geographical information, underlies a good opportunity for the first intellectual advance in urban environmental design since the time of Frederick Law Olmsted.

In a review published as recently as 1970, Smith was able to conclude that significant noise reduction through the use of vegetation might require buffer strips of plants at least 400 feet wide (Smith: 1970). In Nebraska two investigators have measured the reduction in loudness of recorded traffic noise under standardized conditions for a range of distances behind shelterbelts containing various tree and shrub species (Cook and Van Haverbeke: 1971). Their most interesting set of data concerns the sound propagation over suburban lawn with screen plantings as compared with the adjacent street. Traffic noise was half as loud in the lawn as over the street (a difference of more than ten decibels) at equal distances from the source. Aylor has attempted to specify the complex acoustical effects of several kinds of surface and vegetation, performing measurements in maize fields, coniferous forest, hardwood brush, and marshes (Aylor: 1972a, 1972b, 1972c). The results vary with the frequency of the sound, and the distance to the receiver; nevertheless, the general conclusions indicate a major potential for reduction of noise intensity by relatively narrow strips of plant material in urban areas. Several European workers have reported similar findings (citations may be found in Bach: 1972b).

Plants have long been appreciated in rural areas as indicators of hazard zones; there is some possibility of similar use of urban plants. In the western United States certain species of *Astragalus* prefer selenium-rich soils, and warn experienced ranchers to keep their livestock away (Trelease and Beath: 1949). Urban plants can serve as after-the-fact monitors of air pollution, since particular species and varieties respond to extremely small concentrations of particular gaseous compounds: gladioli react to fluorides, pinto beans wither in the presence of ozone and PAN, Bel-W3 tobacco signals ozone, alfalfa shows characteristic symptoms from sulphur dioxide, and even common weeds can be interpreted by specialists (Heck: 1966; Heck and Heagle: 1970; Leone *et al.*: 1964). Interpretation of plant damage by air pollutants is complicated by many factors, such as the age of the individual plants, their state of nutrition and moisture, their previous life-history; the simultaneous presence of several pollutants may enhance tissue damage; and the different genetic constitution of individuals within a single species may give rise to great variation in response (Brandt and Heck: 1968). Higher plants appear to be damaged principally by discrete fumigation episodes, when pollutant levels may rise to many times their long-period average concentrations. Lower plants (lichens and mosses) indicate much more precisely the effective long-term geographical extent of polluted air (Mansfield and Bull: 1972).

Climatic amelioration by city plants can be divided into considerations of air pollution and of heat-water balance. Because urban society is capable of producing airborne wastes in local concentrations greater than plants can survive, it is clear that the principal means of reducing air pollution is reduction of emissions by changing the composition of wastes leaving exhaust pipes and chimneys—that is, technological change, not more plants. A number of these measures have been described by Bach (1972*a*). But there remain residual quantities of pollutants which are extremely difficult to capture except at enormous expense. These will no doubt remain in urban atmospheres for the forseeable future, and for them vegetation can act as an important sink (Hill: 1971). A rough quantitative example of the role of plants in absorbing sulphur dioxide has been offered by Lanphear (1971): given measured absorption rates of SO_2 by Douglas fir (*Pseudotsuga menziesii*) and given the average output of SO_2 by St. Louis in one year, all the annual output of SO_2 could theoretically be absorbed locally by 50 million Douglas fir trees, which could be grown on five percent of the city's land area. Other figures from the literature have been gathered by Smith: removal by alfalfa (*Medicago sativa*) of SO_2 at 7,250,000 lbs. per square mile per year, of NO_2 at 204,000 lbs. per square mile per year; removal by soybean (*Glycine max*) of NH_3 at 11,400 lbs. per square mile per year; removal by soil fungi of CO at 421,000 lbs. per square mile per year (Smith: 1972*b*). In New Haven a sugar maple (*Acer saccharum*) one foot in diameter removes from the atmosphere in a single growing season 60 mg. cadmium, 140 mg. chromium, 820 mg. nickel, and 5800 mg. lead (Smith: unpublished). In addition to active uptake of gases into leaves via stomata, leaf surfaces provide a vast area for the settling of particulates and absorption of further gaseous wastes. Bach has measured the decrease in atmospheric turbidity which occurs across a steep gradient at Cincinnati's heavily vegetated Spring Grove cemetery under polluted conditions (Bach: 1971); others have contrasted the ragweed pollen concentration in open valley fields (high) and hillside coniferous forests (low) in Pennsylvania (Neuberger *et al.*: 1967). One must note that plants release not only pollen into the atmosphere, but also reactive hydrocarbons (Rasmussen: 1972), thus contributing to as well as reducing the burden of atmospheric contaminants. Fortunately, volatile terpenes are perceived by people as "fresh" air rather than "dirty" air. These interactions of plants with air pollutants should receive the careful attention of planners interested in human health and much more information is needed to permit rational field application of present knowledge over a range of urban conditions. For example, it is frequently suggested in the press that urban plants are useful because they exchange oxygen for carbon dioxide. This effect is insignificant, since it is quantitatively small and oxygen is not in short supply (SCEP: 1970); urbanites will choke from excess carbon monoxide long before they run short of oxygen (Broecker: 1970*a*, 1970*b*). Prevailing wind data give a reasonable first approximation to the shape of the lichen desert around cities, but Landsberg has pointed out that under atmospheric conditions of intense fumigation, light winds may blow opposite to the prevailing direction (Landsberg: 1970*a*). Thus sources of inevitable pollution sometimes need to be located upwind rather than downwind from an urban center.

At a very local level, individual homeowners could arrange their vegetation to provide the maximum effect on wind and incoming radiation. Federer suggests this formula for the northern United States (Federer: 1971, p. 27):

> conifers to the west and north for protection against cold winter winds, hardwoods to the south for summer shade and winter sun, and grass or shrubs to the east or southeast for a feeling of openness and for early morning sun.

This kind of advice has been given to suburbanites by landscape architects in countless books and articles for at least a century, with remarkably little result.

The use of shelterbelts of trees and shrubs is well understood from a technical viewpoint (Van Eimern, ed.: 1964), but this knowledge is rarely applied in contemporary American cities. A need for such plantings to counteract wind at ground level in urban canyons is obvious to all frequenters of central business districts.

On the scale of the whole metropolitan area green spaces could have an equally pronounced effect. Oke calculates that two-thirds of total potential evapotranspiration from a completely vegetated surface can occur if plants cover about one-third of a city's land area (Oke: 1973). This evapotranspiration becomes significant in terms of human health during heat waves, when a few degrees' difference in temperature can sharply influence heat prostration (Clarke: 1970). Federer offers the following illustration: a single, isolated tree by evapotranspiring 100 gallons of water per day accounts for 230,000 kcal. of energy, the equivalent cooling of five average room air conditioners (each 2500 kcal/hr.) running 19 hours per day (Federer: 1971). The air conditioners, however, merely shift heat from indoors to outdoors; they do not operate with perfect efficiency, and they ordinarily entail the release of heat elsewhere in the urban area from the combustion of fossil fuel. How the mesoclimatic effects of individual trees are to be aggregated is not yet known; two trees do not transpire twice as much as one if they are competing for limited moisture. Street trees have small soil volumes available for rooting in many instances, and their transpiration could presumably be augmented by increasing available water in summer. Detailed local isotherms showing the effect of a small park in Montreal on surrounding blocks have been mapped by Oke (Oke: 1973), while the human comfort provided by such microenvironmental differences has been calculated by several investigators (Clarke and Bach: 1971; Waggoner: 1963).

All the foregoing economic and engineering benefits from vegetation can be enjoyed by urbanites without much conscious attention, by virtue of the mere presence of plants in the urban landscape. There is insufficient space here to do justice to a set of more complex benefits which people derive from vegetation as a social symbol and an aesthetic object, yet these considerations have influenced most urban vegetation in the past and undoubtedly will remain important. They have received little attention in the literature, and are less easily described than the preceding kinds of benefits. For example, strong connections between social class and vegetational patterns can be found in Chicago residential neighborhoods, where Thorstein Veblen's "pecuniary aesthetic" still persists (Schmid: 1974). The plants of front yards, like the exterior appearance of a house, convey information about the persons within. Thus weeds give public notice that a landowner or tenant is unwilling to contribute to public decency. As ornaments, urban plants are subject to changes in fashion over time, but particular plantings persist in both public and private landscapes long after the fashion has changed. In most cultures plants form a part of the human environment, and are often highly valued even if the space allotted to them is small; yet the desired kinds and arrangements of plants vary widely within and among human societies. The typical American arrangement of grassy lawn, however diminutive, with shade trees recalls the common pasture of northern Europe as the appropriate setting for civilized life (Jackson: 1951). Without vegetation cities would lack green forms, reminders of the changing seasons, which contrast sharply with buildings and help increase pleasurable complexity in a sensually impoverished milieu. If managed by the residents themselves, the gardens of public housing projects can even become foci of community formation (Lewis: 1973). One can measure the quantity of greenery present in an urban area from aerial photographs, but such functions of vegetation as these can only be understood by an observer on foot who can experience the plants in their three-dimensional setting, and can interpret the historical, psychological, and sociological connotations of the local context.

Both urbanites and urban planners have neglected opportunities, in McHarg's phrase, to "design with nature" rather than against its potentialities, when building the landscape of urban-industrial society. Jacobs (1961) has properly questioned whether the plantings so often installed by city planners are appropriate occupants of urban space. If plants are to provide much human benefit, they must provide more than a fragile green surface and they must be located in the immediate presence of people. But intermingling of people and plants is not easily achieved in such a way that both coexist. Parks can either destroy or enliven street life, and people can easily destroy vegetation if it is incorrectly sited. To make their urban space habitable, wealthy urbanites can afford mechanical buffers between themselves and the outdoor environment; they can likewise afford to clean up environmental pollution generated by the buffers. One can agree with Krieger (1973) that astroturf and plastic trees have aesthetic value in places where living organisms would never survive—so long as the viewers are passing by quickly in their automobiles and never have to walk through or examine the imitation at close range. Twentieth-century readers may smile at the romantic excess that led William Kent to build sham ruins and to plant his dead trees for effect in Kensington Gardens, but there is an arrogant indifference toward both man and nature underlying plastic plants that is not amusing but sinister. As in the days of Frederick Law Olmsted, the rich still have both the leisure and the means to leave the city for other environments at will; the poor are confined to its precincts, whatever the environmental quality.

ANIMAL LIFE

Plastic trees support no food chains, so they cannot sustain urban populations of birds, squirrels, or other animals which rely only partially on direct human support. Urban faunas can be surprisingly complex, but to date they have attracted far less attention among ecologists and population biologists than the animal inhabitants of less disturbed areas. (See the discussion by Doughty elsewhere in this volume.)

The animal and plant kingdoms are fundamentally different, even though intimately linked, and few interesting generalizations apply equally well to both. The range of ecological functions within the animal kingdom is vast; thus it is not possible to summarize urban effects on animals in the same way as such effects can be treated for plants. As a result of their comparatively small biomass and their wariness, most animals are hidden from man most of the time, while green plants constitute major landscape features even in cities. Plant ecology is virtually an earth science, while animal ecology is less directly tied to soils and microclimatic exposure because animals are mobile. Thus the distinguished animal ecologist Elton has voiced doubts about the capacity of geography as a synthesizing discipline to manage ecological survey work, even for so small a place as the two square miles of Wytham Woods (near Oxford) with its biota of at least 5,000 species (Elton: 1966, p. 63):

> geography concerns itself with much broader classifications of earth and water and climate, and with the relations between man himself and his crops and landscape, and is a blunt tool for defining habitats that may at the lower end occupy areas as small as half a square foot, or—as with the bodies of animals as habitats for parasites—even less.

Animal ecology is studied at an even smaller microscale than plant ecology. The literature and concepts differ sharply between the two disciplines, as do the personnel, in spite of the existence of joint organs of publication, past attempts to develop unifying biogeographical concepts (Merriam's life zones, Clements and Shelford's biomes), or contemporary interests in nutrient and energy cycling (Watts: 1971) and ecosystem functioning and stability (Regier and Colwell: 1972).

Literature on urban animals exists in proportion to their importance to and interest for man. Thus a large number of studies concerns birds and mammals, and attention has been given to invertebrates significant for human health (e.g., Belding: 1965; James and Harwood: 1969). General books exist on the natural history of London, New York, and Chicago (Fitter: 1945; Kieran: 1959; Dubkin: 1947, 1965, 1972). A number of species adapted to urban open spaces has been studied: the sparrow (*Passer domesticus*) and the red fox (*Vulpes vulpes*) in England (Summers-Smith: 1963; Vesey-Fitzgerald: 1967), the black-bird (*Turdus merula*) in Oxford (Snow: 1958), the coyote (*Canis latrans*) in Los Angeles (Gill: 1970), the grey squirrel (*Sciurus caroliniensis*) in Toronto (Cox: 1970), peregrine falcons (*Falcus peregrinus*) in Montreal (Hall: 1970). Other authors have observed larger groups of animals, such as birds in London (Hudson: 1898; Homes, ed.: 1957; Cramp and Tomlins: 1966), in suburbs in Sardinia, Florida and South Africa (Walter and Demartis: 1972; Woolfenden and Rohwer: 1969; Siegfried: 1968), in Illinois (Graber and Graber: 1963), in Massachusetts (Walcott: 1959; Boyd: 1962), and in Michigan (Wallace, Nickell and Bernard: 1961), ants in Harpenden (Morley: 1944), and slugs in Borne-mouth (Barnes and Weil: 1944, 1945). Animals closely dependent on man have been investigated also: the inhabitants of a Tudor house in southeastern England (Ordish: 1960), rats in Baltimore and Calcutta (Davis: 1953; Spillet: 1968), dogs in Baltimore (Beck: 1973), monkeys in the cities of North India (Southwick *et al.*: 1965; Southwick: 1969), the pests of storehouses (Solomon: 1965), and cockroaches (Guthrie: 1968; Cornwell: 1968).

Some organisms are favored by urban expansion, whereas others are deci-mated or extinguished entirely. Those creatures best able to tolerate disturbance, to adjust their behavior patterns adaptively, to utilize patches of open or woodland-edge habitat, to creep about inside buildings, to tap man's own food supply surreptitiously, to avoid recognizable competition, or to attract human appreciation and esteem, may increase in the urban milieu. Thus large carnivores are banished from cities, but red foxes breed within four miles of London's St. Paul's (Teagle: 1967). The northeast megalopolis of the United States hosts thriving populations of squirrels, rabbits (*Sylvilagus* spp.), raccoons (*Procyon lotor*), skunks (*Mephitis mephitis*), and opossums (*Didelphis marsupialis*) (Morel and Gottmann: 1961). Orange County, New York hires professional hunters to reduce its herds of white-tailed deer (*Odocoileus virginianus*), because public hunting is banned from its growing suburban communities and the deer constitute a hazard to motorists. Birds and insects can readily enter cities, where they find ambient pesticide levels higher than in unfarmed countryside but lower than in orchard and truck-farm districts (Tarrant & Tatton: 1968; Tabor: 1966); many insects, as well as reptiles and amphibians, find cities too dry for optimal habitat. Wetland preserved as wildlife refuge may attract high populations of migrant waterfowl, as at Jamaica Bay within the City of New York. The ever-increasing movement of people and goods enables both animals and plants to escape the geological confinement of Wallace's realms (Elton: 1958), and to contribute to a cosmopolitan urban biota whether people desire the newcomers or not. Patagonian monk parrots (*Myopsitta monachus*) nested in Manhattan's Morningside Park in 1972, presumably part of a shipment accidently released at Kennedy Airport several years before. Urban-industrial pollution has killed fish in thousands of streams by means of toxic wastes, nutrient overloads, temperature increase, and habitat-destroying channelization; yet cold water from New York City's reservoirs has made the upper Delaware once more habitable by trout, and tropical fish inhabit the warm waters of London's power station discharges.

The major attempt to synthesize the literature on urban animals is the work of Bonnett (1971), who has looked in particular detail at London as a city of rich wildlife diversity. London's fauna is perhaps the best studied among major cities (Table 3), because the British are inveterate amateur naturalists; greater London is fortunate to possess a large acreage of green spaces linked with each other and with the surrounding countryside. The significance of the percentage figures of total British biota observed in London is difficult to assess until comparable data are available for other cities. Presumably the London figures are relatively high, but the evidence is not yet in. And why so few kinds of city beetles? Few urbanites would recognize this biota unless they made natural history a hobby of special interest!

Many questions remain concerning the ecology and natural history of urban animals. No one has yet studied in detail how urban species numbers change as habitat is reduced to islands of green within built-up areas. Preliminary indexes of urbanization have been developed only for birds, for which a considerable empirical-descriptive literature exists (Preston and Norris: 1947; Udvardy: 1957). A major effort is currently underway to study megalopolitan wildlife under the auspices of the United States Forest Service (Thomas: 1972), but in the past non-game species have been neglected by American wildlife biologists (Larson: 1971). Aside from the work on industrial melanism in moths (Kettlewell: 1957, 1961), little attention has been given to genetic changes allowing animals to flourish in cities. What happens to the elaborate microfauna of forest soils when leaf litter is replaced by lawn with fertilizer and insecticides in suburban plots? For long-term appraisals of urban biotic change, the accumulated observations of local naturalists over many years is fundamental, yet this is precisely the kind of material which laboratory-minded biologists recommend for removal from university libraries faced by shortages of funds and storage space. Moreover, the reward system for biological researchers favors rapid publication of short-term studies rather than long-term investigations.

What useful purposes might animals serve in cities? The keeping of animals for food is as rare as vegetable gardening in modern cities. Horses are no longer significant for transportation, but have retained status value. A variety of creatures is kept indoors, or encouraged by feeding outdoors, for amusement and companionship. Urban animals can be used as biological monitors; urban

TABLE 3—The Biota of Contemporary London

Kind	Number of Species		London Species as Percent of UK Species
	Seen in London	Seen in the United Kingdom	
Higher Plants	1,835	3,000	61
Insects			
Hemiptera-Homoptera (bugs)	317	390	82
Coleoptera (beetles)	248	3,700	7
Macro Lepidoptera (moths, butterflies)	728	930	78
Diptera (true flies)	2,300	5,200	44
Fishes (fresh and brackish water)	33	45	73
Amphibians	8	12	66
Reptiles	6	10	60
Birds	203	301	66
Terrestrial Mammals	32	52	62
Insectivora (shrews, moles, hedgehogs)	5	6	83
Chiroptera (bats)	10	15	66
Lagomorpha (hares, rabbits)	2	3	66
Rodentia (squirrels, voles, rats, mice)	8	17	47
Carnivora	4	11	36
Artiodactyla (deer)	3	9	33

Compiled by Bonnett (1971) from records of the London Natural History Society (1960-1970), (Fitter: 1963), and (Southern: 1964), for London as defined by a circle of 20 miles radius centered on St. Paul's, *ca.* 1200 square miles.

pigeons (*Columba livia*) have more lead in their bones than do their country cousins (Tansy and Roth: 1970); feral dogs in cities suffer higher incidence of pulmonary disease (Reif and Cohen: 1970) and tonsillar carcinoma (Ragland and Gorham: 1967) than do those living in rural areas; suburban chickens and horses permit precautionary surveillance for St. Louis encephalitis virus in Florida (Nichols and Bigler: 1969).

Domestic animals can be used both for environmental monitoring and for physiological research (Mulvihill: 1972). But these considerations do not explain why wild animals would be thought desirable in cities. It is generally accepted that species diversity contributes to ecosystem stability (Odum: 1969); therefore, an abundance of organisms may help reduce the probability that any one kind will increase in uncontrolled fashion to cause direct or indirect damage to man. At present this remains a matter of faith, not of fact, for urban environments. Perhaps more important, the unexpected encounter with wild creatures appears to strike deep chords of response in human nature, at least in part because man was during most of his biological existence an inhabitant of the natural world (Shepard: 1967). Perhaps wild creatures provide desired stimuli outside the range of experience indigenous to built-up environments, stimuli not associated with the stress of ordinary encounters with people and people's artifacts (Parr: 1966). In part the urbanite's attraction to animals in the cities of European influence reflects his socialization in a cultural tradition which venerates the pastoral "middle landscape" of Europe, which is not completely dominated by man's structures and activities (Schmitt: 1969; Shepard: 1967). Dagg (1970) asked householders in the small Ontario city of Waterloo which wildlife species they had seen and which they preferred, but the more difficult question "why?" remains in the realm of speculation. Geographers have developed a tradition of studying cultural attitudes toward domesticated animals (Simoons: 1961, 1968; Isaac: 1970), which might well be extended to include the household and wild animals of the modern city.

To illustrate the interaction of city animals with people, one may examine the animal whose living biomass is perhaps second only to man's own in modern cities, the dog (*Canis familiaris*). Canine population estimates for major cities are 700,000 for London, 500,000 for New York, Buenos Aires, and Mexico City, 300,000 for Los Angeles and Lima, 90,000 for Baltimore. More than half the nearly 25 million owned American dogs are urbanites, and twenty to fifty percent of the families in city neighborhoods own at least one dog (Schwabe: 1969). People enjoy the presence of household dogs because they provide companionship, protection, entertainment, and a means for fashionable display. In the countryside, even in the outer suburbs, few public constraints on dog ownership are necessary. But the dense populations of dogs in crowded cities are different. Beck estimates that New York City's dogs deposit between 15 and 55 tons of feces and more than 53,000 gallons of urine *daily* (Beck: 1973). Dog feces are a prime source by which eggs of the nematode *Toxocara canis* reach humans, especially children. The resulting human disease, visceral larva migrans, is not readily diagnosed except in its ocular form, which can cause permanent blindness. Both this disease and others associated with dogs lead Beck to recommend that dogs should not be kept by families with small children (Beck: 1973). Stray dogs consume garbage, which they scatter, benefiting both rats and flies. Flies readily breed in feces, and concentration of dog urine hastens the early death of urban trees. Both feces and urine find their way into streams via storm sewers which bypass sewage-treatment plants, thereby contributing to water pollution. Current attempts in New York City to enact legislation requiring a dog's owner to clean up his pet's solid nuisances for the protection of public health are being vociferously resisted. In a classic case of common-property resource misuse, many urbanites decline responsibility for internalizing costs which could be borne conveniently by society in an earlier and less congested era. What is rational for the individual is not rational for the community as a whole. In Baltimore dogs in 1970 accounted for 6,023 bites of humans, whereas only 32 rat bites were recorded. For 1971 the figures were 6,809 and 54 (Beck: 1973). Yet urbanites who advocate the extermination of rats protect ownerless dogs, and make strict enforcement of control ordinances virtually impossible in contemporary American cities. Here is human behavior which bears further investigation.

SOME CONCLUSIONS

In the past men have customarily acted to produce artifacts and to rearrange their habitat without regard to what might happen to other animals, plants, climates, soils, or the very earth beneath their feet. But man has become the ecological dominant of the modern world. His numbers are growing rapidly, and he is congregating in cities even more rapidly, in an implosion that appears to be out of control. Modern science and technology have permitted the lengthening of man's life span and an enormous reduction in infant mortality. Given population control, science and technology may also help solve the problems they have created. But continuing reappraisals of the consequences of actions must now be made, and the reasons for undertaking the actions must be examined critically. The social linkage between public, formerly uncalculated costs, and privately anticipated benefits must be solidly forged: in the long run the preservation of man and the preservation of nature are one and the same, but in the short run there are always too many temptations to sacrifice the latter for the former. Both the physical and the mental health of man require that urban systems of biogeochemical cycling be brought into a new, relatively stabilized relationship. Unfortunately, time is short and men learn slowly (Frank: 1966). It is safe to assume that grievous crises will precede positive action.

To the extent that professional geographers confront environmental problems in modern cities, they can make a contribution to the quality of contemporary life. Society critically needs understanding of the local spatial expression of environmental systems; it needs to know who wants what and who gets what, in spatial as well as socioeconomic terms of reference. And it needs critical appraisals of past behavior for clues to future events. The probability of failure is high. Just a century ago, when American cities were undergoing their first major period of industrial growth, the intellectual community and the profession of landscape architecture lost political control of the metropolis (Fein: 1972; Jackson: 1972). Whether the scientific establishment will succeed this time remains to be seen. But the opportunity currently exists for geographers to join with other scholars along all their many common research frontiers in order to rationalize and humanize the environmental impact of urbanization.

ACKNOWLEDGEMENTS

For helpful criticism of an earlier draft and for useful suggestions, the author is indebted to his former colleagues at Barnard College, D. Ehrenfeld, K. Jackson, J. Oliver, J. Sanders, and F. Warburton; and to correspondents A. Beck, J. Bell, W. Berger, J. Carter, T. Dailey, C. Elton, R. Frischmuth, I. Leone, M. Levandowsky, D. Neely, C. Olmsted, R. Platt, H. Schroeder, W. Smith, G. Stephens, F. Stearns, W. Terjung, D. Watts, and C. Wright. Advice offered has not always been accepted, and the author is fully responsible for errors of fact and interpretation.

REFERENCES

Adams, Robert McC., 1965, *Land Behind Baghdad: A History of Settlement on the Diyala Plains.* Chicago: University of Chicago Press.
_____ , 1966, *The Evolution of Urban Society: Early Mesopotamia and Prehispanic Mexico.* Chicago: Aldine.
_____ , 1972, *The Uruk Countryside: The Natural Setting of Urban Societies.* Chicago: University of Chicago Press.
APCA (Air Pollution Control Association), 1970, *Recognition of Air Pollution Injury to Vegetation: A Pictorial Atlas.* Pittsburgh, Pa.: APCA. Informative Report 1.
Anderson, Edgar, 1949, *Introgressive Hybridization.* New York: Wiley.

_____ , 1952, *Plants, Man and Life*. Boston: Little, Brown.

_____ , 1956, "Man As A Maker of New Plants and New Plant Communities," in Wm. L. Thomas (ed.), *Man's Role in Changing the Face of the Earth*. Chicago: University of Chicago Press, pp. 763-777.

Arkell, W. J., 1947, *Oxford Stone*. London: Faber & Faber.

Ashby, Wm. C. and H. C. Fritts, 1972, "Tree Growth, Air Pollution, and Climate Near La Porte, Indiana," *Bulletin of the American Meteorological Society*, Vol. 53, pp. 246-251.

Aylor, Donald J., 1972a, "Noise Reduction by Vegetation and Ground," *Journal of the Acoustical Society of America*, Vol. 51, pp. 197-205.

_____ , 1972b, "Sound Transmission Through Vegetation in Relation to Leaf Area Density, Leaf Width, and Breadth of Canopy," *ibid.*, Vol. 51, pp. 411-414.

_____ , 1972c, "Muffling Noise With Soil, Plants," *Grounds Maintenance*, August, pp. 20-22.

Bach, Wilfrid, 1971, "Seven Steps to Better Living on the Urban Heat Island," *Landscape Architecture*, Vol. 61, pp. 136-138.

_____ , 1972a, *Atmospheric Pollution*. New York: McGraw-Hill.

_____ , 1972b, "Urban Climate, Air Pollution, and Planning," in Thomas R. Detwyler and M. G. Marcus (eds.), *Urbanization and Environment*. Belmont, California: Duxbury, pp. 69-96.

Baker, Herbert G. and G. L. Stebbins (eds.), 1965, *The Genetics of Colonizing Species*. New York: Academic.

Baker, W. L., 1949, "Studies on the Transmission of the Virus Causing Phloem Necrosis of American Elm, With Notes on the Biology of Its Insect Vector," *Journal of Economic Entomology*, Vol. 42, pp. 729-732.

Bakke, Arthur L., 1913, "The Effect of Smoke and Gases Upon Vegetation," *Proceedings of the Iowa Academy of Science*, Vol. 20, pp. 169-186.

Barkman, J. J., 1958, *The Phytosociology and Ecology of Cryptogamic Epiphytes*. Assen, Neth.: Van Gorcum.

_____ , 1969, "The Influence of Air Pollution on Bryophytes and Lichens," in *First European Conference on the Influence of Air Pollution on Plants and Animals, Wageningen*, pp. 197-210.

Barnes, H. F. and J. W. Weil, 1944, "Slugs in Gardens: Their Numbers, Activities, and Distribution I," *Journal of Animal Ecology*, Vol. 13, pp. 140-175.

_____ , 1945, "Slugs in Gardens II," *ibid.*, Vol. 14, pp. 71-105.

Barton, Nicholas J., 1962, *The Lost Rivers of London*. London: University of Leicester Press and J. M. Dent.

Basile, Dominick V., L. L. Slade and W. A. Corpe, 1969, "An Association Between a Bacterium and a Liverwort, *Scapania nemorosa*," *Bulletin of the Torrey Botanical Club*, Vol. 96, pp. 711-714.

Beck, Alan M., 1973, *The Ecology of Stray Dogs: A Study of Free-Ranging Urban Animals*. Baltimore: York Press.

Belding, D. L., 1965, *Manual of Human Parasitology*. New York: Appleton-Century-Crofts.

Bobek, Hans, 1962, "The Main Stages in Socioeconomic Evolution from a Geographical Point of View (1959)," in Philip L. Wagner and M. W. Mikesell (eds.), *Readings in Cultural Geography*. Chicago: University of Chicago Press, pp. 209-247.

Bonnett, Penelope A., 1971, "Nature In the Urban Landscape: A Review and Bibliography," Unpublished master's thesis. Edmonton: University of Alberta. (See also Gill and Bonnett, below).

Boyd, Elizabeth, 1962, "A Half Century's Changes in the Bird Life around Springfield, Massachusetts," *Bird Banding*, Vol. 33, pp. 137-149.

Bradshaw, A. D., 1970, "Plants and Industrial Waste," *Transactions of the Botanical Society of Edinburgh*, Vol. 41, pp. 71-84.

_____ , 1971, "Plant Evolution in Extreme Environments," in Robert Creed (ed.), *Ecological Genetics and Evolution: Essays in Honour of E. B. Ford*. Oxford: Blackwell, pp. 20-50.

Braidwood, Robert and C. A. Reed, 1957, "The Achievement and Early Consequences of Food Production: A Consideration of the Archaeological and Natural Historical Evidence," *Cold Spring Harbor Symposia in Quantitative Biology*, Vol. 22, pp. 19-31.

Brandt, C. Stafford and W. W. Heck, 1968, "Effects of Air Pollution on Vegetation," in Arthur C. Stern, ed., *Air Pollution*. 2nd ed. New York: Academic Press, pp. 401-443.

Brodo, Irwin M., 1966, "Lichen Growth and Cities: A Study on Long Island, New York," *Bryologist*, Vol. 69, pp. 427-449.

Broecker, Wallace S., 1970a, "Man's Oxygen Reserves," *Science*, Vol. 168, pp. 1537-1539.

_____ , 1970b, "Enough Air," *Environment*, Vol. 12, pp. 26-31.

Brooks, C. E. P., 1952, "Selective Annotated Bibliography on Urban Climates," *Meteorological Abstracts and Bibliography*, Vol. 3, pp. 734-773.

Bryson, Reid A. and J. E. Ross, 1972, "The Climate of the City," in Thomas R. Detwyler and M. G. Marcus (eds.), *Urbanization and Environment*. Belmont, California: Duxbury, pp. 51-58.

Buder, Stanley, 1967, *Pullman: An Experiment in Industrial Order and Community Planning*. New York: Oxford University Press.

Carson, Rachel M., 1962, *Silent Spring*. Boston: Houghton, Mifflin.

Carter, J. Cedric, 1967, *Dutch Elm Disease in Illinois*. Urbana: Illinois Natural History Survey. Circular 53.

Center for Air Environment Studies, 1970, *Proceedings of the Teachers Conference on Conservation of Our Air Environment*. University Park, Pennsylvania: Pennsylvania State University. CAES Publication 182-70.

Chandler, T. J., 1965, *The Climate of London*. London: Hutchinson.

———, 1970, *Selected Bibliography on Urban Climate*. Geneva: World Meteorological Organization. Publication 276 (TP-155).

Changnon, Stanley A., 1968, "The La Porte Precipitation Anomaly–Fact or Fiction?" *Bulletin of the American Meteorological Society*, Vol. 49, pp. 4-11.

———, 1970, "Reply," *ibid.*, Vol. 51, pp. 337-342.

Chow, T. J. and J. L. Earl, 1970, "Lead Aerosols in the Atmosphere: Increasing Concentrations," *Science*, Vol. 170, pp. 577-580.

Ciborowski, Adolf, 1972, "The Impact of the Rural-Urban Relationship in Landscape Planning." Invited paper for 12th Technical Meeting, International Union for the Conservation of Nature and Natural Resources, Banff, Canada.

Clark, Roger N., J. C. Hendee and F. L. Campbell, 1971, "Values, Behavior, and Conflict in Modern Camping Culture," *Journal of Leisure Research*, Vol. 3, pp. 143-159.

Clarke, J. F., 1970, "Some Effects of Urban Structure on Heat Mortality," *Environmental Research*, Vol. 5, pp. 93-104.

Clarke, J. F. and W. Bach, 1971, "Comparison of Comfort Conditions in Different Urban and Suburban Environments," *International Journal of Biometeorology*, Vol. 15, pp. 41-54.

Clayton, Keith M. (ed.), 1964, *Guide to London Excursions*. London: Twentieth International Geographical Congress.

Clinton, G. P. and F. A. McCormick, 1936, *Dutch Elm Disease–Graphium ulmi*. New Haven: Connecticut Agricultural Experimental Station. Bulletin 389.

Cobb, F. W., Jr. and R. W. Stark, 1970, "Decline and Mortality of Smog-Injured Ponderosa Pine," *Journal of Forestry*, Vol. 68, pp. 147-149.

Cohen, Julius B. and A. G. Ruston, 1925, *Smoke: A Study of Town Air*. 2nd ed. London: E. Arnold.

Cole, Henry S. and W. A. Lyons, 1972, *The Impact of the Great Lakes on the Air Quality of Urban Shoreline Areas: Some Practical Applications with Regard to Air Pollution Control Policy and Environmental Decision-Making*. Milwaukee: University of Wisconsin, Center for Great Lakes Studies. Contribution 72.

Commonwealth Bureau of Pastures and Field Crops, 1969, *Application of Sewage and Factory Effluents and Sewage Sludge to Grassland and Crops*. Hurley, Maidenhead, Berks. Annotated Bibliography 1175.

Cook, David I. and D. F. Van Haverbeke, 1971, *Trees and Shrubs for Noise Abatement*. Lincoln: University of Nebraska and U.S. Forest Service. Research Bulletin 246.

Cornwell, P., 1968, *The Cockroach*. Vol. 1. London: Hutchinson.

Cox, P., 1970, "The Squirrels of Queen's Park and Philosopher's Walk." Unpublished report. Toronto: University of Toronto, Department of Zoology.

Cramp, S. and A. D. Tomlins, 1966, "The Birds of Inner London," *British Birds*, Vol. 59, pp. 209-233.

Crowther, Charles and A. G. Ruston, 1911-1912, "The Nature, Distribution, and Effects upon Vegetation of Atmospheric Impurities in and near an Industrial Town," *Journal of Agricultural Science*, Vol. 4, pp. 25-55.

Cunningham, Ernest B., 1970, "An Ecologist's View of National Park Operation and Management," *Canadian Field Naturalist*, Vol. 84, pp. 191-194.

Cusumano, Robert D. and G. L. Wasser, 1965, "A Survey of Practices in Regard to the Air Pollution Aspects of Dutch Elm Disease Eradication," *Journal of the Air Pollution Control Association*, Vol. 15, pp. 230-234.

Dagg, A. I., 1970, "Wildlife in an Urban Area," *Naturaliste Canadien*, Vol. 97, pp. 201-212.

Dancer, W. S. and A. V. Hardy, 1969, *Greater London*. London: Cambridge University Press.

Dansereau, Pierre M., 1957, *Biogeography: An Ecological Perspective*. New York: Ronald.

Davis, D. F., 1953, "The Characteristics of Rat Populations," *Quarterly Review of Biology*, Vol. 28, pp. 373-407.

Davis, John H., 1956, "Influences of Man Upon Coast Lines," in Wm. L. Thomas (ed.), *Man's Role in Changing the Face of the Earth*. Chicago: Univ. Chicago Press, pp. 504-521.

Department of Public Parks, City of New York, 1873, *Annual Report*.

Detwyler, Thomas R. (ed.), 1971, *Man's Impact on Environment*. New York: McGraw-Hill.

——, 1972, "Vegetation in the City," in T. R. Detwyler and M. G. Marcus (eds.), *Urbanization and Environment*. Belmont, California: Duxbury, pp. 135-168.

Detwyler, Thomas R. and M. G. Marcus (eds.), 1972, *Urbanization and Environment: The Physical Geography of the City*. Belmont, Cal. and North Scituate, Mass.: Duxbury Press.

Dubkin, Leonard, 1947, *Enchanted Streets: Adventures of a Nature Lover*. Boston: Little, Brown.

——, 1965, *The Natural History of a Yard*. Chicago: H. Regnery.

——, 1972, *My Secret Places: One Man's Love Affair with Nature in the City*. New York: McKay.

Dubos, René J., 1966, "Man and His Environment: Scope, Impact, and Nature," in Ralph W. Marquis (ed.), *Environmental Improvement: Air, Water, and Soil*. Washington, D.C.: U.S. Department of Agriculture Graduate School Press, pp. 3-21.

Ehrenfeld, David W., 1972, *Conserving Life on Earth*. New York: Oxford University Press.

Eickhorst, Walter, R. Schulenberg, and F. Swink, 1972, *Woody Plants of the Morton Arboretum: A Handlist of Plants Established or Tried in the Woody Plant Collections*. Lisle, Ill.: Morton Arboretum.

Elton, Charles S., 1958, *The Ecology of Invasions by Animals and Plants*. London: Methuen.

——, 1966, *The Pattern of Animal Communities*. London: Methuen.

English, L. L. and W. Hartstirn, 1962, "Systemic Insecticide Control of Some Pests of Trees and Shrubs—A Preliminary Report," *Illinois Natural History Survey Biological Notes*, Vol. 48, pp. 1-12.

Engström, Arne, 1971, *Air Pollution Across National Boundaries: The Impact on the Environment of Sulfur in Air and Precipitation*. Stockholm: Royal Ministry for Foreign Affairs and Royal Ministry of Agriculture.

Eschman, Donald F. and M. G. Marcus, 1972, "The Geological and Topographic Setting of Cities," in Thomas R. Detwyler and M. G. Marcus (eds.), *Urbanization and Environment*. Belmont, California: Duxbury, pp. 27-50.

Evans, D. M., 1966, "The Denver Area Earthquakes and the Rocky Mountain Arsenal Disposal Well," *The Mountain Geologist*, Vol. 3, pp. 23-36.

Federer, C. A., 1971, "Effects of Trees in Modifying Urban Microclimate," in Silas Little and J. H. Noyes (eds.), *Trees and Forests in an Urbanizing Environment*. Amherst, Mass.: University of Massachusetts, Cooperative Extension. Planning and Resource Development Series Publication 17, pp. 23-28.

Fein, Albert, 1972, *Frederick Law Olmsted and the American Environmental Tradition*. New York: Braziller.

Feliciano, Alberto, 1972, *1971 Survey and Assessment of Air Pollution Damage to Vegetation in New Jersey*. New Brunswick, N.J.: Rutgers University Cooperative Extension Service.

Firey, Walter, 1946, *Land Use in Central Boston*. Cambridge, Mass.: Harvard University Press.

Fitter, R. S. R., 1963, *Wildlife in Britain*. Harmondsworth: Penguin.

——, 1945, *London's Natural History*. London: Collins.

Flannery, Kent V., 1969, "Origins and Ecological Effects of Early Domestication in Iran and the Near East," in Peter J. Ucko and G. W. Dimbleby (eds.), *The Domestication and Exploitation of Plants and Animals*. Chicago: Aldine, pp. 73-90.

Flawn, Peter T., 1970, *Environmental Geology: Conservation, Land Use Planning, and Resource Management*. New York: Harper & Row.

Frank, Jerome D., 1966, "Galloping Technology: A New Social Disease," *Journal of Social Issues*, Vol. 22, pp. 1-14.

Franken, E., 1955, "Der Beginn der Forsythienblüte in Hamburg, 1955: Ein Beitrag zur Phänologie der Grossstadt," *Meteorologische Rundschau*, Vol. 8, pp. 113-114.

Frenkel, Robert E., 1970, "Ruderal Vegetation along Some California Roadsides," *University of California Publications in Geography*, Vol. 20, pp. 1-163.

Geiger, Rudolph, 1965, *The Climate Near the Ground*. Revised ed. Cambridge, Mass.: Harvard University Press.

Gilbert, O. L., 1965, "Lichens as Indicators of Air Pollution in the Tyne Valley," in Gordon T. Goodman *et al.* (eds.), *Ecology and the Industrial Society*. New York: Wiley, pp. 35-47.

———, 1968, "Bryophytes as Indicators of Air Pollution in the Tyne Valley," *New Phytologist*, Vol. 67, pp. 15-30.

———, 1969, "The Effect of Sulphur Dioxide on Lichens around Newcastle-upon-Tyne," pp. 223-236 in *First European Conference on the Influence of Air Pollution on Plants and Animals, Wageningen.*

———, 1970a, "Further Studies on the Effect of Sulphur Dioxide on Lichens and Bryophytes," *New Phytologist*, Vol. 69, pp. 605-627.

———, 1970b, "A Biological Scale for the Estimation of Sulphur Dioxide Pollution," *ibid.*, Vol. 69, pp. 629-634.

Gill, Don, 1970, "The Coyote and the Sequential Occupants of the Los Angeles Basin," *American Anthropologist*, Vol. 72, pp. 821-826.

Gill, Don and P. A. Bonnett, 1973, *Nature in the Urban Landscape: A Study of City Ecosystems.* Baltimore: York Press.

Gold, Seymour M., 1972, "Nonuse of Neighborhood Parks," *American Institute of Planners Journal*, Vol. 38, pp. 369-378.

Goldman, Marshall I., 1972, *The Spoils of Progress: Environmental Pollution in the Soviet Union.* Cambridge, Mass.: MIT Press.

Gordon, A. G. and E. Gorham, 1963, "Ecological Aspects of Air Pollution from an Iron-Sintering Plant at Wawa, Ontario, Canada," *Canadian Journal of Botany*, Vol. 41, pp. 1063-1078.

Gorham, Eville and A. G. Gordon, 1960a, "The Influence of Smelter Fumes upon the Chemical Composition of Lake Waters Near Sudbury, Ontario and upon the Surrounding Vegetation," *ibid.*, Vol. 38, pp. 477-486.

———, 1960b, "Some Effects of Smelter Pollution Northeast of Falconbridge, Ontario," *ibid.*, Vol. 38, pp. 307-312.

Graber, Richard R. and J. W. Graber, 1963, "A Comparative Study of Bird Populations in Illinois, 1906-1909 and 1956-1958," *Illinois Natural History Survey Bulletin*, Vol. 28, pp. 383-528.

Gregory, G. F., T. W. Jones and P. McWain, 1971, *Injection of Benomyl into Elm, Oak, and Maple.* Upper Darby, Pa.: USDA Forest Service. Research Paper NE-232.

Guthrie, D., 1968, *The Biology of the Cockroach.* London: E. Arnold.

Hall, G. H., 1970, "The Sun Life Falcons," *Canadian Field Naturalist*, Vol. 84, pp. 210-230.

Hamilton, Douglas H. and R. L. Meehan, 1971, "Ground Rupture in the Baldwin Hills," *Science*, Vol. 172, pp. 333-344.

Hart, John H., 1972, "Control of Dutch Elm Disease with Foliar Applications of Benomyl," *Plant Disease Reporter*, Vol. 56, pp. 685-688.

Healy, John *et al.*, 1968, "The Denver Earthquakes," *Science*, Vol. 161, pp. 1301-1310.

Heck, Walter W., 1966, "The Use of Plants as Indicators of Air Pollution," *International Journal of Air and Water Pollution*, Vol. 10, pp. 99-111.

Heck, Walter W. and A. S. Heagle, 1970, "Measurement of Photochemical Air Pollution with a Sensitive Monitoring Plant," *Journal of the Air Pollution Control Association*, Vol. 20, pp. 97-99.

Heggestad, H. E., 1968, "Diseases of Crops and Ornamental Plants Incited by Air Pollutants," *Phytopathology*, Vol. 53, pp. 1089-1097.

———, 1971, "Air Pollution and Plants," in W. H. Matthews, F. E. Smith, and E. D. Goldberg (eds.), *Man's Impact on Terrestrial and Oceanic Ecosystems.* Cambridge, Mass.: MIT Press, pp. 101-115.

Heiser, Charles B., 1949, "A Study in the Evolution of the Sunflower Species *Helianthus annuus* and *H. bolanderi*," *University of California Publications in Botany*, Vol. 23, pp. 157-208.

———, 1951, "Hybridization in the Annual Sunflowers . . . ," *Evolution*, Vol. 5, pp. 42-51.

Hepting, George H., 1963, "Climate and Forest Diseases," *Annual Review of Phytopathology*, Vol. 1, pp. 31-50.

_____, 1968, "Diseases of Forest and Tree Crops Caused by Air Pollutants," *Phytopathology*, Vol. 58, pp. 1098-1101.

_____, 1971a, "Air Pollution and Trees," in W. H. Matthews, F. E. Smith, and E. D. Goldberg (eds.), *Man's Impact on Terrestrial and Oceanic Ecosystems.* Cambridge, Mass.: MIT Press, pp. 116-129.

_____, 1971b, *Diseases of Forest and Shade Trees of the United States.* Washington: GPO. USDA Forest Service Agricultural Handbook 386.

Hibbard, Walter R., 1968, "Mineral Resources: Challenge or Threat?" *Science*, Vol. 160, pp. 143-149.

Hibben, C. R. and J. J. Walker, 1966, "A Leaf-Roll Necrosis Complex of Lilacs in an Urban Environment," *Proceedings of the American Society for Horticultural Science*, Vol. 89, p. 636-642.

Hill, A. C., 1971, "Vegetation: A Sink for Atmospheric Pollutants," *Journal of the Air Pollution Control Association*, Vol. 21, pp. 341-346.

Himelick, E. B. and H. W. Fox, 1961, *Experimental Studies on the Control of Oak Wilt Disease.* Urbana: Illinois Natural History Survey. Bulletin 680.

Hindawi, Ibrahim J., 1970, *Air Pollution Injury to Vegetation.* Washington: GPO. USHEW Air Pollution Control Administration. Publication AP-71.

Holmes, Francis W., 1956, "Recorded Dutch Elm Disease Distribution in North America as of 1955," *Plant Disease Reporter*, Vol. 40, pp. 351-352.

_____, 1957, "Recorded Dutch Elm Disease Distribution in North America as of 1956," *ibid.*, Vol. 41, pp. 634-635.

_____, 1958, "Recorded Dutch Elm Disease Distribution in North America as of 1957," *ibid.*, Vol. 42, pp. 1299-1300.

_____, 1961, "Recorded Dutch Elm Disease Distribution in North America as of 1959," *ibid.*, Vol. 45, pp. 74-75.

_____, 1962, "Recorded Dutch Elm Disease Distribution in North America as of 1961," *ibid.*, Vol. 46, p. 715-718.

Holscher, Clark E., 1971, "European Experience in Integrated Management of Urban and Suburban Woodlands," in Silas Little and J. H. Noyes (eds.), *Trees and Forests in an Urbanizing Environment.* Amherst: University of Massachusetts, Cooperative Extension. Planning and Resource Development Series Publication 17, pp. 133-138.

Holzman, B. G. and H. C. S. Thom, 1970, "The La Porte Precipitation Anomaly," *Bulletin of the American Meteorological Society*, Vol. 51, pp. 335-337.

Homes, Richard C. (ed.), 1957, *Birds of the London Area Since 1900.* London: Collins.

Hudson, Wm. Henry, 1898, *Birds in London.* London: Dent.

Huling, Edwin E. and T. C. Hollocher, 1972, "Groundwater Contamination by Road Salt: Steady-State Concentrations in East Central Massachusetts," *Science*, Vol. 176, pp. 288-290.

Hursh, C. R., 1948, *Local Climate in the Copper Basin of Tennessee as Modified by the Removal of Vegetation.* Washington: Government Printing Office. USDA Circular 774.

Hutchinson, G. L., R. J. Millington, and D. B. Peters, 1972, "Atmospheric Ammonia: Absorption by Plant Leaves," *Science*, Vol. 175, pp. 771-772.

Iglauer, Edith, 1972, "Our Local Correspondents: The Biggest Foundation (World Trade Center Foundation)," *The New Yorker Magazine*, 4 November, pp. 130 ff.

Isaac, Erich, 1970, *Geography of Domestication.* Englewood Cliffs, N.J.: Prentice-Hall.

Jackson, John B., 1951, "Ghosts at the Door," *Landscape*, Vol. 1, pp. 3-9.

_____, 1972, *American Space: The Centennial Years, 1865-1876.* New York: Norton.

Jackson, W. B., R. K. Bastian, and J. R. Marks, 1972, "Effluent Disposal in an Oak Woods During Two Decades," Unpublished paper presented at the International Geographical Congress, Montreal.

Jacobs, Jane, 1961, *The Death and Life of Great American Cities.* New York: Random House.

_____, 1969, *The Economy of Cities.* New York: Random House.

James, M. T. and R. F. Harwood, 1969, *Medical Entomology.* London: Macmillan.

Jennings, J. D., 1965, "Man as a Geological Agent," *Australian Journal of Science*, Vol. 28, pp. 150-155.

Kalb, Margaret, 1962, "Einige Beiträge zum Stadtklima von Köln," *Meteorologische Rundschau*, Vol. 15, pp. 92-99.

Kardos, Louis T., 1970, "A New Prospect: Preventing Eutrophication of Our Lakes and Streams," *Environment*, Vol. 12(2), pp. 10-27.

_____, 1971, "Recycling Sewage Effluent Through the Soil and Its Associated Biosystems," in *Proceedings of the International Symposium on Identification and Measurement of Environmental Pollutants, Ottawa*, pp. 119-123.

Katz, Morris *et al.*, 1939, *The Effect of Sulphur Dioxide on Vegetation*. Ottawa: National Research Council of Canada. Publication 815.

Kettlewell, H. B. D., 1957, "Industrial Melanism in Moths and Its Contribution to Our Knowledge of Evolution," *Proceedings of the Royal Institution of Great Britain*, Vol. 36, pp. 616-635.

―――, 1961, "The Phenomenon of Industrial Melanism in Lepidoptera," *Annual Review of Entomology*, Vol. 6, pp. 245-262.

Kieran, John, 1959, *A Natural History of New York*. Boston: Houghton, Mifflin.

King, F. H., 1911, *Farmers of Forty Centuries*. Madison, Wisconsin: Mrs. F. H. King.

King, Lawrence J., 1966, *Weeds of the World: Biology and Control*. New York: Wiley-Interscience.

Kom, Tony N., 1959, "An Investigation of Design Considerations for Residential Street Trees," Unpublished master's thesis. Berkeley: University of California.

Krantz, Grover S., 1970, "Human Activities and Megafaunal Extinctions," *American Scientist*, Vol. 58, pp. 164-170.

Kratzer, P. Albert, 1956, *Das Stadtklima*. 2nd. ed. Braunschweig: F. Vieweg. (English Translation available from National Technical Information Service, AD 284776).

Krieger, Martin H., 1973, "What's Wrong with Plastic Trees?" *Science*, Vol. 179, pp. 446-455.

Lacasse, Norman L. and W. J. Moroz, 1969, *Handbook of Effects Assessment―Vegetation Damage*. University Park, Pa.: Pennsylvania State University, Center for Air Environment Studies Publication 47-69.

Landsberg, Helmut E., 1956, "The Climate of Towns," pp. 584-606 in Wm. L. Thomas, (ed.), *Man's Role in Changing the Face of the Earth*. Chicago: University of Chicago Press.

―――, 1970*a*, "Climates and Urban Planning," pp. 364-374 in *Urban Climates*. Geneva: World Meteorological Organization. Publication 254. (TP-141, Technical Note 108).

―――, 1970*b*, "Micrometeorological Temperature Differentiation through Urbanization," pp. 129-138 in *ibid*.

―――, 1970*c*, "Man-Made Climatic Changes," *Science*, Vol. 170, pp. 1265-1274.

Lanphear, F. O., 1971, "Urban Vegetation: Values and Stresses," *Hortscience*, Vol. 6, pp. 332-334.

La Perriere, Louis B. and W. A. Howard, 1971, *Discriminating Pre-Visual Symptoms of Stress Associated with Dutch Elm Disease through Color Infrared Photography*. Denver: University of Denver, Department of Geography. Technical Paper 71-1.

Larson, Joseph S., 1971, "Managing Woodland and Wildlife Habitats in and near Cities," in Silas Little and J. H. Noyes (eds.), *Trees and Forests in an Urbanizing Environment*. Amherst, Massachusetts: University of Massachusetts, Cooperative Extension. Planning and Resource Development Series Publication 17, pp. 125-128.

Law, James P., 1968, *Agricultural Utilization of Sewage Effluent and Sludge: An Annotated Bibliography*. Washington, D.C.: U.S. Government Printing Office.

Le Blanc, Fabius, 1971, "Possibilities and Methods for Mapping Air Pollution on the Basis of Lichen Sensitivity," *Mitteilungen der Förstlichen Bundes-Versuchsanstalt, Wien*, Vol. 92, pp. 103-126.

Le Blanc, Fabius and J. de Sloover, 1970, "Relation between Industrialization and the Distribution and Growth of Epiphytic Lichens and Mosses in Montreal," *Canadian Journal of Botany*, Vol. 48, pp. 1485-1496.

Leighton, Philip A., 1966, "Geographical Aspects of Air Pollution," *Geographical Review*, Vol. 56, pp. 151-174.

Leone, Ida A., E. Brennan and R. H. Daines, 1964, "Weeds Are Sensitive to Pollution of Atmosphere," *New Jersey Agriculture*, Vol. 46, pp. 6-10.

Lewis, Charles A., 1973, "People-Plant Interaction: A New Horticultural Perspective," *American Horticulturist*.

Lihnell, D., 1969, "Sulphate Contents of Tree Leaves as an Indicator of Sulphur Dioxide Air Pollution," in *First European Conference on the Influence of Air Pollution on Plants and Animals, Wageningen*, pp. 341-352.

Likens, Gene E., F. H. Bormann, and N. M. Johnson, 1972, "Acid Rain," *Environment*, Vol. 14, pp. 33-40.

Lindsey, Alton A., 1963, "Accuracy of Duration Temperature Summing and Its Use for *Prunus serrulata*," *Ecology*, Vol. 44, pp. 149-151.

Little, Silas L. and J. H. Noyes (eds.), 1971, *Trees and Forests in an Urbanizing*

Environment. Amherst, Massachusetts: University of Massachusetts, Cooperative Extension. Planning and Resource Development Series Publication 17.

Little, Silas L., H. W. Lull, and I. Remson, 1959, "Change in Woodland Vegetation and Soils after Spraying Large Amounts of Waste Water," *Forest Science*, Vol. 5, pp. 18-27.

Lutz, Harold J., 1945, "Soil Conditions of Picnic Grounds in Public Forest Parks," *Journal of Forestry*, Vol. 43, pp. 121-127.

Lyons, Walter A., 1971, "Mesoscale Transport of Pollutants in the Chicago Area as Affected by Land and Lake Breezes," pp. 973-979 in H. M. Englund and W. T. Beery, (eds.), *Second International Clean Air Congress Proceedings.* New York: Academic Press.

Lyons, Walter A. and L. E. Olsson, 1972, "Mesoscale Air Pollution Transport in the Chicago Lake Breeze," *Journal of the Air Pollution Control Association*, Vol. 22, pp. 876-881.

McCool, M. M. and A. N. Johnson, 1938, "Nitrogen and Sulphur Content of Leaves of Plants at Different Distances from Urban Centers," *Boyce Thompson Institute Contributions*, Vol. 9, pp. 371-380.

Malo, Bernard A. and E. R. Purvis, 1964, "Soil Absorption of Atmospheric Ammonia," *Soil Science*, Vol. 97, pp. 242-247.

_____, 1963, "Find Polluted Air Supplies Nitrogen," *New Jersey Agriculture*, Vol. 45, p. 13.

Mamaev, S. A., 1970, "Current Conditions and Scientific Problems in Studying the Injurious Effects of Industrial Pollutants on Plants and in Developing Methods for Controlling Them in the Urals (1964)," in M. Y. Nuttonson (ed.), *American Institute of Crop Ecology Survey of Russian Air Pollution Literature,* Vol. 3. Silver Spring, Md.: AICE, pp. 23-32.

Mansfield, T. A. and J. N. Bull, 1972, "The Effects of SO_2 Pollution on Plant Life," *The Environment This Month*, August, pp. 29-34.

Martin Paul S. and H. E. Wright (eds.), 1967, *Pleistocene Extinction: The Search for a Cause.* New Haven: Connecticut: Yale University Press.

Matthews, Wm. H., F. E. Smith, and E. D. Goldberg (eds.), 1971, *Man's Impact on Terrestrial and Oceanic Ecosystems* (SCEP—Study of Critical Environmental Problems). Cambridge, Massachusetts: MIT Press.

Mikesell, Marvin W., 1969, "The Deforestation of Mount Lebanon," *Geographical Review*, Vol. 59, pp. 1-28.

Milgram, Stanley, 1970, "The Experience of Living in Cities," *Science*, Vol. 167, pp. 1461-1468.

Millecan, Arthur A., 1971, *A Survey and Assessment of Air Pollution Damage to California Vegetation in 1970.* Sacramento: California Department of Agriculture.

Miller, P. R. and A. A. Millecan, 1971, "Extent of Oxidant Air Pollution Damage to Some Pines and Other Conifers in California," *Plant Disease Reporter*, Vol. 55, pp. 555-559.

Morgan, George B., G. Ozolins, and E. C. Tabor, 1970, "Air Pollution Surveillance Systems," *Science*, Vol. 170, pp. 289-296.

Morley, B. D. Wragge, 1944, "A Study of the Ant Fauna of a Garden, 1934-1942," *Journal of Animal Ecology*, Vol. 13, pp. 123-127.

Morel, H. and Jean Gottmann, 1961, "The Woodlands, Their Uses and Wildlife," in Jean Gottmann, *Megalopolis: The Urbanized Northeastern Seaboard of the United States.* New York: Twentieth Century Fund, pp. 341-383.

Muehrcke, Phillip, 1972, *Thematic Cartography.* Washington, D.C.: Association of American Geographers, Commission on College Geography. Resource Paper No. 19.

Mulvihill, John J., 1972, "Congenital and Genetic Disease in Domestic Animals," *Science*, Vol. 176, pp. 132-137.

Mumford, Lewis, 1938, *The Culture of Cities.* New York: Harcourt, Brace.

_____, 1961, *The City in History: Its Origins, Its Transformations, and Its Prospects.* New York: Harcourt, Brace and World.

Murphey, Rhoads, 1954, "The City as a Center of Change: Western Europe and China," *Annals of the Association of Amerian Geographers*, Vol. 44, pp. 349-362.

Neely, Dan, 1963, *Results of Dutch Elm Disease Control Efforts in Illinois.* Urbana: Illinois Natural History Survey.

_____, 1967, "Dutch Elm Disease in Illinois Cities," *Plant Disease Reporter*, Vol. 51, pp. 512-514.

_____, 1971, *Dutch Elm Disease Control in Illinois Cities: Results of 1970.* Urbana: Illinois Natural History Survey.

_____, 1972, "Municipal Control of Dutch Elm Disease in Illinois Cities," *Plant Disease Reporter*, Vol. 56, pp. 460-462.

Neuberger, H., C. L. Hosler, and W. C. Kocmond, 1967, "Vegetation as Aerosol Filter," in

S. W. Tromp and W. H. Weihe (eds.), *Biometeorology: Proceedings of the Third International Biometeorology Congress, 1963.* Oxford: Pergamon, pp. 693-702.

Nichols, James B. and W. J. Bigler, 1969, "Use of Sentinel Animals in St. Louis Encephalitis Virus Surveillance in Florida Outside the Tampa Bay Area," in *St. Louis Encephalitis in Florida: Ten Years of Research, Surveillance and Control Programs.* Jacksonville, Florida: State Board of Health. Monograph Series 12, pp. 90-94.

Odum, Eugene P., 1969, "The Strategy of Ecosystem Development," *Science*, Vol. 164, pp. 262-270.

Oke, T., 1969, *Toward A More Rational Understanding of the Urban Heat Island.* Montreal: McGill University, Department of Geography. Climatological Bulletin 5.

———, 1973, "Evapotranspiration in Urban Areas and Its Implications for Urban Climate Planning," World Meteorological Organization, *International Colloquium on Building Climatology.* Geneva: WMO.

Olgyay, Viktor, 1963, *Design With Climate: Bioclimatic Approach to Architectural Regionalism.* Princeton, New Jersey: Princeton University Press.

Olschowy, Gerhard (ed.), 1971, *Belastete Landschaft–Gefährdete Umwelt.* München: Goldmann Verlag.

Ordish, George, 1960, *The Living House.* Philadelphia: Lippincott.

Pack, Donald H., 1964, "Meteorology of Air Pollution," *Science*, Vol. 146, pp. 1119-1128.

Parizek, R. R. *et al.*, 1967, "Waste Water Renovation and Conservation," *Penn State Studies*, Vol. 23, pp. 1-71.

Parmeter, J. R. and F. W. Cobb, Jr., 1972, "Long-term Impingement of Aerobiology Systems on Plant Production Systems," in W. S. Benninghoff and R. L. Edmonds (eds.), *US-IBP Aerobiology Program Handbook 2.* Ann Arbor: University of Michigan, pp. 61-68.

Parr, A. E., 1966, "Psychological Aspects of Urbanology," *Journal of Social Issues*, Vol. 22, pp. 39-45.

Peterson, James T., 1969, *The Climate of Cities: A Survey of Recent Literature.* Durham, N.C.: U.S. Department of Health, Education and Welfare. Publication AP-59.

Peucker, Thomas K., 1972, *Computer Cartography.* Washington, D.C.: Association of American Geographers, Commission on College Geography. Resource Paper No. 17.

Poland, J. F., 1972, "Land Subsidence in the Western States Due to Ground Water Overdraft," *Water Resources Bulletin*, Vol. 8, pp. 118-131.

Poland, J. F. and G. H. Davis, 1969, "Land Subsidence Due to Withdrawal of Fluids," *Reviews in Engineering Geology*, Vol. 2, pp. 187-269.

Porter, Lynn K., F. G. Viets, and G. L. Hutchinson, 1972, "Air Containing Nitrogen-15 Ammonia: Foliar Absorption by Corn Seedling," *Science*, Vol. 175, pp. 759-762.

Preston, Frank W. and R. T. Norris, 1947, "Nesting Heights of Breeding Birds," *Ecology*, Vol. 28, pp. 241-273.

Ragland, W. L. and J. R. Gorham, 1967, "Tonsillar Carcinoma in Rural Dogs," *Nature (London)*, Vol. 214, pp. 925-926.

Rasmussen, Reinhold A., 1972, "What Do the Hydrocarbons from Trees Contribute to Air Pollution?" *Journal of the Air Pollution Control Association*, Vol. 22, pp. 537-543.

Regier, Henry A. and E. B. Colwell, 1972, "Applications of Ecosystem Theory, Succession, Diversity, Stability, Stress and Conservation," *Biological Conservation*, Vol. 4, pp. 83-88.

Reif, J. S. and D. Cohen, 1970, "Canine Pulmonary Disease and Urban Environment II," *Archives of Environmental Health*, Vol. 20, pp. 684-689.

Rosenberg, Charles E., 1962, *The Cholera Years: The United States in 1832, 1849, and 1866.* Chicago: University of Chicago Press.

Ross, F. Fraser, 1971, "What Sulphur Dioxide Problem?" *Combustion*, Vol. 43(3), pp. 6-11.

Ruppert, Kurt, 1960, *Der Stadtwald als Wirtschafts- und Erholungswald.* München: BLV Verlags-Gesellschaft.

SCEP (Study of Critical Environmental Problems), 1971, "Work Group on Ecological Effects Report," in W. H. Matthews, F. E. Smith, and E. D. Goldberg, (eds.), *Man's Impact on Terrestrial and Oceanic Ecosystems.* Cambridge, Massachusetts: MIT Press, pp. 4-32.

SCEP, 1970, *Report of the Study of Critical Environmental Problems: Assessment and Recommendations for Action.* Cambridge, Massachusetts: MIT Press.

SMIC (Study of Man's Impact on Climate), 1971, *Inadvertent Climate Modification.* Cambridge, Massachusetts: MIT Press.

Saarisalo-Taubert, A., 1963, "Die Flora in ihrer Beziehung zur Siedlung und Siedlungsgeschichte in den südfinnischen Städten Porvoo, Loviisa und Hamina," *Annales Botanici Fennici* (Societas Zoologica et Botanica Fennica "Vanamo"), Vol. 25, pp. 1-190.

Saunders, P. J. W., 1971, "Modification of the Leaf Surface and Its Environment by Pollution," in T. F. Preece and C. H. Dickinson (eds.), *Ecology of Leaf Surface Microorganisms.* New York: Academic Press, pp. 81-90.

Scheidt, Melvin E., 1967, "Environmental Effects of Highways," *Journal of the Sanitary Engineering Division, Proceedings of the American Society of Civil Engineers*, Vol. 93, pp. 17-25.

Schmid, James A., 1974, *Urban Vegetation: A Review and Chicago Case Study.* Chicago: University of Chicago, Department of Geography, Research Paper (forthcoming).

Schmitt, Peter J., 1969, *Back to Nature: The Arcadian Myth in America, 1900-1930.* New York: Oxford University Press.

Schwabe, C., 1969, *Veterinary Medicine and Human Health.* Baltimore: Williams and Wilkins.

Scully, Vincent J., 1962, *The Earth, the Temple, and the Gods: Greek Sacred Architecture.* New Haven, Connecticut: Yale University Press.

Sestini, Aldo, 1962, "Regressive Phases in the Development of the Cultural Landscape," in Philip L. Wagner and M. W. Mikesell (eds.), *Readings in Cultural Geography.* Chicago: University of Chicago Press, pp. 479-490.

Sheaffer, John R., 1960, *Flood Proofing: An Element in a Flood Damage Reduction Program.* Chicago: University of Chicago, Department of Geography. Research Paper 65.

Shepard, Paul, 1967, *Man in the Landscape: A Historic View of the Esthetics of Nature.* New York: Knopf.

Sherlock, R. L., 1922, *Man as a Geological Agent: An Account of His Action on Inanimate Nature.* London: Witherby.

Siegfried, W. R., 1968, "Ecological Composition of the Avifaunal Community in a Stellenbosch Suburb," *Ostrich*, Vol. 39, pp. 105-129.

Simon, C. and E. F. Ferrand, 1971, "The Impact of Low Sulfur Fuel on Air Quality in New York City," in H. M. Englund and W. T. Beery, eds., *Second International Clean Air Congress Proceedings.* New York: Academic Press, pp. 41-50.

Simoons, Frederick J., 1961, *Eat Not This Flesh: Food Avoidances in the Old World.* Madison: University of Wisconsin Press.

_____, 1968, *A Ceremonial Ox of India: The Mithan in Nature, Culture, and History with Notes on the Domestication of Common Cattle.* Madison: University of Wisconsin Press.

Skye, Erik, 1968, "Lichens and Air Pollution: A Study of Cryptogamic Epiphytes and Environment in the Stockholm Region," *Acta Phytogeographica Suecica*, Vol. 52, pp. 1-124.

Smalley, Eugene B., 1971, "Prevention of Dutch Elm Disease in Large Nursery Elms by Soil Treatment with Benomyl," *Phytopathology*, Vol. 61, pp. 1351-1354.

Smith, Wm. H., 1970, "Trees in the City," *Journal of the American Institute of Planners*, Vol. 36, pp. 429-435.

_____, 1972a, "Lead and Mercury Burden of Urban Woody Plants," *Science*, Vol. 176, pp. 1237-1239.

_____, 1972b, "Air Pollution Effects on the Quality and Resilience of the Forest Ecosystem." Paper presented at the Annual Meeting of the American Association for the Advancement of Science, Washington, D.C.

Snow, D. W., 1958, *A Study of Blackbirds.* London: G. Allen & Unwin.

Solomon, M. E., 1965, "Ecology of Pests in Stores and Houses," pp. 345-366 in Gordon T. Goodman, R. W. Edwards and J. M. Lambert, (eds.), *Ecology and the Industrial Society.* New York: Wiley.

Solotaroff, Wm., 1912, *Shade Trees in Towns and Cities.* New York: Wiley.

Sopper, Wm. E., 1971, "Effects of Trees and Forests in Neutralizing Waste," in Silas Little and J. H. Noyes (eds.), *Trees and Forests in an Urbanizing Environment.* Amherst, Massachusetts: University of Massachusetts, Cooperative Extension. Planning and Resource Development Series Publication 17, pp. 43-57.

Sopper, Wm. E. *et al.*, 1970, "Revegetation of Strip Mine Spoils Banks Through Irrigation with Municipal Sewage Effluent and Sludge," *Compost Science*, November-December, pp. 6-11.

Southern, H. N., 1964, *The Handbook of British Mammals.* Oxford: Blackwell.

Southwick, Charles H., 1969, "Aggressive Behaviour of Rhesus Monkeys in Natural and Captive Groups," in S. Garattini and E. B. Sigg (eds.), *Proceedings of the Symposium on the Biology of Aggressive Behavior (Milan, 1968).* Amsterdam: Excerpta Medica, pp. 32-43.

Southwick, Charles H., C. H. Beg and M. R. Siddiqi, 1965, "Rhesus Monkeys in North

India," in I. DeVore (ed.), *Primate Behavior.* New York: Holt, Rinehart, Winston, pp. 111-159.

Spillett, James J., 1968, *The Ecology of the Lesser Bandicoot Rat in Calcutta.* Bombay: Bombay Natural History Society and The Johns Hopkins University Center for Medical Research and Training (Calcutta).

Stanislawski, Dan, 1946, "The Origin and Spread of the Grid-Pattern Town," *Geographical Review,* Vol. 36, pp. 105-120.

Stark, R. W. *et al.,* 1968, "Incidence of Bark Beetle Infestation in Injured Trees I," *Hilgardia,* Vol. 39, pp. 121-126.

Stearns, Forest, 1970, "Urban Ecology Today," *Science,* Vol. 170, pp. 1006-1007.

——, 1972a, "The City as Habitat for Wildlife and Man," in T. R. Detwyler and M. G. Marcus (eds.), *Urbanization and Environment.* Belmont, California: Duxbury, pp. 261-278.

——, 1972b, "US-IBP Phenology Program, Final Newsletter," Milwaukee, Wis.: University of Wisconsin, Department of Botany.

——, 1973, "Phenology and Environmental Education," in H. Lieth (ed.), *AIBS Phenology Papers.* New York: Springer Verlag (forthcoming).

Stern, Arthur C. (ed.), 1968, *Air Pollution.* 2nd ed. New York: Academic.

Stokinger, Herbert E. and D. L. Coffin, 1968, "Biologic Effects of Air Pollutants," in Arthur C. Stern (ed.), *Air Pollution.* 2nd. ed. New York: Academic Press, pp. 445-546.

Sullivan, Walter, 1973, "Earthquakes: New York is Not Immune," *New York Times,* January 28, p. 12.

Summers-Smith, D., 1963, *The House Sparrow.* London: Collins.

Tabor, Elbert C., 1966, "Contamination of Urban Air through the Use of Insecticides," *Transactions of the New York Academy of Sciences* (Series 2), Vol. 28, pp. 569-578.

Tansy, M. F. and R. P. Roth, 1970, "Pigeons: A New Role in Air Pollution," *Journal of the Air Pollution Control Association,* Vol. 20, pp. 307-309.

Tarrant, K. R. and J. O'G. Tatton, 1968, "Organochlorine Pesticides in Rainwater in the British Isles," *Nature,* Vol. 219, pp. 725-727.

Teagle, W. G., 1967, "The Fox in the London Suburbs," *London Naturalist,* Vol. 46, pp. 44-68.

Thomas, Jack W., 1972, "Non-Game Wildlife Research in Megalopolis: The Forest Service Program." Paper presented at the August Meeting of the American Institute of Biological Sciences, Minneapolis.

Thomas, Jack W. and R. A. Dixon, 1973, "Cemetery Ecology," *Natural History,* Vol. 82, pp. 60-67.

Thornton, Philip L., 1971, "Managing Urban and Suburban Trees and Woodlands for Timber Products," in Silas Little and S. H. Noyes (eds.), *Trees and Forests in an Urbanizing Environment.* Amherst, Massachusetts: University of Massachusetts, Cooperative Extension. Resource and Planning Development Series Publication 17, pp. 129-132.

Trelease, Sam F. and O. A. Beath, 1949, *Selenium: Its Geographical Occurrence and Its Biological Effects in Relation to Botany, Chemistry, Agriculture, Nutrition and Medicine.* New York: by the authors.

Tromp, S. W. (ed.), 1962, *Biometeorology: Proceedings of the Second International Bioclimatology Congress.* Oxford: Pergamon Press.

Tuan, Yi-Fu, 1971, *Man and Nature.* Washington, D.C.: Association of American Geographers, Commission on College Geography, Resource Paper No. 10.

Tyson, Peter D., 1970, *Urban Climatology: A Problem of Environmental Studies.* Johannesburg: Witwatersrand University Press.

Udvardy, M. D. F., 1957, "An Evaluation of Quantitative Studies of Birds," *Cold Spring Harbor Symposia in Quantitative Biology,* Vol. 22, pp. 301-311.

United Nations, 1970, "Report of the Secretary-General on Housing, Building and Planning." New York: United Nations.

——, 1971, "A Concise Summary of the World Population Situation in 1970." New York: United Nations.

U.S. Department of the Interior, Strip and Surface Mine Policy Study Committee, 1967, *Surface Mining and Our Environment.* Washington, D.C.: Government Printing Office.

Van Eimern, Leonard J. *et al.* (eds.), 1964, *Windbreaks and Shelterbelts.* Geneva: World Meteorological Organization, Publication 147.

Vareschi, Volkmar, 1953, "La Influencia de los Bosques y Parques sobre el Aire de la Ciudad de Caracas," *Acta Cientifica Venezolana,* Vol. 4, pp. 89-95.

Vesey-Fitzgerald, B., 1967, *Town Fox, Country Fox.* London: A. Deutsch.

Waggoner, Paul E., 1963, *Plants, Shade and Shelter*. New Haven: Connecticut Agricultural Expt. Station. Bulletin 656.

Waggoner, Paul E. and J. D. Ovington (eds.), 1962, *Proceedings of the Lockwood Conference on the Suburban Forest and Ecology*. New Haven: Connecticut Agricultural Experiment Station. Bulletin 652.

Walcott, Charles F., 1959, "Effects of City Growth on Bird Life," *Massachusetts Audubon*, Vol. 49, pp. 120-122.

Wallace, George J., W. P. Nickell, and R. F. Bernard, 1961, *Bird Mortality in the Dutch Elm Disease Program in Michigan*. Bloomfield Hills, Michigan: Cranbrook Institute of Science. Bulletin 41.

Walter, Hartmut and A. M. Demartis, 1972, "Brutdichte und ökologische Nische sardischer Stadtvögel," *Journal für Ornithologie*, Vol. 113, pp. 391-406.

Watts, David, 1968, "Origins of Barbadian Cane Hole Agriculture," *Barbados Museum and Natural History Society Journal*, Vol. 32, pp. 143-151.

_____, 1971, *Principles of Biogeography*. New York: McGraw-Hill.

Weidensaul, T. C. and N. L. Lacasse, 1970, *Statewide Survey of Air Pollution Damage to Vegetation (1969)*. University Park, Pa.: Pennsylvania State University, Center for Air Environment Studies, Publication 148-70.

Wester, Horace V. and E. E. Cohen, 1968, "Salt Damage to Vegetation in the Washington, D.C. Area during the 1966-67 Winter." *Plant Disease Reporter*, Vol. 52, pp. 350-354.

Wheatley, Paul S., 1971, *The Pivot of the Four Quarters: A Preliminary Inquiry into the Origins and Character of the Ancient Chinese City*. Chicago: Aldine.

White, Gilbert F., 1972, "Environmental Impact Statements," *Professional Geographer*, Vol. 24, pp. 302-309.

Whyte, William H., 1968, *The Last Landscape*. Garden City, New York: Doubleday.

Wolman, Abel, 1956, "Disposal of Man's Wastes," in W. L. Thomas (ed.), *Man's Role in Changing the Face of the Earth*. Chicago: University of Chicago Press, pp. 807-816.

Wolman, M. Gordon, 1973, "The Physical Environment and Urban Planning," in *Geographical Perspectives and Urban Problems*. Washington: National Academy of Sciences, pp. 55-70.

Wolman, M. G. and A. P. Schick, 1967, "Effects of Construction on Fluvial Sediment, Urban and Suburban Areas of Maryland," *Water Resources Research*, Vol. 3, pp. 451-464.

Woodwell, George M., 1970, "Effects of Pollution on the Structure and Physiology of Ecosystems," *Science*, Vol. 168, pp. 429-433.

Woolfenden, Glen E. and S. A. Rohwer, 1969, "Breeding Birds in a Florida Suburb," *Bulletin of the Florida State Museum*, Vol. 13, pp. 1-83.

World Meteorological Organization, 1970a, *Urban Climates*. Geneva: WMO, Publication 254.

_____, 1970b, *Building Climatology*. Geneva: WMO, Publication 255.

_____, 1973, *International Colloquium on Building Climatology* (forthcoming).

Wurster, Doris H., C. F. Wurster, and W. N. Strickland, 1965, "Bird Mortality Following DDT Spray for Dutch Elm Disease," *Ecology*, Vol. 46, pp. 488-499.

Environmental Perception

Thomas F. Saarinen
University of Arizona

Every day, all over the world, men are making decisions which lead to transformations of the earth environment. Although the impact of an individual decision may be small, the cumulative effect of all such decisions is enormous, for both the number of people and the technological power at the command of each is greater than ever before and is growing rapidly. In the regions with the most advanced technology some of the inadvertent side effects of the primary decisions are already producing environmental problems of crisis proportions along with some of the intended benefits.

As the environmental impact of man's decisions grows in significance it becomes imperative to examine the bases on which such decisions are made. This is a major goal of research in environmental perception reviewed in this chapter. A basic assumption of this effort is that environmental decisions and behavior are based on individual or group images of the real world. Thus people presumably base their decisions not so much on the world as it is but rather on the world as they perceive it. This is illustrated in the conceptual schema for research into geographic space perception development by Roger Downs (1970*a*) (Figure 1).

The Downs schema incorporates a number of the basic theories and concepts underlying current research in environmental perception and places it in a broad social science context. Man is viewed as a decision maker, his behavior is considered to be some function of his image of the real world, and he is taken to be a complex information-processing system.

> The basic process in interaction in the schema is as follows. The *real* world is taken as the starting point, and it is represented as a source of *information*. The information content enters the individual through a system of *perceptual receptors*, and the precise meaning of the information is determined by an interaction between the individual's *value system* and their [*sic.*] *image of the real world*. The meaning of the information is then incorporated into the image. On the basis of this information, the individual may require to adjust himself with respect to the real world.

252

This requirement is expressed as a *decision* which can, of course, be one that involves no overt reaction. The links from the concept of a decision are two-fold (although these could be amalgamated). The first link is a re-cycling process, called *search*, whereby the individual searches the real world for more information. This process can continue until the individual decides that sufficient information has been acquired, or some time/cost limitation acts as a constraint to further search. A decision is then made which may be expressed as a pattern of *behaviour* which will in turn affect the *real world*. Since the real world undergoes a change, fresh information may result, and the whole process can continue. The schema therefore allows the space perception process to occur in a temporal as well as a spatial context (Downs: 1970*a*, pp. 84-85).

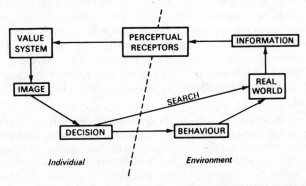

Figure 1. A Conceptual Schema for Research into Geographic Space Perception. Reproduced from Downs: 1970*a*, by permission of the author and Edward Arnold Publishers, Ltd.

Downs suggests viewing the factors which cause people to see the same segment of the real world differently as a set of filters. The constant input of information is then seen as being screened by the physiological filters of our sense receptors and such important psychological filters as language, social class, personal values, value and need, culture, and some form of Gestalt or pattern seeking function.

The power of these psychological filters to alter or select from the incoming information may be illustrated by the example of language, the primary communication system. In the process of adjusting to environment each culture selects from an infinite array of possibilities a certain set of categories to describe and explain what is there. These categories become part of a system of communication and a structure for succeeding generations which aspects of the environment are attended to. A familiar example is the contrast between English with only one word for snow and the Eskimo language with a great variety of words indicating different qualities such as falling snow, snow on the ground, snow packed hard like ice, slushy snow, wind-driven flying snow, and so on (Whorf: 1940). Pitts provides some interesting examples of the degree of differentiation of certain natural phenomena provided by the Japanese words for types of paddy fields, winds, rain and snow (Pitts: 1960). Table 1 indicates the sharp observation, attention to detail, and subtle differences in humidity, temperature and speed which can be expressed by separate words for rain in the

Japanese language. In these examples the elaborate vocabulary indicates the importance to the group of the phenomena considered. In different languages there is great variation not only in vocabulary but in the grammatical structure as well, which may totally change the usual mode of viewing such aspects of experience as time, space, or relationships to nature or other people. But that is only the beginning of the problem, for communication difficulties may be evident not only between people speaking different languages but also between speakers of the same language.

Within any linguistic group the same term may come to have a variety of meanings for different individuals and groups. Burrill's work at the Board on Geographic Names provides some fascinating examples (Burrill: 1968). He warns (p. 4) that "one can easily fall into the trap of regarding categories as entities whose reality is independent of human invention." The connotations of geographic terms like summit, valley, plain, desert, gorge, swamp, archipelago, and creek vary depending on what examples we have seen and what our parents or other authorities may have told us or showed us early in life. Thereafter a great reluctance to change the meaning is apparent, for a surprising amount of anger and frustration are aroused when one's concepts are challenged. Burrill (1968, p. 4) illustrates the difficulty of understanding other people's categories by noting that

> the Atlantic coast *swamp* with all those attributes is a sort of complex, the nature of which is clearly known to the local people who are parties to a tacit understanding about the usage of the term. We who were not parties to the basic regional understanding had been trying to categorize this kind of entity in terms of a single principal attribute rather than in terms of a multi-attribute feature for which we had no pigeonhole, no term, no concept.

It is clear in the illustration of the Atlantic coast swamp that the consensus as to its attributes is arrived at in the context of a relatively small group of local people. In other words, understanding is rooted in feeling which accounts for the anger and frustration Burrill observed when concepts were challenged. This seems to be characteristic of the way communication systems are learned (DeLong: 1972). The codes developed simplify and reduce the complexity of

TABLE 1—Japanese Words for Types of Rain

yūdachi	squall, usually with lightning
shigure	cold, drizzling rain in autumn
samidare	intermittent, almost continual rain in and around May
tsuyu	same; another name for what the Chinese call "plum rains"
niwakaame	sudden rainfall
itosame	rain that comes down like fine threads
nukaame	drizzle as fine and soft as rice bran
kirisame	misty rain
doshaburi	downpour that comes down quite hard
ōame	a big rain
kosame	a slight rain
harusame	spring rain around March or April
murasame	a steady rain which doesn't last long, but longer than a squall
hisame	icy rain in winter

After Pitts: 1960.

the surrounding environment so that effective communication can take place. But effective communication is limited to the context of the small group in which it is learned, and increasing difficulty in communication is experienced as one moves beyond the confines of this group. First the meanings for the same words or other symbols may be modified and eventually even a different set of symbols may be used. It is not surprising, then, to find that different groups of people have different perceptions of environment and that these are often very resistant to change.

Although the importance of subjective views of environment and how these vary from place to place has long been noted, it has only been in the past decade that perception of environment has become a major focus for systematic research. That this was an idea whose time had come is clearly indicated by its quick acceptance and rapid development in a multitude of fields, from the social and biological sciences to design and planning disciplines (Research and Design Institute: 1969). The interdisciplinary nature of the research and the strong common focus on current environmental problems should serve as strengths, for future findings might be directly relevant to environmental design with man as the measure. However, planners should bear in mind the incipient nature of such findings. As in other new fields, research in perception of environment lacks a firm theoretical framework and a well-developed methodology. In addition, there are major measurement problems, for the variables of greatest interest are those which lie in the minds of men. Decisions must be made not only on what should be measured but how it should be measured and how it can then be related to environmental decision-making. The studies by geographers reviewed below illustrate how some or all of these aspects of the problem have been approached.

This chapter is an updated version of an earlier paper (Saarinen: 1970) which in turn was an updated and revised version of a still earlier paper (Saarinen: 1969). Such a situation provides the author with both problems and opportunities. The major problem is that some repetition is inevitable. On the other hand, there is an opportunity to place in perspective the directions and rate of development which have taken place in the past few years. In order to maximize this opportunity, an effort has been made to include wherever possible examples from the most recent research, especially where these indicate the directions such studies appear to be taking.

The organization is by scale. The first section deals with the international level including perception studies concerned with the entire earth or broad multi-national regions. The next level considered is that of a single country. This in turn is followed by the level at which appears the greatest preponderance of geographic studies, that of large conceptual regions. These first three levels illustrate very clearly the paramount importance of ideas, images, or mental conceptions of places, for such areas are clearly too large to be perceived directly by the sense organs. However, the emphasis on cognitive structuring of the physical and social environment holds true for the sections on the city, neighborhoods, small towns, and in even smaller areas.

THE WORLD

Over a hundred years ago Alexander Von Humboldt (1850, p. 62) asserted that "... in order to comprehend nature in all its vast sublimity, it would be necessary to present it under a twofold aspect, first objectively, as an actual phenomenon, and next subjectively, as it is reflected in the feelings of mankind." To accomplish the latter he traced variations in expressed attitudes and feelings toward the nature of peoples of Indo-European speech, ranging from Northern Europe to Indian tropical regions. Early impressions which Humboldt felt could exercise powerful and lasting effects on the youthful mind are derived from such sources as literary descriptions of nature, the art of landscape painting, and the direct contact with natural forms as in botanical gardens with exotic plant species. Each of these sources is discussed at length in the second volume of his *Cosmos*. Groups in different areas had their own characteristic expressions of love of nature. Over time in any one area the writings often changed dramatically as nature descriptions and their effect on emotions became the major objective rather than an incidental part of the background. Humboldt advocated, as an educational device, the opening in large cities of a number of panoramic buildings, containing pictures of landscapes of different geographical latitudes and from different zones of elevation. He felt that the study of nature was markedly influenced by the feelings of mankind as aroused by literary description, landscape painting, and contemplation of exotic plants.

Sweeping in its scope is Glacken's *Traces on the Rhodian Shore* (1967). Three main themes are traced from classical times to the end of the 18th Century: the idea of an earth created by design, the influence of environment on man, and the influence of man on his environment. The attitudes implied in these ideas did not, of course, stop at the 18th Century and the early history of these ideas should make more meaningful modern attitudes toward the earth. For example, the present interest in ecology has deep roots which can be traced in the designed earth idea which tried to see earthly environments as wholes, as manifestations of order. The idea of the influence of man on his environment is more important today than ever before, as the inadvertent side effects of man's actions create problems of crisis proportions in our cities, in our air, and in our water. The idea of environmental influence has also been important in discussions of national character. Writing about the conspicuous interest in national character in 17th Century England, Glacken (p. 451) outlined for our times as well the pros and cons of such studies:

> These writings on national character had their attractive and their seamy sides. They provided an outlet for curious, active, and open-minded intelligence; sharp observation often resulted in valuable descriptions of the workaday world, diet, and regional differences. Their great weakness was their proneness to bias, to insufferable smugness, often to bigotry. Their crudity lay in the assumption that it was possible to label nations or peoples quickly and firmly; peoples had to submit bravely to a single label which summed them up.

Despite their drawbacks studies of national character are fascinating. Campbell suggests that personality should be considered as an element of regional geography (Campbell: 1968). Although often noted in passing as being of some importance, the distribution in space of social attitudes and moral and spiritual values has seldom been used as a basis for the definition of regions. A notable exception is provided by Stanislawski (1972, pp. 1-2) who contrasts the strong individual character of three different cultural units within ancient Greece— Lesbos, Ionia, and Athens—based mainly on evidence from the arts.

... in one there was notable sensitivity, imagination, individuality, and a reverence for life in balance with nature. In the second the dominant theme was aggressive trade and piracy (actually synonymous), but coupled with it was an avidity for the knowledge of measurement and an understanding of the physical world. The third lived in the spirit of organization and productive synthesis.

Despite wars and other disasters these separate culture areas persisted. Furthermore, when colonies of each were transplanted to other areas the same culture traits could be recognized in the new colonies. Further studies focussing on the geographic distribution of ideas and attitudes toward various aspects of environment would be useful to indicate how such ideas and attitudes originate, spread, and persist or change, and how they interact with environmental behavior.

Attitudes toward nature have varied greatly in different areas and ages. Tuan (1969) has demonstrated that the publicized environmental ethos of a culture seldom covers more than a fraction of the total range of environmental behavior. He compared the Chinese and European attitudes toward environment and noted the discrepancy between these attitudes and behavior. Western humanists commonly point out the virtues of the Oriental's adaptive approach toward nature in contrast to the aggressive masculinity of Western man. Certainly the adaptive attitude toward nature does have ancient roots in China. Yet, in spite of this, deforestation occurred there as a result of such practices as the burning of trees to deprive dangerous animals of their hiding places, burning trees to make charcoal for industrial use, and the construction of the old Chinese cities in which timber was the basic structural material. Such practices also had support in ancient ideas. A study by O'Riordan in the current North American context also calls attention to the contrast between "environmental words and environmental deeds" (O'Riordan: forthcoming). The point to be made here is not that environmental attitudes are unimportant, but that they are complex, often contradictory, and interact in ways which may only be predictable for specific situations.

The persistence of old ideas, even in the face of scientific evidence to the contrary, is well documented in another study by Tuan, *The Hydrologic Cycle and the Wisdom of God* (1968). In it he points out the remarkably late awareness of the extent of dry climates in the world. At least one of the factors explaining this was the acceptance as an article of faith of the idea of "the well-watered earth." To acknowledge the extent of deserts would necessitate abandonment of long-held beliefs. Apparently anxiety is aroused when an accepted mental schema becomes challenged as inappropriate. This was noted earlier in connection with the connotation of words and may help to account for the persistence of old ideas which must be reckoned with on many levels of environmental perception.

Perception of environment, at the broadest level, involves such factors as national stereotypes, ethnocentrism, xenophobia, national attitudes, and national character. Teachers wishing to verify the existence of national stereotypes, or ethnocentric views of the world, can do so with a simple exercise. For example, Haddon (1960) asked students to write down in short phrases or single words, the thoughts and images conjured by the name of a particular country. The results provide strong evidence of stereotypic notions of other nations:

France. Ah France! She consists of the Eiffel Tower, the Folies Bergères (which no-one can spell), Christian Dior, and the Riveria. Upon her lives a race of fickle, excitable, politically obsessed people who dine and wine themselves magnificently, wearing berets, in the midst of unmentionable plumbing; and over all looms De Gaulle.

There is generally some element of truth in a stereotype, but people may act on it as if it were totally correct. This may even happen when the stereotype is a myth about oneself. For example, Lowenthal (1972a) notes that some people in the West Indies like to feel that the image of the West Indies is exactly what is written on the tourist brochures and may try to live in keeping with that make-believe world. However, generally the stereotypes may be expected to thrive especially well where limited factual information is available which is one reason for deploring the almost total lack of information about black people in geographical textbooks and journals (Donaldson: 1971). Some psychologists have made a strong case for misperceptions of other nations and their intentions as a cause or contributing factor to international conflict (White: 1966). The importance of such mental images is also recognized in the preamble to the constitution of UNESCO: "Since wars begin in the minds of men, it is in the minds of men that the defenses of peace must be constructed."

An important aspect of international images is that of mankind's geographical horizons. Such a topic was speculated on some thirty years ago by Whittlesey (1945) in a stimulating essay which explored the way in which mankind's geographic horizons have expanded over time. He contrasted the primal, the regional, and the world sense of space.

The outlook of primitive people, and in the earliest period of human history, was almost literally confined to the physical horizon. The major landscape features might be known by their generic names as "the mountain," "the river," or "the village," and the geographic horizon was generally the physical horizon of man's experience. No doubt such narrowly restricted views of the world still survive, and even within modern cities there may be people whose minds only rarely touch on events beyond their block or neighborhood. According to Whittlesey, a broader regional sense of space appeared some 1800 to 2000 years ago as two areas of subcontinental size separately achieved political unity. The Romans and the Chinese, in producing a political unity based on effective internal communication, also provided some of their people with an awareness of a broader geographic horizon. Other regions appeared and former political regions contracted. But it was not until after the 15th century that a new wider geographic horizon began to appear. Following the European Age of Discovery, some of the areas beyond the oceans and the Sahara became known to Eurasian people. A worldwide horizon appeared for the first time at the most advanced frontiers of thought. Whittlesey felt it was reasonable to assume that eventually all of mankind would advance to such a position, but the following remarks (p. 14) clearly indicate that he was sure this had not yet taken place at the time he wrote:

Even in the lands where geography is part of a compulsory school curriculum, and among people who possess considerable information about the earth, the world horizon is accepted in theory and rejected in practice. A parochial outlook injects itself into every consideration of political system more inclusive than the one in vogue, it appears in snap judgments on "foreigners," and it dims the view of existing interdependence in the economic order. The myopia is understandable. The weight of tradition is heavy. Until five centuries ago a primal or regional sense of space dominated human settlements everywhere. In the United States, where society is mobile, it is easy to forget that even now few members of the human species move beyond their native region, and that hardly anybody has fruitful contact with folk who think in patterns different from his own.

While we may expect that the number of people who have a worldwide geographic horizon is greater than ever before there is good reason to question the quality of their knowledge. An excellent perspective for doing so was provided almost fifty years ago by J. K. Wright in *The Geographical Lore of the Time of the Crusades* (1925). He conceived of the regional geographic knowledge of an age as the area within two concentric circles: an inner circle contained knowledge based on clear, reliable observation and first-hand experience, and beyond this an area of second-hand knowledge based on literary sources which at the time of the Crusades were derived largely from tradition, and hence were full of fancy, fables, and wild speculation. No doubt today much of the current popular regional knowledge of the world could still be most accurately placed in the second category. For in the absence of better knowledge humans are probably inclined to accept as fact the second-hand, often exaggerated, stereotypic, biased, and incomplete reports of affairs in other lands as reported in the modern communication media. It would be interesting to test the quality of regional knowledge of various world areas from the various locational or cultural perspectives to see whether there is a zonation as Wright's schema would predict.

A study by the author (Saarinen: 1973) examines student views of the world by means of freehand sketch maps. High school students in Canada, the United States, Finland, and Sierra Leone were given a blank sheet of paper and asked to draw a map of the world. Although certain common features are found, distinctive ethnocentric views of the world tend to emerge for each group. In each case the home continent is exaggerated in size, a reflection perhaps of the perceived importance to the person. For example, Canada in the map of a Canadian student is central, dominant, and highly differentiated. However, the Finnish student relegates a vague abbreviated Canada to an edge position while a vastly-expanded, well-shaped Finland dominates a much-exaggerated Europe. This sketch map technique could prove useful in gaining insights into varying views of the world held by people in different regions.

In spite of the possibilities for instantaneous communication from all parts of the world, parochial outlooks still tend to prevail. In fact they appear to provide a new source of distortion. For example Cole and Whysall (1968) have demonstrated that the available information sources they investigated tend to amplify the importance of the local area and reduce the importance of other regions. Their world maps, with areas drawn proportional to the number of mentions on the B.B.C. and in *Pravda*, show great distortions (Figure 2). Britain is indeed "great" in the B.B.C. map, in fact, larger than any continent. In the *Pravda* version, the U.S.S.R. is large enough to absorb the remainder of the world. Before Americans laugh, they might look at a similar map constructed by Goodey (1969) from places named in one issue of *Time* magazine. In this version, Asia seems to consist of Hanoi, Saigon, Peking, North and South Vietnam, and a few minor surrounding places. Europe has more divisions, but is clearly dominated by London, Paris, and Moscow. The United States, of course, is much larger than all the other areas put together, but as in the other maps of this type cities stand out. This urban dominance is even more pronounced in another world map version, again by Goodey (1969), based on four issues of the *Rolling Stone*, a popular music magazine. Here America consists largely of San

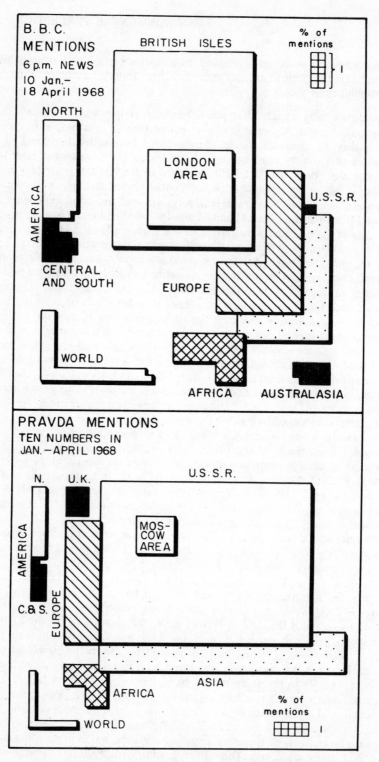

Figure 2. B.B.C. and *Pravda* Views of the World. Reproduced from Cole and Whysall:
1968, by permission.

Francisco and Los Angeles attached to California, and the Northeast largely made up of Chicago and New York. It does not seem likely that the communications media will soon switch to a less biased coverage of the world. Therefore, it is essential that teachers be aware of the existence of this bias so that they can take pains to compensate for it. They might also try to provide their pupils with an empathetic appreciation of the world as seen from various national perspectives.

A paper by Ginsburg (1968) examines the Chinese perception of a world order; the traditional view was Sinocentric, in keeping with the examples above in which the world always seems to center on the nation being studied. One difference in the case of China is the length of time that this perception has persisted. For centuries upon centuries, the Chinese remained unchallenged as the central power in a vast Asian orbit. Surrounding the core area of continuous Chinese control, from ancient times, was a series of roughly concentric zones in which Chinese power and authority diminished gradually in all directions. Ginsburg distinguishes four zones as seen in Figure 3. The Inner Asian Zone includes those areas not in the core area (Zone 1), but over which China has exerted various degrees of control and with which she always had intimate relations. The Outer Asian Zone includes areas somewhat farther removed, which were relatively well known to the Chinese, although, with some exceptions, they were never in true tributary or client relationships with China. The Outer World (Zone 4) contained all areas about which the Chinese were ignorant or indifferent. A vivid view of the type of information the Chinese had of one such area in Zone 4 is provided by Wheatley's article (1964) on Chinese knowledge of East Africa prior to 1500. It seems likely that this traditional view of the world persists in China, with perhaps minor modifications here and there. Without knowledge of this world view it may be difficult to comprehend major decisions in Chinese foreign policy. But if this view is known, the foreign policy is much easier to understand, i.e., Taiwan is regarded as a part of the core area, and certain Soviet provinces were traditionally regarded as a part of Zone 2.

THE COUNTRY

Perception studies at the national level may serve to illustrate several different approaches. Among those noted here are studies of national landscapes and landscape preferences, studies of residential preferences, and studies of regional consciousness within a nation.

Lowenthal and Prince collaborated for two studies on "The English Landscape" (1964) and "English Landscape Tastes" (1965). The emphasis in their articles is on the thesis that landscapes are formed by landscape tastes. What people perceive as the ideal is what they hope to accomplish. The idealized images of the past and present are usually sought by examining travellers' accounts, landscape paintings, literature, and attitudes expressed in speeches, public hearings, newspaper articles, and letters, which require acceptance of the assumption that the articulate minority responsible for such source materials is most influential in creating landscape tastes and hence in molding the landscape. Lowenthal and Prince suggest that the key to summarizing the relationships between the English people and their landscape is the word "amenity." This term is attached to whatever seems to need protection. Thus amenities may at various times be historic buildings and the flavor of the past,

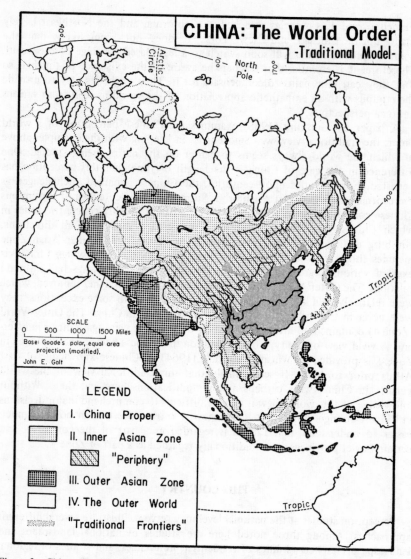

Figure 3.   China: The World Order–Traditional Model. Reproduced from Ginsburg: 1968,
by permission of the author and the University of Chicago Press.

open spaces, views and vistas, facilities for recreation, or access to points of
scenic interest. Government departments and private interests exhibit the
English talent for compromise, and the result is a settled and comfortable land.

Lowenthal later studied the American Scene (1968) which is generally seen
by visitors as being vast, wild, empty, formless, and unfinished, and subject to
violent extremes. But most Americans probably see it in other ways. Lowenthal
states that our whole way of life determines our view of nature. Therefore,
planning and design should be grounded on an intimate knowledge of the ways
people think and feel about environment. Further discussion of American ideas

about nature, parks, wildlife, wilderness, and recreation is found in the chapters by Nelson and Butler and by Doughty in this volume.

Other national landscapes might also be expected to reflect attitudes and ideas of their citizens. This theme has been considered in a number of recent monographs on different national landscapes as, for example, in Parker's (1969) description of the different stages in the development of Soviet attitudes toward the environment (see also Tuan: 1969). An extreme example of the influence of a particular attitude on decision-making is provided by "voluntarism" which prevailed during the Stalinist era. This attitude implied that Soviet society could do as it pleased in defiance of nature. When this attitude was in the ascendancy many ambitious and costly schemes linked with the personal glorification of Stalin were pushed through. Some such proposals were the planting of tree belts in the steppes, construction of dams, irrigation of vast areas of arid land, changing the channels of the Ob and Yenisey Rivers to water the deserts of Central Asia, nuclear power stations to heat up the waters of the Arctic, and schemes to change the climate of Siberia. Since Stalin's death voluntarism has been officially and academically discredited. Now there is apparently more discussion of the pros and cons of such grandiose schemes.

Also at the national level are Gould's studies (1966) on place preferences. Students from different universities were asked to provide rank order listings of their preferences for states in the United States. The scores derived from a principal components analysis of these data were used to construct isoline maps which reflect the relative desirability of various areas to the students. A remarkably similar map of the United States emerged for most of these students. The West Coast was seen as the most desirable area. From a high here the surface slopes downward to a perceptual basin in Utah, and rises once more to the Colorado high. Over the Great Plains there is a general decline eastward with a low point in the Dakotas. Near the 100th meridian, a change takes place with a rise toward the northeast, and a drop in desirability toward the South, the lowest perceptual trough of the entire surface. The map of the California students corresponds rather well to common elements (Figure 4) found on the preference maps from Minnesota and Pennsylvania. The only major exceptions are higher ratings for home areas. However, the maps of Alabama students show a different set of preferences (Figure 5). From their perspective the North is seen as undesirable, the South is more highly differentiated with Alabama the most desirable, and a new low appears over New Mexico. Clearly the home area ranks high in such preference maps. But Goodey's (1969) similar study in North Dakota indicates that there at least the home state is not seen as most desirable. However, he found that the most familiar states, that is, the ones most often visited, showed up as most desirable, and these were also the ones to which North Dakotans most generally migrated. Gould and White (1968) applied the same sort of procedure to determine British school-leavers' residential preferences and Doherty (1968) did a similar study of preference for the cities of the United States. Later studies have examined the pattern of preferences in Tanzania (Gould: 1969b), the Western Region of Nigeria (Gould and Ola: 1970), and Sweden (Gould: 1973). The focus has shifted to a consideration of the development of geographic space preferences through different age groups and on the flows of information from which such images are formed. Preference maps may help explain migrations and movements of people within a country or, if prepared on other scales, world, city, or regional migrations. Although there is generally a tendency to prefer the familiar and places close to home,

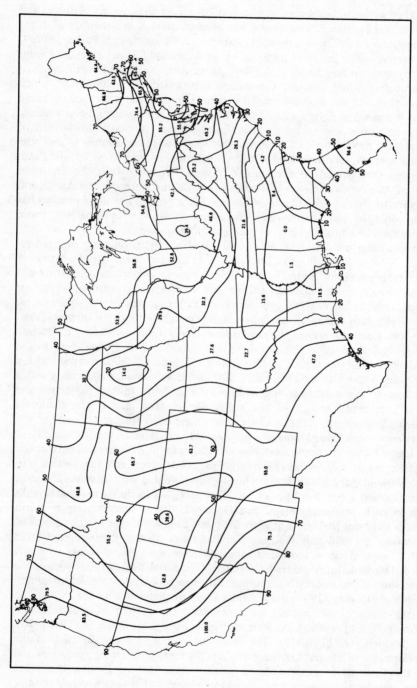

Figure 4. The View from California. Reproduced from Gould: 1966, by permission.

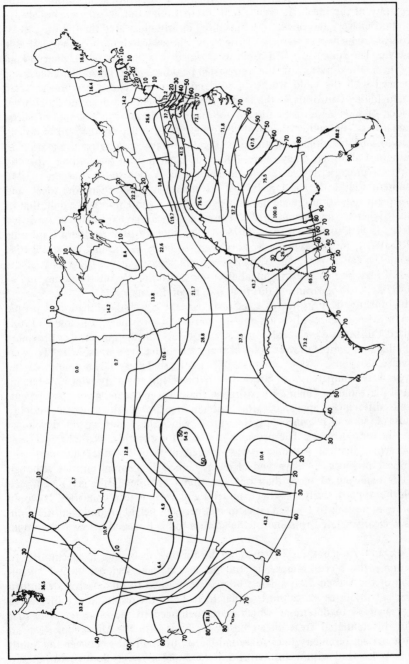

Figure 5.   The View from Alabama. Reproduced from Gould: 1966, by permission.

certain other areas are usually also seen as desirable, for example, California, long the mecca of internal migrations in the United States.

Vance (1972) interprets the settlement of California in terms of the geography of the ideal. He argues that internal migration in America has always fed upon images, and nowhere is this more clearly illustrated than in the case of California which was largely settled by those searching for the desirable life-style. The very name California was coined to represent an imaginary island very near the quarter of the terrestrial paradise. This favorable image was enhanced with the Gold Rush of 1849 and when that ended new images were created billing California as the land of restorative climate or as an agricultural arcadia, or later as an area foreign to American norms and tolerant of social peculiarities. The pull of the ideal could best be afforded by the well-to-do and these formed the dominant group in the first wave of American migration to Southern California. They were followed in each later succeeding wave by people of progressively lesser means and status. Vance states that since 1946 "southern California has largely lost its image as the land of the ideal, and subsequent migration thence has come to reflect a more normative pull, that of money, whereas the geography of the more illusive image has shifted successively poleward, first to the Bay Area (1945-1960), then to rural northern California (1960-1970), and, it seems now, northward to Oregon, Washington, and British Columbia (Vance: 1972, p. 200). By becoming aware of the geography of the ideal, it may be possible to gain a better understanding of America today and of trends likely to appear in the future in other world areas.

In Finland the province as a regional concept is well-developed, and people have a strong sense of belonging to particular provinces. Palomaki (1968) utilized this sense of regional consciousness to delimit the present-day provinces of Finland. A sample of over 5000 primary school teachers was asked, "To what province do you consider your school district belongs?" The results of the survey were compared with previously defined functional provinces based on central place theory (Figure 6). Although there was in general a good agreement, certain differences appeared. Most outstanding are the presence in people's minds of several provinces in the north which have not as yet developed effective central places. The province of Oulu, for example, was split into three parts while that of Rovaniemi was divided in two. In other instances, the historical provinces of Savo and Häme remained conceptual entities although each is made up of more than one functional province. Palomaki's approach could be applied easily in other countries and areas within countries. It would also be interesting to try it in cities to test people's neighborhood identification. This is clearly related to some of the studies to be discussed below at the urban scale.

Cox and Zannaras (1970) used an interesting technique in attempting to determine the sets or subclasses students use in their regional mental organization of the United States. The students were asked to take each state in turn and select the three states most similar to it. Later the results were subjected to factor analysis to determine which states belonged to the same set. The first factor differentiated areas on an East-West basis with the Mississippi River an almost perfect boundary line. A second factor differentiated between the South and New England with a southern borderland and a "Deep South" distinguishable. In addition there was a perceived area of homogeneity in the Midwest, a Mid-continent region, an Appalachian factor, and a contrast between the Pacific Northwest and the Southwest (Figure 7). The perceived similarity of sixty North

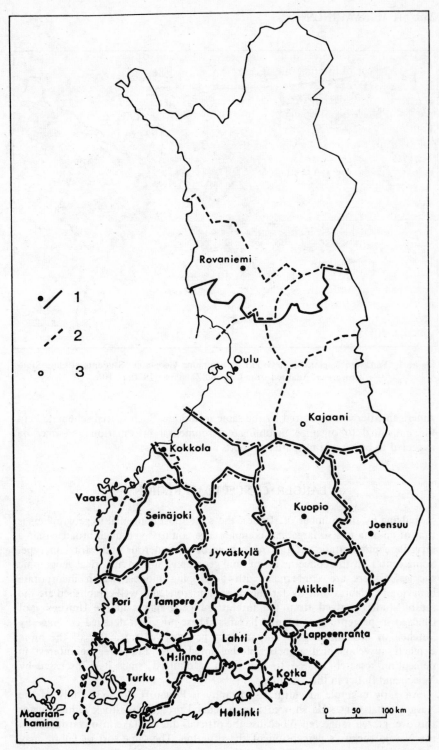

Figure 6. Comparison of Functional and Conceptual Provinces of Finland: (1) Center and boundary of functional province, (2) Boundary of province in the light of public opinion, (3) Lower level center. Reproduced from Palomaki: 1968, by permission of the author and the editor of *Acta Geographica*.

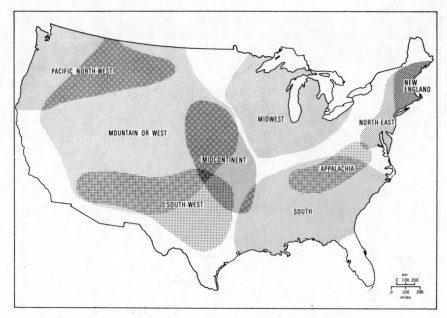

Figure 7.   Perceived Regions of a Group of Beginning Geography Students at Ohio State
University. Adapted from Cox and Zannaras: 1970, p. 106.

American cities was measured by the same technique. Such spatial schemata help
the individual to organize incoming environmental information and may be
expected to be present in spatial contexts at many scales.

LARGER CONCEPTUAL REGIONS

Judging by the number of studies, the scale most congenial to geographers is
that of an area not so large and complex as a country yet much broader than a
city. Perception studies at this scale have been numerous and varied in type.
Some center on the concerns of cultural geography and on historical geographic
themes. Others are concerned with developing models which incorporate
behavioral variables. But by far the most numerous and well-established are the
set of studies derived from the interest of geographers at the University of
Chicago in perception of natural hazards. These are given detailed coverage by
Mitchell in this volume, so only a brief perspective and a few of the more
explicitly psychological aspects will be noted here. Likewise the interest in
perception research related to recreation is omitted, since it is discussed by
Nelson and Butler in this volume.

An early example in cultural geography is Fonaroff's (1963) study of the
Navajo tribal range. He showed how a federal program of stock reduction for
this over-grazed range failed because the officials did not take into consideration
the Navajo society's perception of the situation. The same sort of failure may
attend many, if not most, well-meaning but ill-informed attempts to improve
techniques of people in the non-Western world. In such situations it is essential
to start where the people are, by investigating their perception of the situation.

This is well-illustrated by the study of Blaut and others (1959) in the severely eroded Blue Mountains of Jamaica, where conservation methods were not accepted by farmers because they failed entirely to perceive, or perceived imperfectly, the process of soil erosion in cause and effect terms. In order to introduce the desirable conservation methods in such a situation it would be essential to start any educational program at the level of local beliefs. A positive example is provided by Boxer's (1968) analysis of the urbanization process in a development area of Hong Kong's New Territories. Here a smooth transition to a modern urban-industrial society has been facilitated because the planners and administrators have been sensitive to the *feng-shui* beliefs of the agricultural villagers. These traditional beliefs provided definite ideas on how urban space should be allocated. The officials involved showed an understanding of the importance of the people's ideas by taking great pain to arrive at a consensus. In addition to financial compensation, building rights, and provision of new temples and shrines, the Government also paid for the employment of geomancers to supervise site construction and village removals and to ameliorate the damaging effect on *feng-shui* resulting from topographic alterations.

Differing cultural perceptions about which environmental resources are valued and hence exploited have long been referred to as cultural appraisals. A good example of this is provided by Newcomb (1969) who studied a small area in Northern Jutland, Denmark, from the Stone Age to the advent of the Industrial Revolution. He speculated on the ways in which people apparently perceived the Vester Han Herred district, and how aspects of these perceptions were fulfilled in terms of natural resource exploitation. Four phases are described: The Stone Age mining of flint; the medieval construction of parish churches out of glacial debris; the replanning of the rural landscape by means of enclosure; and the more recent impact of reclamation projects. Each of these phases involved a precise perception of particular resources, and each has left clearly demonstrable effects on the present-day land surface.

Perception approach has been applied with even greater frequency in historical geography. Already noted earlier were studies which indicate the differences in world view or geographic horizon at different time periods, the idea that landscapes are products of landscape tastes and the concept of cultural appraisal. An excellent review showing the diversity of approaches which have and could be applied is provided by Prince (1971). Here only one further study will be noted, an interesting application by John Allen (1972) of Wright's framework (1925) to analyze the exploratory process.

Allen selected the Lewis and Clark expedition of 1804-1806 to study the relationship between the exploratory process and man's understanding of his world. Gradations in the accuracy of regional knowledge both real, as compared to current knowledge, and perceived, were the bases of the assessment. Figures 8, 9, and 10 illustrate the relationship between the zonation of real and perceived knowledge and how these relate to the actual field operations. The real boundaries of first degree knowledge based on commercial, diplomatic, ecclesiastical, military, and scholarly enterprise are shown in Figure 8. Clearly these are much more circumscribed than the zone of first degree knowledge as perceived by the explorers (Figure 9), which extends well into the area for which only travellers' accounts and/or fairly reliable hearsay information was available. However, this is not known by the explorer until he passes the boundary of real first degree knowledge and begins to notice the discrepancies between his best information about the region and the local conditions he observes (Figure 10).

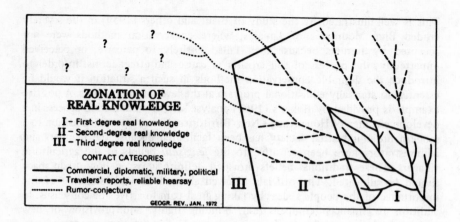

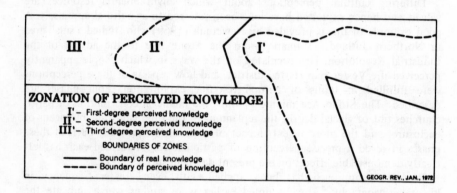

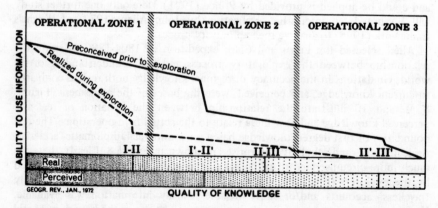

Figures 8, 9, 10. Zonation of Real Knowledge, Perceived Knowledge, and Zones of Operation. Reproduced from Allen: 1972 by permission of the author and the American Geographical Society.

The success or failure of an expedition may rest on how quickly the explorers are able to shift to a greater reliance on field observations and detailed lore from local people. Eventually through effective exploration the real and perceived zones of first degree knowledge may be merged. In the case of the Lewis and Clark expedition a new image of the West was developed. This image was more realistic than the old and lacked a major dream element, the Passage to India, so important as an original motive for the mission.

A burgeoning research theme in geography, which involves consideration of perception, is that of spatial diffusion (Gould: 1969a). Studies of this type have had a strong emphasis on model building. They attempt to work out systematically the spatial dimensions of the communication process basic to an understanding of the diffusion of innovation in a community or region. Most of these are derived from the work of Hägerstrand in Sweden. Wolpert (1965), for example, demonstrated that a sample of population of farmers in Sweden did not optimize their resource productivity, in part because they lacked perfect information due to the unpredictable change and lag in the communication and perception of information. Other studies have attempted to develop models to help explain the communication process (Cox and Golledge: 1969).

The geographic work on perception of natural hazards is reviewed comprehensively by Mitchell in this volume. He notes, as does an earlier review of Burton, Kates, and White (1968), the paradox presented by growing damages due to natural hazards, even as man's capabilities to manipulate or control certain aspects of nature increase. Geographers have long been curious about the behavior of people who persistently return to resettle areas after devastation by floods, volcanoes, earthquakes, drought, or other natural disasters. Although it seems likely that modern man is more aware of the risks of repeated disasters, the reinvasion of hazard zones probably continues as in the past. In fact, even more pressure is probably placed on these areas as population numbers grow and man and his works continue to spread over the earth. And, with increasing pressure on resources, a more delicate adjustment to nature becomes necessary.

To understand the long-term human adjustment to hazard, the inhabitants' view of the hazard is sought. This provides the possibility of assessing man's ability to perceive and understand the world around him and to choose appropriate courses of action. Improved public policies may be achieved by educating and informing in areas where knowledge is deficient. In many cases this could mean providing the people involved with a broader view of the complete range of theoretically possible adjustments. As can be seen in Table 2, there are many more possibilities than the prevailing public approach of offering immediate relief followed by a technological solution, as when dams follow floods and irrigation projects follow droughts. Clearly there are many alternatives. The problem of flood damage, for example, might be more wisely handled by preventing dense development on flood plains rather than relying on the commonly perceived solutions of bigger dams and levees. With a more rational adjustment, much loss of life and other damage could be avoided both on a national and a global level.

The perception of hazard, whether due to flood, drought, snow, landslides, tidal waves, or coastal storms, involves a high degree of abstraction and generalization of a complex reality. Although experts are able to work out with some precision the chances of recurrence of various hazards, they cannot, of course, predict exactly when they will occur in any one area. Non-professionals are even less at home with the probabilities of risk and uncertainty. Some of the

TABLE 2–Theoretical Range of Adjustments to Geophysical Events

Class of Adjustment	Event		
	Earthquakes	Floods	Snow
Affect the cause	No known way of altering the earthquake mechanism	Reduce flood flows by: land-use treatment; cloud seeding	Change geographical distribution by cloud seeding
Modify the hazard	Stable site selection: soil and slope stabilization; sea wave barriers; fire protection	Control flood flows by: reservoir storage; levees; channel improvement; flood fighting	Reduce impact by snow fences; snow removal; salting and sanding of highways
Modify loss potential	Warning systems; emergency evacuation and preparation; building design; land-use change; permanent evacuation	Warning systems; emergency evacuation and preparation; building design; land-use change; permanent evacuation	Forecasting; rescheduling; inventory control; building design; seasonal adjustments (snow tires, chains); seasonal migration; designation of snow emergency routes
Adjust to losses:			
Spread the losses	Public relief; subsidized insurance	Public relief; subsidized insurance	Public relief; subsidized insurance
Plan for losses	Insurance and reserve funds	Insurance and reserve funds	Insurance and reserve funds
Bear the losses	Individual loss bearing	Individual loss bearing	Individual loss bearing

common responses to the uncertainty of natural hazards are indicated in Table 3. Society's handling of extreme natural events might be considerably improved if the average man could be educated to think rationally about random events. When rare random events are considered from a global perspective, they no longer appear infrequent or unusual. For example, Hewitt (1969) notes that the "once-in-two-thousand year" event for a 10,000 square mile area in North America may turn out to have an average global recurrence of several times per year.

A major thrust of the hazard research has been the attempt to indicate the interaction between public attitudes toward environment and environmental decision-making. To accomplish this aim most studies have used questionnaires to probe the attitudes and ideas of the public and of the key decision-makers involved in particular resource uses. In an early discussion of this topic White (1966) suggested that although the role of attitudes is still far from clear, they appear to enter into decisions in three ways: first, through the personal attitudes of those making the decisions; second, through their opinions as to what others prefer; and third, through their opinions as to what others should prefer. One problem is that too many decisions are made on the basis of someone's opinions

TABLE 3—Common Responses to the Uncertainty of Natural Hazards

Eliminate the Hazard		Eliminate the Uncertainty	
DENY OR DENI-GRATE ITS EXISTENCE	DENY OR DENI-GRATE ITS RE-CURRENCE	MAKING IT DE-TERMINATE AND KNOWABLE	TRANSFER UN-CERTAINTY TO A HIGHER POWER
"We have no floods here, only high water."	"Lightning never strikes twice in the same place."	"Seven years of great plenty. . . . After them seven years of famine."	"It's in the hands of God."
"It can't happen here."	"It's a freak of nature."	"Floods come every five years."	"The government is taking care of it."

Source: Burton, Kates, and White: 1968.

of other people's attitudes without any real knowledge of these attitudes. For example, officials in New York assumed a preference for pure, upland water supplies and thought that most people would be unwilling to drink water from closer polluted sources, such as the Hudson River. The important point is not whether this was true or not, but that the officials made the decision on the basis of an untested assumption as to the people's preferences or, perhaps, what the officials thought they should prefer. Since this basis for decisions is not uncommon, it becomes important to probe the attitudes of the decision-makers. One significant finding of the research on this topic is that decision-makers often feel a strong professional identification which tends to shape their perception of environmental problems. McMeiken (1970) found that Public Health officials in British Columbia perceived water quality problems in terms of potential impacts on human health. By comparing these views with actual decisions or recommendations made by the officials in particular water quality situations, she indicated a close connection between such views and behavior. It is clear that the perceptions and attitudes of Public Health officials differ from the views of other groups on the nature of the water quality problems, the solutions to be applied, and the appropriate role of various participants in the decision-making process. Yet many are loath to involve the general public or other agencies because they fear it would make decision-making cumbersome, inefficient, or perhaps even impossible. Sewell (1971) extended these findings by comparing them with a similar study of engineers. He found (p. 40) that,

> the perceptions and attitudes of the two groups of professionals studied have all the characteristics of a closed system. Their views tend to be highly conditioned by training, adherence to standards and practices of the respective professions and allegiance to the agency's or firm's goals or mission.

He concluded that the solution to the emerging environmental crisis will require at least three major changes. First the adoption of a holistic rather than fragmented view of the problem is necessary. Second the public will have to be much more directly involved in the planning process. Finally, changes in administrative structures, laws, and policies are necessary to ensure that a broader view is taken, enabling the various aspects of environmental quality problems to be considered in an integrated fashion with public participation.

The emphasis on the decision-maker has led to an increased appreciation of the role of personality in man-environment relations. Some of the studies which have attempted to measure personality variables in hazard research are discussed by Mitchell in this volume. Here only brief mention is made of a model of environmental personality developed by Sonnenfeld (1972). His model (Figure 11) brings together a variety of elements which may account for variability in environmental behavior. Environmental personality is seen as a function of stimulus situation plus personality variables grouped into categories of awareness, operational style, action/reaction style, and motivation. Sonnenfeld is concerned with qualities of the environment dependent on man such as predictability, complexity, and resilience rather than climate, landforms, and vegetation. He boldly states: "I am willing to predict that consistent environmental personality types will be found among all populations, regardless of the contrast in cultural values otherwise distinguishing between them, and regardless of the contrast in environments they occupy" (Sonnenfeld: 1969, p. 97). Research on environmental personality has also been undertaken by psychologists who are developing an inventory of environmental responses (Craik: 1970;

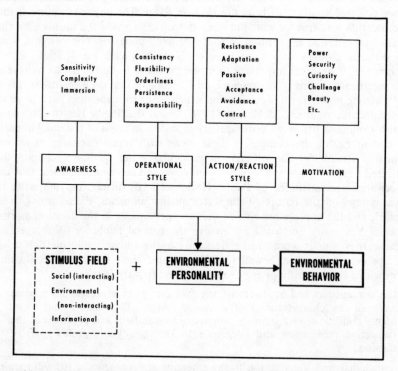

Figure 11.   A Model of Environmental Personality and Behavior. Adapted from Sonnenfeld: 1972.

McKechnie: 1970). An operational environmental personality scale would be of great value to work on perception at many levels.

THE CITY

In moving from a consideration of broad conceptual regions to the scale of the city, or smaller areas, the number of geographic studies of perception drops rapidly. Two reviews of aspects of the literature on perception as related to urban areas completed in 1968 by geographers at the University of Toronto illustrate the paucity of empirical work by geographers. Moreover, the reviews of both Bunting (1968) and Punter (1968) consist essentially of studies by people in other disciplines. Goodey's (1971) review for urban and regional studies relies more on the work of geographers, but his intention is different. His study pulls together research at many different scales to illustrate how they could be used in urban and regional research. This is a useful approach since the techniques developed in studies of a particular scale can probably be applied fruitfully at other smaller or larger scales.

More recently geographers have demonstrated a growing interest in perception studies at the city scale. These represent the diffusion into geography of concepts or approaches from other social sciences. For the purposes of this chapter a few representative studies have been selected, more to illustrate the diversity of approaches than to generalize about current research results.

At the broadest level are studies concerned with the entire urban area. Examples include Rooney's study (1967) on the urban snow hazard in the United States. This is an application of hazard research and really fits on a broader scale. Many cities are compared in terms of the degree of disruption due to snow. Another example is the article of Lycan and Sewell (1968) on perception of air and water pollution in the urban environment of Victoria, British Columbia. This study can also be considered as an extension of the research on natural hazards with a more recent move toward questions of how people perceive the man-created hazards of air and water pollution. An even broader range of environmental problems in one city has been considered in later extensions of the same theme. Hewitt and Burton in *The Hazardousness of a Place* (1971) discuss all the hazards that occur at London, Ontario and adjacent parts of the province, while Saarinen and Cooke (1971) examine public perception of environmental quality in Tucson, Arizona.

The Saarinen and Cooke study is based on a questionnaire survey of a sample of residents in the city of Tucson and its environs. Here the advantages apparently far outweigh the disadvantages for a favorable image is found, dominated by the advantage of a fine climate. However several problems do appear to be considered serious, most notably littering, air pollution, and traffic congestion. Visibility and personal experience of the problems seem to be important in their identification. Air pollution, though not extreme by comparison with other areas, is probably considered serious because of the noticeable deterioration in the quality of air, for virtually all of those who considered it a problem felt it had been getting worse in recent years. A clear illustration of the rather parochial manner in which environmental problems may be perceived is provided by responses to the question of noise pollution. Comparison of respondents' locations with a map showing noise intensity contours (Figure 12) reveals that the noise pollution problem is considered somewhat serious or very

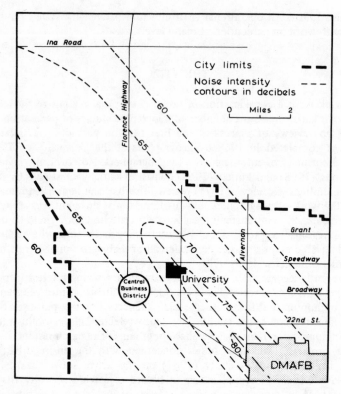

Figure 12. Zones of Aircraft Noise, Tucson, Arizona. Reproduced from Saarinen and
Cooke: 1971.

serious by all those in the zone of greatest intensity (Table 4). However the
proportions who perceive a noise pollution problem diminish regularly through
the zones of lesser intensity. Any action group wishing to obtain public support
to combat noise pollution would be well advised to concentrate its efforts in the
high decibel zones for elsewhere it is generally not even considered to be a
problem. For most problems analyzed, the respondents felt that technological

TABLE 4—Rating of Seriousness of Noise Pollution According to Noise Level

Noise Level in Decibels	Very Serious Number	%	Somewhat Serious Number	%	Not Serious Number	%	No Answer Number	%
Over 80	3	50	3	50	0	0	0	0
75-79	0	0	0	0	0	0	0	0
70-74	11	55	7	35	2	10	0	0
65-69	10	39	14	54	2	7	0	0
60-64	11	18	20	32	30	48	1	2
Less than 60	3	12	5	19	18	69	0	0
0	2	7	3	11	20	74	2	7

Source: Saarinen and Cooke: 1971.

solutions could be found, but they were more pessimistic about the possibility that action would actually be taken.

A technique which provides input for comprehensive design of cities is that advanced by Kevin Lynch (1960) and since applied by others in many different fields at various scales. The main aim of such studies is to provide information as to how people use the city and find their way around in it. By having a person sketch a map, and describe the parts felt to be most distinctive, an individual image of the city is obtained. This can be described in terms of paths, edges, districts, nodes, and landmarks.

Studies in Tucson and Chicago indicate that, in spite of individual and group variations, there is a high degree of conformity and consistency in the major elements, so that one can speak of the "public image." This was the case in a study of the University of Arizona Campus (Saarinen: in press) and the Chicago Loop (Saarinen: 1964) (Figures 13, 14). In the latter case, three groups were tested. Each drew maps and listed the most distinctive areas in the Loop. Certain areas and elements were included or omitted from the composite maps of all three groups. The grid pattern was noted. The distinctiveness of the image diminished westward and north-south streets were dominant. Major elements which appeared to some degree in all maps were State Street with its department stores, the contrast between the open space of Grant Park and the massive wall of Michigan Avenue, the canyon-like LaSalle Street dominated by the Board of Trade Buildiing, and the vista of major landmarks lining the north branch of the Chicago River. However, workers within the Loop area tended to have a more

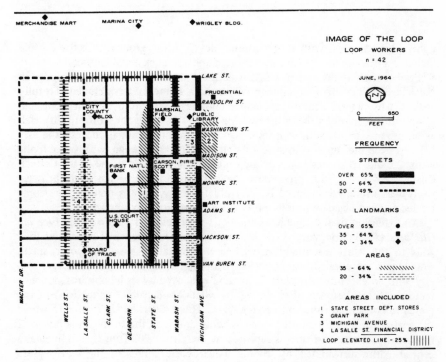

Figure 13. Image of the Chicago Loop: Loop Workers. Reproduced from Saarinen: 1964.

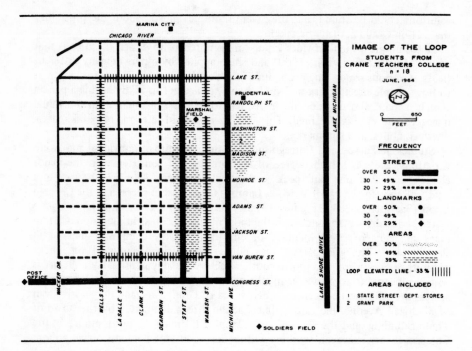

Figure 14.   Image of the Chicago Loop: Crane Teachers College Students. Reproduced from Saarinen: 1964.

tightly defined area, with more internal detail, while groups from the outside included a broader area, with much more emphasis on external landmarks.

Studies such as the one just discussed are concerned with what is included in the image of the city, rather than why certain elements are included. To fully answer why would require an understanding of the role of sentiment and symbolism. A master's thesis by Bunting (1967) discusses the Toronto City Hall as an urban symbol. Although its design won an international contest, the city hall has been the center of controversy. It has a striking design, with two curving walls, 27 and 20 stories tall, shielding the centrally placed dome of the Council Chambers. Whether this progressive symbol was reacted to positively or negatively was strongly influenced by individual value systems. Conservative people tended to react negatively to it and to the kind of city it symbolizes.

An extension of the Lynch technique is provided by Denis Wood in *Fleeting Glimpses* (1971). He starts with his own unabashedly personal views and then adds to the usual essentially visual image information based on color, smell, sound, and temporal differences. San Cristobal, Chiapas, Mexico, emerges as a city with an exceptionally clean image and one loved by its inhabitants. A major factor in the coherence of the image is what Wood calls "replication" or the recreation of similar forms on varying scales. This is illustrated in Figure 15 where the spatial form of the house is seen as being similar to the form of the *barrio* or neighborhood which in turn is repeated at the city scale. Thus each home has a central patio surrounded by rooms which corresponds to the *barrio* plaza surrounded by individual houses and to the main plaza or *zocalo* surrounded by the separate neighborhoods. The patio serves as the main recreational area for children, the *barrio* plaza for young adolescents, and the *zocalo* for older adolescents and adults. Politics, religion, and fiestas are similarly evident on all

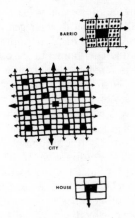

Figure 15.   Idealized City Plan Showing the Individual Home, the *Barrio*, and the City. Reproduced from Wood: 1971, by permission.

levels, so that skills learned at the lowest level are easily transferable to each succeeding level of the hierarchy. The barrio or neighborhood is a critical intermediate level in this process of replication which binds the home to the city. It is one which Wood emphasizes is lacking in Anglo-American cities. He suggests that his results be correlated with information concerning satisfaction, health, spiritual well-being, and so on in an investigation of the relationship between the coherence of city image and physical and spiritual health of city inhabitants.

A recent development along similar lines is that which stresses the importance of the image in relating environmental behavior to perception. Downs and Stea (1970) advocate a research focus on these images, mental maps, conceptual spaces, and schemata or cognitive maps in order to explain environmental behavior (Downs and Stea, eds.: 1973). They suggest three major research foci, centering on the elements that comprise cognitive representations and the relationships between elements. A study by Downs (1970*b*) shows the cognitive complexity of a single spatial element. He interviewed women in Bristol to investigate the dimensions on cognitive categories they thought most important in evaluating an urban shopping center. Other studies have investigated such topics as subjective distances (Golledge *et al.*: 1968), or the ages at which children develop map skills (Blaut: 1969; Blaut and Stea: 1969). A fine review by Hart and Moore (1971) indicates how recent work on the development of spatial cognition relates to the fundamental philosophical concepts of space and the major psychological theories of cognitive development such as those of Piaget. Their review indicates the present knowledge of the stages through which people pass from infancy to adulthood in the general progression from concrete to abstract representation and thought about space. A grounding in this theoretical framework would provide a firm foundation for further research on cognitive maps at all scales.

A series of studies by Lowenthal and Riel (1972) demonstrates a methodology which could be useful for measuring responses to the urban outdoor environments of different cities. They had several groups of subjects walk along one-half mile set paths in New York, Boston, Cambridge, and Columbus. The paths were selected as being quintessentially New York, Boston, and so on in flavor. The subjects were asked to record their general impressions and to make judgments about each milieu in terms of 25 attribute pairs previously selected as being significant for comparing environmental responses (Table 5). The studies differ from most others considered in this chapter in that they are concerned with direct perception of the environment through the senses rather than simply conceptions or ideas about the environment. When the associations of attributes of the subjects who actually experienced the environment through the walks were compared with a control group who did not, interesting contrasts appeared. The mental structure based on semantic responses differed from that based on observation and experience in the outdoor world. The structuring on perception by language already noted in the introduction to this chapter is clearly seen by Lowenthal and Riel, who conclude that ". . . while language at times reinforces environmental experience, at other times the two are opposed. The differences help to show how and explain why the way we think we see the world is in many respects not the way we actually do see it" (Lowenthal and Riel: 1972, p. 206). Their studies compare and contrast the impressions of the four cities which the research revealed. The authors provide a list of implications which may be of some value to planners. A major implication is the need for input from human experience and response in the development of design vocabularies, concepts, and building blocks.

SMALL TOWNS, NEIGHBORHOODS, AND SMALLER AREAS

Perception of environment studies have not been prominent at the level of the small town. However some of the essays of J. B. Jackson which appeared in *Landscape* magazine deal with the varying perception of smaller American cities and towns (Zube: 1970). "Other-Directed Houses" (Jackson: 1957), and "The

TABLE 5—Environmental Attribute-Pairs Responded to in Urban Walks

1. Natural-Artificial	14. Old-New
2. Contrast-Uniform	15. Quiet-Noisy
3. People-Things	16. Vivid-Drab
4. Ugly-Beautiful	17. Self Awareness-Awareness of Surroundings
5. Appearance-Meaning	
6. Smelly-Fresh	18. Pleasant-Unpleasant
7. Vertical-Horizontal	19. Business Use-Living Use
8. Ordered-Chaotic	20. Clean-Dirty
9. Moving-Motionless	21. Dense-Empty
10. Smooth-Rough	22. Suburban-Urban
11. Poor-Rich	23. Individual Features-Overall Views
12. Open-Bounded	
13. Boring-Interesting	24. Like-Dislike
	25. Dark-Light

Source: Lowenthal and Riel: 1972.

Stranger's Path" (Jackson: 1957) provide perceptive analyses of certain ubiqui-tous features of the American scene. The first is concerned with the way the public perceives and uses the highway strips leading out of our towns. The second discusses in the vivid empathetic manner of a participant the probable sequence of scenes and activities encountered by the stranger as he enters any small American city. Another article discusses "The Almost Perfect Town" (Jackson: 1952) where certain of the citizens wish to tear down the courthouse, make a parking lot of courthouse square, and institute a series of one-way streets in order to attract new business and prosperity from passing motorists. These and other Jackson essays reflect a keen awareness of the psychological frame of mind which may induce small-town planners imbued with the conventional planning wisdom to destroy some of the few remaining sources of local character and vitality in a perhaps illusory effort to attract new outside sources of revenue.

A similar situation is described in a more recent article by Lewis (1972), who treats American small towns on two levels. First he considers them as a group and then he examines the small town of Bellefonte, Pennsylvania as a case study. He contends that their importance is far greater than their current population numbers would indicate, for small town imagery and mythology are central to the American experience. Americans have loved small towns. This is reflected in American literature where small towns may grow stronger as images of their neighborliness and stable community relations contrast with a feeling of loss of control in larger more anonymous and even dangerous urban areas. Changes in technology may also enable small towns to play a new role in contemporary society. However, in spite of changes in taste and technology, Lewis foresees difficulties which may prevent small towns from playing a new role. In the case of Bellefonte, three generations of economic stagnation and loss of population have led to great physical and psychological damage. The atmosphere of despair and pessimism has created a grim conservatism which leads to reluctance to entertain new ideas and a clinging to established patterns of thought and behavior. Yet in their desperate effort to induce growth the town has narrowed its options still further as highway building and urban renewal have led to a demolition of distinguished old buildings and their replacement by gas stations and outlets for chain stores or restaurants. Unfortunately it is mainly outsiders and returned native sons who see the possibilities of retention and restoration of the earlier architectural atmosphere to create a physically attractive town and to shore up the ebbing community spirit. Most locals are sure it wouldn't work.

Information on neighborhoods and how they are perceived and used has also developed as an outcome of the mistakes and failures of major urban renewal projects (Duhl: 1963). Much of this work has been done by psychologists and sociologists, but geographers have also shown a recent surge of interest. Among the earlier studies by geographers on neighborhood perception were those by Zannaras (1968) and Metton (1969) who both defined neighborhoods by using individual delimitations of the area on maps provided. The summation of individual action spaces produced a common spatial area which could be designated as the neighborhood for the majority of respondents. Metton, whose data were derived from a densely built-up area of Paris, found that the form and size of the neighborhood depended on the relative locations of the home, the market, and local commercial establishments. In his area, the size was on a pedestrian scale, that is, limited to a distance that people would find convenient to cover on foot. Similar studies would be useful in less densely built-up areas where the automobile is dominant. One good reason for making studies of neighborhoods might be to avoid the kind of situation described by Doeppers (1967), which occurred in the Globeville neighborhood in Denver. Here a freeway was constructed which cut through the social fabric of an old ethnic neighborhood and contributed to its decline.

A more recent framework for evaluating the design of residential areas is provided by Anne Buttimer (1972). She states (p. 313) that "to discover the principles that underlie ordinary behavior in urban social worlds, and then to design a physical framework to accommodate it, are the challenge and hope of the seventies." She suggests that the efficacy of residential area design can be assessed in terms of the individual's expectations. Some of the factors which influence the individual expectations are illustrated in Figure 16 which contrasts the socio-spatial reference systems of two hypothetical polar types of resident: the "localite," and the "urbanite." The social interaction pattern, activity spaces, sense of territoriality, and site character expectation of each are markedly different. It is important, then, to identify the degree to which the population of a particular area is localite, urbanite, or some intermediate category, since the planning implications are different for each group. For example, the localite group tends to develop a strong sense of territoriality and prefers an environment which provides for neighborly relations, communal activities, and convenient services and institutions. The urbanite, on the other hand, does not identify strongly with place and is concerned with the high quality and status of services. Amenity, visual quality, and accessibility to the city are more important than interaction with neighbors. Buttimer's framework incorporates much of the current work of sociologists which may be seen in the review of Michelson (1970).

An example of an extremely strong sense of territoriality is provided by Boal (1969) in a study of Belfast, long the scene of intense inter-group conflict. He interviewed people in the Shankill-Falls area of the city where the Protestant and Roman Catholic groups are residentially segregated from each other but in close spatial proximity. Figures 17 and 18 show the location of the study area in relation to the pattern of street decorations for the Orange (Protestant) celebrations on July the Twelfth, and households where at least one member has a surname or first name that could be classified as "Roman Catholic." The two patterns are almost reversed images of each other. The study area contains two distinct territories separated by the "divide" of Cupar Street. The people on opposite sides of this divide live in entirely different mental worlds. Furthermore their activity patterns are almost totally separated with no socially meaningful connections linking the two portions of the study area in spite of their proximity. This study provides a striking example of the importance of the largely invisible landscape which may exist in people's minds and condition their behavior and activity patterns, yet not be readily discernible in physical form to the outside observer. The strict observance of territorial limits in Belfast no doubt serves to reduce the amount of direct confrontation and conflict. This is a major function of territoriality in animals and recent applications of the concept to studies of human behavior indicate strong parallels (Esser: 1971).

A different approach to metropolitan neighborhoods is that of Julian Wolpert and his associates at the University of Pennsylvania, where the major concern is with conflict in locational decisions (Wolpert, Mumphrey, and Seley: 1972). They provide a model of land-use change which represents broadly what happens in a metropolitan neighborhood. The outcome depends on the actions of the

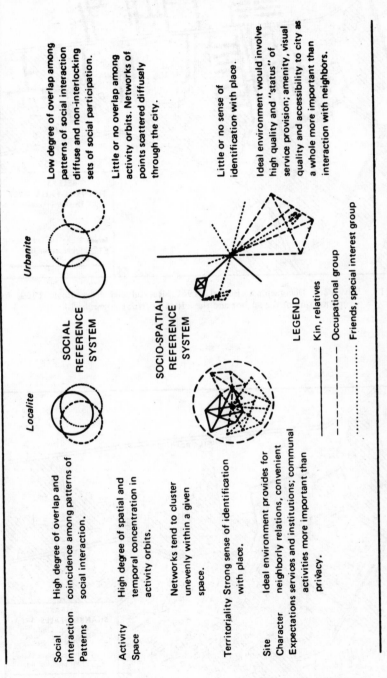

Figure 16. Idealized Sketches of Socio-Spatial Reference Systems. Reproduced from Buttimer: 1972, by permission of the author and Sage Publications, Inc.

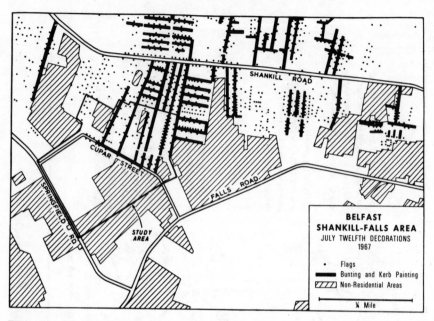

Figure 17. July 12th Decorations: Belfast, 1967. Reproduced from Boal: 1969, by permission of the author and the editor of *Irish Geography*.

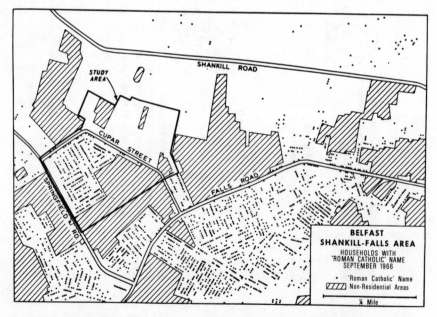

Figure 18. Households with "Roman Catholic" Names: Belfast, 1966. Reproduced from Boal: 1969, by permission of the author and the editor of *Irish Geography*.

neighborhood actors as they participate in contests over land-use change. The principal actors involved are the neighborhood property owners (who may or may not be residents), the residents of the neighborhood, and the local government. Each of these has different goals which lead to the original conflict situation. Whether the changes that occur result from decisions within the neighborhood or from outside forces depends on the degree of community organization and participation. The authors outline a range of possibilities using case studies from metropolitan neighborhoods.

A scale, almost totally ignored by geographers, which has a thriving tradition of research in environmental perception is that of personal space and room geography. This has largely been the domain of psychologists and anthropologists (Hall: 1966; Sommer: 1969; Proshansky, Ittelson, and Rivlin: 1970). An interesting exception is the recent geographic work by Kimber (1973) on the spatial patterning of the dooryard gardens of Puerto Rico. She illustrates the variety of types of dooryard gardens and variation in behavior associated with them indicating that these provide clues to codified cultural patterns. The principal design elements involved are the dwelling, other buildings, bare earth, and the arrangement of trees, shrubs, herbs, and flowering plants. The major variation in spatial patterning is a result of two contrasting traditions, the vernacular and the high-style. In the vernacular tradition "man's relationship with plants is direct and his concern is with the function of the plant—for ornament, food, medicine, construction, fiber, or forage." In contrast the high-style tradition uses the plants "to create artifical landscapes, to decorate the dwelling, and to express the esthetic taste of the owner or the local landscape architect" (Kimber: 1973, p. 23). Kimber also found that plants are used as objects in gardens to create fixed spaces in which different human activities are performed and that garden spaces function as human territories. For example, in certain types of garden design large amounts of bare earth are left around the dwelling. Such near space is an extension of the dwelling and contains enough room to accommodate the household members as they go about their activities. The social space of hospitality also appears to extend beyond the house to encompass this near space. A curious habit observed is that of tending the land on the other side of the road if it is not a part of the near space of someone else's holding. Kimber suggests that it may be maintained as a part of the visual space of those who habitually regard it.

CONCLUSIONS

The number of studies concerned with how people perceive their environment is rapidly increasing in a variety of disciplines and geography is no exception. Within geography two notable trends are evident in the past four years in addition to the general increase in number of studies. One is the tendency to apply the available techniques to a greater variety of scales and the other is the increased sophistication in the application of psychological and other social science methodologies. The broad regional scale is still the one at which the most geographic effort has been applied. But the conceptual framework and methods of perception study have been used at all scales with a noticeable increase in interest in areas of smaller size. Today there are many more geographers investigating how people perceive their environment than a few years ago. Neighborhoods and even smaller areas have also begun to receive some attention. As geographers have become more involved in perception studies they have adopted and adapted a wide range of techniques from the social and behavioral sciences and become more aware of advancing frontiers of research in these disciplines. Thus, for example, recent work in cognitive maps has attempted to place current geographical research within the broader theoretical framework of developmental psychology and philosophy of space. This allows the testing of specific hypotheses which provide a firm foundation for succeeding studies whether in geography or other disciplines. Such attempts by geographers to place their own research within a broader social and behavioral science framework is indicative of a new phase in research on perception of environment. It indicates a concern that the proliferation of studies might lead to a scattering of energies in a variety of disjointed research directions with no common vocabulary or theoretical framework. A sustained effort will be required to reconcile the differences in disciplinary philosophies, vocabularies, and research directions (Lowenthal: 1972b). But the fact that the initial phase of preliminary research has passed, indicates that the focus on people's perceptions of environment is a fruitful approach. From now on it may be expected that an integral part of environmental education will be an effort to elucidate the importance of the relationship between man's environmental perceptions and his behavior.

REFERENCES

Allen, John L., 1972, "An Analysis of the Exploratory Process: The Lewis and Clark Expedition of 1804-1806," *Geographical Review*, Vol. 62, pp. 13-39.

Blaut, J. *et al.*, 1959, "A Study of Cultural Determinants of Soil Erosion and Conservation in the Blue Mountains of Jamaica," *Social and Economic Studies*, Vol. 8, pp. 402-20.

Blaut, J. M., 1969, "Studies in Developmental Geography," *Clark University Place Perception Research Report No. 1*.

Blaut, J. M., and David Stea, 1969, "Place Learning," *Clark University Place Perception Research Report No. 4*.

Boal, F. W., 1969, "Territoriality in the Shankill-Falls Divide, Belfast," *Irish Geography*, Vol. 6, pp. 30-50.

Boxer, Baruch, 1968, "Space, Change and Feng-Shui in Tsuen Wans Urbanization," *Journal of Asian and African Studies*, Vol. 3, pp. 226-40.

Bunting, Trudi, 1967, "Symbolic Urban Images: A Case Study of the New City Hall in Toronto," unpublished Master's Thesis, University of Western Ontario.

———, 1968, "Perception: Paradigm for Urban Environmentalism," unpublished paper.

Burrill, Meredith F., 1968, "The Language of Geography," *Annals of the Association of American Geographers*, Vol. 58, pp. 1-11.

Burton, Ian, Robert Kates, and Gilbert F. White, 1968, "The Human Ecology of Extreme Geophysical Events," *Natural Hazard Working Paper No. 1*, Toronto: Department of Geography, University of Toronto.

Buttimer, Anne, 1972, "Social Space and the Planning of Residential Areas," *Environment and Behavior*, Vol. 4, pp. 279-318.

Campbell, Robert D., 1968, "Personality as an Element of Regional Geography," *Annals of the Association of American Geographers*, Vol. 58, pp. 748-59.

Cole, J. P. and P. Whysall, 1968, "Places in the News, a Study of Geographical Information," *Bulletin of Quantitative Data for Geographers*, No. 7.

Cox, J. J. and R. G. Golledge, 1969, *Behavioral Problems in Geography: A Symposium*, Evanston, Illinois: Northwestern University Papers in Geography.

Cox, Kevin and Georgia Zannaras, 1970, "Designative Perceptions of Macro-Spaces: Concepts, a Methodology and Applications," *EDRA Two* Proceedings of the 2nd Annual Environmental Design Research Association Conference, October 1970.

Craik, Kenneth, 1970, "Environmental Psychology," *New Directions in Psychology IV*, New York: Holt, Rinehart and Winston.

De Long, Alton J., 1972, "The Communication Process: A Generic Model for Man-Environment Relations," *Man-Environment Systems*, Vol. 2, pp. 263-313.

Doeppers, Daniel F., 1967, "The Globeville Neighborhood in Denver," *Geographical Review*, Vol. 57, pp. 506-22.

Doherty, J. M., 1968, "Residential Preferences for Urban Environments in the United States," *London School of Economics Graduate School of Geography Discussion Paper No. 29.*

Donaldson, O. Fred, 1971, "Geography and the Black American: The White Papers and the Invisible Man," *Journal of Geography*, Vol. 70, pp. 138-149.

Downs, Roger M., 1970*a*, "Geographic Space Perception: Past Approaches and Future Prospects," *Progress in Geography*, Vol. 2, pp. 65-108.

———, 1970*b*, "The Cognitive Structure of an Urban Shopping Center," *Environment and Behavior*, Vol. 2, pp. 13-39.

Downs, Roger and David Stea, 1970, "Environmental Cognition and Behavior," *EDRA Two* Proceedings of the 2nd Annual Environmental Design Research Association Conference, October 1970, Pittsburgh, Pennsylvania, session two, pp. 95-142.

——— (eds.), 1973, *Image and Environment*. Chicago: Aldine.

Duhl, Leonard J., 1963, *The Urban Condition*, New York: Simon and Shuster.

Esser, Aristide H., 1971, *Behavior and Environment: The Use of Space by Animals and Men*, New York: Plenum Press.

Fonaroff, L. Schuyler, 1963, "Conservation and Stock Reduction on the Navajo Tribal Range," *Geographical Review*, Vol. 53, pp. 200-23.

Glacken, Clarence, 1967, *Traces on the Rhodian Shore: Nature and Culture in Western Thought from Ancient Times to the End of the Eighteenth Century*, Berkeley: University of California Press.

Ginsburg, Norton, 1968, "On the Chinese Perception of a World Order," in Tang Tsou (ed.) *China's Policies in Asia and America's Alternatives*. 2 vols., Chicago: University of Chicago Press, Vol. 2, pp. 73-91.

Golledge, R. *et al.*, 1968, "A Pilot Study of the Geographical Perception of North Dakota Students," unpublished paper.

Goodey, Brian R., 1969, "Messages in Space: Some Observations on Geography and Communications," *North Dakota Quarterly*, Vol. 37, pp. 34-49.

———, 1971, "Perception of the Environment," *University of Birmingham Centre for Urban and Regional Studies Occasional Paper No. 17.*

Gould, Peter, 1966, "On Mental Maps," *Michigan Inter-University Community of Mathematical Geographers Discussion Paper No. 9.*

———, 1969*a*, *Spatial Diffusion*, Commission on College Geography Resource Paper No. 4, Washington, D.C.: Association of American Geographers.

———, 1969*b*, "The Structure of Space Preference in Tanzania," *Area*, No. 4, pp. 29-35.

———, 1973, "Geographic Exposition, Information and Location," National Academy of Sciences, *Geographical Perspectives and Urban Problems*, Washington, D.C.: National Academy of Sciences, pp. 25-40.

Gould, P. and D. Ola, 1970, "The Perception of Residential Desirability in the Western Region of Nigeria," *Environment and Planning*, Vol. 2, pp. 73-87.

Gould, Peter, and R. R. White, 1968, "The Mental Maps of British School Leavers," *Regional Studies*, Vol. 2, pp. 161-82.

Haddon, John, 1960, "A View of Foreign Lands," *Geography*, Vol. 65, pp. 286-89.

Hall, Edward T., 1966, *The Hidden Dimension*, New York: Doubleday.

Hart, Roger A., and Gary T. Moore, 1971, "The Development of Spatial Cognition: A Review," *Clark University Place Perception Research Report No. 7.*

Hewitt, Kenneth, 1969, "A Pilot Survey of Global Natural Disasters of the Past Twenty Years," *Natural Hazard Research Working Paper No. 11* Toronto: Department of Geography, University of Toronto.

Hewitt, Kenneth and Ian Burton, 1971, *The Hazardousness of a Place: A Regional Ecology of Damaging Events*, University of Toronto Department of Geography Research Publication No. 6.

Jackson, J. B., 1952, "The Almost Perfect Town," *Landscape*, Vol. 2, also in Erwin H. Zube (ed.), 1970, *Landscapes: Selected Writings of J. B. Jackson*, Amherst: University of Massachusetts Press, pp. 116-31.

———, 1957, "Other-Directed Houses," *Landscape*, Vol. 6, pp. 29-35.

———, 1957, "The Stranger's Path," *Landscape*, Vol. 7 pp. 11-15.

Kimber, Clarissa T., 1973, "Spatial Patterning in the Dooryard Gardens of Puerto Rico," *Geographical Review*, Vol. 63, pp. 6-26.

Lewis, Peirce F., 1972, "Small Town in Pennsylvania," *Annals of the Association of American Geographers*, Vol. 62, pp. 323-51.

Lowenthal, David, 1968, "The American Scene," *Geographical Review*, Vol. 58, pp. 61-88.

———, 1972, "Research in Environmental Perception and Behavior: Perspectives on Current Problems," *Environment and Behavior*, Vol. 4, pp. 333-42.

———, 1972a, *West Indian Societies*, New York: Oxford.

———, 1972b, "The Nature of Perceived and Imagined Environments," *Environment and Behavior*, Vol. 4, pp. 189-207.

Lowenthal, David and Hugh C. Prince, 1964, "The English Landscape," *Geographical Review*, Vol. 54, pp. 309-46.

———, 1965, "English Landscape Tastes," *Geographical Review*, Vol. 55, pp. 188-222.

Lowenthal, David and Marguita Riel, 1972, *Publications in Environmental Perception*, (1) Environmental Assessment: A Case Study of New York City; (2) Environmental Assessment: A Case Study of Boston; (3) Environmental Assessment: A Case Study of Cambridge, Mass.; (4) Environmental Assessment: A Case Study of Columbus, Ohio; (5) Environmental Assessment: A Comparative Analysis of Four Cities; (6) Structures of Environmental Associations; (7) Milieu and Observer Differences in Environmental Associates; (8) Environmental Structures: Semantic and Experiential Components, New York: American Geographical Society.

Lycan, D. R., and W. R. D. Sewell, 1968, "Water and Air Pollution as Components of the Urban Environment of Victoria," *Geographical Perspectives*, Vancouver, B. C.: Tantalus Press.

Lynch, Kevin, 1960, *The Image of the City*, Cambridge, Mass.: M. I. T. Press.

McKechnie, George E., 1970, "Measuring Environmental Dispositions with the Environmental Response Inventory," *EDRA Two* Proceedings of the 2nd Annual Environmental Design Research Association Conference October 1970, Pittsburgh, Pennsylvania, pp. 320-26.

McMeiken, Joan Elizabeth, 1970, "Public Health Professionals and Attitudes in Environmental Quality Decision-Making in British Columbia," unpublished Masters Thesis, University of Victoria.

Metton, Alain, 1969, "Le Quartier: Etude Géographique et Psycho-Sociologique," *Canadian Geographer*, Vol. 13, pp. 299-316.

Michelson, William, 1970, *Man and His Urban Environment: A Sociological Approach*, Reading, Mass.: Addison-Wesley.

Newcomb, Robert M., 1969, "Environmental Perception and Its Fulfillment During Past Times in Northern Jutland, Denmark," *Skrifter Fra Geografisk Institut Ved Aarhus Universitet Nr. 26*.

O'Riordan, Timothy, forthcoming, "Environmental Words and Environmental Deeds" (unpublished manuscript).

Palomaki, M., 1968, "On the Concept and Delimitation of the Present-Day Provinces of Finland," *Acta Geographica*, Vol. 20, pp. 279-95.

Parker, W. H., 1969, *The Soviet Union*, Chicago: Aldine.

Pitts, Forrest R., 1960, "The Japanese Landscape as Mood and Intensity," unpublished manuscript; a shorter version appeared in 1960 as "A Mirror to Japan," *Landscape*.

Prince, Hugh C., 1971, "Real, Imagined and Abstract Worlds of the Past," *Progress in Geography*, Vol. 3, pp. 1-86, London: Edward Arnold.

Proshansky, Harold M., William H. Ittelson, and Leanne G. Rivlin, 1970, *Environmental Psychology: Man and His Physical Setting*, New York: Holt, Rinehart and Winston.

Punter, John V., 1968, "Urban Design: A Review of Its Actual and Potential Contribution to Improving the Central-City Environment," unpublished Masters Thesis, University of Toronto.

Research and Design Institute, 1969, *1969 Directory of Behavior and Environmental Design*, Providence, R.I.: Research and Design Institute.

Rooney, John F., Jr., 1967, "The Urban Snow Hazard in the United States," *Geographical Review*, Vol. 57, pp. 538-59.

Saarinen, Thomas F., 1964, "Image of the Chicago Loop," unpublished paper.

———, 1969, *Perception of Environment*, Commission on College Geography Resource Paper No. 5, Washington, D.C.: Association of American Geographers.

———, 1970, "Environmental Perception," in Phillip Bacon (ed.), 1970, *Focus on Geography: Key Concepts and Teaching Strategies*, Washington, D.C.: National Council for the Social Studies, pp. 63-99.

_____ , 1973, "Student Views of the World," in Roger M. Downs and David Stea (eds.), *Image and Environment*. Chicago: Aldine, pp. 148-161.

_____ , forthcoming, "The Use of Projective Techniques in Geographic Research," in W. H. Ittelson (ed.), *Environment and Cognition*, New York: Academic Press.

Saarinen, Thomas F. and Ronald U. Cooke, 1971, "Public Perception of Environmental Quality in Tucson, Arizona," *Journal of the Arizona Academy of Science*, Vol. 6, pp. 260-74.

Sewell, W. R. Derrick, 1971, "Environmental Perceptions and Attitudes of Engineers and Public Health Officials," *Environment and Behavior*, Vol. 3, pp. 23-59.

Sommer, Robert, 1969, *Personal Space, the Behavioral Basis of Design*, Englewood Cliffs, N.J.: Prentice-Hall.

Sonnenfeld, Joseph, 1969, "Equivalence and Distortion of the Perceptual Environment," *Environment and Behavior*, Vol. 1, pp. 83-99.

_____ , 1972, "Social Interaction and Environmental Relationship," *Environment and Behavior*, Vol. 4, pp. 267-77.

Stanislawski, Dan, 1972, "Culture Areas of the Ancient Aegean Area: Selective Contact and Persistence," Presidential Address, Association of Pacific Coast Geographers, Hayward, California, June 15, 1972. To be published in the *Yearbook of the APCG*, 1973.

Stea, David and Roger Downs (eds.), 1970, "Cognitive Representations of Man's Spatial Environment," *Environment and Behavior*, Vol. 2, entire issue.

Tuan, Yi-Fu, 1968, *The Hydrologic Cycle and the Wisdom of God: A Theme in Geoteleology*, Toronto: Department of Geography Research Publication No. 1, University of Toronto.

_____ , 1969, *China*, Chicago: Aldine.

Vance, James E., Jr., 1972, "California and the Search for the Ideal," *Annals of the Association of American Geographers*, Vol. 62, pp. 185-210.

Von Humboldt, Alexander, 1850, *Cosmos: A Sketch of a Physical Description of the Universe*, New York: Harper.

Wheatley, Paul, 1964, "The Land of Zanj: Exegetical Notes on Chinese Knowledge of East Africa Prior to AD 1500," in R. W. Steel, and R. M. Prothero, (eds.), *Geographers and the Tropics: Liverpool Essays*, London: Longman, pp. 139-88.

White, Ralph K., 1966, "Misperception and the Vietnam War," *The Journal of Social Issues*, Vol. 22, entire issue.

Whittlesey, Derwent, 1945, "Horizon of Geography," *Annals of the Association of American Geographers*, Vol. 35, pp. 1-36.

Whorf, Benjamin Lee, 1940, "Science and Linguistics," *Technology Review*, Vol. 44, pp. 229-31, 247, 248; reprinted in Eleanor E. Maccoby, Theodore M. Newcomb, and Eugene L. Hartley (eds.), 1958, *Readings in Social Psychology*, New York: Holt, Rinehart and Winston.

Wolpert, Julian, 1965, "The Decision Process in Spatial Context," *Annals of the Association of American Geographers*, Vol. 54, pp. 537-58.

Wolpert, Julian, Anthony Mumphrey, and John Seley, 1972, *Metropolitan Neighborhoods: Participation and Conflict Over Change*, Commission on College Geography, Resource Paper No. 16, Washington, D.C.: Association of American Geographers.

Wood, Denis, 1971, *Fleeting Glimpses*, Clark University: Cartographic Laboratory.

Wright, John K., 1925, *The Geographical Lore of the Time of the Crusades*, American Geographical Society Research Series No. 15, New York: American Geographical Society, republished in 1965 as a Dover paperback.

Zannaras, Georgia, 1968, "An Empirical Analysis of Urban Neighborhood Perception," unpublished Master's Thesis, Ohio State University.

Zube, Erwin H. (ed.), 1970, *Landscapes: Selected Writings of J. B. Jackson*, Amherst: University of Massachusetts Press.

Recreation and the Environment

J. G. Nelson and R. W. Butler
University of Western Ontario

The impact of recreation on the environment has been profound and promises to be more so as incomes, mobility, and leisure time increase. Indeed, in North America at least, society may be on the verge of a new age in which automation and technology will largely free men from productive concerns, leaving an increasing amount of discretionary time or leisure for such non-economic activities as recreation (Mumford: 1966; Mesthene: 1970; Parker: 1972). What have such activities been in the past, especially in North America? What resources do they require? What are their effects on vegetation, wildlife and other aspects of landscape? What will be their effects in the future? Not all such questions can be answered adequately within the scope of this brief essay, and the emphasis here is on recreational land use with particular regard to the establishment and management of national parks and other large public reserves in North America. The approach is essentially historical, with emphasis on ideas, perceptions and attitudes and the way in which these have influenced the use, management, and change of landscape (Lowenthal: 1966; White: 1966; Sewell and Burton: 1971). An understanding of the way in which our ideas about recreation and environment have evolved is basic to better management in the future.

Meanings tend to vary among users so that something should be said at the outset about terminology. Environment is used to refer to all aspects of the world around us, such as noise, pine forests, advertising, marinas, parking lots. Environment is a comprehensive term, but hardly more so than ecosystem with which its meaning overlaps. Ecosystem is a biological concept which can be defined as the elements and processes interacting with and supporting an organism or organisms in space and time. As discussed by David Watts in an earlier essay, the processes of energy flow and cycling of phosphorus, nitrogen, carbon dioxide and other nutrients necessary to maintain organic life, are basic to ecosystem dynamics. Recently as ecologists have become more sensitive to human effects they have attempted to apply ecological concepts to agriculture, mining, lumbering and other cultural processes (Odum: 1971). Landscape is essentially a geographical and cultural concept (Sauer: 1925). The term refers to the assemblage of plants, animals, land use patterns and other elements and processes at work on or near the earth's surface at some point in time. Landscape stresses morphology, mappable forms and the cultural and biophysical processes accounting for them.

Recreation itself can be categorized in various ways (Outdoor Recreation Resources Review Commission: 1962; Clawson and Knetsch: 1966). For example, Clawson and Knetsch (1966) have divided recreational areas into three classes; user-oriented, intermediate and resource-oriented. User-oriented areas are usually located in urban and suburban environments and include playgrounds, schoolgrounds, swimming pools, parking lots, and many other facilities. Such facilities must cater to large numbers of people and problems of litter, crowding and noise are frequently acute. Resource-oriented areas generally are much larger and are located more than a few hours from major population centers. Snowmobiles, power boats and associated facilities are excluded or controlled to prevent unwanted changes in vegetation, animals, erosion rates, scenery and other resources which make the area attractive to users in the first place. National parks are prime examples of resource-oriented areas (Nelson and Scace: 1968).

As their name implies, the location and the biophysical and cultural character of intermediate areas place them somewhere along the spectrum between user- and resource-oriented areas. Typically, they are regional or state parks located about half a day's drive from home. They offer diverse recreational opportunities; for example, overnight camping, picnicking, fishing, hiking and downhill skiing. But campsites may be large and perceived as crowded and noisy, especially if all-terrain vehicles, motor boats and other modern recreational tools are used in the area.

The effects of new recreational technologies are not dealt with adequately in classification schemes like that of Clawson and Knetsch. In particular, there is the implication that the biophysical and cultural impact of technology can be nicely demarcated spatially, the intensive areas closest to the cities being subject to the greatest impact and the more distant intermediate and resource-oriented areas to lesser effects. The impact of recreational technology in more remote areas such as Yellowstone or Mammoth Cave National Parks is obscured by such a classification system. In this context, other researchers have made a general distinction between facilities-oriented and non-facilities-oriented types of recreation (Nelson: 1970). In the latter category are activities such as hiking, photography, canoeing, backpacking and other pursuits, where little equipment is required and the effects of technology are relatively limited. Facilities-oriented recreation includes snowmobiling, skiing, and other activities which require trails and roads, parking lots, ski tows, motels, gas stations, and other facilities which can cause much change in ecosystem or landscape.

LAND FOR RECREATION

In recent years there has been a dramatic increase in demand for outdoor recreation facilities. This, together with increasing pressure on land resources resulting from population growth and suburbanization, has created new values for reservoirs, scenic areas and wildernesses and stimulated attempts to identify areas with high value for recreation and related conservation uses. These systematic approaches to identifying potential recreation areas, for example, include the scenic corridors and nodes of Lewis (1963), the overlays of physical and social characteristics of McHarg (1971) and Hills' (1966) capability approach, utilizing physical elements, particularly soils and landforms (Belknap and Fustado: 1967). In addition, efforts to measure more intangible factors such as the quality of scenery or the uniqueness of an area have met with some success (Leopold: 1969; Linton: 1968).

Most of these methods, however, have been developed for use outside the cities. Indeed, historically, recreation has always had a low priority in urban areas. Little effort appears to have been made to provide a variety of recreation areas in or around urban centers. Landscape architects such as Capability Brown rose to prominence in the eighteenth and nineteenth centuries by designing gardens and parks for private rural estates in England and on the continent (Johnson: 1971; Shepard: 1967). Early industrial cities such as Manchester, Birmingham, and Edinburgh had little more than paths and roads for recreation, these cities of the industrial revolution being devoted to the factory and to commerce. Even in Philadelphia, New York and other New World urban centers about 1800, little formal allocation of land was made for recreation (Huth: 1972; Nash: 1967). On the other hand, these towns were small and many citizens found recreation along the boulevards, the canals, and in nearby rural areas. In the early nineteenth century landscaped cemeteries were introduced and their lawns and shrubbery became a focus for walks, picnics and other activities. In New York at this time, prominent architects such as Frederic Law Olmsted worked for the establishment of Central Park against opposition from commercial and other interests. We know little, however, about the historical development of such public recreation areas in most North American cities and would benefit from studies aimed at a better understanding of their establishment and development.

How many cities have recreational and park histories similar to that of Calgary, for example? In the early 1900's a European architect, Mawson, was invited to visit a number of expanding urban centers in Western Canada. His task was to offer advice on future urban form and function. For downtown Calgary he proposed a land use plan far different from the present concentration of commercial, financial and other high rise structures. The flood plain of the nearby Bow River was to be left largely free of development. Wide boulevards and small parks were to be interspersed in the downtown area so as to provide an attractive townscape and ample recreational opportunities. What forces came into play to cancel this plan? What forces brought encroachments on many of the parks established in Calgary through the years?

The problems of not only acquiring recreation space in urban areas but also of maintaining such land as open space are severe (Little: 1969). In the last three decades, a number of attempts have been made to formulate open space standards designed to ensure a degree of access to recreational areas to all residents of an urban area. However, no uniformly accepted standards have appeared, in part because of difficulty in developing accurate social, psychological, or other measures of space needs which vary with individual, group and cultural differences (Hall: 1966). It is unlikely that these difficulties will be resolved. Moreover, as Clawson and Knetsch (1966) have bluntly indicated, the amount of available open space depends upon the amount of money people are prepared to invest in recreation and related land use. As cities face ever increasing financial problems, the proportion of budgets devoted to recreation and park provision cannot be expected to rise sharply. It is therefore unlikely that many cities will reach the ideal standards that they have set for themselves (Butler: 1971; Lanzen: 1972). Furthermore, achieving a certain level of open space per head of population does not guarantee that all residents will have equal opportunity to reach or use recreational areas (Conservation Foundation: 1972). Downtown core areas of most major cities are deficient in open space and recreational facilities, a factor which contributes in no small way to the general problem of social unrest evident in many cities today (Muller: 1970). A re-examination of standards, together with studies of the development, character and distribution of urban open space would clarify the situation for both the public and the politicians and help make improvements possible.

Far more is known about the development of land for recreation and related uses in rural areas. Here the idea of the park seems to have found its most fertile ground (Shepard: 1967). Thousands of years before the birth of Christ, rulers and nobles in Mesopotamia established large areas amid the grasslands and savannas of the flood plains and foothills where they could camp and tent, escaping the heat and unpleasantness of summer. Vegetation and animals such as deer and tigers were protected in these parks for hunting. Alexander the Great and other Europeans are said to have found such parks attractive and to have taken the idea back to Greece and the Mediterranean, although it apparently manifested itself less frequently than various religious shrines which typically enclosed small areas of trees and rocks. Whatever their antecedents, gardens were also an integral part of the Greek and Roman landscape. Here the emphasis was not on grassy pastoral savannas or parks but on the detailed design and arrangement of terraces, rocks, and plants. In the eighteenth century, large formal gardens of this type were found in central Europe, Versailles being the outstanding example.

European artists of the seventeenth and eighteenth centuries painted images of their ideal landscape, a kind of savanna with scattered forests, grassy swards, trees, antlered deer, sheep and shepherds, as well as crumbling castles and ruins, evidence of an emerging interest in antiquity. This landscape, and the idea of the garden, seem to have blended into the scattered trees, forest copses, extensive lawns, and herds of deer characteristic of the great English estate parks of the eighteenth and nineteenth centuries.

Shepard (1967), Huth (1972) and Nash (1967) have written at length on the history of American ideas about nature, parks, wilderness and recreation. Although not always in agreement, the point is generally made that in the early nineteenth century Americans sought a cultural status equal to that of Europe. Little opportunity existed for competition with Old World cities or art. However, this "search," together with the emerging interest in antiquity, led to renewed emphasis on the natural landscape. In America, such artists, poets and writers as William Cullen Bryant, Thomas Cole, James Fenimore Cooper, and George Catlin, slowly developed the theme of "wilderness." The uniformity of their view of such a landscape is open to question, but their attitudes seem to have been influenced at least in part by the concept of the English park or tame savanna. Indeed, many Americans had been exposed to this ideal while travelling in Europe. Thus in Catlin's early 1830's call for the preservation of a large part of the American Great Plains, for example, there appears to be little of English park thought; yet the antecedents of Catlin's views are still largely European. His image is a romantic one, of a region where a Blackfoot or a Crow Indian might be seen "in his classic attire, galloping his wild horse . . . amid the fleeting herds of elk and buffaloes. What a beautiful and thrilling specimen for America to preserve and hold up to the views of her refined citizens and the world, in future ages. A nation's Park containing man and beast, in all the wild and freshness of their nature's beauty" (Catlin: 1841, pp. 261-262). It is note-worthy, too, that men such as Catlin definitely perceived the native people as part of the wilderness landscape, an idea that failed to take hold as the concept of wilderness evolved to the point where today it often seems devoid of any sign of man.

DEVELOPMENT OF NATIONAL PARKS

By about the middle of the nineteenth century at least three basic threads had emerged which led to the establishment of national parks and similar reserves. These threads can be described as an interest, first, in the preservation and protection of nature, wilderness, and resources; second, in planning for the recreational and aesthetic needs of the people; and, third, in income from businesses associated with recreation and tourism.

American appreciation for nature, wilderness, and outdoor experiences, was honed in the 1840's and 1850's by men such as Thoreau (1960). This coincided with and was reinforced by a growing concern over deforestation, over-grazing, and other effects of settlement on potential resources. George Perkins Marsh synthesized much of this thought in his classic work *Man and Nature; or, Physical Geography as Modified by Human Action*, published in 1864. Marsh warned Americans of the need for better land management. His book was republished a number of times and appears to have had considerable influence on educators, administrators, politicians, and the public. His work preceded establishment of the Forestry Bureau and other government management agencies later in the century. It appears to have been a basic force for the development of what has been called the utilitarian concept of conservation, as exemplified later by Gifford Pinchot and others.

The interest of architects and planners in preserving scenic landscapes, as well as in recreational planning and design, led to the establishment of the first great rural park in the United States, Yosemite, in 1862. Prominent among the workers for this park was Frederic Law Olmsted who left New York in part because of problems arising from the conflict over Central Park. He and his colleagues seem to have seen the Yosemite area in the context of the English park idea; but they and the men who later pushed for the establishment of a Yellowstone National Park were also influenced by scientific considerations.

As a result of the work and thought of Darwin (1859), Wallace (1962) and others, important new perceptions of the landscape arose in the middle and latter part of the nineteenth century. The ideas of evolution and uniformitarian-ism were advanced and students of geology and biology began to make great progress in interpreting the earth and its history. People slowly began to perceive landscape not as static, intricate, cosmic ruins created by an unfathomable god, but as intellectually attractive, with dynamic structures and landforms. In the 1850's the painter Ayres portrayed Yosemite with massive, geologically feature-less walls, enclosing a valley floor done in the English park image with extensive grassland and savanna, a camp fire, smoke, men and quietly grazing horses (Ewers: 1965). In contrast, the work of early Yellowstone artists such as Moran, whose portraits derived from his visit to the park with the Hayden Expedition of

1871, reflect devoted attention to geological detail. Bedding planes, joint systems, travertine terraces, weathered canyons, are all shown, albeit somewhat extravagantly. It was work like this which helped persuade Congress to create Yellowstone Park in 1872 and which led to the government purchase of Moran's Yellowstone Falls canvas for $10,000.

In his outstanding work, *Man in Landscape*, Paul Shepard (1967) has taken pains to develop the idea that the English park and paradise image was important in both Yosemite and Yellowstone as well as other early American parks. The scattered trees, winding streams, grass and glades resembled the estate grounds, landscaped to blend into the rural countryside. "No artificial arrangements of trees could have been more perfect" (Shepard: 1967, p. 253). The landscape also evoked biblical, religious and spiritual thought. It made men feel small in the presence of God's great works, helpless "to even comprehend the mighty architecture of nature . . ." (Shepard: 1967, p. 252). But Shepard also lays much stress on the importance of geology. The Washburn-Langford Expedition members of 1870, whose work led to the establishment of the Yellowstone Park, observed rock formations that were "geologically novel and architecturally suggestive." Their resemblance to buildings provoked thoughts of "ruins." As a result, to quote Shepard, the Washburn-Langford party responded to the Yellowstone area (Shepard: 1967, pp. 248-49):

> with all the momentum of American tourists unleashed in Rome or in the Rhineland. While Hudson Valley aristocrats were copying old Gothic or wishing that they could import Scottish castles intact, Langford, Hedges, and Doane were discovering an unchartered heritage of castles, fortresses, and ramparts already in the American landscape. Minarets, water towers, turrets, lined the canyon of the Yellowstone. . . . [The geysers were perceived as fountains and the terraced hot springs as] exactly the kind of adjunct that one might expect in a Villa garden.

These cultural or allegorical aspects were, however, not the only stimulus provided by the geology. The new scientific ideas had their effect as well. The rocks were thought of in terms of geologic or geomorphic process. "Looking out from Mount Washburn, Doane grasped at once that the whole plateau was a complex volcano" (Shepard: 1967, p. 250). Response to the "wonders" of the area did not, of course, require scientific training; Niagara Falls, the "Mecca" of many early American and European tourists, found its counterpart in the falls and canyons of Yellowstone.

Other significant forces were at work in the United States and Canada in the last half of the nineteenth century, notably an interest in deriving income from the commerce associated with recreation, national parks, and similar public reserves. Lengthy and expensive transcontinental railroads were constructed in western North America in the middle to late 1800's. These routes traversed vast areas with low population, yielding little income to the companies which searched vigorously for resources that would raise funds from "empty areas." The companies were interested not only in the mining of gold, copper, coal and other commodities, in lumbering and other extractive industries, but also in recreation and tourism based on scenery, the mountains, the forests, and the hot springs. When parks such as Yellowstone and Banff began to develop in the last decades of the nineteenth century, the railroads built lines and constructed hotels and other facilities in and near them (Ise: 1961; Nelson: 1970).

Interest in the first Canadian national park at Banff began with the discovery of hot springs in the 1880's (Brown: 1970; Byrne: 1968; Scace: 1968). These springs were seen as offering great recreational and health advantages and were included within a ten square mile public reserve established in 1885. The federal government and the Canadian Pacific Railroad entered a kind of partnership designed to develop the area and attract visitors to the west. There was, of course, some interest in landscape or environmental protection, but in the early stages it seems to have been largely geological rather than biological in orientation. As appreciation of the scenery and the landscape grew, so did the park. By about 1900 the government had extended the boundaries to the Rocky Mountain foothills. Unlike the general policy in the United States, townsites were permitted in the national parks. Indeed, contrary to popular opinion, Banff townsite, which now exceeds 4,000 people, is not a prenational park historical anachronism which developed from an early railroad siding, but a planned community, a spa in the European tradition, providing amenities to visitors taking the hot baths or enjoying the mountains.

The introduction of the automobile brought a series of remarkable and largely unforeseen changes in the parks after about 1910. Visitors from Los Angeles, San Francisco and other centers, for example, began to drive in ever increasing numbers to Yosemite. Road networks developed as well as visitor service areas. More and more entrepreneurs began to operate in the parks. Governments were interested in promoting commerce and assisted by subsidizing many services, including water supply facilities, garbage disposal, police, and the like (Ise: 1961; Nelson: 1970). The pronounced seasonal nature of the tourist trade and other uncertainties also encouraged the governments of both Canada and the United States to grant monopolies on restaurant, touring, and other operations in the park. Entrepreneurs were protected from competition and expected to maintain a high level of service during the tenure of their lease. These businessmen have developed a strong interest in and influence on park policy which is maintained to this day (Conservation Foundation: 1972). The desire to attract the masses of recreationists in the post war years was particularly strong, and manifests itself in large scale provision of facilities in many recreational areas. As the recreationist began to travel considerable distances, so grew the desire to transport with him an ever increasing array of recreational equipment, from portable televisions to trail bikes. The result has been that recreation facilities in some areas now cater to forms of recreation considerably divorced from their physical surroundings. Indeed the facilities themselves often become the major attraction rather than the environment in which they are found. Campsites in some national parks have become virtual towns under canvas with attendant social and criminal problems because of the desire to cater to the large numbers of urban recreationists.

In early decades then, the commercial aspects of the national parks were emphasized, pioneering activities were widespread, and the ideas of the preservationist school played a relatively minor role. Many years after its establishment in 1872, Yellowstone National Park was the scene of much hunting and trapping (Chittenden: 1964). Visitors to the parks were careless, and forest fires and destruction of trees and wildlife habitat common. A similar state of affairs existed in Canadian national parks such as Banff and Jasper in Alberta, and Glacier in British Columbia (Byrne: 1968; Nelson and Byrne: 1966). Dynamite was employed to obtain large quantities of fish from streams and lakes. Timber berths were allocated and an unknown amount of cutting occurred. Prospectors and surveyors deliberately or carelessly burned the parks. Railroad construction and operation caused many fires. Mining also was carried out in some parks, certain park superintendents in Banff, for example, seeing nothing paradoxical in the growth of coal mining towns within park boundaries.

These activities and their effects on vegetation succession and character, wildlife, and other aspects of the landscape, have frequently been ignored by the many parks officials interested in establishing the idea of park landscapes as extensive tracts of relatively undisturbed wilderness—"much as it was when the white man first saw it."

Similarly, the effects of man on vegetation and other landscape patterns are often inadequately considered in making zoning or other land use decisions in recreational reserves. Thus, climax vegetation reflecting relatively little sign of human impact can be considered as a more likely candidate for wilderness zoning than an earlier successional stage whose status owes much to human interference through burning or other processes. However, such landscape characteristics and differences should be considered within the appropriate cultural and physical setting. Thus there is a controversy over whether eastern American forests, whose species composition and successional status have been changed considerably by Caucasians in the last few hundred years, should be designated as wilderness under the Wilderness Act of 1964. Some perceive them as not having the "quality" commensurate with landscapes in the west which were set aside earlier under this Act. Indeed, the idea of "wilderness quality" has become the focal point of a struggle among politicians and government officials attempting to control large tracts of eastern wildland.

The reaction against early pioneering activities and their effects on land and life began earlier in the United States than in Canada and other countries. The preservationist school of thought really began to gather strength in the late 1890's and early 1900's (Nash: 1967; Burton and Kates: 1965). The focal point was Yosemite where proposals were made to construct a dam and reservoir in the Hetch Hetchy Valley in order to provide water for the city of San Francisco. The fight against the project was led by John Muir. He had already inveighed against grazing within the boundaries of the park, being especially opposed to sheep, "locusts" which preyed on the park (Ise: 1961; Nash: 1967). Muir's strong speeches and writing conveyed an image of wilderness that transcended the concepts of the ruin, the garden, the English Park or the savanna. All kinds of landscapes—forests, alpine meadows, glaciated landscapes, tundra—were seen as worthy of protection from economic exploitation in the wild state.

In the Hetch Hetchy affair Muir entered into conflict with Gifford Pinchot and the utilitarian school of conservation (Nash: 1967). By about 1900, concern over the rate of resource destruction and depletion had led to a political conservation movement headed by Theodore Roosevelt. In this movement the major concern was for "wise use," sustained yield and "multiple use management." Proponents of such utilitarian thinking generally were not sympathetic to preservationist ideas. These were seen as leading to a locking up of trees, animals and minerals which could not then be used by man. They would age, decay, and be "wasted." Pinchot and others supported the construction of the Hetch Hetchy Reservoir and Muir and his associates eventually lost the fight. But the defeat became a hallmark for the wilderness thinkers. After 1910 they began to form associations such as the Sierra Club which have fought for preservation ever since.

Although relatively little has been written about the attitudes of early Canadians towards particular types of landscape, it is only in the last two decades that a strong preservationist movement has emerged (Brown: 1970; Nash: 1968b). Reaction to the hunting, mining and other economic and pioneering activities of the late nineteenth and early twentieth century, for example, was essentially confined to the provision of some funds and a few park wardens in the early 1900's. A more important change came with the establishment of the Dominion Parks Branch as an overall management unit for the park and forest reserves that had previously been operated as separate units. For years, much of the ensuing thrust for recreation and conservation seems to have come from the administration rather than the public, and perhaps largely from one man, J. B. Harkin (National and Provincial Parks Association of Canada: 1972).

Harkin was appointed first Commissioner of National Parks in 1911, five years before Steven B. Mather assumed a comparable post as Head of the United States National Park Service. In the twenty-five years or so of his tenure, Harkin left a deep imprint on the Canadian landscape. He appears to have been a devotee of the idea and value of wilderness, perhaps as a result of contact with American ideas. He was interested in developing the parks for recreation, in part because of a strong belief in this activity, and in part because as a pragmatic and effective administrator, he saw that this activity would provide the interest, support and funds needed to develop a Canadian National Park system. In the period from about 1911 to 1940, Harkin and his colleagues slowly promoted the preservation and protection of park landscapes, particularly in the biological sense.

As in the United States, strict fire control practices were introduced and continue to the present, with the result that much burned and denuded forest has regenerated. The protection of animals was encouraged, though not uniformly. Elk and other ungulates were perceived as "nice" or desirable animals and the predators as pests, dangerous to man and beast. Elk, deer, sheep and other wildlife populations, of course, had been seriously reduced in many parks in North America by 1910 (Banfield: 1958; Noble: 1972; Ise: 1961). Elk were reintroduced into the Banff Park in 1917 from Yellowstone and multiplied vigorously in the next twenty years, presumably due to the combined effects of fire and predator control, to the regrowth of poplar, willow and other forage, and to other changes. By the 1940's the elk were considered to be over-grazing the range and control programs were introduced which continue to the present (Clarke: 1942; Cowan: 1943). Today the wolf is gone from most North American parks outside the north. The grizzly was eliminated from much of its western range by the late nineteenth and early twentieth centuries. It has, however, been protected in northern U.S. and Canadian Parks such as Glacier in Montana and Banff in Canada. During the 1930's and 1940's many of the bears began to change their behavior as a result of human interference; for example, garbage or spoil around campsites, trails and townsites has become a major source of food (Herrero: 1972). With the increase in bears and in hikers since World War II, encounters between man and the bear have gone up rather sharply, although the number of incidents and injuries have been lower in Canadian than in United States parks such as Yellowstone or Glacier. As a result of these encounters both Canadian and U.S. authorities are introducing measures designed to control garbage and litter disposal and to make the animal more self-reliant, thereby lowering the hazard to humans and reducing pressure to eliminate grizzly populations in heavily used parks.

PUBLIC POLICY AND THE MANAGEMENT OF NATIONAL PARKS IN THE MID-TWENTIETH CENTURY

Zoning and Land Use Controls

The growing demand for outdoor recreation facilities has created new management problems for park administrators. Attempts to introduce zoning and other land use controls in public reserves, for example, is a reflection of the discontinuous distribution of problems caused by changes in recreation demand as well, of course, as by the growing number of visitors. The Canadian National and Historic Parks Branch is now using a five part zoning system. Recreational areas are zoned for particular activities and designated as: (1) intensive; (2) general outdoor recreation; (3) natural environment; (4) wilderness recreation; or (5) special (cultural and ecological) areas (National and Historic Parks Branch: 1971). In intensive areas, such as Banff townsite in Banff National Park, services and facilities of all kinds are permitted. Roads, campsites, and associated facilities are allowed in general outdoor recreation zones. Natural environment areas are often described as buffers between the general outdoor recreation and the wilderness zones. Ideally, little more than trails or rudimentary wooden shelters are permitted in the wilderness areas. Even less development may be allowed in special zones where stress is on the protection of relatively unique or sensitive features such as Bighorn sheep range or archaeological sites. The United States, New Zealand, and other countries use zoning arrangements quite similar to that developed in Canada.

However, zoning and land use controls in recreation areas suffer from a common problem (Doolittle: 1971). How are the types and levels of land use in an area to be defined and established? Or, to phrase the problem differently, how do we determine the carrying capacity of a zone or a park? The presence of too many people or of certain types of activities or machines such as snowmobiles, can alter vegetation and wildlife associations, as well as detract from recreational enjoyment in other ways. How can we measure and determine whether a change in vegetation is significant? Some biologists speak of irreversible or irretrievable changes in the ecosystem as a result of human activities (Wagar: 1964). What does this mean in terms of recovery time and character? Will the system never return to something close to its predisturbance condition or will this occur only in forty or fifty or two hundred years? How can one measure and determine when people's enjoyment has decreased significantly as a result of crowding, noise or some other process (Brougham: 1969)? How many people must share this perception before management controls are introduced? Relatively few studies have been carried out on such problems.

The classic research of Lucas in the Boundary Waters Canoe Area of northern Minnesota still remains a most instructive example of perceptual differences among users and the relevance of these differences to zoning (Lucas: 1962).

Apart from logging, the main activity in the forests, streams and lakes of the Boundary Waters Canoe Area is recreation, including canoeing, motor boating, and camping. Lucas' analysis revealed significant differences in the way in which the various types of users defined and delimited "wilderness." He interviewed canoeists, motor boaters and others in various parts of the area and concluded that, from a perceptual standpoint, there were two wildernesses, that of the canoeist and that of the motor boater. The canoeist's wilderness was the most sensitive, being reduced by road construction, encounters with motors, and similar changes. Remoteness and signs of logging were not as important influences on wilderness. As a result of his study, Lucas suggested that in order to conserve the canoeist's wilderness, the Forest Service should zone the Boundary Waters Canoe Area into the two perceived wildernesses and regulate the number of users in each zone.

More research is required on the general problem of recreational activities and technology and their relationship to user perceptions, zoning concepts, management policies, and environmental change. Case studies of conflict situations would be useful as would perception and environmental impact studies. Some significant work on motorized recreation vehicles and their impact is now available (Butler *et al.*: 1972; Baldwin: 1970; Chubb: 1971). Some relevant research in similar directions has been undertaken by the Nature Conservancy in Great Britain and by the Forest Service in the United States (Duffy: 1967; Nature Conservancy: 1968).

Recreation Systems

In addition to zoning, recreational pressures can be reduced by the development of an integrated recreation system (Hart: 1966). Such a complex of urban, regional, state and national parks where, at least in theory, different volumes and types of recreational activity are allowed, has long been advocated for the United States. In recent years the National Park Service has been attempting to develop such a system in the United States (National Park Service: 1968) and the resulting array of recreation areas range from small urban and historic parks to national parks exceeding two thousand square miles. Included in the National Park Service System are the Great Arch in St. Louis, the Gettysburg battlefield and other military monuments, canals and railroads such as the Chesapeake and Ohio, wild and scenic areas such as parts of the Green and the Snake Rivers, marine parks in Florida, national recreation areas such as Fort Peck on the Missouri River, and educational reserves or benchmarks designed to provide environmental education opportunities for students in schools and universities. This national system is further extended through such federal agencies as the Bureau of Outdoor Recreation, the Bureau of Land Management and the Forest Service which manage other general recreational areas as well as wilderness areas.

In the United States, some attempts have been made to integrate the recreational areas managed by different agencies. The outstanding example is the Wilderness Act of 1964, which defines wilderness as essentially a roadless area in which the effects of human activities are transitory (McCloskey and Gilligan: 1969). Areas of 5000 acres or more under federal jurisdiction can be classified as wilderness under the Act and together constitute a national wilderness system. A few areas in the national parks and many areas in the forest reserves and wildlife refuges have been similarly designated and the system is expanding steadily.

Although this wilderness legislation gives a high degree of control over technology, the landscape continues to be affected by the growing numbers of recreationists (Schwartz: 1969). Millions of people are now hiking, backpacking, photohunting, birdwatching, camping, canoeing, and mountain climbing in remote wilderness areas each summer. The tramping of their feet, the accumulation of their litter, and the effect of their presence on wild animals are all bringing often unwanted changes in landscape character and wilderness experience (Ripley: 1962). Such increasing use of back-country is forcing administrators to establish carrying capacities as well as to introduce systems of reservation and rationing. Such controls were employed in three National Parks in the United States during the summer of 1972. The basis for estimating user levels was apparently the experience and wisdom of the administrators.

The foregoing discussion raises the basic problem of how to define wilderness, or, for that matter, landscape goals in general in national parks and similar reserves. In the United States, the Leopold Committee addressed this problem in the early 1960's (Leopold et al.: 1963a, 1963b, 1963c). The Committee recommended that the desirable national park landscape was that extant when the white man came. Although establishing the character of these early landscapes might provide fruitful research opportunities for geographers and ecologists (Gibbons and Heady: 1964), the Leopold Committee recommendation offers some practical difficulties. It is not always easy to re-establish landscape character at the time of the white settlement. In western Canada, for example, Indian trade routes made it possible for the Blackfeet, the Shoshoni, and others to move away from their subsistence, stone-age culture to the commercial hunting of beaver and other animals with iron tools, while the fur trade posts were still hundreds of miles away. A fine temporal division of the Indian and the "white man's" landscape is therefore hard to establish and perhaps not realistic.

Another problem with the Leopold scheme is its scientific and educational restrictiveness. Landscapes other than those existing at the time of white settlement are of equal interest as are the long term evolutionary changes occurring in the environment. Changes in vegetation and wildlife species, in erosion and land forms, have occurred in response to changes in climate and other biophysical processes as well as in response to human activity. In this context, any decision to control or prohibit human activities in national parks and similar reserves can be questioned with regard to indigenous groups whose hunting, burning, and other actions have had a functional place in the ecosystem for centuries. What do we mean by "nature" under these circumstances (Lowenthal: 1959)? Is it not quite arbitrary to decide at what time human agency should be considered "unnatural" and should consequently be controlled?

A final reason for questioning the value of a park policy aiming at the establishment and maintenance of landscapes as they were at the time of arrival of the white man is the lack of enthusiasm such a goal is likely to generate among non-white groups. These peoples are likely to conceive of landscapes that are of much greater historical significance to them.

In the United States and Canada, attempts have been made to deal with the problem of goals through the concepts of era and evolutionary landscapes (National and Historic Parks Branch: 1971). Era landscapes are those where disease, fire, and other processes are managed in order to maintain the land as it was at the time of the fur trader, the rancher, or early gold miner. Evolutionary landscapes are those where no human interference is contemplated and the landscape is allowed to change "naturally," independent of man. Contrary to common opinion, however, such evolutionary landscapes are still being managed by man, who has simply taken the policy decision not to interfere directly in their development.

Relatively few parks or reserves actually seem to be managed as era or evolutionary landscapes. One exception, however, is the Yosemite National Park. Here historical studies have shown that oak savanna and grassland were much more extensive in the lower valley in early Caucasian days, when fire control had not been introduced and when cedar and other trees had not yet established themselves as extensively as today (Gibbons and Heady: 1964). Controlled burning is now being conducted on the valley floor in an attempt to remove the conifers and recreate the savannas and grasslands of old. In Yellowstone National Park, large evolutionary zones have been set aside where grizzly bear, bison, and other animals roam freely. Recreational use is strongly controlled and human interference is minimized. Some roads traverse these areas allowing for sightseeing, but visitors are warned not to venture far from cars at risk of injury. The policy is to let fire, cyclic variations in animal populations, "over-grazing," and other processes run their course, although if such processes occur on a scale large enough to threaten the viability of a particular species or the character of the landscape, control measures would be introduced.

ECONOMIC AND SOCIAL ASPECTS
OF NATIONAL PARKS

The United States National Park Service and other agencies have sponsored studies of the economic value of recreation in the national parks in order to protect them against increasing pressures from lumbering, mining, and commercial uses; to support increased appropriations for the purchase of new park land; and to encourage other nations to establish national parks and comparable reserves. Probably the most ambitious economic impact study is Swanson's (1969) research on the effect of national parks on the entire economy of the United States. He found that in 1967 national parks contributed as much as $6.4 million to the sales of American firms and generated a personal income of $4.7 billion. Travel to the national parks was estimated to have produced $950 million in taxes alone. Swanson also estimated that the annual government appropriations to the national parks generated about 55 times that amount when income was stated as Gross National Product. Swanson concluded that the national parks represent an asset or a resource that few others can eclipse.

Such estimates of park value, however, include many intangible benefits not readily susceptible to economic analysis (Hines: 1969; Coomber and Biswas: 1972). Economists have recognized that there is as yet no satisfactory quantitative measure of the extent to which recreation makes for a more highly developed human being, a more productive worker, or a better citizen (Nelson: 1972; Hayes: 1967; Herr and Associates: 1969; Rajender et al.: 1967; Beyers: 1970). Nor, in addition, does economic analysis have much to say about the values of parks as gene pools from which useful plant and animal hybrids might some day be derived. Some observers also point out that all economic judgments are anthropogenic in orientation (Darling: 1969). They say nothing of values independent of man.

In countries outside the United States and Canada it is the increasing economic returns from recreation and tourism that seem to have encouraged the recent establishment of many national parks or similar reserves. There are exceptions of course. The New Zealand system is an old one, the first national park having been established on Maori sacred land at Tongariro in 1885. While many changes are underway, there has been no large expansion of national parks area in recent years even though the economic value of tourism is strongly recognized in a country heavily dependent on a few agricultural products (Lucas: 1970). On the other hand about 9 percent of the country is in national parks, compared to about 1 percent in Canada, and much land is available to accommodate tourism and related activities.

National parks and similar reserves in the United Kingdom have developed in response to both an increasing local demand for recreation and a desire to encourage tourism, a major earner of foreign exchange. The parks are located on freehold land which has been used for agriculture and other economic purposes for centuries (Johnson: 1971; Hobhouse: 1947). The necessity for this arrangement derives from the fact that very little public or crown land remained in Britain at the time the parks were established under the original National Parks and Access to the Countryside Act of 1949. Furthermore, little, if any, of the national parks landscape can be considered as "natural" or "wild" in the American sense. Park management really means preservation of cultural landscapes as part of the overall scene. Special attention is paid to maintaining the economic viability of communities located within the park boundaries, some of which are quite large. For example, over 25,000 people live in the Peak District National Park (Edwards: 1962). The British national parks now fall under the aegis of the Countryside Act of 1968 which emphasizes conservation and access by the population at large. Easements and stringent land use controls are emphasized to realize these goals (Johnson: 1971). Arrangements also include compensation to landowners for economic opportunities foregone when land is incorporated into the parks. The overall success of the British system should be increased by the decision to develop a new class of regional parks, termed country parks, where the emphasis will be primarily upon meeting the short-term recreation needs of the largely urban population.

Methods similar to those employed in the United Kingdom could certainly be used more extensively in the United States and Canada, where reliance traditionally has been placed on public ownership and outright control of land and development rights, which is an increasingly costly approach. When notices of intent to establish new national parks, such as Point Reyes, California, are made, land prices climb markedly in the designated area at the general public's expense. Other means will have to be found of providing for recreation and conservation of landscapes. The United Kingdom system offers some valuable guides.

It is in the so-called developing countries of Africa and Asia that potentially very large economic returns from tourism appear to have had the greatest impact on the establishment of national parks. Such is the message of Ouma (1970) in his *Evolution of Tourism in East Africa.* In justifying his book, Ouma notes that many publications have appeared on agricultural development but nothing on recreation. Yet since 1948, tourism has ranked one, two and six respectively in Kenya, Uganda, and Tanzania as a source of foreign funds. In Kenya alone, tourism earns more foreign currency than coffee or any other crop.

Ouma's work suggests, however, that the East African national parks derive originally from Western attempts to protect wildlife for recreational, conservational, and scientific purposes. Acts to protect birds, white rhinoceroses, and other declining species were established in the early years of this century under colonial governments. But the funds provided to protect such reserves were inadequate and the institutional arrangements ineffective. Pressures on lions, elephants, and other fauna increased with independence and economic and population growth. Cultivators such as the Kikuyu pressed for more agricultural land which together with the grazing activities of people such as the Masai put increasing pressure on wildlife. With rising incomes in Europe and other western countries, and with the introduction of improved air transport, visitor numbers and hunting and other recreational pressures also began to rise. The importance of wildlife and wild landscape became increasingly apparent as did the threats to these valuable resources.

Most of the national parks in East Africa have been established since the end of the colonial regimes (Ouma: 1970; Harroy: 1971). Nairobi National Park was created in Kenya in 1946 and thirteen other reserves have since been set aside in that country. The largest are Tsavo East and Tsavo West which cover thousands of square miles of mountains, foothills and plains. These are the main reserves for the typical Kenyan fauna, including elephants, black rhinoceroses, lions and leopards, as well as many species of antelope. Today these areas are said to be strictly protected, with no exploitation reportedly allowed except for one isolated mine and the piping of water from the Mzima Springs to Mombasa. However, an unknown amount of poaching goes on in the African Parks, a reflection of the traditional dependence of many peoples on wildlife as sources of meat. Pastoralists also frequently encroach on park lands. Volcanoes National Park, Rwanda, has been described as a strict nature preserve, but Tutsia pastoralists reportedly graze cattle on the upper mountain slopes and cultivators have invaded the park fringes. Similar problems in Tanzania have resulted in the removal of the Ngorongoro Crater from the fauna-rich Serenegeti National Park. Wildlife in the crater area is, however, still in a conservation unit and subject to some protective measures.

Like those in other developing countries, many of the East African Parks and reserves are small and it is difficult to maintain landscape character with growing recreational use. On the other hand, in Kenya, Tanzania, and other countries, an increasing array of different types of public and private reserves, not unlike those in the United States, are being set aside to serve recreationists and to protect landscape to varying degrees (Myers: 1972).

Ouma (1970) devotes some space in his book to the social effects of recreational developments. As a promoter of tourism, he recommends changes in education, occupations, investment patterns, language, dress and other attributes in order to stimulate foreign visits and expenditures in East Africa. In doing so, however, he is aware of the possible effects on the basic way of life of the people. Ouma encourages his countrymen to try to maintain the important aspects of their culture, although he is not too helpful in saying how this should be done. The impact of many members of a foreign culture on indigenous host populations is, of course, a major problem, particularly for those concerned about disappearing cultures and values and the diminishing richness and variety of the human tapestry. Such cultural changes may also destroy the very things that many tourists come to see.

In parts of North America, the Caribbean and Africa, people have been relocated to allow visitors access to certain areas or to provide labor for construction or for service industries (Curry-Lindahl: 1972; Nelson and Scace: 1968). Many changes in tastes and styles have occurred, from a liking for Coca-Cola to miniskirts, often followed by sanctions against such trends. The barring of certain traditional activities or of access to areas traditionally used for fishing or hunting, can cause much resentment, hindering rather than fostering the greater intercultural understanding that tourism is sometimes said to promote.

CONCLUSION

Recreation has had a profound effect on environment. It has led to the establishment of many national parks and related reserves in the United States, Canada, and elsewhere. Under evolving human management, these reserves have led to the protection and preservation of individual life and land forms. The reserves have also contributed to the creation of a variety of new cultural landscapes, ranging from the "wilderness" of Jasper, Canada, or Fiordland, New Zealand, through the pastoral vistas of the English Peak District to urbanized service centers and townsites such as Banff. More than a thousand national parks and similar reserves now exist throughout the world (Harroy: 1971).

The future role of such parks and reserves in the preservation of species and creation of new cultural landscapes is, however, clouded by the growth of tourism. In the past, many ecologists and other scientists supported tourism in national parks because it not only made them appear useful to the public but also provided the income needed to operate the parks and to protect the flora, fauna, and features of scientific value. The opinion was also widely held that exposure to nature in the parks would prompt tourists to appreciate and support such reserves. But tourism is now increasingly recognized as a commercial and technical operation that brings major physical and social changes comparable to those of other western industries. It involves large numbers of people; the more there are the higher the profits, but the greater its spatial impact. Protected species such as the grizzly are increasingly threatened as they become "hazards" for the growing number of visitors. The technological load of tourism is high; roads, hotels, and other equipment bring deep changes in landscape and way of life.

The traditional view of tourism as a handmaiden for parks and conservation is therefore being increasingly questioned. The result undoubtedly will be a new system involving some of the arrangements discussed in this paper. These will have an as yet unforeseen impact on landscapes, ecosystems and environments around the world. Furthermore, the problems of estimating future patterns and impact are made even more difficult by growing energy problems in the United States and other countries whose citizens provide most of the recreation traffic. If energy problems do bring sharp increases in travel costs then the pressure for more facilities and more use of the parks could lessen substantially as would their promise as economic enterprises. In such circumstances, the thrust for more recreational opportunity of all kinds in and near the cities would gather additional strength.

SOURCES

A vast amount of literature is, of course, available on recreation, national parks, public land and environment, of which we are able to list only certain major items. A number of periodicals can and should be consulted regularly by those interested in this field. Some of these are noted in this list of sources. Others are the *Journal of Leisure Research, Journal of Applied Ecology, Regional Studies, Annals of the Association of American Geographers,* the *Journal of Environmental Education, Geographical Journal, The Ecologist, Sierra Club Bulletin, National Parks Magazine, The Living Wilderness, Audubon Magazine,* and *Nature Canada.* No maps of park systems or data on visitors have been included in this chapter because of the ease with which this information can be found in the sources and because of the rapidity with which such information becomes outdated. Maps of the United States Public Land system, the Canadian National Parks, the East African public reserves, the New

Zealand national parks and the United Kingdom national parks are in the *National Atlas of the United States*, *Park News* (April, 1972), Ouma (1970), Lucas (1970) and Johnson (1971), respectively. Records of hearings on national parks and related matters, master plans, current visitor data and other information are available from Congress or other legislative bodies and from relevant government departments such as the National Park Service or the Bureau of Outdoor Recreation. Master plans contain many useful resources and other maps of value for the teacher. Those interested in keeping up to date on recreational and related matters on a week to week basis can consult such sources as *Conservation Report*, National Wildlife Federation (1412 Sixteenth Street, N.W., Washington, D.C. 20036), *The Conservation Foundation Letter* (1717 Massachusetts Ave., N.W., Washington, D.C. 20036) and *S.F.I. Bulletin*, Sport Fishing Institute (608-13th St., N.W., Washington, D.C. 20005). A useful Canadian source is *Man and Resources*, Canadian Council of Resource and Environmental Ministers, 1170 Beaver Hall Square, Montreal 111, Quebec.

REFERENCES

Baldwin, M. F., 1970, *The Off the Road Vehicle and Environmental Quality*. Washington, D.C.: Conservation Foundation.

Banfield, W. A. F., 1958, *Mammals of Banff National Park, Alberta*. National Museum of Canada, Bulletin 159, Ottawa: Queens Printer.

Belknap, R. K. and J. G. Fustado (eds.), 1967, *Three Approaches to Resource Analysis*. Washington, D.C.: Conservation Foundation.

Beyers, W. B., 1970, *An Economic Impact Study of Mt. Rainier and Olympic National Parks*. Seattle: Department of Geography, University of Washington.

Brougham, J. E., 1969, "An Evaluation of the Impact of Crowding Upon the Quality of the Recreation Experience." Unpublished M.A. Thesis, University of Western Ontario.

Brown, R. C., 1970, "The Doctrine of Usefulness: Natural Resource and National Parks Policy in Canada, 1887-1914," in J.G. Nelson (ed.), *Canadian Parks in Perspective*. Montreal: Harvest House, pp. 46-62.

Burton, Ian and R. W. Kates (eds.), 1965, *Readings in Resource Management and Conservation*. Chicago: University of Chicago Press.

Butler, R. W., 1971, *London Parks—Adequacy Study*. London: Department of Geography, University of Western Ontario.

Butler, R. W., P. S. Elder, H. N. Janish, and B. M. Petrie (eds.), 1972, *Proceedings of Symposium on Snowmobiles and All Terrain Vehicles*. London: Faculty of Law, University of Western Ontario.

Byrne, A. R., 1968, *Man and Landscape Change in the Banff National Park Area Before 1911*, Studies in Land Use History and Landscape Change, National Park Series, No. 1. Calgary: University of Calgary Press.

Catlin, G., 1841, *Letters and Notes on the Manners, Customs and Conditions of the North American Indians*. New York: Wiley and Putman.

Chittenden, H. M., 1964, *The Yellowstone National Park*, (edited and with an introduction by R. A. Bartlett). Norman: University of Oklahoma Press.

Chubb, M. (ed.), 1971, *Proceedings of Snowmobile and Off the Road Vehicle Symposium*. East Lansing: Michigan State University.

Clarke, C. D. H., 1942, *Wildlife Investigations in Banff and Jasper National Parks, 1942*. Ottawa: Canada National Parks Bureau.

Clawson, M. and J. Knetsch, 1966, *Economics of Outdoor Recreation*. Baltimore: Johns Hopkins Press.

Conservation Foundation, 1972, *National Parks for the Future*. Washington, D.C.: Conservation Foundation.

Coomber, N. H. and A. K. Biswas, 1972, *Evaluation of Environmental Intangibles*. Ottawa: Environment Canada.

Cowan, I. M., 1943, *Report on Game Conditions in Banff, Jasper and Kootenay National Park, 1943*. Ottawa: Canada National Parks Bureau.

Curry-Lindahl, K., 1972, "Some Comments on National Parks and Surrounding Human Populations in Africa," in R. V. Osten (ed.), *World National Parks—Progress and Opportunities*. Brussels: Hayez, pp. 370-71.

Darling, F. F., 1969, *Wilderness and Plenty*. London: Ballantine.

Darwin, Charles, 1859, *On the Origin of Species by Means of Natural Selection.* London: Murray.

Doolittle, W. T. (ed.), 1971, *Recreation Symposium Proceedings.* Upper Darby, Pa.: U.S. Forest Service.

Duffy, E. (ed.), 1967, *Biotic Effects of Public Pressures on the Environment.* London: Nature Conservancy.

Edwards, R. C., 1962, *The Peak District.* London: Collins.

Ewers, J. C., 1965, *Early Artists of the Old West.* Garden City, New York: Doubleday and Co.

Gibbons, R. P. and H. F. Heady, 1964, *The Influence of Modern Man on the Vegetation of Yosemite Valley.* Berkeley: Division of Agriculture Science, University of California.

Hall, E. T., 1966, *The Hidden Dimension.* Garden City, New York: Doubleday.

Harroy, J. P. (ed.), 1971, *United Nations List of National Parks and Equivalent Reserves.* Brussels: International Union for the Conservation of Nature and Natural Resources.

Hart, W. J., 1966, *A Systems Approach to Park Planning.* Morges: International Union for the Conservation of Nature and Natural Resources.

Hayes, D. R., 1967, *An Economic Study of Dare County, North Carolina.* Raleigh, North Carolina: North Carolina State University.

Herrero, S. (ed.), 1972, *Bears: Their Biology and Management.* Morges: International Union for the Conservation of Nature and Natural Resources.

Herr and Associates, 1969, *Cape Cod National Seashore: Economic Impact Study.* Final Report prepared for the U.S. Department of the Interior: National Parks Branch. Boston, Mass.

Hills, G. A., 1966, *The Ecological Basis for Land Use Planning Research Branch.* Toronto, Canada: Ontario Department of Lands and Forests.

Hines, L. G., 1969, "Wilderness, Economic Choice, Values, and the Androscoggin," in M. E. McCloskey and J. P. Gilligan (eds.), *Wilderness and the Quality of Life.* San Francisco: Sierra Club, pp. 74-80.

Hobhouse, A., 1947, *Report of the National Parks Committee* (England and Wales), Ministry of Town and Country Planning. London: H.M.S.O.

Huth, H., 1972, *Nature and the American.* Lincoln: University of Nebraska Press.

Ise, J., 1961, *Our National Park Policy: A Critical History.* Baltimore: Johns Hopkins Press.

Johnson, W. A., 1971, *Public Parks on Private Land in England and Wales.* London: Johns Hopkins Press.

Lanzen, J., 1972, *Edmonton Parks and Recreation Master Plan, 1970-1980.* City of Edmonton.

Leopold, A. S. *et al.*, 1963a, "Wildlife Management in the National Parks," *Sierra Club Bulletin*, Vol. 48, pp. 4-11.

＿＿＿, 1963b, *Report of the Advisory Board on Wildlife Management.* Washington, D.C.: United States Park Service.

＿＿＿, 1963c, *A Report by the Advisory Committee to the National Park Service on Research.* Washington, D.C.: National Academy of Sciences.

Leopold, L. B., 1969, "Landscape Esthetics: How to Quantify the Scenics of a River Valley," *Natural History*, Vol. 45, pp. 36-45.

Lewis, P. H., 1963, *Landscape Development, Lake Superior South Shore Area.* Madison, Wisconsin: Wisconsin Department of Resource Development.

Linton, D. L., 1968, "The Assessment of Scenery as a Natural Resource," *Scottish Geographical Magazine*, Vol. 84, pp. 219-38.

Little, C. E., 1969, *Challenge of the Land.* New York: Pergamon Press.

Lowenthal, D., 1966, "Assumptions Behind the Public Attitudes," in H. Jarrett (ed.), *Environmental Quality in a Growing Economy.* Baltimore: Johns Hopkins Press, pp. 127-47.

＿＿＿, 1959, "The American Creed of Nature as Virtue," *Landscape*, Vol. 9, pp. 24-25.

Lucas, P. H. C., 1970, *Conserving New Zealand's Heritage.* Wellington: Government Printing Office.

Lucas, R. C., 1962, *The Quetico-Superior Area: Recreational Use in Relation to Capacity.* Unpublished Ph.D. Thesis, University of Minnesota.

Marsh, G. P., 1864, *Man and Nature; or, Physical Geography as Modified by Human Action.* New York: Scribner.

McCloskey, M. E. and J. P. Gilligan (eds.), 1969, *Wilderness and the Quality of Life.* San Francisco: Sierra Club.

McHarg, I., 1971, *Design with Nature.* Philadelphia: Falcon Press.

Mesthene, E., 1970, *Technological Change: The Impact on Man and Society.* New York: New American Library.

Muller, H. J., 1970, *The Children of Frankenstein: A Primer on Modern Technology and Human Values.* Bloomington: Indiana University Press.

Mumford, L., 1966, *The Story of Utopias.* New York: Viking Press.

Myers, N., 1972, "National Parks in Savannah Africa," *Science*, Vol. 178, pp. 1255-63.

Nash, R. (ed.), 1968*a*, *The American Environment.* Reading, Mass.: Addison Wesley.

———, 1968*b*, "Wilderness and Man in North America," in J. G. Nelson and R. C. Scace (eds.), *The Canadian National Parks: Today and Tomorrow.* Calgary: University of Calgary Press, pp. 66-93.

———, 1967, *Wilderness and the American Mind.* New Haven: Yale University Press.

National and Historic Parks Branch, 1971, *Banff National Park Provisional Master Plan.* Ottawa: Department of Indian Affairs and Northern Development.

National and Provincial Parks Association of Canada, 1972, "How it all Began," *Park News*, Vol. 8, pp. 5-13.

National Park Service, 1968, *Administrative Policies for Natural Historical and Recreational Areas*, Department of the Interior. Washington, D.C.: Government Printing Office.

Nature Conservancy, 1968, *Nature Conservancy—Progress 1964-1968.* London: H.M.S.O.

Nelson, J. G., 1972, "Some Economic and Social Effects of National Parks on Surrounding Communities," in R. V. Osteen (ed.), *World National Parks—Progress and Opportunities.* Brussels: Hayez, pp. 363-69.

———, 1970, "Man and Landscape Change in Banff National Park: A National Park Problem in Perspective," in J. G. Nelson (ed.), *Canadian Parks in Perspective.* Montreal: Harvest House, pp. 63-98.

Nelson, J. G. and A. R. Byrne, 1966, "Man as an Instrument of Landscape Change: Fires, Floods and National Parks in the Bow Valley, Alberta," *Geographical Review*, Vol. LVI, pp. 226-33.

Nelson, J. G. and R. C. Scace (eds.), 1968, *The Canadian National Parks: Today and Tomorrow.* Calgary: University of Calgary Press.

Noble, L. B., 1972, "Man and Grizzly Bear in Banff National Park, Alberta." Unpublished M.A. Thesis, University of Calgary.

Odum, H. T., 1971, *Environment, Power and Society.* New York: Wiley.

Ouma, J., 1970, *Evolution of Tourism in East Africa.* Nairobi: East African Literature Bureau.

Outdoor Recreation Resources Review Commission, 1962, *Study Reports, 1-27.* Washington, D.C.: Government Printing Office.

Parker, S., 1972, *The Future of Work and Leisure.* London: Paladin.

Rajender, G. R., F. K. Harmston and D. N. Wood, 1967, *A Study of the Resources, People and Economy of Teton County.* Laramie, Wyoming: University of Wyoming, Division of Business and Economic Research.

Ripley, T. H., 1962, *Recreation, Impact on Southern Appalachian Campgrounds and Picnic Sites*, U.S. Forest Service, S.E. Experiment Station, Paper No. 153. Ashville, N.C.: U.S. Forest Service.

Sauer, C. O., 1925, "Morphology of Landscape," *University of California Publications in Geography*, Vol. 2, pp. 19-54.

Scace, R. C., 1968, *Banff: A Cultural Historical Study of Land Use and Management in a National Park Community to 1945*, Studies in Land Use History and Landscape Change, National Park Series, No. 2. Calgary: University of Calgary Press.

Schwartz, W. (ed.), 1969, *Voices for the Wilderness.* New York: Ballantine.

Sewell, W. R. D. and I. Burton, 1971, *Perceptions and Attitudes in Resources Management*, Resource Paper No. 2. Ottawa: Department of Energy, Mines and Resources.

Shepard, P., 1967, *Man in the Landscape.* New York: Ballantine.

Swanson, E. W., 1969, *Travel and the National Parks—An Economic Study.* Washington, D.C.: National Park Service.

Thoreau, Henry David, 1960, *Walden and Civil Disobedience.* New York: Signet Classic, New American Library.

Wagar, J. A., 1964, *The Carrying Capacity of Wild Lands for Recreation*, Forest Series Monograph, 7. Washington, D.C.: United States Forest Service.

Wallace, Alfred Russell, 1962, *The Malay Archipelago.* New York: Dover.

White, G., 1966, "Formation and Role of Public Attitudes," in H. Jarrett (ed.), *Environmental Quality in a Growing Economy.* Baltimore: Johns Hopkins Press, pp. 105-27.

ADDITIONAL READINGS

Adams, A. B. (ed.), 1962, *First World Conference on National Parks.* Washington, D.C.: Government Printing Office.

American Society of Planning Officials, 1965, *Standards for Outdoor Areas*, Report No. 194. Chicago.

An Foras Forbatha, 1970, *Planning for Amenity Recreation and Tourism.* Dublin: Bord Failte.

Brockman, F., 1959, *Recreational Use of Wild Lands.* New York: McGraw-Hill.

Bureau of Outdoor Recreation, 1967, *Outdoor Recreation Space Standards.* Washington, D.C.: Government Printing Office.

Burton, T. L., 1971, *Experiments in Recreation Research.* London: George Allen and Unwin.

_____ (ed.), 1970, *Recreation Research and Planning.* London: George Allen and Unwin.

Butler, G. D., 1961, *Introduction to Community Recreation.* New York: Prentice-Hall.

Cahn, R., 1968, *Will Success Spoil the National Parks?* Boston: Christian Science Monitor.

Caldwell, L. K., 1970, "The Ecosystem as a Criterion for Public Land Policy," *Natural Resources Journal*, Vol. 10, pp. 203-21.

Chretien, J. Hon., 1968, "Our Evolving National Parks System," in J. G. Nelson and R. C. Scace (eds.), *Canadian National Parks: Today and Tomorrow.* Calgary: University of Calgary Press, pp. 7-14.

Chubb, M., 1964, "Outdoor Recreation Land Capacity, Concepts Usage and Definitions." Unpublished M.Sc. Thesis, Michigan State University.

Clawson, M., 1959, *Methods of Determining Demand for and Value of Outdoor Recreation*, Reprint No. 10. Washington, D.C.: Resources for the Future.

Clawson, M., R. B. Held and C. H. Stoddard, 1960, *Land for the Future.* Baltimore: Johns Hopkins Press.

Crow, B. W. Associates, 1969, *A Study of the Leisure Needs and Leisure Activities of Canadians*, Vol. 4, Summary Report. Toronto.

Darling, F. F. and D. Eichorn, 1967, *Man and Nature in the National Parks.* Washington, D.C.: Conservation Foundation.

Darling, F. F. and J. B. Milton (eds.), 1966, *Future Environments of North America.* Garden City, New York: Natural History Press.

Detwyler, T. R. (ed.), 1971, *Man's Impact on Environment.* New York: McGraw-Hill.

De Vos, A. and R. H. Bailey, 1970, "The Effect of Logging and Intensive Camping on Vegetation in Riding Mountain National Park," *Forest Chronicle*, Vol. 46, pp. 49-55.

Ditton, R. B. and T. L. Goodale (eds.), 1972, *Environmental Impact Analysis—Philosophy and Methods.* Madison: University of Wisconsin Press.

Douglas, R. W., 1969, *Forest Recreation.* London: Pergamon.

Dower, J., 1958, *National Parks in England and Wales.* London: H.M.S.O.

Everhart, W. C., 1972, *The National Park Service.* New York: Praeger.

Foster, H. D. and W. R. D. Sewell (eds.), 1970, *Resources, Recreation and Research*, Western Geographical Series, Vol. 3, Department of Geography, University of Victoria.

Galbraith, J. K., 1964, "Economics and the Quality of Life," *Science*, Vol. 145, pp. 117-23.

Hines, L. G., 1951, "Wilderness Areas: An Extra-market Problem in Resource Allocation," *Journal of Land Economics*, Vol. 27, pp. 306-13.

International Union for the Conservation of Nature and Natural Resources, 1966, *Ecological Impact of Recreation and Tourism Upon Temperate Environments.* Morges.

Jaarvinen, J. A. and W. D. Schmidt, 1971, "Snowmobile Use and Winter Mortality of Small Mammals," in M. Chubb (ed.), *Proceedings of Snowmobile and Off the Road Vehicle Symposium.* East Lansing: Michigan State University, pp. 130-40.

Jarrett, H. (ed.), 1969, *Perspectives on Conservation.* Baltimore: Johns Hopkins Press.

_____, 1966, *Environmental Quality in a Growing Economy.* Baltimore: Johns Hopkins Press.

_____, 1961, *Comparisons in Resources Management.* Lincoln: University of Nebraska Press.

Kates, R. W., 1966, "The Pursuit of Beauty in the Environment," *Landscape*, Vol. 16, pp. 21-25.

Knetsch, J. L., 1969, "The Identification of Recreation Demand," *Recreation, 1969.* Waterloo: Planning and Resources Institute, University of Waterloo, pp. 15-22.

_____, 1963, "Outdoor Recreation Demands and Benefits," *Land Economics*, Vol. 39, pp. 387-96.

Kostelanetz, R. (ed.), 1968, *Beyond Left and Right: Radical Thought for Our Times.* New York: Morrow.

Leighly, J. (ed.), 1963, *Land and Life*. Berkeley: University of California Press.
Leopold, L. B., 1969, *Quantitative Comparison of Some Aesthetic Factors Among Rivers*, U.S. Geological Survey Circular 620. Washington, D.C.: Government Printing Office.
Leopold, L. B., *et al.*, 1971, *A Procedure for Evaluating Environmental Impact*, U.S. Geological Survey Circular 645. Washington, D.C.: Government Printing Office.
Le Page, W. F., 1971, "Cultural 'Fogweed' and Outdoor Recreation Research," in W. T. Doolittle (ed.), *Recreation Symposium Proceedings*. Upper Darby, Pa.: United States Forest Service, pp. 186-93.
Lerner, L. J., 1962, "Quantitative Indices of Recreational Values," *Economics in Outdoor Recreation Policy*, Report No. 11, Committee on Water Resources and Economic Development of the West, Western Agricultural Economics Research Council.
Lowenthal, D., 1968, "The American Scene," *Geographical Review*, Vol. 58, pp. 61-88.
Lucas, R. C., 1966, "The Contribution of Environmental Research to Wilderness Policy Decisions," *Journal of Social Issues*, Vol. 22, pp. 115-26.
_____, 1964, "Wilderness Perception and Use: The Example of the Boundary Waters Canoe Area," *Natural Resources Journal*, Vol. 3, pp. 394-411.
Massland, D. E. L., 1970, "Conservation and the City," Paper presented at the 25th Annual Meeting of Soil Conservation Society of America. Toronto.
Mercer, D. C., 1970, "Geography of Leisure—A Contemporary Growth Point," *Geography*, Vol. 55, pp. 261-73.
Mitchell, L. S., 1967, "An Empirical Study of Urban Recreation Units," Unpublished Ph.D. Thesis, Ohio State University.
National and Historic Parks Branch, 1970, *Economic Impact of National Parks in Canada*. Ottawa: Department of Indian Affairs and Northern Development.
_____, 1964, *National Parks Policy*. Ottawa: Department of Indian Affairs and Northern Development.
Nelson, J. G. (ed.), 1970, *Canadian Parks in Perspective*. Montreal: Harvest House.
Nelson, J. G., L. D. Cordes, and J. Masyk, 1972, "The Proposed Master Plans for Banff National Park: Some Criticisms and an Alternative," *Canadian Geographer,* Vol. XVI, pp. 29-49.
Nicol, J. I., 1970, *The Economic Impact of National Parks in Canada, A Summary*. Ottawa: Department of Indian Affairs and Northern Development.
Osten, R. V. (ed.), 1972, *World National Parks, Progress and Opportunities*. Brussels: Hayez.
Pascoe, J. D. (ed.), 1971, *National Parks of New Zealand*, 2nd edition. Wellington: Government Printing Office.
Patmore, J. A., 1970, *Land and Leisure*. London: Penguin.
Pruitt, W. O., 1972, "Some Ecological Effects of Snowmobiles," in R. W. Butler *et al.* (eds.), *Proceedings of Symposium on Snowmobiles and All Terrain Vehicles*. London: Faculty of Law, University of Western Ontario, pp. 103-107.
Royal Society of Arts, 1970, *The Countryside in 1970*. London.
Saarinen, T., 1969, *Perception of Environment*, Commission on College Geography Resource Paper No. 5. Washington, D.C.: Association of American Geographers.
Sonnenfeld, J., 1966, "Variable Values in Space and Landscape: An Inquiry into the Nature of Environmental Necessity," *Journal of Social Issues*, Vol. 22, pp. 71-82.
Taylor, G. D., 1967, *Techniques in the Evaluation of Recreation Use*. Ottawa: Department of Indian Affairs and Northern Development.
_____, 1965, "An Approach to the Inventory of Recreational Lands," *Canadian Geographer*, Vol. IX, pp. 84-91.
Toffler, A., 1971, *Future Shock*. New York: Bantam.
Tumard, C. and B. Pushkarev, 1967, *Man-made America*. New Haven: Yale University Press.
United States Department of the Interior, 1970, *National Atlas of the United States*. Washington, D.C.: Government Printing Office.
Wanek, W., 1971, "Snowmobiling Impact on Vegetation, Temperatures and Soil Microbes," in M. Chubb (ed.), *Proceedings of Snowmobile and Off the Road Vehicle Symposium*. East Lansing: Michigan State University, pp. 116-129.
Wolfe, R. I., 1966, "Recreational Travel, The New Migration," *Canadian Geographer*, Vol. X, pp. 1-14.
_____, 1964, "Perspective on Outdoor Recreation," *Geographical Review*, Vol. 54, pp. 203-38.

Natural Hazards Research

James K. Mitchell
Rutgers University

Few people are aware that the Bezymianny eruption of March 30, 1956, was the world's most powerful volcanic event of recent years. Since it took place in an almost uninhabited part of Kamchatka and caused no known casualties, the eruption was largely a scientific curiosity (Latter: 1969). In contrast, the extrusion of a small volume of lava from a secondary cone on the slopes of Tristan da Cunha became a focus of global interest during October of 1961. By smothering a lobster processing plant and menacing the island's only settlement, the lava flow disrupted the economic system and compelled total evacuation of the three hundred residents to England.

Extreme natural events are often marked by such contrasting effects. In the United States, "[snow] . . . disruption at cities which average less than 20 inches a year is in many cases more frequent and more severe than the disruption at places recording considerably greater accumulations" (Rooney: 1969, p. 397). Although many nations are subject to major earthquakes, Iran has suffered 41 percent of the world's earthquake related deaths during recent decades (Latter: 1969). Hurricane Camille (1969), one of the most intense tropical cyclones to affect the United States, killed 248 persons. A storm of similar magnitude—the Bangladesh cyclone of November 1970—was responsible for between 250,000 and 500,000 deaths (Fournier d'Albe: 1971).

The preceding examples demonstrate that natural hazards are not defined solely by the characteristics of natural events, but by the interaction of those events with the human use systems of affected areas (Kates: 1971). This conception is a central tenet of natural hazard research, an emerging field of inquiry concerned with the human occupance of hazardous environments. Such a theme satisfies several motivations for geographic research, and it focusses disciplinary skills upon a worldwide humanitarian and practical problem. Although fewer than one thousand persons die as a direct result of natural hazards in the United States each year, annual losses from geophysical hazards alone total $2-3 billion (Burton, Kates and White: 1968). The costs of biological hazards and man-made pollutants are considerably greater (Burton and Kates:

1964; Council on Environmental Quality: 1971). In the developing world, confrontations between man and extreme natural events are more starkly dramatic: "For most of the world's people it is drought rather than pollution that endangers health, and the invasion of locusts rather than the extinction of endangered species threatens the quality of life" (Kates: 1972, p. 520).

Attempts to survive and prosper under conditions of environmental uncertainty are " . . . symptomatic of a variety of resource problems accompanying the increase of man's numbers and the spread of his works" (Kates: 1962, p. 144). Hence, the insights of natural hazard research may aid in developing general theories of man-environment relations. The possibility exists that models of human response to environmental threat may also function as analogs for research on man's adjustment to more pervasive forms of social stress. Finally, by virtue of its position at the interface of natural, social and policy sciences, natural hazard research provides an excellent opportunity for geographers to engage in interdisciplinary cooperation.

AN OUTLINE OF NATURAL HAZARD RESEARCH

Natural Hazard Research provides a theme for the integration of many disciplinary interests and geographers have made basic contributions to its development. A geographic tradition of hazard research can be traced back for half a century in the United States. Harlan Barrows' observations on the concept of human adjustment to environment provide the philosophical basis for this field of inquiry (Barrows: 1923). "From that viewpoint man interferes with the complex systems of air, water, soil and life that surround him, and seeks to isolate himself from many aspects of the natural world, to reconstruct others, and to adjust in varied ways to the rhythms and discontinuities of the resulting environment" (Burton, Kates and White: 1968, p. 4). Similar views are implicit in the writings of the French geographer Jean Brunhes (1920).

Since subsequent developments in the growth of natural hazard research have been amply documented elsewhere (White: 1973a), only a brief synopsis is given here. In a series of studies of United States flood problems undertaken at the University of Chicago, Gilbert F. White and his students applied the theoretical concept of adjustment to the analysis of human responses to hazard (White: 1945; White, et al.: 1958; Murphy: 1958; Sheaffer: 1960; White et al.: 1961; Burton: 1962; Kates: 1962; White: 1964; Kates: 1965). In this context, adjustments were regarded as actions taken by man to ameliorate or offset the effects of floods.

During the past decade behavioral science methodology has been widely employed to analyze adjustment decisions made by resource managers in areas susceptible to hazard (Kates: 1962; Saarinen: 1966; White: 1966). Particular attention has been paid to the role of perception in structuring these decisions. Complex theoretical, methodological, and policy questions raised by this research have stimulated a significant degree of interdisciplinary liaison between geographers, psychologists, economists, engineers, and community planners. Such multi-disciplinary initiatives currently receive National Science Foundation support through a major "Assessment of Natural Hazards Research" program.

Hazard researchers have addressed themselves to five principal areas of investigation. These include (1) assessing the extent of human occupance of hazard zones, (2) identifying the full range of possible human adjustments to hazard, (3) studying human perception and estimation of hazard, (4) describing the process of adopting hazard adjustments, and (5) estimating the optimal set of adjustments and its social consequences (Burton, Kates and White: 1968).

The International Geographical Union's Commission on Man and Environment has played a central role in stimulating and coordinating the hazard research activities of geographers in many countries. This has helped to focus attention on a wide variety of extreme events in contrasting cultural settings. Among others these include drought (Kenya, Tanzania, Australia, Mexico, U.S.A.), air pollution (Canada, United Kingdom, New Zealand, Japan, Hungary, Yugoslavia), tropical cyclones (Bangladesh, Puerto Rico, U.S.A.), avalanches (Norway, Austria), riverine floods (India, England), coastal erosion (U.S.A.), frost (U.S.A.), volcanoes (U.S.A.), earthquakes (U.S.A.), and tornadoes (U.S.A.). The early focus on meteorological and geomorphic events has been broadened to include studies of human response to air and water pollution (Auliciems and Burton: 1971). Cross-sectional investigations of specific types of hazard in one or more study sites have recently been supplemented by research on all of the hazards in a single community (Hewitt and Burton: 1971). Researchers have also begun to investigate aspects of collective adjustment decisions—a previously neglected field of inquiry. Typologies of natural hazards based upon their physical domain (Table 1), size and frequency of events, speed of onset, degree of social preparedness, duration of impact, and scale of damages are being superseded by more sophisticated classifications of the semantic images of hazards (Golant and Burton: 1969b), damage processes, energy and hazard "types" (Hewitt and Burton: 1971). Recently, Kates has outlined a general systems model of hazard adjustment which incorporates the results of this research (Figure 1). Field investigations are presently under way in many parts of the world to test the validity of this formulation.

It would be misleading to imply that geographers have only examined natural hazards from the perspective of natural hazard research programs. Geomorphologists and biogeographers have long studied the physical dimensions of catastrophic events; historical geographers have assessed the influence of real and imagined hazards on the trend of pioneer settlement, and medical geographers have analyzed the environmental parameters of disease. There is also an extensive body of literature from other disciplines which can usefully illuminate aspects of human response to hazard (Cochran: 1972). Wherever appropriate, this material has been integrated into the subsequent discussion.

Since the effects of natural hazards frequently generate immediate public and scholarly interest, these require initial consideration.

EFFECTS OF NATURAL HAZARDS

One of the principal motivations behind research on natural hazards is a concern for reducing the losses which they inflict upon society. Yet, relatively little is known about these losses and available data are apt to be misleading. Recognizing these deficiencies, geographers have been active in (1) helping to point out limitations of existing hazard-cost data, (2) developing improved procedures for making damage estimates, and (3) defining global patterns of loss. In common with other researchers they have paid little attention to the identifiable benefits of hazards and even less to the host of intangible effects which hazards produce.

TABLE 1—Common Natural Hazards by Principal Causal Agent

Geophysical		Biological	
Climatic and Meteorological	Geological and Geomorphic	Floral	Faunal
Blizzards & Snow	Avalanches	Fungal Diseases *For example:*	Bacterial & Viral Diseases
Droughts	Earthquakes	Athlete's foot Dutch elm	*For example:*
Floods	Erosion (including soil erosion	Wheat stem rust Blister rust	Influenza Malaria
Fog	& shore and beach erosion)	Infestations:	Typhus Bubonic
Frost		*For example:*	Plague Venereal
Hailstorms	Landslides	Weeds Phreatophytes	Disease
Heat Waves	Shifting Sand	Water hyacinth	Rabies Hoof & Mouth
Hurricanes	Tsunamis	Hay Fever	Disease Tobacco
Lightning Strokes & Fires	Volcanic Eruptions	Poison Ivy	Mosaic
			Infestations *For example:*
Tornadoes			Rabbits Termites Locusts Grasshoppers
			Venomous Animal Bites

Source: Burton and Kates: 1964.

Costs and Losses

Damage estimates are subject to a variety of errors and problems of interpretation. Individual assessors utilize varying loss evaluation criteria. Some classes of damage are exaggerated or "double counted" (White: 1964), while others are omitted from reports altogether (Sewell: 1965). Trends in adjustment to hazard are rarely taken into account (Russell: 1970). Strikingly different estimates of loss can be achieved by varying the economic assumptions upon which the evaluations are based (Kates: 1965; Russell, Arey and Kates: 1970). Hence, it is common to find widely divergent loss estimates among reporting agencies (Burton and Kates: 1964).

In an attempt to overcome some of these deficiencies, White and Kates have formulated methods for constructing flood damage estimates. These make provision for different types of hazard adjustment strategy (White: 1964; Kates: 1965). Total losses are calculated by aggregating the amounts of damage which would occur in specific types of structure for flood heights of varying frequency. Similar improvements in estimating damages are more difficult to achieve for

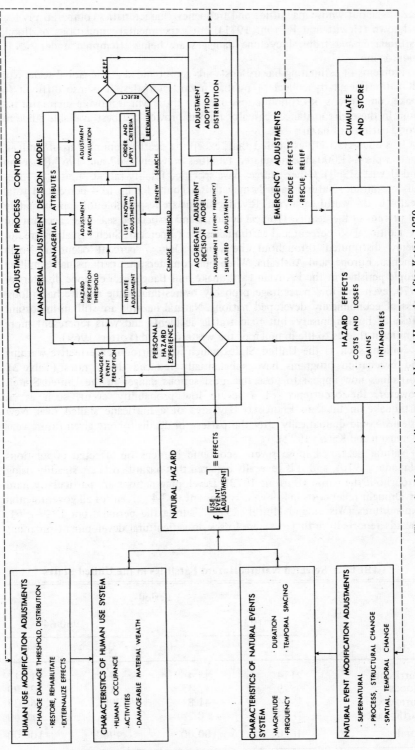

Figure 1. Human Adjustment to Natural Hazards. After Kates: 1970.

hazards about whose magnitude and frequency characteristics comparatively less is known (Hewitt and Burton: 1971), but experimental simulations of flood, earthquake, and tropical cyclone damages are being attempted under N.S.F. sponsorship.

Problems of estimating hazard costs are compounded at the global scale. Not all nations regularly collect or publish hazard statistics. It is also difficult to make comparisons of economic loss data for those which provide such information. In these circumstances casualty reports provide the best available guide to world patterns of hazard loss.

It is conservatively estimated that, excepting deaths stemming from famines, there were 441,000 hazard related fatalities between 1947 and 1967 (Sheehan and Hewitt: 1969). Other sources have specified fatality rates of up to ten times this magnitude. Natural hazards may thus account for up to 4 percent of total deaths in the world each year. Riverine floods are responsible for approximately 40 percent of the deaths. Tropical cyclones and associated sea surges account for an additional 35 percent and earthquakes for 13 percent. Such casualties are not evenly distributed throughout the world. Only 7 percent occur in North America, Europe, and Australia. When one considers that perhaps half a million people perished in the Peruvian earthquake and Bangladesh cyclone disasters of 1970, even this low percentage probably overestimates the relative hazardousness of economically developed nations. Natural hazards are still an important cause of human misery, but road traffic accidents and wars reperesent more significant threats to life in much of the western world (Latter: 1969).

Nations such as the United States which have introduced effective warning and evacuation programs have substantially reduced death rates (Table 2). Tornadoes now appear to pose the most serious danger in the United States. However, the occurrence of a severe low probability event, such as an earthquake in the San Francisco Bay area or a hurricane stalled over New Orleans, could dramatically alter the pattern of deaths for any given future year (Baumann and Kates: 1972).

Natural hazards impose severe economic burdens on affected populations (Maunder: 1970), and it is generally believed that hazard costs are steadily rising throughout the world (Burton: 1972). Developing nations are particularly hard hit. Drought relief costs in Kenya may amount to 3-4 percent of all governmental expenditures (Wisner and Mbithi: 1972). During the period from 1949-1961, hazards reportedly inflicted severe losses on agricultural development programs

TABLE 2—Selected Natural Hazard Fatalities in the United States

Hazard	1925-29 N	1925-29 %	1960-64 N	1960-64 %
Hurricanes	2114	45.46	75	15.12
Floods	579	12.45	119	23.99
Tornadoes	1944	41.81	299	60.29
Earthquakes	13	0.28	3	0.60
Totals	4650	100.00	496	100.00

in China (Freeberne: 1962). Annual losses from Japanese hazards are equivalent to between ½ percent and 1 percent of the Gross National Product of that country (Nakano, *et al.*: 1972). Although recent economic expansion in Japan has resulted in a declining ratio of damage to Gross National Product, total losses are not decreasing. Comparable estimates are not available for the U.S.A., but it is thought that total hazard costs are at least keeping pace with G.N.P. (Dacy and Kunreuther: 1969). In some cases losses may even have exceeded public investments for hazard protection (White, *et al.*: 1958). Costs of individual natural disasters in the United States are impressive. The Alaska (1964) and San Fernando (1971) earthquakes inflicted estimated damage of $311 million and $504 million respectively. Hurricane Camille is credited with total losses of more than $1.4 million and it is expected that damages attributable to tropical storm Agnes (1972) will eventually exceed $2.0 billion.

Types of damage caused by natural hazards are extremely varied, ranging from total and permanent destruction of all life and property improvements in areas covered by lava flows to the loss of a single tree from a lightning stroke. Figure 2 summarizes the range of damages which one hazard—tropical cyclones— can inflict. Current estimates of the annual costs of such hurricanes in the United States approximate a half billion dollars.

Beneficial Aspects of Natural Hazards

Natural hazards are popularly regarded as undesirable phenomena. Since the bulk of public policy is directed towards their reduction or elimination it is also assumed that they produce no beneficial effects. This assumption cannot always be justified, for it is abundantly clear that apparently hazardous events can produce substantial economic, aesthetic, and other benefits for some members of society. In the United States snow sustains a growing winter sports industry, provides essential meltwater reservoirs for irrigated lands and is valued as an adornment for otherwise monotonous winter landscapes (Rooney: 1969). For those whose trees escape serious damage, frosts often increase the value of surviving fruit crops by inducing relative market scarcity and hence raising prices. Growers also benefit from the shorter time required to gather the smaller crop and lower wage rates for temporary harvest labor (Ward: 1972). In Africa, floodplain cropping and grazing activities, which depend heavily upon seasonal inundation, contribute a disproportionately large share of the continent's agricultural production (Thomas and Whittington: 1969).

Unfortunately, benefits which accrue to individual resource managers frequently result from redistributions of income rather than genuine additions to national wealth and well-being. For example, fruit growers' gains are partly at the expense of crop harvesters' salaries. Again, when heavy snowfalls disrupt a central business district, demand may be transferred to neighborhood stores but the community as a whole does not benefit. Even individual beneficiaries may fail to reap all of the economic returns expected from transferred demand. After severe natural disasters, market prices for locally available goods may be depressed by the influx of relief supplies (Dacy and Kunreuther: 1969).

At present one can only guess at the scale of benefits which accrue to natural hazards. It is known that the value of rainfall provided to drought-prone areas on the periphery of tropical cyclone tracks can outweigh the deleterious consequences of these storms elsewhere (Sugg: 1967). In this context, it has been estimated that 90 percent of the hurricanes which affected Puerto Rico between

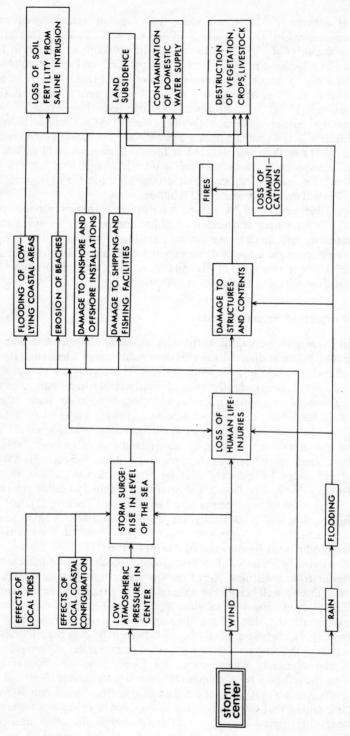

Figure 2.   Types of Potential Damage from Tropical Cyclones. Reproduced from A. White: 1972, by permission.

1899 and 1929 were beneficial to the island as a whole (Fassig: 1930). By cleaning coral reefs of silt and redistributing food producing areas, hurricane Carla (1961) is reported to have increased fish catches along the coast of the Gulf of Mexico (Moore, *et al.*: 1964). A Topeka tornado produced one of the more bizarre benefits on record by demolishing condemned structures along the path of a proposed superhighway (Dacy and Kunreuther: 1969).

Accurate cost-benefit analysis of natural hazards are generally lacking. One reason for this is the difficulty of evaluating many effects of hazards. How much benefit did San Francisco derive from the functionally efficient central business district which it acquired after the 1906 earthquake (Bowden: 1970)? What is the value of healthy rangeland vegetation when a severe drought increases stock mortality and thereby reduces overgrazing (Perry: 1962)?

Attempts to assess the significance of long-term hazard consequences raise even more complex issues. Many of these revolve around the question of benefits derived from post-disaster governmental investment in resource development projects. For example, Heathcote has pointed out that Australian droughts bring with them the prospect of increased public spending on rural facilities (Heath-cote: 1969*a*). After the eruption of Paricutin (1943), development of adjacent villages was strongly affected by governmental action. As Rees (1970, pp. 7-25) indicates, "With the direct intervention of the outside world, the resettlement villages were modernized ten to twenty years ahead of other Tarascan villages in the Meseta Tarasca. The Government introduced water storage and piping installations, electricity, medical clinics and poultry raising projects soon after resettlement." We know little about the benefits of such rehabilitation schemes because retrospective evaluations are rarely made. In any case, by drawing attention to the plight of stagnant economies or underprivileged groups, hazards are sometimes perversely beneficial.

Local benefits have clearly been generated by federal investment in water control schemes and public services in the American Great Plains (Borchert: 1971). Public spending has also affected dramatic changes in the economic health of small islands devastated by tropical cyclones. A prosperous banana industry was developed on Grenada after nutmeg and cacao plantations were decimated by a hurricane. The latter crops had long dominated a moribund agricultural economy (Weaver: 1968). Similar occurrences on the islands of Guadeloupe and Martinique also took place in the wake of severe storms. However, public investment does not invariably follow a natural disaster. Most of the world's population probably rely on their own resources or at best emergency relief to recover from such events.

Intangible Consequences of Natural Hazards

There are many effects of natural hazards which cannot readily be evaluated on a cost-benefit basis. A number of these have particular significance for theories of landscape development and social change.

Some of the more striking examples of fundamental social changes which may be attributable to the occurrence of extreme natural events can be found in the reported eclipse of ancient societies (Sestini: 1962). For example, it is now thought that the Minoan civilization on Crete (2500-1400 B.C.) was terminated by a major volcanic explosion at Santorini. This coated the island with volcanic ash and generated tsunamii which may have destroyed the city of Knossos (Latter: 1969). A similar fate probably befell inhabitants of the eleventh century

Hindu-Javanese state of Mataram. Precise factors accounting for the demise of Mohenjo-daro, Harappa, and contemporary Indus valley communities (*ca.* 1500 B.C.) are still in dispute. Some observers argue that tectonic uplift in the lower valley impounded waters which backed up and flooded the cities (Raikes: 1964). Others have identified periodic shifts in river courses as the chief cause of their extinction (Lambrick: 1967). Judging by the prevalence of similar catastrophic events in the folk myths of most societies, it is probable that natural hazards also achieved the unrecorded destruction of other groups.

Given the hazardous location of early urban civilizations in seasonally flooded river valleys, their compact nature and the lack of significant external resources with which to speed post disaster recovery, it is easy to understand why natural hazards might have effected critical changes in the evolution of ancient societies. When one considers the relatively localized character of such hazards and the areal spread of present human populations, the prospect that similar changes might be induced in the modern world is remote indeed. Man-made environmental hazards, such as atmospheric and oceanic pollution, are more frequently portrayed as potential agents of global catastrophe.

Social and economic changes of lesser magnitude may, nevertheless, be influenced by natural hazards. Glacken has reported on the reappraisals of religious and secular philosophy which were stimulated by the disastrous Lisbon earthquake of 1755. "This frightful catastrophe and the accompanying tsunami dramatized the problem of evil and the role of physical catastrophe affecting living things indiscriminately; it also raised questions, about the order and harmony on earth and the fitness of the environment, and the validity of final causes in nature" (Glacken: 1967, pp. 521-524).

Anthropologists have observed that some cultural changes can be facilitated by natural hazards. The propagation of Christianity in the western Pacific was assisted by nineteenth century typhoon disasters (Beaglehole: 1957). Heavy mortality among the elderly during the Mount Lamington volcanic eruption permanently deprived local groups in New Guinea of traditional customs and myths known only to their senior members (Schwimmer: 1969). Stresses produced by prolonged drought have been identified as factors precipitating the breakup of extended family life among the Arizona Navaho (Downes: 1965). Firth and Spillius have documented significant social changes following a series of droughts and typhoons on Tikopia (Firth: 1959; Spillius: 1957).

However, it is rarely possible to be sure that the apparent social or economic effects of natural hazards would not have occurred in the absence of such events. Thus, relocation of villagers affected by the Mount Lamington eruption was in part a response to the volcano hazard and in part a long established component of government policy. Lessa has also concluded that post-typhoon changes in tribal leadership, the role of women, diet, and local economy on the Pacific atoll of Ulithi, merely reflected the acceleration of existing trends toward modernization (Lessa: 1964).

Whether one can conclude that natural hazards tend to speed the process of social change in all developing areas is still open to question. Further data on the hazard responses of native cultures throughout the world is required before that contention can be verified, although many studies have highlighted the effects of typhoons and droughts on Pacific islanders (Schneider: 1957; Sahlins: 1962; Yamashita: 1965; Young: 1971).

Even less is known about the intangible effects of hazards in the developed world. While some researchers have commented on the amenity and aesthetic importance of volcanoes, eroded areas and other hazard related features, no attempts have been made to investigate their social value. In a society whose members' day to day lives are largely insulated from contact with the natural environment, the stimulus value of low risk events such as snowfalls have not been explored. There is also a possibility that populations which live in hazardous regions are self-selected risk takers. Russell implied this when observing that " ... [the prospect of] tornadoes [may] have influenced many people against settling in the tornado belt" (Russell: 1956, p. 459). Perhaps there are fundamental psychological differences between hazard zone occupants and the rest of the population.

Researchers are often sharply divided over the interpretation of information pertaining to natural hazards and processes of change in the physical environment. Some geomorphologists claim that storms affect only transitory changes in coastal landforms. For example, Hayes has suggested that, after the passage of a hurricane, wave cut inlets are rapidly closed, beach scarps are reduced, vegetation recolonizes eroded dunes, and shore profiles return to the forms which they assumed during periods of calmer weather (Hayes: 1967). Similar observations have been made by Blumenstock (1961), Stoddart (1971), and Steers (1953). Conversely, Ball and his colleagues have concluded that hurricanes accomplish virtually all of the supertidal sedimentation in parts of south Florida (Ball, et al.: 1967). Most permanent coastline recessions occur during storms (Shepard and Wanless: 1971; Langfelder, et al.: 1970), and a variety of other permanent shoreline changes have been ascribed to storm action (Brown: 1939; El-Ashry and Wanless: 1965; High: 1969).

Increased attention is being paid to the role of contemporary and prehistoric floods in shaping landforms. These studies " ... suggest that a re-thinking of the concept of dominance by low magnitude high-frequency events (Wolman and Miller, 1960) may be in order, at least in some geomorphic contexts" (Dury: 1972, pp. 45-72). If so, the terms "neocatastrophism" and "catastrophic uniformitarianism" have been suggested as possible titles for this type of theorizing (Zenger: 1970; Dury: 1972).

Widely held assumptions concerning vegetation succession and climax communities are difficult to justify in the light of findings on natural hazards. Raup has demonstrated that hurricanes have long been responsible for maintaining forests of even-aged trees in New England, thereby precluding the realization of theoretical succession sequences and vegetation climaxes (Raup: 1957; 1964). Lightning also appears to be a highly significant factor affecting the nature of forest ecosystems (Taylor: 1971).

In summary, natural hazards produce considerable damage, some benefits, and a host of consequences which defy precise evaluation. Society is mainly concerned with the first set of consequences, and hazard losses appear to be increasing in most parts of the world. What accounts for this trend? Available data suggest that increasing human occupance of hazard zones is the primary cause. Fuller reporting of damages and possible changes in the temporal and spatial patterns of extreme events are contributory factors.

TRENDS IN HUMAN OCCUPANCE OF HAZARD ZONES

Locations which are characterized by permanent extremes of aridity, altitude, exposure, or temperature tend to offer few incentives to human occupance. Conversely, settlement is not deterred from areas susceptible to extreme natural events of a temporary nature. Indeed, one of the basic findings of recent geographical research is that many intermittently hazardous zones are attracting human occupance at a more rapid rate than nominally "safer" areas. This trend has been documented for riverine flood plains and coastal lowlands exposed to storm damage in many parts of the world (White, *et al.*: 1958; Burton: 1962; Kates: 1962; White: 1964; Sewell: 1965: Burton, Kates, and Snead: 1969; White: 1970; Islam: 1971; 1972). Few extreme events have been examined so thoroughly as flooding. Thus, it is not yet possible to make clear-cut generalizations about human occupance in areas affected by other hazards. Nevertheless, it does seem likely that rapidly rising demands for scenic amenity and outdoor recreation are exposing larger numbers of people to the dangers of avalanches, landslides, forest fires, and volcanoes (White: 1973*b*).

A corollary of the preceding findings is that the occurrence of a natural disaster usually does not produce any significant permanent out-migration of population from affected areas. On the contrary, even though they may have suffered severe losses, hazard-zone residents tend to return to their original locations (Burton and Kates: 1964; Burton, Kates, and White: 1968; Burton: 1972). This is frequently followed by large-scale investment of capital in redevelopment with only minimal provisions for reducing future hazard losses (Bowden: 1970; Kates: 1970).

A few examples are known of permanent exodus from hazardous locations. Droughts have produced large scale out-migrations of population from Northeast Brazil (Brooks: 1971). It is also believed that future droughts will accelerate existing rural depopulation trends in parts of the Great Plains (Borchert: 1971). Exposed islands off the coast of Louisiana have been abandoned by their occupants after hurricanes, although Russell believes that " . . . such radical changes are ordinarily limited to places which had somewhat marginal value to begin with" (1956, p. 458). The incidence of environmental diseases such as Trypanosomiasis (sleeping sickness) and Onchocerciasis (river blindness), also appears to be a major factor affecting the abandonment of settlement in some parts of Africa (Deshler: 1960; Hunter: 1967; Knight: 1971). The latter diseases represent semi-permanent hazards rather than relatively short-term environmental extremes.

By concentrating wealth and population, urbanization undoubtedly increases the damage potential of specific sites and hence the likelihood of a "super-disaster" (Baumann and Kates: 1972; Latter: 1969). Conversely, prospects for rapid post-hazard recovery are often better in urban areas. Public services are more easily restored and relief supplies more effectively distributed in cities than in rural regions (Islam: 1972). The process of suburbanization may also make important contributions to increasing hazard potential by forcing populations with the least economic resources to live in the most hazardous locations (Eschman and Marcus: 1972). Worldwide trends toward urbanization and suburbanization pose an interesting question. Is increasing transiency of occupance accompanied by decreasing awareness of local hazards? If this is so, public decision makers may be required to bear a heavier burden of responsibility towards protecting private citizens against hazard.

The apparent paradox of rapid population growth in areas of serious hazard can be explained by a combination of factors:

(1) Hazard zones frequently offer comparative advantages to prospective occupants. Fertile alluvial and volcanic soils are premium resource

endowments in agricultural economies. Floodplains and unstable hill-slopes may provide cheap housing sites to low income residents. The occupants of exposed shorelines can take advantage of attractive vistas or proximity to maritime recreation.

(2) Persons living in hazard prone areas may also fail to perceive the true degree of risk. For example, many resource managers are overly optimistic about the protective capacities of flood control structures. We will return to the significant body of evidence relating to hazard perception later in the chapter.

(3) Institutional and social factors may prevent occupants from leaving the hazard zone. Public relief and rehabilitation programs often impede attempts to reconstruct facilities in less hazardous locations (Islam: 1972; Kates: 1970). Pressures to "normalize" the post hazard economy encourage local officials to continue previous modes of operation and patterns of development (Bowden: 1970). In some cases public agencies have even taken steps to recreate the psychological, social, and physical characteristics of pre-disaster life in an effort to ensure that natural hazards will not effect any major socio-cultural changes (U.N. Technical Assistance Board: 1968).

Geographers and anthropologists have pointed out that evacuees from disaster-stricken areas frequently fail to make the necessary adjustments to life among alien cultural groups. It was for that reason that most former residents of Tristan da Cunha returned from Britain two years after abandoning settlement on that remote volcanic island. Similar problems caused peoples living on the slopes of Mount Lamington to repossess land affected by a disastrous nuée ardente (Schwimmer: 1969). Attempts to settle villagers whose homes were overrun by lava from Mexico's Paricutin volcano also failed when the new villages were established beyond the traditional cultural area (Rees: 1970). Hence, under some circumstances, cultural pressures may function as a fourth constraint on maintaining levels of hazard-zone occupance.

The preceding factors need not all operate with equal influence. Residents of the coastal lowlands of Bangladesh are well aware of the cyclone hazard and do not migrate from this vulnerable region even when they know of opportunities elsewhere. Incentives to remain include the prospect of acquiring more land as a result of public dyking and embanking schemes, family ties, and the existence of relief and rehabilitation programs which encourage a rapid return to the precyclone status quo (Islam: 1972). Conversely, many occupants of Megalopolitan shores do not accurately perceive the frequency of coastal storms, but continue to invest in vacation homesites for amenity and recreational advantages, even when the prospect of substantial public reimbursement for flood or erosion damage is small (Burton, Kates, and Snead: 1969).

VARIATIONS IN THE PATTERN OF EXTREME EVENTS

Students of natural hazards have rarely attempted to investigate the physical nature of extreme events per se. This is more properly the task of geomorphologists, meteorologists, biogeographers, and specialists in the natural sciences. Nevertheless, through frequent contact with geophysical and meteorological data, hazard researchers have become aware that changes in the pattern of extreme events are partially responsible for rising hazard losses. Such changes are a function of the lengthening historical record and the extension of systematic data gathering procedures to previously unmonitored parts of the world as well as of periodic variations in the spatial pattern of hazard.

While records of floods on the Nile go back to antiquity, few nations began to compile detailed data on natural hazards before the turn of the century. Events of great magnitude which occurred prior to the establishment of data recording programs are frequently omitted from consideration when estimates of hazard frequency are compiled. Thus, the actual severity of future events may be underestimated. For example, Tazieff has pointed out the potential dangers of "extinct" volcanoes and ignimbrite flows. The latter are highly fluid "aerosols" of pumice and magmatic gases which spread quickly over large areas (Tazieff: 1966). Although only one such eruption is thought to have occurred during historical time, and that in a thinly populated area of Alaska, ignimbrite deposits have covered significantly large areas since the late Tertiary period. "If, however, such a disaster were to occur again in Indonesia, as it has in the past, and if this were to happen in a densely populated part of, for example, Java, it is not improbable that casualties might rise as high as one or two million" (Latter: 1969, p. 369).

As more and better data become available each year, the frequency of extreme natural events appears to increase. Thus, during 1969, floods in Tunisia were four times larger than the estimated 100 year maxima (Mensching, et al.: 1970). When settlement spread across the United States, " . . . the apparent center of maximum tornado incidence moved southwestward, from western Illinois to Iowa and Missouri, to Kansas, and now to central Oklahoma" (Court: 1970). The trend towards recording more extreme events is likely to be reinforced as more is learned about the environmental parameters of developing areas. As Sheehan and Hewitt have noted, " . . . the 'one-in-two-thousand-year' event for a 10,000 square mile area in North America may turn out to have, say, an average global recurrence of several times per year" (1969). Furthermore, as a consequence of the modernization process itself, and the development of formerly marginal agricultural lands, the cost of hazard related losses in developing areas is likely to increase.

With respect to the limitations of our present knowledge of hazard frequencies one further point is worthy of mention. It has been suggested that further knowledge of the probability characteristics of extreme events will not be forthcoming so long as we analyze those events as abstractions from normal physical processes of which they are a part. For example, proper understanding of fluctuations in river water levels below the flood damage threshold may be essential to the analysis of flood frequency. Yet, these sub-threshold changes are often ignored in frequency calculations (Hewitt: 1970). Similar problems frequently arise in the analysis of other hazards.

When one recalls that Boston, Massachusetts and Charleston, South Carolina have suffered damage from major earthquakes in 1765 and 1886 respectively, it is clear that the spatial pattern of extreme natural events varies through time. Indeed, many of the areas which appear to be hazard free on current maps may merely be passing through a temporary period of quiescence. Such changes are well illustrated by shifts in the zone of maximum seismic activity in the Middle East. This has moved repeatedly between northern and southern regions over periods of many hundred years. Tracks followed by tropical cyclones affecting the United States also appear to vary from decade to decade, sometimes focusing on the Gulf of Mexico and in other periods following routes along the Atlantic coast. Temporal variations in the location of serious Great Plains droughts have also been noted. Like changes in the cyclone tracks, these appear to be " . . . associated with contemporaneous rhythmic shifts in the general circulation pattern of the atmosphere on a large scale" (Borchert: 1971, p. 9).

The problem of interpreting data on extreme natural events is further complicated by the increasing scale of human interference in natural processes. Certain types of earthquakes can now be generated by impounding water behind dams and injecting it into oil fields (Healy, Rubey, Griggs, and Raleigh: 1968). The failure of dams at Johnstown (1889), Buffalo Creek, West Virginia (1927), and Rapid City, South Dakota (1972) reminds us that man can make major contributions to the generation of some catastrophic floods. Reduction of infiltration surfaces throughout urbanizing river basins may also cause streams to flood up to five or six times more often than previously (Schaake: 1972). Table 3 illustrates the varying contributions of man and nature to the generation of one hazard—coastal erosion.

TABLE 3—Causes of Coastal Erosion

Types of Erosion	Causal Agents	
	Natural Erosion	Man-Induced Erosion
Accelerated Destruction (*in situ*)	1. Increased Wave Energy (wind waves, storm surges, seiches, tsunamis) 2. Frost Action (cliffs) 3. Ice Scouring 4. Wind Action (dunes) 5. Mass Movements (landslips, slumping) 6. Corrasion, Corrosion, Attrition and Hydraulic Action (rocky coasts) 7. Marine Fauna 8. Floodwater (exiting through breached dunes) 9. Changes in water levels (tectonic, isostatic and eustatic movements)	1. Beach Excavation 2. Offshore Dredging 3. Destruction of Vegetation (or replacement with species having fewer sand retaining qualities) 4. Permafrost Melting (near Arctic oil fields)
Beach Starvation	1. Natural Starvation (deep water offshore, submarine canyons) 2. Null Points (offshore foci from which sediment supply diverges) 3. Natural Inlets	1. Interception of Littoral Drift (groynes, jetties, "improved" inlets) 2. Arrest of Supply at Source (river dredging, dams, "armoring" of headlands)

More accurate information about contemporary and historical worldwide patterns of extreme events would be helpful in assessing the degree of risk associated with occupying hazardous locations. Better accounting procedures would also ensure more comprehensive damage totals and greater international comparability of losses. Yet, neither of these actions would aid our understanding of how resource managers can better adjust to hazards. For this it is necessary to analyze hazard adjustment decisions.

HAZARD ADJUSTMENT DECISIONS

Social scientists have utilized principles of game theory to explain fishing strategies, crop combinations, and cattle herding practices in hazardous areas (Gould: 1963; Gould: 1965; Davenport: 1960; Lipton: 1968). Perhaps because it entails making questionable assumptions about rational behavior on the part of individual resource managers, this technique has not been widely applied in natural hazard research. Instead, White has made the basic hazard research contribution to the analysis of adjustment decisions with a model which can also be used to explain other resource use choices (White: 1961). In Kates' most recent version, this formulation portrays adjustments as the products of a three stage filtering process. This involves (1) the manager's perception of hazard, (2) his awareness of possible adjustments, and (3) his evaluation of these adjustments in terms of their suitability for the environmental setting, technical feasibility, economic efficiency, and conformance with social guides (Kates: 1971).

While collective decisions may be explained with respect to this model, in practice it has been used mainly to analyze processes of adjustment selection utilized by individual resource managers (Mitchell: 1973). In that capacity it works equally well when applied to professional decision makers in public agencies concerned with hazard management or private individuals living in hazardous areas. Each of these groups exhibits characteristically different patterns of response (Burton, Kates, and White: 1968). For example, it has been alleged that technical decision makers are often overspecialized (Sewell: 1971), professionally misinformed (Baumann: 1969; Hewings: 1968), biased (Schiff: 1966), elitist (Kasperson: 1969a), and conservative (MacIver: 1970; Hewings: 1968). While these qualities are not the sole property of professionals there is evidence to suggest that technical and public perceptions of specific resource issues are often quite different (Craik: 1970).

Initially it was thought that hazard adjustments adopted by resource managers might be explained in terms of socio-economic variables. However, " . . . these always correlated poorly with observed behavior, and a better explanation seemed to lie in the direction of hazard perception" (Burton: 1972, p. 190). Kates was among the first to recognize the influence of managerial perception on adjustment decisions (Kates: 1962). In a study of flooding at La Follett, Tennessee, he utilized an extended questionnaire to solicit information on respondents' awareness of flood hazard, the subjective probabilities which they attached to flood frequency and their knowledge and adoption of adjustments. Data thus derived suggested that a variety of personal perceptions of the flood hazard and the efficacy of available adjustments accounted for resource managers' decisions to remain in floodplains. Differences in the degree of flood hazard perception among several communities were a function of the actual frequency of flooding (Kates: 1962; Kates: 1963).

This type of investigation has been extended to other hazards. As evidenced by papers delivered at a recent symposium, researchers have variously broadened Kates' basic questionnaire format to include information on respondents' perceptions of (1) hazard causes, (2) spatial variations of hazard, (3) salience of hazard, and (4) responsibility for losses (White: 1973b).

Cultural geographers have also made significant contributions to our understanding of hazard perception. Their research demonstrates that perceptions of risk are strikingly resistant to change, even in the face of evidence to the contrary. Heathcote has noted the persistent failure of Australian farmers and public officials to recognize the full dimensions of drought hazard (1969b). The folk myth that "rainfall follows the plough" appears to have exerted a strong influence on farmers' drought perceptions in the United States Great Plains and South Australia (Meinig: 1962). Widespread public acceptance of erroneous "miasmatic" theories of disease was an important factor affecting the unfavorable nineteenth century perception of California's central valley (Thompson: 1969).

Geographers have been able to make more detailed assessments of hazard perception with the aid of psychological tools. Saarinen laid the groundwork for this type of research in a pioneering application of the Thematic Apperception Test to the topic of drought perception among Great Plains farmers (1966). This technique was further developed in a study of farmers' responses to sudden storms (Sims and Saarinen: 1969). A number of other tests have proved helpful in determining how resource managers discriminate among different types of hazard and respond to specific hazardous situations (Barker and Burton: 1969; Golant and Burton: 1969a; 1969b). Sentence completion tests are now the most widely favored psychological field research instrument (Sims and Baumann: 1972). Although the application of psychological techniques has yielded considerable insights into human behavior in hazardous areas of western society, there is some indication that they may be more difficult to translate into the context of other cultures.

MANAGERIAL PERCEPTIONS OF HAZARD

Results of the aforementioned studies support the hypothesis that hazard perception is a process which is affected by four main variables: (1) the resource manager's past experience, (2) his interpretation of the physical characteristics of hazard events, (3) personality traits, and (4) the situational characteristics of adjustment decisions.

Experience

It has been generally confirmed that persons with greater experience of floods and droughts tend to perceive and adopt more adjustments (Kates: 1962; Burton: 1962; Burton, Kates, and Snead: 1969; Sims and Baumann: 1972; Saarinen: 1966). Perceptions and evaluations of volcano hazard adjustments are also strongly related to hazard experience (Murton and Shimabukuro: 1972).

However, future expectation of hazard is not always guided by resource managers' past experiences. More than 30 percent of respondents who had experience of coastal flooding did not assess the likelihood of future flood damage as significant. Twenty-seven percent of riverine flood plain residents and 20 percent of persons who had experienced coastal erosion were similarly disposed to overlook the prospect of future hazard (Mitchell: 1973). Most San Franciscans who have experienced local earthquakes appear to evaluate future risks as negligible (Jackson and Mukerjee: 1972). Such misperceptions of future hazard have been explained in terms of managerial responses to conditions of uncertainty. These include, denying or denigrating the existence of reoccurrence of a hazard, imposing oversimplified subjective probability models upon complex natural events and transferring responsibility for resolving uncertainty to God or "the government" (Burton, Kates, and White: 1968). For some resource managers, their mental models of future natural events are "nonoperational" (Kirkby: 1972a), while others simply refuse to speculate about the future on religious grounds (Roder and Dupree: 1972). Elsewhere, managers utilize complicated techniques for divining forthcoming environmental conditions, but fail to act upon the information which these provide. This applies to the Australian farmer's practice of keeping raingauge records (Heathcote: 1972), and the complex moisture calendars (*cabanuelos*) of Mexican peasants (Parra: 1972).

The dominant association between heightened perception of hazard and previous experience raises an interesting question. Does repeated exposure to extreme natural events produce a population which is particularly sensitive to hazard—a "disaster culture" (Haas: 1968). Anderson has pointed out that chronic environmental threats can be incorporated into the familiar schemes of "normal" cultural problems (1968). There is also some evidence that contemporary perceptions of hazard may be distorted by recollections of previous severe local disasters. In some cases this may result in the underestimation of hazard severity—perhaps as a compensation for the stress of living with a chronically threatening situation (Mitchell: 1973). Elsewhere, resource managers may be "inordinately fearful" of possible future hazards. Thus memories of the destructive 1925 Tri-State tornado in southern Illinois have been thought to influence present day behavior of local residents during the tornado season. "In particular, older women would call with alarm for the gathering of the family in the storm shelter or basement at the first sight of any dark cloud, regardless of whether any severe storm warnings had been issued" (Changnon: 1970, p. 39).

Variations in the Natural Events System

Several studies have revealed that differences in the physical characteristics of extreme natural events can strongly influence the perception of hazard. Burton and Kates have suggested that hazard perception is related to the frequency of such events (1964). Saarinen has confirmed that perception of drought varies with degree of aridity (1966). Russell has also noted that hazard frequency is an important factor affecting resource manager decisions about citrus crop production: "The probability that most of the citrus trees will be killed once in fifty years is not sufficient to prohibit the raising of oranges commercially near the mouth of the Mississippi River; but inland, where the frequency of disaster caused by killing frost may be as often as once in ten years, man appraises the risk as excessive" (1956, p. 457). Private resource managers also appear to systematically underestimate the frequency of relatively unspectacular hazards such as frost and drought—even when these are common occurrences (White: 1973b; Saarinen: 1966).

Contrasts between the perception of man-made and natural hazards are even more striking. In a series of studies of air pollution in British cities, it was concluded that many types of pollutants are not easily detected by the human senses until they reach chronic proportions. Thus hazard perception is more strongly influenced by the availability of information on the problem, disseminated through the mass media and interpersonal contacts, than by the degree of individual exposure to the physical stimulus of pollution (Kirkby: 1972b; Auliciems and Burton: 1971). This research also revealed that significant differences in perception and response to quasi-natural or man-made hazards were accounted for by the respondent's age and socio-economic status—characteristics which do not appear to influence the perception of natural hazards. There are indications that these findings may also be valid for cities in other parts of Europe (White: 1973b). If these conclusions are generally confirmed, they suggest that persons who control the timing, form and content of "messages" which the resource manager receives, can exercise a strategic influence on the nature of adjustments to man-made hazards.

Personality Traits

Research on relationships between personality traits and perception of hazard is still at an early stage. Nevertheless, a few conclusions can still be stated with some degree of confidence. Saarinen suggests that there is a clear connection between the inability of Great Plains farmers, in areas affected by drought, to resolve the issue of achievement in TAT stories, and the uncertain character of the environment in which they live (1966). The same conflict is mirrored in their responses to sudden storms. Here, " ... the primary reaction to the threat is the mobilization of (their) own resources towards rational, task-oriented action. However, uncertainty remains and this is reflected in a subsidiary theme in which attempts to alleviate anxiety are made by the essentially religious appeal to transcendental powers to lessen or stay the environmental threat" (Sims and Saarinen: 1969, p. 677).

Sims and Baumann have indicated that differences in the tornado death rates of Illinois and Alabama can partly be explained by contrasting personality traits of the affected populations. The results of a sentence completion test reveal " ... Illinoisans to be more autonomous, more prone to see themselves as responsible for directing their own lives, and more confident in their own efficaciousness ... Alabamans are seen to be more heteronomous, feeling themselves to be moved by external forces—fate, luck, and, particularly God. They are consequently less confident in themselves as causal agents, less convinced of their ability to engage in effective action" (Sims and Baumann: 1972, p. 1391). These characteristics are reflected in the attention paid to the tornado warning system in Illinois and its relative neglect by Alabama residents.

Preliminary results from a cross cultural study suggest that there may be similar significant differences in human response to hurricanes. When compared with more fatalistic Puerto Ricans, residents of the United States appear to be less concerned with the threat of hurricanes and more active in post hazard restoration (Baumann and Sims: 1972).

Responses to volcano hazard in Hawaii may, in part, also be a function of different conceptions of "fate control" among the state's ethnically diverse population. Hawaiians and Filipinos appear to be distinguished by their emphasis on cooperation as the means to success, whereas the Japanese regard hard work as the most important factor (Murton and Shimabukuro: 1972).

Situational Characteristics

There is considerable evidence that perception of hazard is a function of resource use. Farmers are particularly sensitive to environmental threats. This was first demonstrated in the United States flood hazard studies (Burton and Kates: 1964), but subsequent research suggests that farmers in areas susceptible to drought, volcanic eruption, and frost are also more aware of hazard than adjacent non-agriculturalists (Saarinen: 1966; Jackson: 1972; Ward: 1972; Murton and Shimabukuro: 1972). Conversely, urban and industrial resource managers apparently perceive hazard less readily. It has been found that manufacturers in eastern Colorado fail to perceive meteorological conditions as threats to business operations (Bickert and Browne: 1966). Municipal water managers in Massachusetts did not perceive the beginning of a drought until a year and a half after it had actually started (Russell, Arey, and Kates: 1970).

MANAGERIAL SELECTION OF HAZARD ADJUSTMENTS

When a natural event is perceived as being sufficiently hazardous to warrant some responsive action by a resource manager the second stage of the adjustment decision process commences. At this point resource managers list known adjustments and proceed to evaluate their potential utility. Such adjustments are of four basic types. Managers may choose to (1) affect the hazard cause, (2) modify the hazard, (3) modify the loss potential, and (4) adjust to the losses (Burton, Kates, and White: 1968; Taylor: 1970). For any given hazard a large number of adjustments are theoretically possible but, in practice, only a few are usually known to individual managers (Sewell: 1969). Factors influencing resource manager awareness of adjustments include socio-economic status and role responsibility (Kates: 1970).

Ranges of adjustments practiced in North America have been outlined for riverine and coastal floods (Sewell: 1969; Burton, Kates, and Snead: 1969), drought (Saarinen: 1966), earthquakes and snow (Burton, Kates and White: 1968), and coastal erosion (Mitchell: 1973). Global spectra of adjustments to these and other hazards are presently being specified in the work of the Commission on Man and Environment of the International Geographical Union.

Although the importance of perception is widely acknowledged, comparatively little is known about other factors which influence the process of adjustment adoption. Many studies have suggested that age, education, socio-economic status, and experience exert little influence on adoption decisions (Burton, Kates, and White: 1968). However, this may not be true of all hazards. Recent research on the San Francisco earthquake hazard suggests that there is a direct relationship between experience of past earthquakes and adjustment adoptions (Jackson and Mukerjee: 1972).

Strong associations have been reported between numbers of adjustments adopted and the frequencies of flood, frost, and drought in the United States (Kates: 1962; Saarinen: 1966; Burton, Kates, and Snead: 1969; Ward: 1972). However, more recent findings indicate that this relationship is not so obvious in other areas. For example, in parts of East Africa most adjustments are adopted in areas of moderate drought intensity (Heijnen and Kates: 1972). Furthermore, in these areas it is " . . . not so much the purposive adjustments in response to a specific drought but rather the adjustments embedded in the fabric of everyday life that serve to mediate the differentials of environmental opportunity" (Heijnen and Kates: 1972, p. 21). Thus, farm size, crop diversity, distributions of plots, and degree of surplus production are more important factors affecting adjustment to drought than migration to alternative sources of income, dry farming practices, irrigation, or appeals to rainmakers. At present, research on hazard adjustments in culturally diverse areas is at an early stage. Nevertheless, initial results indicate that human responses are considerably more complex than in relatively homogeneous Western societies.

The influence of environmental, technological, economic, and social constraints on adjustment adoptions has been explored in detailed studies of water supply and recreation decisions (Wong: 1968; Baumann: 1969; MacIver: 1970; Johnson: 1971). Thus far, ramifications of these factors have not been as thoroughly investigated in the context of hazard research. From what is known it is clear that such constraints can severely limit the practicability of adopting perceived adjustments.

Peasants who are subject to the dictates of "rent capitalism" (Bobek: 1962), usually lack money, technology, and political power to implement perceived adjustments (Parra: 1972). It is believed that the social attractiveness of frequent participation in ceremonial celebrations associated with the sharing of surplus grain, restrains personal initiatives towards maximum crop productivity in arid sections of Mexico's Oaxaca Valley (Kirkby: 1972*b*). Wisner and Mbithi have commented on contrasts between the failure of many colonial rural development projects in East Africa and the comparative success of similar schemes in the post-independence period (1972). Unwillingness to contravene the will of the goddess Pele has been held responsible for the failure of elderly Hawaiians to evacuate lava-threatened possessions to safer locations. In contrast, for most other residents, evacuation has become the socially expected pattern of behavior (Murton and Shimabukuro: 1972). The successful evacuation of people from areas of Bangladesh threatened by cyclones, to community shelters, is frustrated by local traditions. "For women to walk in public a long distance is not regarded as desirable under any circumstances. . . . people prefer to take shelter with known persons or relatives" (Islam: 1971, p. 21).

In summary, processes by which individual resource managers adopt adjustments to hazard are broadly understood, but much field research is required before details of specific hazard adjustment systems can be uncovered. Few hazards other than floods and droughts have been comprehensively explored. Relatively little is known about spatial and temporal patterns of adjustment diffusion. Collective adjustment decision processes are even less well understood (Kasperson: 1969*b*; O'Riordan: 1971*a*; 1971*b*; Mitchell: 1973). The latter is particularly unfortunate since governmental action may be necessary in areas where individual adjustment strategies are relatively ineffective. For example, in parts of Tanzania private hazard adjustments " . . . seem to only slightly moderate the differentials of environmental opportunity while providing minimal sustenance to all" (Heijnen and Kates: 1972, p. 23). In other developing areas, there is widespread expectation of, and dependence upon, public protection against natural hazards.

Despite a lack of detailed studies of collective adjustment decisions, especially at the local community level, information on governmental activity in the field of hazard control is not totally lacking. Several analyses of national public policy on selected natural hazards have been carried out.

NATURAL HAZARDS AND PUBLIC POLICY

A recent appraisal of United States public policy on natural hazards has concluded that centrally administered "technological fix" strategies of adjustment have been favored by the federal government during most of the twentieth century (Arey and Baumann: 1971). This emphasis is now undergoing a change, influenced in part by the research contributions of Gilbert F. White and his colleagues (White: 1969). A resurgent interest in resource conservation and concern over environmental quality have aided this process. Combinations of technological, social and legal adjustments are now being promoted and applied at various administrative levels. One example of this change in emphasis, built directly upon the research contributions of geographers, concerns federal policy in riverine flood control (U.S. House of Representatives, 1966). Here, large water management schemes constructed by the U.S. Army Corps of Engineers have been supplemented by a flood hazard evaluation program, which applies to all federally financed buildings, flood plain information reports, and a flood insurance scheme. Such measures have the effect of transferring much of the cost and responsibility for adjusting to floods away from the federal government and towards individual flood plain users. Although less comprehensive in scope, current activities for the reduction of losses caused by droughts and hurricanes are said to exhibit " . . . distinct parallels [with] . . . the past development of flood control policies" (Arey and Baumann: 1971, p. 82).

The preceding trend conforms to the sequence of techno-social adjustment stages which have been recognized by hazard researchers. Thus societies tend to move from adopting patterns of flexible, low cost, individual measures against hazard (folk adjustments), through emphasis on inflexible, high cost, technological devices (modern technological adjustments) to mixtures of both strategies (comprehensive adjustments) (Burton, Kates, and White: 1968).

Due to a lack of detailed information it is presently impossible to assess hazard adjustment policies in other nations. It has been reported that only 58 countries possess formal plans for coping with natural disasters (*New York Times*, December 16, 1971). A similar disparity of interest has been revealed in a recent survey of hazard warning and research programs (Figure 3). Most commonly promoted public policy responses include prediction and warning systems, evacuation programs, structural defenses and emergency relief (Fournier d'Albe: 1971).

Although the bulk of the world's population probably utilizes "folk adjustments," many public policy makers appear to favor "technological fix" strategies of hazard control (Islam: 1972; Latter: 1969). The introduction of sophisticated technological adjustments into the traditional societies of developing lands can have far-reaching consequences. For example, in the Oaxaca valley of Mexico, publicly sponsored flood control and irrigation schemes have been viewed as panaceas for all local problems (Kirkby: 1972a). Despite the potentially undesirable consequences of misapplied industrial technology (Farvar and Milton: 1972), this course of action receives the endorsement of many persons. Recently, observers have detected signs of change towards more varied "comprehensive" mixes of hazard adjustments in several nations (White: 1970; Oya: 1970).

Reflecting an interest in broadening the practical range of alternatives available to resource managers, hazard researchers have aided in the design and improvement of specific types of adjustments. Sheaffer's work on "flood proof-

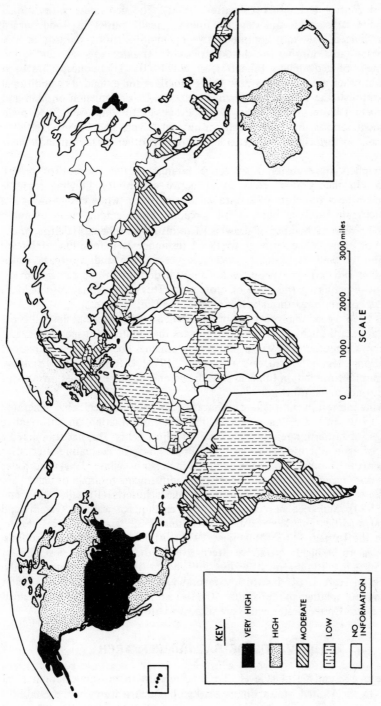

Figure 3.   Levels of Interest in Natural Hazards: National Research, Forecasting, and Warning Activites. Data from Smithsonian Institution: 1972.

ing" buildings represents one of the few excursions by geographers into the area of hazard control technology (Sheaffer: 1960). The geographer's traditional concern for cartographic analysis has found a ready outlet in flood hazard mapping. Indeed, the only comprehensive mapping of flood hazards in any metropolitan area in the world took place in Greater Chicago under the management of geographers (Sheaffer, et al.: 1970). This concept has been adopted in other nations and is now being modified and extended to additional hazards through the mapping program of the I.G.U. Commission on Man and Environment (White: 1973; Oya: 1970). Proposals for improved flood plain management services have also been formulated (Cypra and Peterson: 1969). These can, in principle, be extended to cover other hazard management programs.

Geographers have fostered an active interest in the concept of hazard insurance. In theory this offers an attractive system for allowing resource managers to bear the costs of hazard zone occupance, while cushioning them against extreme financial burdens by spreading losses among many premium holders. There are a number of drawbacks to insurance schemes (Felton, et al.: 1971). For example, receptivity to flood insurance is a function of hazard perception as well as property value, structural age and mortgage status (Cymanske: 1967). Hence, people who foresee little future flood damage are less interested in acquiring this type of protection. This outlook may also account for low receptivity to earthquake insurance in the United States.

It has been argued that provision of comprehensive insurance against all types of natural hazard might offer more advantages than policies for specific hazards (Dacy and Kunreuther: 1969). Although such schemes operate in several nations with varying degrees of success (Vaughan: 1971; O'Riordan: 1971c), they require careful formulation to avoid subsidizing or inducing increased investment and occupance in hazard zones.

Growing interest in comprehensive hazard adjustment strategies has generated a need to provide decision makers with better information on the relative advantages of hitherto rarely utilized types of adjustments. This has stimulated a number of economic efficiency analyses. Procedures for evaluating alternative adjustments to flooding have been explored in detail by White (1964) and Kates (1965). More recently, costs and benefits of adjustments to urban drought have been assessed for several communities in Massachusetts (Russell, Arey, and Kates: 1970). Mukerjee has concluded that earthquake warning systems and structural modifications have cost/benefit ratios of 22.7:1 and 17.92:1 respectively in the United States (Mukerjee: 1971). At least on economic grounds, both appear to be highly attractive alternatives to the methods of post disaster relief and rehabilitation most widely utilized at the present time. Finally, Mukerjee has calculated that highly favorable cost/benefit ratios make water harvesting and weather modification attractive supplements to irrigation in areas of the western United States which are subject to drought (1972).

THE VALUE OF HAZARD RESEARCH

There is presently a high level of public interest in the subject of natural hazards. In the United States this is marked by such features as the establishment of an N.S.F. hazard research program, a federal Task Force on Earthquake Problems, improved tornado identification, and flash flood warning systems, formulation and publication of evacuation maps for areas of coastal storm hazard, and widespread state government enactment of flood plain zoning regulations. At the United Nations, member countries have sponsored a resolution calling for increased governmental cooperation to curb damages from tropical storms. An international Coordinator of Disaster Relief has been appointed by the United Nations, and the North Atlantic Treaty Organization has developed a program for improving disaster relief coordination among its members and other states (Committee on the Challenges of Modern Society: 1972). It has also been proposed that a specially equipped International Disaster Relief Force be established, consisting of mobile military units based near likely disaster areas.

These activities underscore the pervasiveness and importance of hazard problems. Given the undesirable consequences of poorly applied "technological fix" adjustments and considerations of financial limitation, professional expertise and political self interest, it is neither feasible nor desirable that hazard control be solely a governmental responsibility or an opportunity for the blanket application of expensive technological "solutions." It seems highly desirable to incorporate the knowledge, skills, and resources of individual resource managers into the comprehensive adjustment process. For this to be done successfully requires a thorough knowledge of public and private adjustment decision processes and the natural hazard systems which operate in a specific area.

Geographers have already developed some impressive credentials in this field of research. As evidenced by the flood hazard gaming simulations of the High School Geography Project of the Association of American Geographers (published as *Geography in an Urban Age*, Unit V, "Habitat and Resources": 1965, 1967, 1969, 1970) and the existence of several university courses in natural hazards, findings have also begun to filter back to the classroom. Whether it will eventually be shown that present models of the hazard adjustment process are accurate formulations remains to be seen. These models are currently undergoing close scrutiny and it is anticipated that major reinterpretations of much of the data reviewed in this paper may be forthcoming. Whatever the outcome of such reassessments, it is clear that natural hazard research provides an admirable opportunity to bring together and test disparate strands of geographic theory on man-environment relations, to focus research skills on a topical and significant practical problem, and to provide a stimulating "real world" setting for the teaching of geographic contributions to environmental education.

REFERENCES

Anderson, Jon W., 1968, "Cultural Adaptation to Threatened Disaster," *Human Organization*, Vol. 27, pp. 298-307.

Arey, David G. and Duane D. Baumann, 1971, *Alternative Adjustments to Natural Hazards*. National Water Commission Research Report No. NWC 70-029. Carbondale, Illinois: Southern Illinois University, Department of Geography.

Auliciems, Andris and Ian Burton, 1971, *Perception and Awareness of Air Pollution in Toronto*. Natural Hazard Research Working Paper No. 13. Toronto: University of Toronto, Department of Geography.

Ball, M. M., E. A. Shinn and K. W. Stockman, 1967, "The Geologic Effects of Hurricane Donna in South Florida," *Journal of Geology*, Vol. 75, pp. 583-597.

Barker, Mary and Ian Burton, 1969, *Differential Response to Stress in Natural and Social Environments: An Application of a Modified Rosenzweig Picture-Frustration Test*. Natural Hazard Research Working Paper No. 5. Toronto: University of Toronto, Department of Geography.

Barrows, Harlan H., 1923, "Geography As Human Ecology," *Annals of The Association of American Geographers*, Vol. 13, pp. 1-14.

Baumann, Duane D., 1969, *The Recreational Use of Domestic Water Supply Reservoirs: Perception and Choice*. Chicago: University of Chicago, Department of Geography Research Paper No. 121.

Baumann, Duane D. and Robert W. Kates, 1972, "Risk From Nature in The City," *Urbanization and Environment*. Edited by Thomas R. Detwyler and Melvin G. Marcus. Belmont, California: Duxbury Press.

Baumann, Duane D. and John Sims, 1972, "Human Response to Hurricanes: A Comparative Study." Unpublished Paper. International Geographical Union, Commission on Man and Environment. Commission Meeting, Calgary, Alberta, July 23-30, 1972.

Beaglehole, Ernest, 1957, *Social Change in the South Pacific: Rarotonga and Aitutaki*. New York: Macmillan.

Bickert, Carl von E. and Theodore D. Browne, 1966, "Perception of the Effects of Weather on Manufacturing: A Study of Five Firms," *Human Dimensions of Weather Modification*. Edited by W. R. D. Sewell. Chicago: University of Chicago, Department of Geography Research Paper No. 105.

Blumenstock, D. J., F. R. Fosberg and C. G. Johnson, 1961, "The Re-Survey of Typhoon Effects on Jaluit Atoll in The Marshall Islands," *Nature*, Vol. 189, pp. 618-620.

Bobek, Hans, 1962, "The Main Stages in Socio-Economic Evolution from a Geographical Point of View," in Philip L. Wagner and Marvin W. Mikesell (eds.), *Readings in Cultural Geography*. Chicago: University of Chicago Press.

Borchert, John R., 1971, "The Dust Bowl in the 1970s," *Annals of The Association of American Geographers*, Vol. 61, pp. 1-22.

Bowden, Martyn J., 1970, "Reconstruction Following Catastrophe: The Laissez-Faire Rebuilding of Downtown San Francisco After the Earthquake and Fire of 1906," *Proceedings of The Association of American Geographers*, Vol. 2, pp. 22-26.

Brooks, Reuben, 1971, "Human Response to Recurrent Drought in Northeastern Brazil," *The Professional Geographer*, Vol. 23, pp. 40-44.

Brown, C. W., 1939, "Hurricanes and Shore-Line Changes in Rhode Island," *Geographical Review*, Vol. 29, pp. 416-430.

Brunhes, Jean, 1920, *Human Geography*. Chicago: Rand McNally.

Burton, Ian, 1962, *Types of Agricultural Occupance of Flood Plains in the United States*. Chicago: University of Chicago, Department of Geography Research Paper No. 75.

———, 1972, "Cultural and Personality Variables in the Perception of Natural Hazards," *Environment and the Social Sciences: Perspectives and Applications*. Edited by J. F. Wohlwill and D. H. Carson. New York: American Psychological Association.

Burton, Ian and Robert W. Kates, 1964, "The Perception of Natural Hazards in Resource Management," *Natural Resources Journal*, Vol. 3, pp. 412-441.

Burton, Ian, Robert W. Kates, and Gilbert F. White, 1968, *The Human Ecology of Extreme Geophysical Events*. Natural Hazard Research Working Paper No. 1. Toronto: Department of Geography, University of Toronto.

Burton, Ian, Robert W. Kates, and Rodman E. Snead, 1969, *The Human Ecology of Coastal Flood Hazard in Megalopolis*. Chicago: University of Chicago, Department of Geography Research Paper No. 115.

Changnon, Stanley A., Jr., 1970, "Major Hailstorms Retrace Tri-State Tornado Track in Illinois," *Transactions of The Illinois Academy of Science*, Vol. 63, pp. 34-41.

Cochran, Anita, 1972, *A Selected Annotated Bibliography on Natural Hazards*. Natural Hazard Research Working Paper No. 22. Toronto: University of Toronto, Department of Geography.

Committee on The Challenges of Modern Society, 1972, *Disaster Assistance Pilot Study— Final Report by the Pilot Country*. Document AC/274-D/20. North Atlantic Treaty Organization.

Council on Environmental Quality, 1971, *Environmental Quality*. Washington, D.C.: U.S. Government Printing Office.

Court, Arnold, 1970, *Tornado Incidence Maps*. Technical Memorandum ERLTM-NSSL-49. Norman, Oklahoma: U.S. National Severe Storms Laboratory.

Craik, Kenneth H., 1970, "Environmental Psychology," *New Directions in Psychology IV*. New York: Holt, Rinehart and Winston, Inc.

Cymanske, David Y., 1967, "Receptivity to Flood Insurance." Unpublished M.A. Thesis. Department of Geography, University of Chicago.

Cypra, Kenneth and George L. Peterson, 1969, *Technical Services for the Urban Floodplain*

Property Manager: Organization of the Design Problem. Natural Hazard Research Paper No. 12. Toronto: University of Toronto, Department of Geography.

Dacy, Douglas C. and Howard Kunreuther, 1969, *The Economics of Natural Disasters: Implications for Federal Policy.* New York: The Free Press.

Davenport, William, 1960, "Jamaican Fishing: A Game Theory Analysis," *Yale University Publications in Anthropology*, Vol. 59, pp. 3-11.

Deshler, Walter, 1960, "Livestock Trypanosomiasis and Human Settlement in Northeastern Uganda," *Geographical Review*, Vol. 50, pp. 542-554.

Downes, James F., 1965, "The Social Consequences of a Dry Well," *American Anthropologist*, Vol. 67, pp. 1387-1416.

Dury, George H., 1972, "Some Current Trends in Geomorphology," *Earth Science Reviews*, Vol. 8, pp. 45-72.

El-Ashry, M. T. and H. R. Wanless, 1965, "Birth and Early Growth of a Tidal Delta," *Journal of Geology*, Vol. 73, pp. 404-406.

Eschman, Donald F. and Melvin G. Marcus, 1972, "The Geologic and Topographic Setting of Cities," *Urbanization and Environment.* Edited by Thomas R. Detwyler and Melvin G. Marcus. Belmont, California: Duxbury Press.

Farvar, M. Taghi and John P. Milton (eds.), 1972, *The Careless Technology: Ecology and International Development.* New York: Natural History Press.

Fassig, O. L., 1930, "On the Frequency of Hurricanes in the Vicinity of Puerto Rico," *Monthly Weather Review*, Vol. 58, pp. 326-327.

Felton, Robert S., William K. Ghee and John E. Stinton, 1971, "A Mid-1970 Report on the National Flood Insurance Program," *Journal of Risk and Insurance*, Vol. 39, pp. 1-14.

Firth, Raymond, 1959, *Social Change in Tikopia: Re-Study of a Polynesian Community After A Generation.* London: George Allen and Unwin Ltd.

Fournier d'Albe, E. M., 1971, "On Cyclones and Other Natural Disasters—Reflections of a Geophysicist," *UNESCO Courier*, February, pp. 24-27.

Freeberne, Michael, 1962, "Natural Calamities in China, 1949-61: An Examination of the Reports Originating from the Mainland," *Pacific Viewpoint*, Vol. 3, pp. 33-72.

Glacken, Clarence J., 1967, *Traces on the Rhodian Shore: Nature and Culture in Western Thought from Ancient Times to the End of the Eighteenth Century.* Berkeley: University of California Press.

Golant, Stephen and Ian Burton, 1969a, *Avoidance-Response to the Risk Environment.* Natural Hazard Research Working Paper No. 6. Toronto: University of Toronto, Department of Geography.

_____, 1969b, *The Meaning of a Hazard-Application of the Semantic Differential.* Natural Hazard Research Working Paper No. 7. Toronto: University of Toronto, Department of Geography.

Gould, Peter R., 1963, "Man Against His Environment: A Game Theoretic Framework," *Annals of The Association of American Geographers*, Vol. 53, pp. 290-297.

_____, 1965, "Wheat on Kilimanjaro: The Perception of Choice Within Game and Learning Model Frameworks," *General Systems*, Vol. 10, pp. 157-166.

Haas, J. Eugene, 1968, "Sociological Aspects of Human Dimensions of the Atmosphere," *Human Dimensions of the Atmosphere.* Edited by W. R. Derrick Sewell, *et al.* Washington, D.C.: National Science Foundation.

Hayes, Miles O., 1967, *Hurricanes as Geological Agents: Case Studies of Hurricane Carla, 1961 and Cindy, 1963.* Report of Investigation No. 61. Austin: University of Texas, Bureau of Economic Geology.

Healy, John, W. W. Rubey, D. T. Griggs and C. B. Raleigh, 1968, "The Denver Earthquakes," *Science*, Vol. 161, pp. 1301-1310.

Heathcote, R. L., 1969a, "Die Dürre als Faktor der Australischen Wirtschaft (Drought as a Factor in the Australian Economy)," *Geographische Rundschau*, Vol. 21, pp. 308-315.

_____, 1969b, "Drought in Australia: A Problem of Perception," *Geographical Review*, Vol. 59, pp. 175-194.

_____, 1972, "Human Adjustment to Agricultural Drought in South Australia." Unpublished Paper. International Geographical Union, Commission on Man and Environment. Commission Meeting, Calgary, Alberta, July 23-30, 1972.

Heijnen, J. and Robert W. Kates, 1972, "Drought in Northeast Tanzania: Comparative Observations on Farm Experience and Adjustment at 13 Sites." Unpublished Paper. International Geographical Union, Commission on Man and Environment. Commission Meeting, Calgary, Alberta, July 23-30, 1972.

Hewings, J. M., 1968, *Water Quality and the Hazard to Health: Placarding Public Beaches.*

Natural Hazard Research Working Paper No. 3. Toronto: University of Toronto, Department of Geography.

Hewitt, Kenneth, 1970, "Probabilistic Approaches to Discrete Natural Events: A Review and a Discussion," *Economic Geography*, Vol. 46, pp. 332-349.

Hewitt, Kenneth and Ian Burton, 1971, *The Hazardousness of a Place: A Regional Ecology of Damaging Events.* University of Toronto, Department of Geography Research Publication No. 6. Toronto: University of Toronto Press.

High, Lee R., Jr., 1969, "Storms and Sedimentation Processes Along the Northern British Honduras Coast," *Journal of Sedimentary Petrology*, Vol. 39, pp. 235-245.

High School Geography Project, Association of American Geographers, 1965, 1967, 1969, 1970, *Geography in an Urban Age.* New York: Macmillan.

Hunter, John M., 1967, "Population Pressure in a Part of the West African Savanna: A Study of Nangodi, Northeast Ghana," *Annals of The Association of American Geographers*, Vol. 57, pp. 101-114.

Islam, A. I., 1971, *Human Adjustment to Cyclone Hazards: A Case Study of Char Jabbar.* Natural Hazard Research Working Paper No. 18. Toronto: University of Toronto, Department of Geography.

——, 1972, "Hazard and Choice Perception in Coastal Bangladesh." Unpublished Paper. International Geographical Union, Commission on Man and Environment. Commission Meeting, Calgary, Alberta, July 23-30, 1972.

Jackson, Edgar and Tapan Mukerjee, 1972, "Human Adjustment to Earthquake Hazard in San Francisco, California." Unpublished Paper. International Geographical Union, Commission on Man and Environment. Commission Meeting, Calgary, Alberta, July 23-30, 1972.

Jackson, Richard, 1972, "Perception of Frost Hazard in the Wasatch Front, Utah." Unpublished Paper. International Geographical Union, Commission on Man and Environment. Commission Meeting, Calgary, Alberta, July 23-30, 1972.

Johnson, James F., 1971, *Renovated Waste Water: An Alternative Source of Municipal Water Supply in the United States.* Chicago: University of Chicago, Department of Geography Research Paper No. 135.

Kasperson, Roger E., 1969*a*, "Political Behavior and the Decision-Making Process in the Allocation of Water Resources Between Recreational and Municipal Use," *Natural Resources Journal*, Vol. 8, pp. 176-211.

——, 1969*b*, "Environmental Stress and the Municipal Political System," *The Structure of Political Geography.* Edited by Julian V. Minghi and Roger E. Kasperson. Chicago: Aldine Publishing Company.

Kates, Robert W., 1962, *Hazard and Choice Perception in Flood Plain Management.* Chicago: University of Chicago, Department of Geography Research Paper No. 78.

——, 1963, "Perceptual Regions and Regional Perception in Flood Plain Management," *Papers and Proceedings of The Regional Science Association*, Vol. 11, pp. 217-227.

——, 1965, *Industrial Flood Losses: Damage Estimation in the Lehigh Valley.* Chicago: University of Chicago, Department of Geography Research Paper No. 98.

——, 1970, "Human Adjustment to the Earthquake Hazard," *The Great Alaska Earthquake of 1964: Human Ecology.* Committee on the Alaska Earthquake, Division of Earth Sciences, National Research Council. Washington, D.C.: National Academy of Sciences.

——, 1971, "Natural Hazard in Human Ecological Perspective: Hypotheses and Models," *Economic Geography*, Vol. 47, pp. 438-451.

——, 1972, review of *Perspectives of Resource Management*, by T. O'Riordan, *Annals of the Association of American Geographers,* Vol. 62, pp. 519-520.

Kirkby, Anne V., 1972*a*, "Perception of Rainfall Variability and Agricultural and Social Adaptation to Hazard by Peasant Cultivators in the Valley of Oaxaca, Mexico." Unpublished Paper. International Geographical Union, Commission on Man and Environment. Commission Meeting, Calgary, Alberta, July 23-30, 1972.

——, 1972*b*, "Perception of Air Pollution as a Hazard and Individual Adjustment to It in Three British Cities." Unpublished Paper. International Geographical Union, Commission on Man and Environment. Commission Meeting, Calgary, Alberta, July 23-30, 1972.

Knight, Gregory C., 1971, "The Ecology of African Sleeping Sickness," *Annals of the Association of American Geographers*, Vol. 61, pp. 23-44.

Lambrick, H. T., 1967, "The Indus Flood Plain and the 'Indus' Civilization," *Geographical Journal*, Vol. 133, pp. 483-494.

Langfelder, Leonard J., Donald B. Stafford and Michael Amein, 1970, "Coastal Erosion in

North Carolina," *Journal of The Waterways and Harbors Division*, Proceedings of the American Society of Civil Engineers (May), pp. 531-545.

Latter, J. H., 1969, "Natural Disasters," *Advancement of Science*, Vol. 25, pp. 362-380.

Lessa, William A., 1964, "The Social Effects of Typhoon Ophelia (1960) on Ulithi," *Micronesia*, Vol. 5, pp. 1-47.

Lipton, Michael, 1968, *A Game Against Nature: Theories of Peasant Decision Making.* Communication No. 4. Sussex: University of Sussex, Institute of Development Studies.

MacIver, Ian, 1970, *Urban Water Supply Alternatives: Perception and Choice in the Grand Basin, Ontario.* Chicago: Department of Geography Research Paper No. 126.

Maunder, W. J., 1970, *The Value of the Weather.* London: Methuen and Company Ltd.

Meinig, D. W., 1962, *On the Margins of the Good Earth: The South Australian Wheat Frontier 1869-1884.* Association of American Geographers Monograph No. 2. Chicago: Rand McNally and Company.

Mensching, H., K. Gressner and G. Stuckmann, 1970, "Die Hochwasserkatastrophe in Tunesien im Herbst 1969. Beobachtungen über die Auswirkungen in der Natur und Kulturlandschaft (The Flood Catastrophe in Tunisia, Autumn 1969. Observations of the Effects Upon the Natural and Cultural Landscape)," *Geographische Zeitschrift*, Vol. 58, pp. 81-94.

Moore, Harry E. *et al.*, 1964, . . . *And The Winds Blew.* Austin: Hogg Foundation for Mental Health, University of Texas.

Mitchell, James K., 1973, *Community Response to Coastal Erosion: A Study of Conditions on the Atlantic Shore.* University of Chicago, Department of Geography Research Paper (forthcoming).

Mukerjee, Tapan, 1971, *Economic Analysis of Natural Hazards: A Preliminary Study of Adjustments to Earthquakes and Their Costs.* Natural Hazard Research Working Paper No. 17. Toronto: University of Toronto, Department of Geography.

_____ , 1972, *Economic Analysis of the Alternative Adjustments to Drought in the Great Plains.* National Water Commission Report. Stockton, California: University of the Pacific, Department of Economics.

Murphy, Francis C., 1958, *Regulating Flood-Plain Development.* Chicago: University of Chicago, Department of Geography Research Paper No. 56.

Murton, Brian J. and Shinzo Shimabukuro, 1972, "Human Adjustment to Volcanic Hazard in Puna District, Hawaii." Unpublished Paper. International Geographical Union, Commission on Man and Environment. Commission Meeting, Calgary, Alberta, July 23-30, 1972.

Nakano, T. *et al.*, 1972, "Natural Hazards and Field Interview Research—Reports from Japan." Unpublished Paper. International Geographical Union, Commission on Man and Environment. Commission Meeting, Calgary, Alberta, July 23-30, 1972.

O'Riordan, Timothy, 1971*a*, "Towards a Strategy of Public Involvement," *Perceptions and Attitudes in Resource Management.* Edited by W. R. D. Sewell and Ian Burton. Resource Paper No. 2. Ottawa: Department of Energy, Mines and Resources, Policy Research and Coordination Branch.

_____ , 1971*b*, "Public Opinion and Environmental Quality," *Environment and Behavior*, Vol. 3, pp. 191-214.

_____ , 1971*c*, *The New Zealand Earthquake and War Damage Commission—A Study of a National Natural Hazard Insurance Scheme.* Natural Hazard Research Working Paper No. 20. Toronto: University of Toronto, Department of Geography.

Oyà, Masahiko, 1970, "Land Use Control and Settlement Plans in the Flooded Area of the City of Nagoya and Its Vicinity, Japan," *Geoforum*, No. 4, pp. 27-36.

Parra, Carlos G., 1972, "Droughts in Ticula, Yucatan, Mexico." Unpublished Paper. International Geographical Union, Commission on Man and Environment. Commission Meeting, Calgary, Alberta, July 23-30, 1972.

Perry, R. A., 1962, "Notes on the Alice Springs Area Following Rain in Early 1962," *Arid Zone Newsletter*, pp. 85-91.

Raikes, R. L., 1964, "The End of the Ancient Cities of the Indus," *American Anthropologist*, Vol. 116, pp. 284-289.

Raup, Hugh M., 1957, "Vegetation Adjustment to the Instability of the Site," *Proceedings of the 6th Technical Meeting, International Union for Conservation and Natural Resources.* London: IUCN.

_____ , 1964, "Some Problems in Ecological Theory and Their Relation to Conservation," *Journal of Ecology*, Vol. 52, pp. 19-28.

Rees, John D., 1970. "Paricutin Revisited: A Review of Man's Attempts to Adapt to Ecological Changes Resulting from Volcanic Catastrophe," *Geoforum*, No. 4, pp. 7-25.

Roder, Wolf and Herb Dupree, 1972, "Coping with Drought in a Preindustrial, Pre-Literate Farming Society." Unpublished Paper. International Geographical Union, Commission on Man and Environment. Commission Meeting, Calgary, Alberta, July 23-30, 1972.

Rooney, J., 1969, "The Economic and Social Implications of Snow and Ice," *Water, Earth and Man: A Synthesis of Hydrology, Geomorphology and Socio-Economic Geography.* Edited by Richard J. Chorley. London: Methuen and Company Ltd.

Russell, Clifford S., 1970, "Losses from Natural Hazards," *Journal of Land Economics,* Vol. 46, pp. 383-393.

Russell, Clifford S., David G. Arey and Robert W. Kates, 1970, *Drought and Water Supply: Implications of the Massachusetts Experience for Municipal Planning.* Baltimore: Johns Hopkins Press.

Russell, Richard J., 1956, "Environmental Changes Through Forces Independent of Man," *Man's Role in Changing the Face of the Earth.* Edited by William L. Thomas. Chicago: University of Chicago Press.

Saarinen, Thomas F., 1966, *Perception of the Drought Hazard on the Great Plains.* University of Chicago, Department of Geography Research Paper No. 106.

Sahlins, Marshall D., 1962, *Moala: Culture and Nature on a Fijian Island.* Ann Arbor: University of Michigan Press.

Schaake, John C., 1972, "Water and the City," *Urbanization and Environment.* Edited by Thomas R. Detwyler and Melvin G. Marcus. Belmont, California: Duxbury Press.

Schiff, Ashley L., 1966, "Innovation and Administrative Decision Making: The Conservation of Land Resources," *Administrative Science Quarterly,* Vol. 11, pp. 1-30.

Schneider, D. M., 1957, "Typhoons on Yap," *Human Organization,* Vol. 16, pp. 10-15.

Schwimmer, Eric G., 1969, *Cultural Consequences of a Volcanic Eruption Experienced by the Mount Lamington Orokaiva.* Eugene: University of Oregon, Department of Anthropology.

Sestini, Aldo, 1962, "Regressive Phases in the Development of the Cultural Landscape," in Philip L. Wagner and Marvin W. Mikesell (eds.), *Readings in Cultural Geography.* Chicago: University of Chicago Press.

Sewell, W. R. Derrick, 1965, *Water Management and Floods in the Fraser River Basin.* Chicago: University of Chicago, Department of Geography Research Paper No. 100.

_____, 1969, "Human Response to Floods," *Water, Earth and Man.* Edited by Richard J. Chorley. London: Methuen and Company, Ltd.

_____, 1971, "Environmental Perceptions and Attitudes of Engineers and Public Health Officials," *Environment and Behavior,* Vol. 3, pp. 23-60.

Sheaffer, John R., 1960, *Flood Proofing: An Element in a Flood Damage Reduction Program.* Chicago: University of Chicago, Department of Geography Research Paper No. 65.

Sheaffer, John R., Davis W. Ellis and Andrew M. Spieker, 1970, *Flood-Hazard Mapping in Metropolitan Chicago.* U.S. Geological Survey Circular 601-C., Washington, D.C.

Sheehan, Lesley and Kenneth Hewitt, 1969, *A Pilot Survey of Global Natural Disasters of the Past Twenty Years.* Natural Hazard Research Working Paper No. 11. Toronto: University of Toronto, Department of Geography.

Shepard, Francis P. and Harold R. Wanless, 1971, *Our Changing Coastlines.* New York: McGraw-Hill Book Company.

Sims, John and Duane D. Baumann, 1972, "The Tornado Threat: Coping Styles of the North and South," *Science,* Vol. 176, pp. 1386-1392.

Sims, John and Thomas F. Saarinen, 1969, "Coping with Environmental Threat: Great Plains Farmers and the Sudden Storm," *Annals of the Association of American Geographers,* Vol. 59, pp. 677-686.

Smithsonian Institute, 1971, *Natural Disaster Research Centers and Warning Systems: A Preliminary Survey.* Center for Short-Lived Phenomena, Cambridge, Mass.

Spillius, James, 1957, "Natural Disaster and Political Crisis in a Polynesian Society: An Exploration of Operational Research," *Human Relations,* Vol. 10, pp. 3-27, 113-125.

Steers, James A., 1953, "The East Coast Floods, 31 January-1 February, 1953," *Geographical Journal,* Vol. 119, pp. 280-298.

Stoddart, David R., 1971, "Coral Reefs and Islands and Catastrophic Storms," *Applied Coastal Geomorphology.* Edited by J. A. Steers. London: Macmillan.

Sugg, Arnold E., 1967, "Economic Aspects of Hurricanes," *Monthly Weather Review,* Vol. 95, pp. 143-146.

Taylor, Alan R., 1971, "Lightning–Agent of Change in Forest Ecosystems," *Journal of Forestry,* Vol. 68, pp. 477-480.

Taylor, James A. (ed.), 1970, *Weather Economics.* Oxford: Pergamon Press.

Tazieff, Haroun, 1966, "Volcano Survey," *Earth Science Reviews,* Vol. 1, pp. 299-335.

Thomas, M. F. and G. W. Whittington (eds.), 1969, *Environment and Land Use in Africa.* London: Methuen and Co. Ltd.

Thompson, Kenneth, 1969, "Irrigation as a Menace to Health in California: A Nineteenth Century View," *Geographical Review,* Vol. 59, pp. 195-214.

United Nations Technical Assistance Board, 1968, *Village Planning and Reconstruction of the Earthquake Zone In the Ghazvin Area, Iran.* Teheran.

U.S. House of Representatives, 1966, *A Unified National Program for Managing Flood Losses.* House Document 465, 89th Congress, Second Session, Washington, D.C.

Vaughan, Christopher K., 1971, *Notes on Insurance Against Loss from Natural Hazards.* Natural Hazard Research Working Paper No. 20. Toronto: University of Toronto, Department of Geography.

Ward, Robert M., 1972, "Models of Weather Hazard Perception and Decision Making in Florida Agriculture." Unpublished Paper. International Geographical Union, Commission on Man and Environment. Commission Meeting, Calgary, Alberta, July 23-30, 1972.

Weaver, David C., 1968, "The Hurricane as an Economic Catalyst," *Journal of Tropical Geography,* Vol. 27, pp. 66-71.

White, Anne M., 1972, Global Summary of Human Response to Natural Hazards—Tropical Cyclones. Unpublished Paper. International Geographical Union, Commission on Man and Environment. Commission Meeting, Calgary, Alberta, July 23-30, 1972.

White, Gilbert F., 1945, *Human Adjustment to Floods: A Geographical Approach to the Flood Problem in the United States.* University of Chicago, Department of Geography Research Paper No. 29.

———, 1961, "The Choice of Use in Resource Management," *Natural Resource Journal,* Vol. 1, pp. 23-40.

———, 1964, *Choice of Adjustment to Floods.* University of Chicago, Department of Geography Research Paper No. 93.

———, 1966, "Formation and Role of Public Attitudes," in Henry Jarrett (ed.), *Environmental Quality in a Growing Economy.* Baltimore: Johns Hopkins Press.

———, 1969, *Strategies of American Water Management.* Ann Arbor: University of Michigan Press.

———, 1970, "Recent Developments in Flood Plain Research," *Geographical Review,* Vol. 60, pp. 440-443.

———, 1973a, "Natural Hazards Research," in Richard J. Chorley (ed.), *Directions in Geography* (forthcoming).

——— (ed.), 1973b, *Natural Hazard Perception and Choice.* Oxford: Oxford University Press.

White, Gilbert F. *et al.,* 1958, *Changes in Urban Occupance of Flood Plains in the United States.* University of Chicago, Department of Geography Research Paper No. 57.

——— *et al.,* 1961, *Papers on Flood Problems.* University of Chicago, Department of Geography Research Paper No. 70.

Wisner, Benjamin and Philip Mbithi, 1972, "Drought in Eastern Kenya: Comparative Observations of Nutritional Status and Farmer Activity in 17 Sites." Unpublished Paper. International Geographical Union, Commission on Man and Environment. Commission Meeting, Calgary, Alberta, July 23-30, 1972.

Wolman, M. G. and J. P. Miller, 1960, "Magnitude and Frequency of Forces in Geomorphic Processes," *Journal of Geology,* Vol. 68, pp. 54-74.

Wong, Shue Tuck, 1968, *Perception of Choice and Factors Affecting Industrial Water Supply Decisions in Northeastern Illinois.* University of Chicago, Department of Geogaphy Research Paper No. 117.

Yamashita, A. C., 1965, "Attitudes and Reactions to Typhoon Karen (1962) in Guam," *Micronesia,* Vol. 6, pp. 15-23.

Young, Michael W., 1971, *Fighting With Food: Leadership, Values and Social Control in a Massim Society.* Cambridge: Cambridge University Press.

Zenger, Donald H., 1970, "The Role of Rapid Events in Earth History," *Journal of Geological Education,* Vol. 18, pp. 42-43.

The Savanna Biome:
A Case Study of Human Impact
on Biotic Communities

Theo L. Hills
McGill University

The savanna biome encompasses approximately 7 million square miles or 18 million square kilometers of the world's land surface, slightly more than a tenth of its total area (Figure 1). One hundred million human beings and countless small and large mammalian herbivores and predators occupy this biome, although they are distributed most unevenly. The African savannas are by far the most heavily populated, whereas those in South America and Australia are relatively lightly populated (Table 1). The major objective of this chapter is to describe the savanna biome and to investigate the nature and intensity of human impact on its biotic communities.

The savanna biome is one of the major biosystems or ecosystems on the earth's surface. Other major biosystems and ecosystems are the tundra, the temperate grasslands, the tropical rainforest, and the desert. The savanna biome is the largest land community unit which can be recognized conveniently. It is a total community unit, in that the major physical and biological components—climate, substrate, and both flora and fauna—interact to produce a homogeneity which characterizes the biome. Although most biomes are named for the dominant plant formation or the lifeform of the vegetation, it is the combination of plant formation and regional biota that produces the biome. Under natural conditions the two live in harmony with each other. Although the term savanna is occasionally used to describe the combination of grasses, sedges, and woody species in subtropical and mid-latitude regions, it is used here to refer to tropical regions.

The biome can also be considered as a level of scale, or type of ecosystem, with the ecosystem defined as a functioning and interacting system comprised of one or more living organisms and their effective environments, physical, biological, and cultural. Not only is it convenient to consider the whole of the savanna biome as an ecosystem but also the whole wide range of distinct communities within it, such as a discrete savanna in the heart of the Amazon Basin or a small pond in the heart of the Venezuelan Llanos. Studying the savanna biome or any part of it within the context of the ecosystem concept has

342

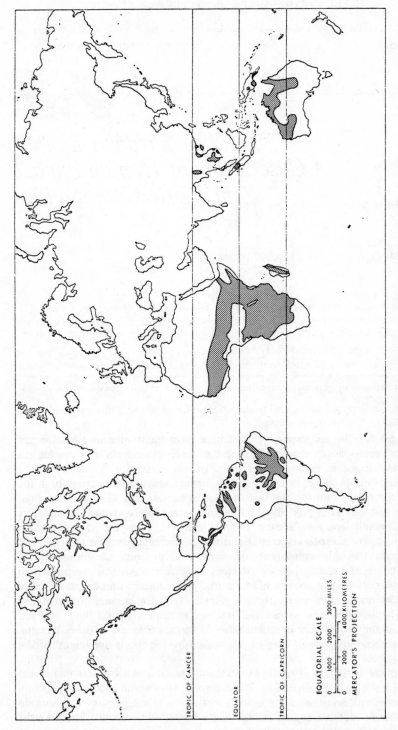

Figure 1. World Distribution of the Savanna Biome. This map attempts to portray the distribution of the existing savanna biome. It is not a map of the potential natural savanna vegetation. Therefore, the savanna biome is not represented on the Indian subcontinent.

TROPIC OF CANCER

EQUATOR

TROPIC OF CAPRICORN

EQUATORIAL SCALE

0   1000   2000   3000 MILES

0   2000   4000 KILOMETRES

MERCATOR'S PROJECTION

TABLE 1—Extent and Population of Savanna Regions

Region	Area*	Population	Population Densities per sq. km.
Africa	3,915,000 sq. mi. 10,297,000 sq. km.	90,000,000	Av: 7 5 – 400
Australia	1,002,000 sq. mi. 2,800,000 sq. km.	50,000	−1 to 2 or 3
South America	1,170,000 sq. mi. 3,027,000 sq. km.	2,500,000	−1 to 15
Central America and Mexico	336,000 sq. mi. 885,000 sq. km.	500,000	−1 to 20
Asia and Pacific	416,000 sq. mi. 1,094,000 sq. km.	1,250,000	--
Total	6,839,000 sq. mi. 18,103,000 sq. km.	94,300,000	

* Figures obtained by planimeter measurements of savanna as delimited on most authoritative vegetation maps.

advantages for the geographer in that man must be studied as one of many biological components, thus minimizing the tendency, especially of the human geographer, to see man always at the center of every system.

Biomes exist in space, and thus have a distinct geographic expression. In the case of the savanna biome, the keynote of this expression is savanna vegetation. Savanna can be defined as plant formation, comprising a virtually continuous and ecologically dominant stratum of more or less xeromorphic plants, of which herbaceous plants, especially grasses and sedges, are frequently the principal and occasionally the only components. However woody plants, usually the size of shrubs but occasionally the size of trees, generally occur and are present in varying densities. Any savanna biome is likely to contain components of other vegetation types, such as riparian or galeria forest forms, small forest inliers (bush islands, islets, and so on) and marshes, swamps, palm communities, and pure grassland. These may represent edaphic and subclimaxes or developmental stages (successions), which may be dominated by life forms not typical of the savanna biome.

Given this definition of savanna vegetation, the savanna biome can be defined as a tropical biome dominated by savanna vegetation which is characteristically herbaceous with some woody species. It reflects adjustment both to a concentrated low to medium annual rainfall and a lengthy dry season (three to eight months) accompanied by frequent burning. It produces a major basic source of food harvested by grazing animals, both domesticated and wild mammalian herbivores (Figure 2).

DISTRIBUTION, DESCRIPTION, AND DIFFERENTIATION

The savanna biome, although zonal, occurs discontinuously within the tropics, north and south of the equatorial rain forest, in contrast to the northern conifer forest biome which almost continuously straddles the 60° line of latitude on land. Only in Africa would it be possible to cross the continent latitudinally entirely within the savanna biome. As already indicated in Figure 1, over half of the earth's savanna biome is located in Africa, while Australia and South America each possess about one-sixth. In South America the biome is considerably fragmented especially in and around the periphery of the Amazon basin (see Figure 6).

A simple descriptive model of the savanna biome, consisting of an itemization of generalizations about the biome, will serve both to characterize the biome and to differentiate between one sub-type and another.

(1) The savanna biome occurs predominantly on surfaces of little relief, generally senile landscapes such as old alluvial plains and planation surfaces of Tertiary age.

(2) Poor drainage is characteristic because of the low relief and because many savanna soil types are affected unfavorably by internal physical structure, such as impermeable horizons formed by clays that are

Figure 2. The Dynamic Edge of the Savanna Biome, Rupununi District, Southern Guyana. In the foreground is a typical herbaceous savanna with scattered trees. In the background savanna is advancing into the previously forest-covered Guiana Highlands. (Photo by T. L. Hills.)

frequently laterized, occasionally by laterite which generally gives rise to perched water tables, and also by excessively drained horizons.

(3) Elevations within the savanna biome range from sea-level to about 5,000 feet (1525 m.) with levels between 2,000 to 3,000 feet (600-900 m.) predominating.

(4) The savanna biome occurs under a great variety of climatic conditions, but most commonly under a seasonality dependent upon occurrence and non-occurrence of rainfall rather than of temperature. Annual rainfall totals range from approximately 15 inches to over 150 inches (380-3800 mm.), with one or two rainy seasons and a high degree of concentration (50-90 percent during the maximum rainy period). Dry seasons range in length from 2 to 8 months. A relatively high constancy and speed of winds during the main dry season have a significant impact upon rates of evapotranspiration, the rapid drying out of soils and surface litter, and thus upon the effectiveness of fires.

(5) The hydrological cycle in savanna regions is characterized by extreme seasonal fluctuations and annual variability. Many lowland savanna biomes are almost completely inundated from one to four months each year. Many rivers, especially tributary streams, are intermittent, and will break up into ponds during the latter half of the dry season. Generally speaking, savanna biome rivers carry much more water in South America than in Africa and Australia. Fluctuations in river levels in South America are also much greater than in Africa and Australia, with differences of 20 feet (6 m.) between the dry and rainy season being common. Rivers in South America produce much greater inundations than elsewhere.

(6) Most soils of the savanna biome are characterized by a low nutrient status that is probably most extreme in deep, highly leached latosols from which soluble nutrients have been completely removed.

(7) Savanna vegetation varies greatly. On a biome-wide basis the only classification of any value is one based upon structure and physiognomy, because of the relative uniformity of these elements in formations, associations, and communities on each of the continents. Within the continental unit a floristic classification becomes useful. The following primary categories and sub-formations can be recognized.

  (a) Herbaceous savanna, savanna grassland, or *campo limpo* (Brazilian).
  (b) Shrub savanna or *campo sujo*, low tree savanna, or xerophilous savanna. Shrubs and woody plants 1 to 3 meters high with a canopy cover of less than 2 percent.
  (c) Open savanna woodland, parkland, orchard savanna, or *campo coberto*. Shrubs and trees, over 3 meters high with a canopy cover of 2-20 percent.
  (d) Savanna woodland, *campo cerrado*, or tropophilous savanna. Mainly trees with a canopy cover of 20-50 percent.
  (e) Closed savanna woodland or *cerradao*. Trees with a complete canopy.

Only broad associations between these categories and other environmental factors can be drawn. There is little doubt, for example, that savanna woodland predominates on old lateritic soils and planation surfaces, while grasslands predominate on watersheds, lowlands and floodplains. Open savanna woodland tends to correspond with areas of better drainage under any of the above conditions.

(8) Seasonality varies in part with the degree of deciduousness. Most trees in the savanna are deciduous although this is not true of the *campo cerrado* or savanna woodland of the New World tropics. However, during the latter half of the dry season, regardless of the degree of deciduousness, fire will often cause leaves to fall. Generally the combination of dryness, deciduousness, and fire greatly reduces the amount of foliage and thus the screening effect of plants.

(9) The savanna biome has a boundary with one form or another of tropical or sub-tropical rainforest; some form of semi-arid scrub, dry deciduous forest, or coastal vegetation. The actual boundary is usually extremely abrupt, a condition which in many areas is due to fire in the savanna vegetation (Figure 3). The configuration of the boundary varies from the fairly regular to the irregular. An irregular configuration may be due to physical and/or cultural factors. Where plateaus within the savanna biome are being dissected, forest may occupy the valleys. The penetration of adjacent forest by roads and railroads accompanied by settlement may also lead to savanna indentations. Along such boundaries a mosaic of forest and savanna may mark the savanna's advance as it surrounds islands of forest.

(10) Most savanna vegetation is burned frequently, in some areas two to three times in two years. Savanna vegetation is well adapted to fire and many plants are "pyrophytes," i.e., plants that are burned to the ground surface and which may have more wood below ground than above. Many pyrophytes are insulated by a thick corky bark and may be impregnated by a fire resistant substance. Such plants may also have

Figure 3. An Amerindian Village 2 to 3 Miles (3.2-4.8 km.) from a Typical Abrupt Forest/Savanna Boundary. A sand and gravel ridge elevates the village site about 30 feet (9 m.) above the 3-to-4 month-long rainy season inundation. (Photo by T. L. Hills.)

seeds which are resistant to fire, or be precocious and produce flower and fruit while less than three feet tall. Fire undoubtedly controls woody species in a variety of ways, and some may eventually survive because of a lack of combustible material. Fire generally promotes grasses and herbs at the expense of woody species.

If fires are frequent and not severe, they will not alter the physical properties of soils, but erosion and loss of productivity will occur. The ash of savanna burns is generally washed too deep to be recycled.

(11) There is a specialized savanna fauna, which is most marked in Africa, especially East Africa where a wide spectrum of wild herbivores are to be found in large numbers. In parts of East Africa, well over 20 species of wild ungulates may live and feed in the same area. Australia with its kangaroos and wallabies is very poor in wildlife species compared to East Africa, but significantly richer than the New World savanna biome which can lay claim only to a variety of rodents and a deer which has now virtually disappeared.

(12) Termites are active in most savanna regions, although those in Australia and the New World biome cannot compare in the intensity of their modifying action on savanna soils and landscapes to their African counterparts. On the other hand, ants would appear to be much more active in the New World savanna biome. Another group of insects feeds directly and indirectly upon the herbivores. Many of these pose no major threat to animals and humans. However, there are the biting flies such as the tsetse (*Glossina spp.*) which is a major menace to both man and domesticated livestock over vast areas of savanna woodland in Africa, and ticks, which reduce the efficiency of domesticated livestock throughout the savanna biome.

(13) Productivity levels vary significantly throughout the savanna biome with net production levels ranging from less than 100 to 2000 grams per square meter per year. For the greater part there is a clear relationship between the length of growing season which corresponds to the major wet season and net production rates based upon above ground peak standing crop data for herbaceous vegetation (Table 2).

(14) Man and other animals are severely restricted in their choice of "niches" in the savanna biome. Both seek those areas where the nutrient, water and energy cycles combine to produce a more favored habitat, one characterized by higher soil fertility, a perennial water supply, and a higher productivity level. Africa would appear to be most favorable, with a higher frequency of the coincidence of the above three character-istics, while the New World savanna biome comes a poor second, and that of Australia a very poor third. Both man and animal exploit the best of the two adjacent biomes. Man while locating his settlement in the savanna biome and hunting, fishing and grazing there, will also exploit the forest biome for cultivation, hunting, and collecting. Some animals also move from one biome to the other.

(15) The restricted nature, number, and distribution of these niches helps to explain the distribution of the human population. Prior to Westerniza-tion, population was primarily agricultural, or pastoral and migratory with the exception of West Africa where there was a small degree of urbanization. Today, population remains primarily rural and dependent upon some form of agriculture in which pastoralism continues to play a

TABLE 2—Productivity Levels

Location	Vegetation Type	Annual Rainfall (mm)	Growing Season (days)	Grams per sq. metre per year	References*
Nigeria Olokemeji	Derived savanna	1168	270	680	Hopkins: 1965, 1966
Ivory Coast Lamto	Forest/Savanna mosaic	1070 1660	270	2,000	Roland: 1967
Nigeria Shika	Guinean savanna	1118	200	340	Rains: 1963
Chad Tébédé	Sahelian savanna	320	40	325	Gillet: 1960
Rhodesia Matapos	Savanna woodland	650	–	145	Bourlière and Hadley (West, personal communication): 1970
South Africa Pretoria	Andropogon/Combretum veld	607	–	75-110	Robinson (J. O. Grunow, personal communication): 1970
Australia Katherine	Native pasture 1959/60 1960/61 1961/62	838 635 508	150 110 60	157 179 109	Norham: 1963
Venezuela Llanos	Trachypogon dominant	1300	130	240-404	Blydenstein: 1962, 1963

* As quoted in Bourlière and Hadley: 1970.

major role. Cultivation in the savanna biome is restricted almost entirely to Africa where quick-maturing grains predominate except where limited irrigation is possible. Symmetrically arranged mounds and ridges rising several feet above ground level provide evidence of intensive cultivation supporting dense populations in late pre-Columbian times in the savanna biomes of Venezuela, Colombia, and Bolivia (Denevan: 1970). Urbanization in the savanna biome is limited and existing towns can be explained largely in terms of administration and agricultural marketing activities, transportation networks, and mining activities.

HUMAN IMPACT ON THE SAVANNA BIOME

One useful way of assessing the degree of human impact on a biome is to attempt to contrast the functioning of the energy, nutrient or biochemical, and water or hydrological cycles under both natural and human-influenced conditions. The major limitation of this approach is that we do not always know what the natural conditions are or were, nor can we readily obtain data on cycling. An attempt is made in Figure 4 to highlight changes in some of the macro-relationships in a savanna biome which affect one or more of the three cycles. This simple model also provides the opportunity of contrasting the savanna and forest biomes.

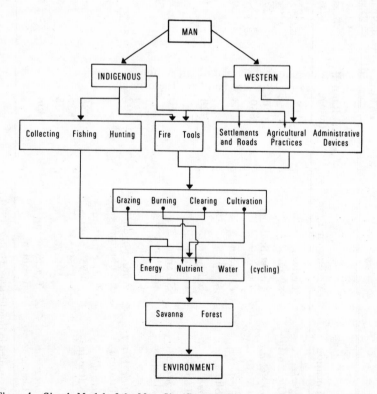

Figure 4.   Simple Model of the Most Significant Relationships in the Savanna Biome.

In using this model it is imperative to remember that any ecosystem or a biome is a highly complex natural unit composed of a variety of organisms and their inorganic environment. All components of the system are linked by processes, such as the fixation of energy, intake of nutrients, movement of nutrients and energy through food chains, release of nutrients by the decomposition of organic matter, and release of nutrients by weathering. In addition, any ecosystem or biome is linked to adjacent land or water.

In contrast to the natural rain forest biome which is characterized by a closed-nutrient cycle and in which nutrients and water are fairly uniformly available, the typical savanna biome is characterized by complexity and disconformity in the distribution and availability of nutrients and water. In the tropical rain forest a low to medium density shifting cultivation occupance generally results in very little interference with the energy, nutrient, and water cycles. Likewise in a savanna biome, indigenous peoples relying for their livelihood upon the natural surplus of herds of native herbivores do little to upset the cycles. The forest area decreases as population increases and without the use of advanced technology will eventually result in impoverishment of the vegetation. Thus the nutrient supply declines (unless soils are naturally very fertile), runoff increases contributing to both loss of nutrients and water and eventually to a decline in the energy supply readily available to man. Similar changes will occur in the savanna biome if the vegetation is impoverished. However, the intensity of the change may well be greater, because a reduction in the vegetation cover as well as surface litter exposes the soil to more direct radiation, higher temperatures, and more direct rainfall.

The establishment of political boundaries and the building of fences, roads, and railroads has greatly restricted the natural and logical movements of indigenous man and fauna in many parts of the world's savanna biome during the last century. Restrictions in the form of boundaries, fences, and roads have either prevented or hindered the natural migrations of men and fauna between one nutrient or water niche and another. These results are discussed in more detail later in this chapter.

THE GUIANA HIGHLANDS–AMAZON SAVANNAS

The Rupununi savannas of southern Guyana have been chosen for a more detailed illustration of human impact upon the savanna biome, primarily because of the author's studies in this area for the past decade as part of a continuing multi-disciplinary research program (Figure 5).

The Rupununi savannas are a portion of what ordinarily appears on vegetation maps of South America as a section of the savanna biome extending from French Guiana, through southern Surinam and Guyana, to the northernmost tip of Brazil, and to the Gran Sabana of Venezuela. The savanna biome occupies no more than a half of this total area. Accurate mapping indicated that the Guyana share of this savanna amounts to about 5,000 square miles (12,949 square kilometers) which is merely an appendage of the far more extensive 16,000 square miles (41429.8 square kilometers) Rio Branco savanna region of Brazil. The savannas are completely surrounded by forest. Figure 6 indicates that the Rio Branco-Rupununi savanna region is one of the many discrete savannas located within and around the periphery of the Amazon Basin.

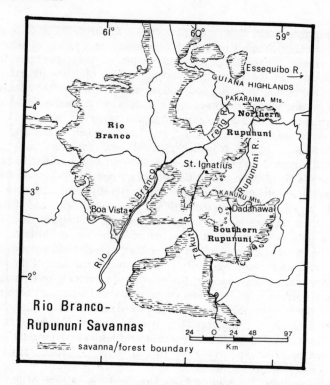

Figure 5. Rio Branco–Rupununi Savannas.

A peripheral location may be suggestive of a highland, watershed location, but only in the latter respect is this true of the Rupununi savannas, which straddle the Amazon-Essequibo divide from a lowest elevation of only 200 feet (61 m.) to about 900 feet (274 m.). This lowest level is quite extraordinary considering that the divide is approximately 1500 miles (2414 km.) by river from the mouth of the Amazon. Associated with the low elevation is flatness, which frequently leads, at the height of the rainy season, to a coalescence of the waters of the Amazonian and Guiana drainage. The flat plain of the low divide gives way in the south to higher undulating surfaces from which rise isolated peaks of a maximum height of 3,000 feet (914 meters). The whole is enclosed by mountain ranges and upland surfaces which rise from heights of 1500 feet (457 meters) to 4,000 feet (1219 meters). The northern boundary is formed by ridges of the Guiana Highlands.

The vegetation cover encompasses all five major categories of savanna, although herbaceous savanna and open savanna woodland predominate, with herbaceous savanna occupying the flat plain of the low divide and open and occasionally closed savanna woodland occupying the higher rolling upland surfaces.

Geologically this part of southern Guyana belongs to the Pre-Cambrian Guiana Shield of northeastern South America. The Pre-Cambrian is most obvious in the southern half of the region and around the periphery, while Quaternary fluvio-lacustrine deposits and gravel ridges primarily of lateritic origin predominate elsewhere. The entire landscape represents part of a Late Tertiary planation surface. Upon this bevelled surface the contemporary landscape has

Figure 6. Savannas of the Amazon Basin. The savanna biome as represented within and around the periphery of the Amazon basin. The small patches of savanna within the Amazon basin are primarily a mosaic of forest and savanna, with the savanna along the ridges and on escarpments.

been fashioned by Quaternary deposition and erosion.

The northern Rupununi corresponds to the lowland and flood plain landscapes of the Amazon basin while the southern Rupununi corresponds to uplands that rise above the Amazon planalto. The Plio-Pleistocene plateau of Amazonia is usually at 450 to 600 feet (150-200 meters) elevation. The northern Rupununi in this respect has a great deal in common with the Llanos de Mojos of the Beni Basin of northeastern Bolivia, which is also formed by a great depth of Quaternary sediment overlying a Pre-Cambrian basement. A significant difference is that these sediments are primarily derived from the younger rocks of the Andes, whereas those of the Rupununi are derived from the Pre-Cambrian rocks of the Guiana Highlands. Also common to the two regions is the degree of inundation during the rainy season; as much as three-fourths of the Llanos de Mojos is under several feet of water between December and June. These ecological conditions favor a herbaceous cover of grasses and sedges rather than savanna woodland.

The southern Rupununi has more in common with Tertiary and Pleistocene pediplanation landscapes of the southern upland periphery of the Amazon Basin. Low nutrient status, and slightly freer drainage, in spite of the occurrence of impermeable clay layers and fossil laterite, tend to favor savanna woodland rather than herbaceous savanna.

The origin and contemporary ecology of the Amazonian savanna has been explained in a variety of terms, primarily climatic, pedologic, edaphic, biotic, and anthropogenic. All these explanations would appear to suffer in one major respect—that they postulate the primacy of a particular determinant. Surely a causal role should only be attributed to an individual factor in the sense that it is immediate in chronological terms and limited in explicative relevance. The following hypothesis is presented not only as an illustration of the latter, but in an attempt to explain the nature, origin, and present distribution of the savanna vegetation of the Amazon Basin.

In many parts of the Amazon Basin climate predisposes the environment towards the development of savanna vegetation. A distinctive dry season of up to eight months as in the Rio Branco-Rupununi savanna often makes the presence of forest problematical. Low soil fertility and laterite are frequently considered as prime determinants of savanna vegetation, but here they are considered as features associated with the savanna biome. Occasionally they may be resultant factors, as when the nutrient cycle is broken following the disappearance of a forest. Fire, which is also frequently considered a prime determinant, is generally a maintaining factor, but in limited areas may be causal in the sense that it is immediate in chronological terms. Fire may well be the final act in a long series of regional environmental changes which have led to the development of a savanna biome at the expense of a rain forest biome. The stage of geomorphic evolution, relief, and slope and the dominant geomorphic processes in the landscape most directly influence the position and behavior of the water table, the soil moisture regime, the nutrient cycle, and the climates of the region, and thus in turn, the distribution of rain forest and savanna.

Implicit in the statement that climate predisposes the vegetation cover of parts of the Amazon Basin to some type of savanna vegetation rather than rain forest is the assumption that related climatic parameters such as the Moisture Index (Thornthwaite: 1948), evapotranspiration and dry months (months with a moisture deficit of less than 4 inches [10.2 cm] is illustrated in Table 3.) In some locations, such as the southern Rupununi, patches of forest occur in a region where there is normally a moisture deficit in eight months of the year. In parts of the Amazon Basin, the forest vegetation is undoubtedly a relict of a period of greater availability of soil moisture, when the environment generally predisposed the vegetation cover to forest rather than savanna. All paleobotanical evidence suggests wide fluctuations in the distribution of rain forest and savanna vegetation (Sombroek: 1966). The Amazonian rain forest which has for so long been portrayed as one of the most stable vegetation formations on the surface of the earth, has fluctuated considerably in extent, with the Guiana and Central Brazilian highlands serving as alternate reservoirs for forest and savanna. Given the present environmental predisposition of such extensive areas of the Amazon Basin towards savanna rather than forest, the concern of many conservationists regarding the likely impact of an intensive road building program upon the "luxuriant" tropical rain forest can be clearly understood.

The Rupununi savanna biome would thus appear to be set in a region of some ecological instability. This is extremely significant in assessing man's impact upon biotic communities. From the beginning of this century, there is plentiful evidence of this state of instability both within and around the limits of the Rupununi savanna biome. This evidence has been accumulated in the course of the McGill University Savanna Research Project in Guyana from 1958 to the present and is available in the project's publications (Savanna Series No. 1-15). Some forest enclaves have disappeared or are in the process of destruction, while others have developed on old Amerindian habitation sites. Around the greater

TABLE 3–Selected Climatic Parameters, Amazon Basin

	Location	Annual rainfall mm.	Number of dry months	Moisture Index[1]	
				Driest month	Wettest month
A	São Gabriel	2824	0	28(B_1)	186 (A)
B	Belem	2732	2	−33(B_1)	292 (A)
C	Santarem	1963	5	−74(E)	194 (A)
D	Dadenawa	1482	8	−82(E)	145 (A)
E	Yupukarri	1183	9	−95(E)	111 (A)
F	Manaus	1994	5	−74(E)	105 (A)
G	Clevelandia	3264	3	−75(E)	372 (A)
H	Coari	2258	3	−53(D)	155 (A)
I	Nunchia	2923	4	−92(E)	344 (A)
J	Porto Velho	2232	4	−88(E)	172 (A)
K	Santa Ana	1842	6	−88(E)	91 (B_4)
L	Mato Grosso	1345	6	−79(E)	89 (B_4)

[1] For complete explanation of Moisture Index see Thornthwaite: 1948.

part of the forest-savanna boundary and in many of the riverine areas, savanna is clearly advancing at the expense of the forest, but there are examples of the reverse. Whether or not the changing ecological status of the Rupununi savanna within the Amazon Basin over this period is exceptional or normal, it is well

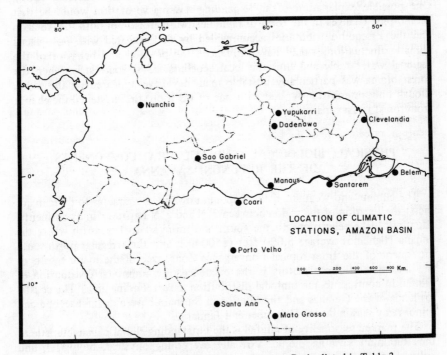

Figure 7. Location of Climatic Stations, Amazon Basin, listed in Table 3.

known. However, there is evidence of the existence of the savanna biome in some form or another for approximately the past 20,000 years (Wymstra and Van der Hammen: 1967). Pollen evidence and radio carbon dating indicate the presence during this period of all the major herbaceous and woody species, and of wide fluctuations in the proportional presence of forest elements, savanna woody species, compositae and other herbs, cyperaceae, and gramineae. These data provide evidence of presence and not of extent. In fact, the pollen could have come entirely from the nearby Guiana highlands at a time when the rain forest biome was more extensive and the highlands served as a savanna reservoir.

If the Rupununi was forest covered 20,000 years ago, or at least at the end of the last glacial epoch, how could it have eventually become a savanna? Could the change be explained entirely or largely in physical and biological terms, or could man have been primarily responsible? As far as man's role is concerned we have to hypothesize because the available archaeological evidence provides no proof of man in the region earlier than 400 years ago (Evans and Meggars: 1960). However, there is evidence of man's presence in the highland regions of Venezuela about 7000/8000 BP (Rouse and Cruzent: 1963), and it appears that there were continuous outward migrations from the Central Amazon starting about 2,500 BP, which could well have brought people into the Rupununi, via the Rio Negro and the Rio Branco, although not necessarily for long periods of occupance (Lathrap, 1966). It may well be pure coincidence, but Van der Hammen (1967), on the basis of pollen analysis from the Rupununi, reports on a rapid increase in the presence of several genera of Cyperaceae, which are considered to be fire resistant, during the period 3000 BP to 2000 BP. Although Van der Hammen suggests that fire was responsible, it is not clear that the presence of these plants is a response to frequent burning (Dansereau: 1967). One possible explanation of an expanding savanna vegetation would be that geomorphic changes in the form of rapid headward erosion of both the Amazon and the Essequibo tributaries accompanied by or associated with post-glacial climatic fluctuations would have influenced the position and behavior of the regional water table and thus the local ecoclimates. At some stage when the forest biome was particularly unstable man may have appeared on the scene, though only intermittently, and with one of his tools, fire, hastened the change from forest to savanna.

PHYSICAL, BIOLOGICAL, AND CULTURAL COMPONENTS OF THE RUPUNUNI SAVANNA

The climate and weather of the Rupununi owe their character to three major facts: the location of the region between 2°N and 5°N Latitude, in a continental situation; higher elevations to the south and more so to the north where the Guiana Highlands average 5,000 feet (1500 m.); and the irregular north-south movement of the Intertropical Convergence Zone. One of the major results of the interplay of these factors is the existence of a unimodal distribution of rainfall in contrast to the bimodal distribution in surrounding areas. The coastal lowlands of the Guianas and the interior of Surinam have a distinct second and minor rainy season during December and January.

The marked seasonality of rainfall is the outstanding climatic characteristic of the Rupununi savanna biome. Virtually everything physical, biological, and cultural is affected by it. At nearly all locations (Figure 7) 85 percent of the rainfall is concentrated between mid-April and mid-September with the bulk of it falling in May, June, and July, and the onset of the rains comes everywhere at the same time. As a general rule the annual total decreases with increasing distance from the forest edge, but the difference is accounted for by a greater wet-season rainfall rather than a more even distribution. The standard deviation ranges from about 12 inches (300 mm.) to 16 inches (400 mm.) with Station D (Table 3) having a 15 inch (381 mm.) deviation, based upon a mean of about 60 inches (1500 mm.), a maximum of about 85 inches (2160 mm.), and a minimum of about 37 inches (940 mm.). Variability is greater within the heart of the savanna. A half of each year's rain is produced by about 10 major storms during each rainy season. The incidence of rainfall thus results from the seasonal weather cycle superimposed on the normal diurnal cycle which is based upon convection. The time of maximum precipitation by volume progresses in an orderly fashion from the early morning hours in April and May, to early afternoon almost exclusively in August and September. Short showers can, however, be expected at any time of day because convection is continuous. During the dry season, the limited rainfall results primarily from thunderstorms, which increase in frequency to the north during December (Frost: 1968; Atwoki: 1969; Hutchinson: 1970).

Seasonality, with associated drought, is intensified by high rates of evapo-transpiration during the dry season. Throughout the dry season pan evaporations range between 0.16 (3 mm.) and 0.40 inches (10 mm.). The factors contributing to this high rate are: (a) dry-season mean temperatures of between $84°F$ ($29°C$) and $86°F$ ($30°C$) with a seasonal range of $4-6°F$ ($2.2-3.2°C$); (b) low humidity; and (c) strong winds from midnight to sunset, averaging 9 mph (4 m/s) persistently from the east and northeast. The resulting water balance for a five-year period is illustrated in Figure 8. The outstanding feature of this water balance is that soil moisture storage is rapidly depleted with the onset of each dry season. There is at least one month of serious drought each year.

A major result of the strong seasonality and the water balance is a marked hydrological imbalance, with the result that all low-lying areas are inundated and rivers flood their banks. This flooding takes place in spite of the fact that the Takutu and Ireng rivers (tributaries of the Rio Branco) are incised 30 to 50 feet (9-15 m.) below the adjacent savanna surfaces. The regional drainage system is not able to cope with the high volume of surface runoff during the height of the rainy season. However, towards the end of the rainy season, much of the surface flood water rapidly disperses and is accompanied by a regional lowering of water levels. An increased ground water gradient is thus established and ground water drainage is accelerated, which is greatly facilitated by the occurrence of porous sand and gravel substrata. In a few places ground water drainage is impeded by clay within silty horizons, and ponds and lakes persist for several months. A measure of river fluctuation is the annual range of 40 feet (12 m.) in the Takutu River at St. Ignatius (Figure 5). Elsewhere ranges of 10 to 30 feet (3-9 m.) are typical. The annual variation in the depth of the water table is in phase with the rainfall regime. In the north the water table is generally 10 to 15 feet (3-4 m.) below the wet season peak at the end of the following dry season, while in the south it would appear to be slightly less. These hydrological characteristics are important in identifying the following major terrain units of the savanna biome.

(1) *Alluvial plains, river terraces, and floodplains.* These landforms are primarily found in the north in the area of the divide between the

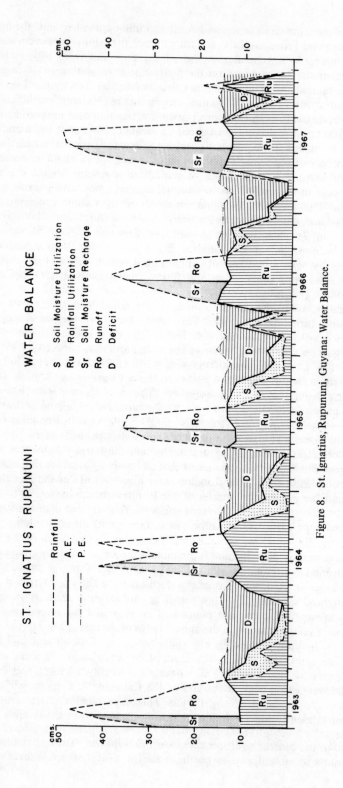

Figure 8. St. Ignatius, Rupununi, Guyana: Water Balance.

Amazon and the Essequibo but also to a limited extent in the south and along the Amazonian tributaries. This is obviously the terrain that experiences the greatest degree of flooding and waterlogging. Fluvio-lacustrine deposits with some recent silt clay and sand predominate. There are two major soil types, low-humic glei soils and ground water laterite soils, both of which are poorly drained, extremely acid, and very infertile with especially low amounts of sodium and potassium. Water-logging for so long a period is a condition that cannot be tolerated by trees so that sedge-dominant herbaceous savanna predominates. Swamps with associated palms (*Mauritia flexuosa*) and ponds abound in this terrain.

(2) *Undulating to rolling gravel ridges, gentle sheetwash slopes, and sandy flats.* This complex is the residue of an earlier extensive lateritic surface which once reached to the slopes of the Kanuku Mountains. The quality of drainage depends upon the degree to which either sheetwash colluvium or fluvial terrace deposits overlay the gravel. All soils are better drained than their lowland counterparts to the north. They are strongly weathered, extremely acid, highly porous, erodable, and extremely infertile. In part as a response to the better drainage, woody species increase and the various types of shrub savanna woodland predominate.

(3) *The low pediments and sheetwash slopes of the northern part of the southern Rupununi.* Most of the parent material has been derived from local crystalline rocks, primarily in the form of exfoliating granitic outcrops. The relief is one of alternate undulating flats and long gentle slopes. The soils are primarily ground water laterites but they are better drained than those to the north. However very low fertility prevails and in the dry season the upper 4 to 5 inches (10-15 cm.) crack badly. The vegetation cover is a mosaic of herbaceous and savanna woodland.

(4) *Rolling to moderately steep hill country* of the southern plateau from which rise residual peaks of inselbergs reaching elevations of 1000-3000 feet (305-915 m.). The underlying crystalline rocks have been deeply weathered to form sand and sandy loam soils which are highly quartzose and slightly acid to acid in reaction. The level of fertility is no higher than elsewhere. The vegetation cover again ranges from shrub through open savanna woodland to savanna woodland. However, most of the landscape has a parkland appearance.

Within these terrain types a range of seasonally influenced climatic conditions can be identified. At one extreme there is the dry savanna climate with alternating dry and wet phases associated with most of the better drained terrains, while at the other there is the wet savanna climate with alternating dry and excessively wet phases, obviously associated with the most poorly drained low-lying areas. Between these extremes the terrain and climatic conditions are immensely variable. This variability helps to explain the very great spatial distribution in the many vegetation types occurring in the Rupununi savanna.

The Vegetation Cover of the Rupununi

The vegetation cover of the Rupununi closely approximates that of the model of the savanna biome, to the extent that a variety of vegetation types other than savanna are present, in addition to five major types of savanna. However the Rupununi is floristically poor compared with many other savanna regions, especially those in Africa. Species lists from the Rupununi (Goodland: 1966), from Surinam (Donselaar: 1965) and the Venezuela Llanos (Lasser: 1955) are roughly comparable in size. Five major structural and physiognomic types of savanna are readily recognized: closed savanna woodland, savanna woodland, open savanna woodland, shrub savanna, and herbaceous savanna. However, the pattern of distribution is a mosaic with open savanna woodland and herbaceous savanna predominating. Floristically the savanna vegetation comprises a ground layer of grasses, sedges, forbs, and a varied tree and shrub layer made up of small trees, tree-like shrubs, sub-shrubs, woody herbs, occasional climbing plants, and rare epiphytes and succulents. The herbaceous layer covers from 10 to 95 percent of the ground with an average coverage of about 50 percent. The area of covered soils is about the same as the area of bare soil. The average density of trees is about 50 per acre (130 per hectare) with a maximum density of about 175 per acre (455 per hectare), the equivalent of a dense orchard with an almost closed canopy.

Over the entire Rupununi savanna, grasses although only second in terms of presence, occupy by far the largest area, and comprise the greater part of the weight of the vegetation. One grass, *Trachypogonplumosus*, may be responsible for 80 percent or more of both occurrence and weight. It is absent only in the lowest depressions. Other grasses of secondary importance are species of *Paspalum, Andropogon Angustatus, Aristida setifolia, Axonopus chrysites,* and *Mesosetym Loliiforme.* These and other grasses occur as both short bunch-grass savanna and as tall-grass savanna.

Sedges and forbs are by far the most important in terms of presence. The commonest genera are *Fimbristylis* and *Bulbostylis* which dominate the moister meadows, and *Rhynchospora* and *Dichromena* on the drier sites. Forbs such as *Polygala* and species of *Cassia* are everywhere common elements in the sward. Intermediate in habit between ground herbage and the larger shrubs and trees is the frequently abundant *Byrsonima verbascifolia,* whose woody growth is so little in evidence that it often passes as a broad-leaved herb.

Curatella americana, locally known as the "sand-paper tree," is the most common of the trees, usually occurring as a small tree or shrub. It is the most ubiquitous tree or shrub of the New World savanna biome. It has a wide ecological tolerance and can tolerate both a water surplus and a water deficit. The commonest genus is *Byrsonima* and there are several species of the dimensions of trees in addition to the herb-like *B. verbascifolia.* Of the other trees, *Plumeria inodora,* which is the tallest tree of the savanna, *Bowdichia Virgilioides,* and *Roupala complicata* are the most common.

With *Trachypogon* and *Curatella* as such overwhelming dominants, most of the savanna outside the pure herbaceous savanna could be designated as a *Trachypogon/Curatella* association.

There are four forest types encountered in the Rupununi savanna biome. One forest type is similar to the main surrounding forest and occurs in the form of "bush" islands. These islands are undoubtedly forest remnants. The forest on the residual or inselberg-like formations is of a tropical-montane type. There are also the "bush" islands on old Amerindian or ranch habitat sites, generally initiated by abandoned mango trees (*Mangifera indica*) and cashew bushes (*Anacardium occidentale*). Finally there is the riverine or galeria forest. In addition to the forest components there are the communities associated with sources of perennial water-supply: aquatic vegetation, palm swamps, marshes, and sedge meadows.

Fauna

The only true savanna fauna with the exception of fish are some rodents, termites, and the ant eaters that are predatory upon them. The deer which is usually thought of as a specialized savanna animal is really a forest creature. Even though fossil evidence shows the existence of large numbers of grazing animals in the South American savanna biome during the Pleistocene, they are absent today with the exception of introduced cattle, horses, small numbers of sheep and goats, and some water buffalo (*Bos bubalis*) brought into the region at the turn of the century from the coastal rice lands. The absence of a significant savanna fauna is usually attributed to the predominant grasses which are coarse and unpalatable (and probably always have been) and are deficient in essential minerals, especially phosphorus. In spite of the restricted nature of the true savanna fauna, a larger and more diverse fauna does in fact make use of the savanna biome (Table 4).

Much of the fauna that is truly a forest fauna, is associated with the savanna biome because it is frequently encountered there. Animals and birds pass back and forth between the surrounding forest, the bush islands, and the riverine forest or the dense savanna woodland in search of prey which may be encountered in the savanna, and from time to time for the more accessible grazing and water on the savanna.

There are some other obvious environmental associations such as the presence of most of the flying insects during the wet season and their occurrence close to water bodies. Termites and earthworms are associated with micro-landforms, specific soil types and moisture (Figure 9) conditions. The grazing animals obviously prefer those niches where the most palatable grasses and water are in close proximity.

The Rupununi has a very rich and complex fish fauna, contributed both by the Essequibo and Amazon drainage systems. Over 150 species more than 5 cm long have been recorded and these include *Arapaima gigas*, reputedly the largest freshwater fish in the world, and *Potamotrygon hystrix*, a freshwater sting-ray.

TABLE 4—Wild Fauna of the Rupununi Savanna Biome

Mammals

Predatory:
jaguar — *Felis onca*
puma — *Felis concolor concolor*
ocelot — *Felis pardales*
margay cat — *Felis macoura*
wild bush dogs — *Speothos vanaticus vanaticus*
bats (numerous families and subfamilies)

Others:
armadillo — *Dasypodidae*
otters — *Lutra enudris enudris*
spider monkey — *Ateles paniscus paniscus*
sloths — *Bradypodidae*
deer—white tailed — *Odocoilius gymnotis*
      —red brocket — *Mazama americana*
paca — *Cuniculus paca paca*
capybara — *Hydrochoerus capybara*

TABLE 4 (Cont'd)

agouti	*Dasyprocta aguti*
adouri	*Dasyprocta acuchy*
tapir	*Tapirus terrestris terrestris*
peccary	*Dictyles labiatus*
giant anteater	*Myremecophaga tridactyla*
porcupine	*Coendou prehensilis prehensilis*

Reptiles

iguana	*Iguana tuberculata*
water turtles	*Podocnemis unifilis*
rattle snake	*Crotalus horridus*
anaconda	*Eunectes murina*
boa constrictor	*Constrictor constrictor*
bushmaster	*Lachesis mutus*
caiman	*Caiman*

Birds

ducks	*Carina moschata*
parrots	*Amazona ochrocephala*
macaws	*Macrocerus araranna*
quail	*Ortyx cristatus*
snipe	*Genus Capella*
pigeon	*Columba rufina*
toucan	*Aulacoramphus sulcatus*
woodpeckers	*Picas multicolor*

Insects

Major pests to man:
sandflies	*Simulium sp.*
cockroaches—order	*Blattaria*
flying ants	
blow fly—family	*Caliphoridae*
spiders—order	*Araneida*
scorpion—order	*Scorpionida*
mosquito	*Anopheles sp.*

Others:
termites	*Syntermes snyderi*
earthworms—family	*Lumbricidae*
ants	*Atta sp.*

Fish

huri	*Haplias malabaricus*
foxfish	*Acestrorhynchus spp.*
silver pacu	*Metynnis spp.*
wabure	*Pygopristis denticulatus*
red pirai	*Serrasalmus nattereri*
lukanani	*Cichla ocellaris*
salmon patawa	*Acaronia nassa*
giant arapaima	*Arapaima gigas*
black pirai	*Serrasalmus niger*
arapaima	*Arapaima*

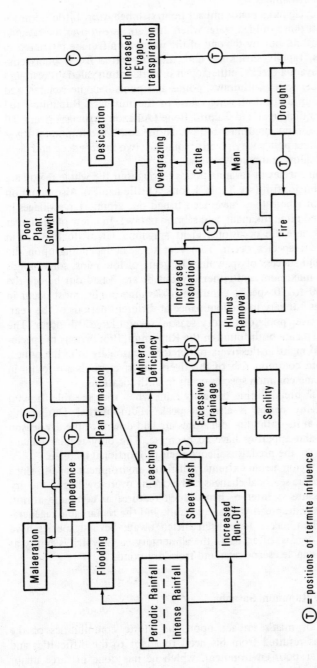

Figure 9. The Influence of Termites Partially Negates Three of the Causal Factors of Savannas. Their burrowing improves drainage and irrigation, thus reducing waterlogging, and permits the establishment of roots of *phreatophytes* through the pan soil although it is possible that clay from eroding termitaria may ultimately give rise to pan formation. Termites may, over time, increase soil nutrients by bringing subsoil to the surface and the more vigorous vegetation found at the base of termitaria may reduce fire.

Ⓣ = positions of termite influence

Some 45 percent of these are characids, 27 percent nemtograth catfish of various families, 14 percent cichlids, and 6 percent gymnotids. The remaining 12 species belong to nine different families.

The hydrological cycle has a major impact upon fish behavior. Little is known about fish behavior at times of high water when they are spread over the savanna and are difficult to catch, but by the end of the wet season fish are restricted to open savanna ponds, rapidly shrinking, dark, deoxygenated forest pools containing leaf debris, savanna creeks, either open or dark within galeria forest, and the main rivers. As the water withdraws, ponds and pools become isolated and fish are imprisoned until the following rains. In the northern Rupununi, the Rupununi (Essequibo drainage) and Takutu/Ireng (Amazon drainage) rivers fall greatly in the dry season but continue to flow. To the south the Rupununi River dries into pools. Savanna ponds vary greatly; some are two meters deep and clear but others are very shallow and muddy.

The most common species in savanna ponds throughout the whole region are the predatory huri and foxfish (see Table 4 for scientific names). Also common are silver pacu (except where they have been fished out around large villages in the south), wabure, red pirai, lukanani, and salmon patawa. In a few of the larger ponds in the north, there are occasional giant arapaima. Great fluctuations in abundance of different species occur from year to year depending upon the degree of flooding and success of spawning. In years of low rains, some ponds are not filled to the maximum and either dry out or are fished out before the next rains. Of the 60 to 70 species common to savanna ponds, most occur in both drainage systems but vary in predominance at different periods of the year.

In the rivers and river pools of the dry season, several large fish occur. The black pirai and arapaima are both found in the Rupununi. Proportions of species vary between day and night in the rivers rather than seasonally as in the ponds. Very few of the more common fish of the rivers and river pools are found in savanna ponds, but some common species occur in both locations.

Most Rupununi fish breed during the early rains when they are able to swim farther afield. The rainy period is also the peak feeding period. During this season food supply is at its optimum, and stores are laid down for the dry season when food is scarce and appetites have to decrease. The only regular feeders during the dry season are the predators, hence their proportional increase.

The waters of this region are an extremely difficult environment for fish since they are subject to drastic seasonal changes and extreme overcrowding in the dry season. Predator pressure is intense, hence such features as complete armor, night immobility, the widespread viviparous habit, and the remarkable regeneration of some fish when pieces have been bitten away. Several species have accessory respiratory organs, often using the alimentary canal which is empty at the dry season. These enable escape overland from dry ponds.

Human Impact on the Rupununi Savanna

The greater part of man's impact upon the biotic communities of the Rupununi savanna has resulted from his need to adapt to the difficulties and limitations of a rather poor environment, which he has done in three major ways. First, man has had to supplement the meager nutrient supply that comes from hunting, collecting, and cultivating in the forest, by fishing in order to supplement protein supply; and by hunting in the savanna. Second, cattle grazing has been organized (initially by open range and more recently by fencing) to allow for wet and dry season grazing, and shifting cultivation has been retained in order to utilize the forest soils without fertilizer. Third, fire has been used for reducing the adjacent rain forest to ash and for enriching the soils for cultivation, for reducing the hazards of the savanna grass cover, and for temporarily improving the palatability of savanna grasses.

The human population of the Rupununi is about 9,000 and is composed largely of Amerindians of the Wapisiana and Macushi tribes, who have probably only settled in the savanna biome during the last two centuries (Evans and Meggars: 1960). The non-Amerindian population comprises a mixed European/Amerindian group, some colored Guyanese and Indian settlers from the coastal lowlands, and about 250 missionaries and government officials. This small element is both scattered on ranches and to a limited extent in the Amerindian villages, and is nucleated in the main administrative and commercial center of Lethem. More than 90 percent of the Amerindian population is concentrated in 10 villages which are within 10 miles of the forest edge including the cluster of bush islands in the heart of the southern Rupununi. In fact more than 80 percent of the population is located within three miles of the forest edge and within this peripheral zone the density of population rises to a mean of 6 per square mile, and a maximum of 10 or more (10-16 per square kilometer). This pattern is obviously a response not only to the distribution of nutrient supply in the region, but also to administrative dictates. The government of Guyana has located villages for convenience of education, health, transportation, and communications since the 1920's. Such nucleation has had two major results. First, the provision of educational, religious, sanitation, health, and religious services has led to a very rapid increase in the population. The 1950 Amerindian total was about 5,000 while in 1970 it was about 8,500. Second, this degree of concentration has served to reduce the fallow period in the areas of shifting cultivation immediately adjacent to the villages. The ideal fallow period is 15 to 20 years. That amount of forest growth provides the quantity of nutrients necessary for a good yield from one crop of cassava and other crops. In some areas the fallow has been reduced to eight or nine years with a resultant reduction in yields. An additional result of this change is that fields are being located too close to the forest edge. If dry conditions prevail following harvest and a strong savanna fire approaches the forest edge, the result may be an extension of the savanna. The seed of savanna species will be carried into an old field by wind, by cattle, and by birds. Figure 10 illustrates a typical situation of forest retreating and savanna advancing.

The more specific treatment of impact that now follows, should be read with one eye on Figure 4, by means of which relationships within the two ecosystems (savanna and forest) can be traced. For example, there is a clear relationship between western and indigenous man, tools, clearing savanna, forest, and the environment. The provision by western man of steel axes and to a limited extent chain saws has provided the Amerindian with a more efficient and effective means of clearing forest and selectively cutting woody savanna species for firewood. These actions in turn affect the energy, nutrient, and water cycles. For example, effective clearing of the forest followed by a good burn will initially produce more nutrients for crop production, but the efficiency of the clearing operation may well slow up the whole process of forest regeneration, thus aiding the process of savanna advance as described above.

Figure 10.   A Dynamic Forest/Savanna Boundary, Rupununi Savannas, Guyana. This photo illustrates many features associated with Amerindian shifting cultivation close to the forest edge and in the riverine forest, between 6 and 12 miles (9.6-19.2 km.) from a village. The savanna biome is advancing at the expense of the forest. Key: (1) bush island, a forest remnant, (2) bush island developed on old habitation site, (3) riverine forest, (4) savanna developing within main forest, (5) main rain forest, (6) angular nature of boundary indicative of old field invaded by savanna, (7) recently established savanna, (8) recently established savanna, and (9) typical savanna woodland. (Photo by permission of Government of Guyana.)

The types of impact now to be described are selective and illustrative; they do not represent the total impact of man on the Rupununi savanna.

Collecting and Gathering. Gathering of firewood by Amerindians from selected woody species in the savanna woodlands surrounding villages or along paths to villages results in these species being kept at the shrub level which, in turn, encourages the herbaceous species. The cashew fruit *Anacardium occidentale* collected from the savanna for the well-known nut is brought into the Amerindian villages for preparation, consumption, and occasional sale with the result that cashew thickets tend to develop close to village sites. Prior to nucleation of settlement these thickets, which developed close to the individual and isolated but nutrient-enriched habitation sites (Figure 10) on which mango trees (*Mangifera indica*) also grew, provided an attraction for birds which frequently brought to the site the seeds of forest species. Many such sites have developed into small bush islands.

Hunting. Prior to the arrival of the rancher in the latter half of the 19th century, the occasional explorer described scenes of deer by the dozen grazing peacefully or deer by the hundreds being chased by fierce savanna fires lit purposely by Amerindians in order to facilitate the hunt. The increased Amerindian population and competition from cattle grazing have resulted in a reduction in deer numbers to the point that they are rarely seen in many parts of the Rupununi today. The tapir, giant otter, giant anteater, two species of peccary, and most of the cats are now also few and far between, as a result of hunting both for zoos and museums, and for skins. Prices of from $5 to $100 or more for cat skins, especially the jaguar, have been largely responsible for the very rapid reduction in numbers during the last two decades.

Fishing. In the past all the reasonable sized streams rivers, and ponds have been useful for fishing, but today in some streams the supply has been greatly diminished, due to poisoning and over-fishing.

Whereas shooting with a shotgun and chopping methods, using a machete, are mostly used in rivers and creeks, fish taken from ponds and river pools are frequently poisoned. Several different types of poison are used, such as haiara and ishal (*Lonchocarpus spp.*) some of which are respiratory and others not. If a part of a large pool is to be poisoned, Amerindians pile up a stone stop-off barrier and then beat the water with the haiara or ishal bush ropes until dead fish come to the surface. This type of poison is selective in that some species disappear ahead of others, cichlids and characids are usually affected first, then gymnotids and later nematognaths. Such poisons are commonly used around the villages in the far south, while to the north a respiratory poison (rotenone) is more common. Only fish that can use atmospheric air, such as the large arapaima, are not killed by this process. The bow and arrow are still frequently used for fishing behind barriers, while the blow-gun is rapidly becoming an historical curiosity.

In recent years hook fishing has increased especially in the creeks and the castnet is used in drying ponds, but the traditional methods are still the most important. With fast increasing populations and highly wasteful fishing methods, such as poisoning, many popular fishing areas near the large settlements are now fished out. The most serious result of the decline in fishing is the consequent reduction in protein intake by Amerindians.

Fire. Fires are frequent in the Rupununi savanna as they would appear to be in all other savanna areas of the Amazon. "Frequent" means at least once a year, and in some areas as many as three times. Areas burned in September, a month after the cessation of the rains, may well be burned in December and/or January and then again in late March. Virtually all the savannas show evidence of frequent burning over long periods of time. Without doubt, natural fire has occurred in the past and still occurs today, but where lightning strikes the area may have already been burned by man. The Amerindians burn the grass to improve grazing conditions, to drive game from cover, to kill menacing animals and insects, to make travel easier, to protect villages from natural fire, and simply for the enjoyment of seeing flames. The latter reason has become even more significant in recent years, with the increased availability of matches in local trade stores.

Until recently, many of the ranchers also practiced burning on a large scale with the idea of removing the old unpalatable grass in order to make way for fresh growth aided by the added nutrient supply from the ash and the first rains. However, it is now realized that the effects of indiscriminate burning are extremely short-lived and in the long-run result in a progressive deterioration of the rangeland. Thus ranchers, aided by government officials, police, and school teachers, are attempting to halt the process, although some judicious burning in order to protect habitation sites and fences remains necessary. Fire is undoubtedly an important factor in maintaining and increasing the extent of savanna. In those isolated areas where there is a tendency for the forest, either the main forest, the riverine, or the bush island forest to advance, frequent fires will probably destroy any forest species that do develop beyond germination in the savanna soils. Reference has already been made (Figure 10) to one way in which fire aids in the advance of savanna. In addition to the direct impact of fire upon plants, there is the long-term effect that frequent cultivation and burning has upon the viability of the seeds of forest species. This is a topic that is not yet fully understood, but it appears likely that a reduction of viability may well take place, which would be a most significant fact, especially in those areas where the continued existence of the forest is already problematical for climatic and other reasons.

Ranching and Cattle. The development of ranching in the Rupununi has not only resulted in today's cattle count of about 60,000, but in support of or as a result of the presence of these cattle a significant variety of administrative, managerial, and technological devices have been introduced into the region. The most important of the administrative devices has been the establishment of Amerindian reservations, purportedly for the protection of Amerindian villages, but also quite clearly for the protection of ranch lands. The fences used to delimit these reservations on the savannas, as well as those constructed by the ranchers, have restricted the movements of Amerindians and the fauna they hunt. Fences have also led to the over-fishing of some savanna ponds and river locations. Due to the spread of foot and mouth disease into the Rupununi from the Rio Branco, a hundred miles or more of fencing has been constructed twice in the last thirty years in Guyana along the border with Brazil. These fences have certainly aggravated an already difficult situation for the Amerindians. Of course fences have also played a vital part in better management of grazing so that some areas that were overgrazed under an earlier open-range period, have been able to regenerate. Roads, airstrips, and cattle trails have all led to the disturbance of the savanna surface and, in many locations, have accelerated soil erosion. Especially where roads have not been well maintained the adjacent savanna surface has become deeply furrowed by myriad land rover tracks, with some furrows eventually becoming deep gullies. However, roads, airstrips, and cattle trails do serve as good firebreaks.

In addition, and most importantly, airstrips since the early 1950's and a major cattle trail from the Rupununi to the Intermediate Savannas of the coastal lowlands constructed during the 1930's and 40's have permitted the culling of cattle, amounting in number to the natural increase of the herd, for sale in Georgetown on the coast of Guyana. This annual depletion of the herd has been a major factor in reducing the degree and extent of overgrazing. Failure to reduce the number of cattle grazing in a given area, where frequent burning and perhaps grazing of natural fauna has so depleted the vegetation that it can no longer support the existing cattle at a reasonable grazing level, can be considered as overgrazing. The general deterioration of the savannas, in terms of vegetation height and percentage of cover for the principal grasses and sedges, and the spread of the sedge *Genus Sciprus*, which is usually an excellent indicator of overgrazing or general range depletion, is evidence of the degree and extent of overgrazing.

One of the objectives of fencing has been controlled breeding. During the open-range period, which survived until the 1940's, there were only very limited attempts to improve the quality of cattle. Some European breeds, more particularly the Hereford, were introduced; however, the impact was negligible. It was not until purebred bulls could be flown to the Rupununi that upgrading was taken seriously. Brahman, Zebu, Santa Gertrudis, and Charolais breeds have all reached the region and are slowly improving the herds. However the final product can only be as good as the weakest link in the chain, and to date ranchers have not succeeded in improving the grazing in spite of myriad experiments. The high cost of air freight has discouraged the use of fertilizers.

Another lesser development in ranching has been the feeding of corn to ranch horses. Ranchers have encouraged Amerindians in several areas to grow corn, and its cultivation has ordinarily been in addition to the normal field cultivation. The result has been that in those areas closest to the main ranches, i.e., in the concentration of bush islands in both the north and south, the necessary fallow has been drastically reduced to the point that some bush islands are now disappearing.

The Future. Finally, in the consideration of man's impact in the Rupununi savanna it is of interest to look into the future. Within the next two or three years it will probably be possible to reach the region from Georgetown by road, and even sooner it will be possible during the dry season to drive from Caracas, Venezuela across the Rio Branco to the Guyana border. Within five years the region will be connected by road to all parts of the Americas. Will man use these roads to leave the region or will he stay and suffer the first unfortunate consequences of a greatly increased acculturation? Present experiences in central Brazil and southern Venezuela should be a warning to the government of Guyana. Man should also zone land-use very carefully to take into account the ecological disequilibrium of the region.

CONTINENTAL COMPARISONS

To conclude this treatment of the savanna biome the experience of the Rupununi and the other savannas of the Amazon basin will be compared with man's impact in other major savanna regions. These comparisons will have to be largely descriptive as very little quantitative data are available. However, overgrazing and consequent accelerated soil erosion are generally similar wherever they occur, as is the change of savanna woodland to herbaceous savanna, or the advance of savanna at the expense of the rain forest. Three types of impact will be considered: changes in the productivity of the non-cultivated areas, changes in the numbers of and ratio of wild fauna to domesticated livestock, and the extent of cultivation and irrigation.

In the three major savanna regions of the New World (central Brazil, the Colombian Llanos, and the Venezuelan Llanos) there appears to have been a deterioration of the vegetation cover and a consequent decrease in plant productivity, similar to that in the Rupununi. The "Africanization" and subsequent improvement of pastures developed on cleared rain forest land has not as yet significantly affected the New World savannas. More particularly, in Colombia and Venezuela, scrub and woodland have increased. In some areas the explanation has been in terms of overgrazing and depletion of the herbaceous cover, while in others it has been in terms of under-grazing. As stated earlier, the wild fauna was never significant and what there was has virtually disappeared. The carrying capacity of these savannas varies from about one head of cattle to 60 acres (23 ha.) to one cattle to 20 acres (8 ha.). In spite of the overall deterioration of the grazing, productivity has been maintained or even increased by management improvements such as increasing the number of watering places (waterbores and windmills), by upgrading the cattle herds, by the production of supplemental fodder, and by the provision of supplemental minerals. In addition, the location of abattoirs and canning factories in the savanna regions has permitted fuller use of existing production.

In only two regions has there been a significant increase in cultivation. In the central Venezuelan Llanos several thousand acres are now under rice and the naturally available water is supplemented by irrigation. In the southeastern section of the Brazilian savanna and especially around Brasilia cultivation of *campo cerrado* lands is increasing rapidly. A variety of crops are grown with the assistance of fertilizers.

The Australian experience, in terms of deterioration of grazing, has been very similar, although at no time has there been present equal densities of cattle. One reason for this has been the competition with the native fauna, especially the kangaroos, although probably of equal significance has been the more difficult environment of northern Australia. However, large numbers of marsupial animals, mostly kangaroos (1.5 million for Australia as a whole), are now being harvested annually (UNESCO: 1970), although rather indiscriminately, partly for internal consumption and partly for export.

The northern Australian savanna biome has over the past half century experienced a great variety of experiments in both cultivation and improvement of pasture. Most of these sorghum and rice producing schemes have failed. However, a new scheme at Willeroo, south of Darwin in the Northern Territory, comprising a block of 2,262 square miles (5,814 square kilometers) promises well, partly because of the large amounts of Australian and Japanese capital available and the large markets presently available in Japan and the United States.

In so many respects the African experience has been different, a consequence of the much greater densities of wild fauna and human beings. Also, whereas occupance of the Australian and New World savannas during the past centuries has been primarily for the purpose of Western type ranching, occupance of the African savannas has remained primarily indigenous in form. Although the population of these savannas has been estimated at about 90 million, this population is highly concentrated and much of the biome remains very sparsely populated. The prevalence of human and livestock diseases contributes to this sparse population. For example, in Nigeria most of the cattle are confined, because of diseases, to the northern quarter of the country. It is the concentration of population and fauna that has created the typical savanna problems of overgrazing, soil erosion, general impoverishment of the vegetation cover, and the retreat of the forest.

Even though cultivation is far more important than in the other continents it affects only about 5 percent of the total area. Most of the farming is of the shifting or bush-fallowing type and population pressure and a hesitancy to break with traditional methods of cultivation, result in a reduction of the fallow-cultivation cycle to a point where the environment begins to deteriorate very rapidly. Fortunately there are some areas where the African farmers have adopted improved techniques such as the use of fertilizer and anti-erosion measures. The greatest changes have been in a few selected areas, such as the Gezira area of the Sudan and at several localities on the Niger River, where irrigation and mechanization have been possible.

However, in recent years, the major theme in the African savanna biome, especially in the central, eastern and southern regions has probably been the ecological and economic role of the national parks. These parks now occupy almost 100,000 square miles (258,900 square kilometers), but it is rapidly becoming obvious that although they presently produce substantial economic benefits, they are producing a myriad of ecological headaches.

In Kenya, a country blessed with many excellent parks, tourism generates 3 percent of the gross national product. In 1971 there were 400,000 visitors and that figure is projected to increase at 20 percent annually (Myers: 1972). The ecological dilemma results in part from the impact of these tourists in the parks, in part from the rapid increase of some types of animals and the rapid decrease of others (endangered species), and in part also from conflicting policies as to how open parks should be to the natural migrations of game ordinarily outside the parks.

The dilemma of the African national parks, although on a much greater scale, is similar to the dilemmas that are likely to be faced by many countries, in which significant areas of savanna exist, as advanced technologies attempt to move into the core of savanna biome regions.

ACKNOWLEDGEMENTS

The author wishes to acknowledge his debt in the writing of this paper to those students and colleagues who have participated in the McGill University Savanna Research Project. In addition to those already cited (C. Atwoki, D. B. Frost, R. J. A. Goodland, and I. Hutchinson), the following also contributed either to the field project and/or to the publication series: E. Waddell, M. Eden, D. A. M. Lea, N. K. P. Sinha, P. Maycock, R. Salisbury, J. B. Bird, and J. Perry. Thanks are also offered to C. McCallum for valuable assistance during the preparation of this paper.

REFERENCES

Allan, W., 1965, *The African Husbandman*. London: Oliver and Boyd.

Atwoki, C., 1969, "A Dynamic Climatology of the Rupununi." Unpublished M.Sc. Thesis, McGill University.

Beard, J. S., 1953, "The Savanna Vegetation of Northern Tropical America." *Ecological Monographs*, Vol. 5, No. 2, pp. 149-215.

Bourlière, F. and M. Hadley, 1970, "The Ecology of Tropical Savanna," in R. F. Johnson, P. W. Frank, and C. D. Michener (eds.), *Annual Review of Ecology and Systematics*. Palo Alto: Annual Review, Inc.

Brown, L., 1965, *Africa: A Natural History*. New York: Random House.

Budowski, G., 1956, "Tropical Savannas: A Sequence of Forest Felling and Repeated Burnings," *Turrialba*, Vol. 6, pp. 23-33.

Carr, A. *et al.*, 1964, *The Land and Wildlife of Africa*. New York: Life Nature Library.

Cole, M. M., 1960, "Cerrado, Caatinga, and Pantanal: The Distribution and Origin of the Savanna Vegetation of Brazil," *Geographical Journal*, Vol. 126, pp. 168-179.

Dansereau, P., 1967, Personal communication.

Denevan, W. M., 1970, "The Aboriginal Population of Western Amazonia in Relation to Habitat and Subsistence," *Revista Geografica*, No. 72, pp. 61-86.

Donselaar, J. Van, 1965, *An Ecological and Phytogeographic Study of Northern Surinam Savannas*. Amsterdam: North Holland Publishing Company.

Eden, M. J., 1964, "The Savanna Ecosystem: Northern Rupununi, British Guiana," *Savanna Research Series*, McGill University, No. 1.

Evans, C. and B. J. Meggars, 1960, *Archaeological Investigations in British Guiana*. Washington, D.C.: Smithsonian Institution, Bureau of American Ethnology, Bulletin 177, pp. 326-347.

Frost, D. B., 1968, "The Climate of the Rupununi Savannas," *Savanna Research Series*, McGill University, No. 12.

Goodland, R. J. A., 1966, "On the Savanna Vegetation of Calabozo, Venezuela and Rupununi, British Guiana," *Boletin, Sociedad Venezolana de Ciencias Naturales*, Vol. 24, No. 110, pp. 241-359.

Grigg, D., 1970, *The Harsh Lands: A Study in Agricultural Development*. New York: Macmillan.

Heyligers, P. C., 1963, "Vegetation and Soil of a White-Sand Savanna in Surinam," in I. A. De Hulsten (ed.), *Vegetation of Surinam*, Vol. 3. Amsterdam: Von Eedenfonds.

Hopkins, B., 1965, *Forest and Savanna: An Introduction to Tropical Plant Ecology with Special Reference to West Africa*. London: Heinemann.

Hutchinson, I., 1970, "Tree Growth and Edaphic Control in the South Rupununi Savannas." Unpublished M.Sc. Thesis, McGill University.

Johannessen, C., 1963, "Savannas of Interior Honduras," *Ibero Americana*, No. 46. Berkeley: University of California Press.

Keast, A., 1966, *Australia and the Pacific Islands: A Natural History*. New York: Random House.

Lasser, T., 1955, "Esbozo preliminar sobre el origen de las formaciones vegetales de nuestros llanos," *Boletin, Sociedad Venezolana de Ciencias Naturales*, Vol. 16, pp. 173-200.

Lathrap, D. W., 1966, "The 'Hunting' Economies of the Tropical Forest of South America: An Attempt at Historical Perspective," in *Symposium: Biota of the Amazon*. Belem, Brazil. Manuscript.

Laubenfels, D. J. de, 1970, *A Geography of Plants and Animals*. Dubuque Iowa: Wm. C. Brown Company.

Lowe, R. H., 1964, "The Fishes of the Rupununi Savanna District of British Guiana, South America," *Journal of the Linnaeus Society* (Zoology), Vol. 45, No. 304, pp. 103-144. (Most of the data on fish were obtained from this paper with the author's permission.)

Moss, R. P., 1972, "The Ecological Background to Land-Use Studies in Tropical Africa with Special Reference to the West," *Environment and Land-Use in Africa*. London: Methuen, pp. 193-238.

Myers, N., 1972, "National Parks in Savanna Africa," *Science*, Vol. 178, pp. 1255-1263.

Parsons, J. J., 1955, "The Misquito Pine Savanna of Nicaragua and Honduras," *Annals of the Association of American Geographers*, Vol. 45, pp. 36-63.

Proceedings of the I.G.U. Humid Tropics Commission Symposium, Venezuela, 1964, "The Ecology of the Forest/Savanna Boundary."

Riley, D. and A. Young, 1966, *World Vegetation*. Cambridge: Cambridge University Press.

Rouse, I. and J. M. Cruzent, 1963, *Venezuelan Archaeology*. New Haven: Yale University Press.

Savanna Research Series, McGill University, 1964-1973, Nos. 1-16.

Sombroek, W. C., 1966, *Amazon Soils*. Wageningen: Center for Agricultural Publications and Documentation.

Teunissen, P. A. and J. T. Wildschut, 1970, *Vegetation and Flora at the Brinckheuvel Nature Reserve, Northern Surinam*. Amsterdam: North Holland Publishing Company.

Thornthwaite, C. W., 1948, "An Approach Toward a Rational Classification of Climate," *Geographical Review*, Vol. 38, pp. 55-94.

Tricart, J., 1972, *Landforms of the Humid Tropics Forests and Savannas*. London: Longman.

UNESCO, 1961, *Tropical Soils and Vegetation*. Abidjan: UNESCO.

_____, 1970, *Use and Conservation of the Biosphere*. "Natural Resources Research," No. 10. Paris: UNESCO.

Van der Hammen, T., 1967, personal communication.

Wood, J. G. and R. J. Williams, 1960, *Vegetation in the Australian Environment*. Melbourne: Commonwealth Scientific and Industrial Research Organization.

Wymstra, T. A. and T. Van der Hammen, 1967, "South American Savannas: Comparative Studies: Colombia and Guyana," *Savanna Research Series*, McGill University, No. 6, pp. 71-83.

AUTHOR INDEX

A

Abbott, C. C., 159
Abeles, F. B., 138
Adams, R. McC., 220
Agble, W. K., 189
Aldrich, J. W., 167
Alexander, M., 195
Allchin, F. R., 70
Allee, W. C., 163
Allen, D. L., 155, 164
Allen, J. A., 159, 167
Allen, J. L., 269, 270
Allen, R. P., 160
Allison, F. E., 192
American Chemical Society, 194, 195
Ames, P. L., 198
Ammerman, A. J., 66
Anderson, D. G., 95
Anderson, D. W., 198
Anderson, E., 230
Anderson, G. C., 191
Anderson, J. W., 328
APCA (Air Pollution Control Association), 228
Arey, D. G., 314, 330, 332, 334
Arkell, W. J., 217
Armstrong, T. R., 8
Ashby, W. C., 226
Atwater, M. A., 114, 132
Atwoki, C., 357
Atzert, S. P., 154
Aubert, G., 69
Auliciems, A., 313, 329
Aylor, D. J., 232
Ayres, E., 10

B

Bach, W., 42, 112, 115, 116, 226, 232, 233, 234
Baerreis, D. A., 120
Bailey, R. G., 92
Baker, H. G., 230

Baker, W. L., 230
Bakke, A. L., 227
Baldwin, M. F., 161, 300
Ball, M. M., 321
Banfield, W. A. F., 298
Bardach, J. E., 159
Barker, M., 327
Barkman, J. J., 228
Barnes, H. F., 236
Barrett, E. W., 130, 132, 133, 135, 138, 140, 141
Barrows, H. H., 3, 312
Barrows, W. B., 167
Barton, N. J., 216, 221
Basile, D. V., 228
Basilevic, N. I., 48, 49
Bastian, R. K., 223
Bates, M., 181
Baumann, D. D., 316, 322, 326, 327, 329, 331, 332
Beaglehole, E., 320
Beath, O. A., 232
Beck, A. M., 236, 239
Beckinsale, R. P., 79, 89, 99
Beer, J. V., 167
Beeton, A. M., 191
Belding, D. L., 236
Belknap, R. K., 292
Bellrose, F. C., 167
Bennett, C. F., 163, 164
Bennett, E., 189
Bennett, H. H., 64, 67, 71, 72
Ben-Tuvia, A., 163
Berg, G. G., 198
Berger, A. J., 168
Berger, R., 66, 136
Bernard, R. F., 236
Bernstein, L., 89, 91, 99
Beug, H. J., 68
Beyers, W. B., 302
Bickert, C. von E., 330
Biesecker, J. E., 81
Bigler, W. J., 238

SUBJECT INDEX

A

Accelerated soil erosion. *See* Soil erosion.

Aerosols, 112, 114, 116, 128, 130, 131, 132, 133, 139, 146, 324. *See also* Dust; Particulates; Turbidity.

Agricultural systems, 34-35, 36, 47, 181, 182, 188, 192, 194, 203
  modern (neotechnic), 35, 36, 45, 182, 186, 187, 188, 192, 201, 202, 203
  traditional (paleotechnic), 35, 182, 201

Albedo, 107, 108, 110, 111, 115, 119, 120, 121, 122, 123, 124, 125, 128, 130, 131, 132, 133, 136, 140, 142, 146

Alien species, introduction of, 167-168

Alluviation, 62, 66, 68. *See also* Sedimentation.

Audubon Society, 153, 173

B

Backscattering, 110, 128, 132, 133

Biogeochemical cycles, 189-194, 219, 240. *See also* Chapter 2.

Biological magnification, 196

Biomass, 24, 32, 33, 38, 40, 42, 47, 48, 49, 51

Biotic modification, 186

Burning, 52, 53, 64, 134, 163, 257, 301, 302, 344, 347-348, 356, 365, 367-368, 369

C

Carbon cycle, 39-42

Carbon fixation, 40, 41

Cascading system, 80

Channelization, 85, 97, 237

Channel manipulation, direct, 80, 84-89, 97

Chlorinated hydrocarbons, 195-198, 199, 204-205. *See also* Pesticides.

Climate, 58, 59, 62-63, 68, 69, 71. *See also* Chapter 5.
  savanna, 354, 355, 356, 359
  urban, 224-226

Climatic modification. *See* Chapter 5.

Climatology,
  rural, 119-121
  urban, 111-119

Cloud seeding, 94, 100, 140

Cognitive maps, 279, 286

Commoner, Barry, 9, 181, 190, 192, 203

Community respiration, 33, 187-188, 191

Comparative advantage, 6-8, 13, 20

Conservation,
  movement, 1, 154, 169
  preservationist, 296, 297, 298
  resources, 170, 213, 332
  soil, 57-58, 59, 69, 72-74, 188, 269. *See also* Crop rotation; Intercropping; Reforestation; Strip Cropping; Terracing.
  utilitarian, 294, 297
  wildlife, 152, 154-155, 158-159, 165, 169-174, 303, 304

Controlled breeding, 170-171, 369

Crop rotation, 64, 204

Cultivation, 35, 57, 58, 59, 60, 61, 64, 65, 66, 68, 69, 73, 94, 137, 164, 182, 188, 191, 220, 348, 350, 351, 364, 365, 369, 370, 371. *See also* Chapter 8.

D

Dam and reservoir construction, 84-85

Decision-making, 12, 252-253, 255, 263, 272-274, 322, 326-327, 330-331, 334

Denitrification, 43, 190, 191